INORGANIC
CHEMISTRY

INORGANIC CHEMISTRY

C. S. G. PHILLIPS

MERTON COLLEGE, OXFORD

AND

R. J. P. WILLIAMS

WADHAM COLLEGE, OXFORD

II

METALS

1966

OXFORD UNIVERSITY PRESS

NEW YORK AND OXFORD

© Oxford University Press 1966
Library of Congress Catalogue Card Number: 65-27666
Second printing, 1970
PRINTED IN THE UNITED STATES OF AMERICA

PREFACE

As was stressed in the general preface in Vol. I, it has been our purpose to concentrate on the comparative chemistry of the elements rather than on the compilation of information element by element. It seems to us that this purpose is best served by dividing the metals into four classes:

1. The pre-transition metals (especially the alkali and alkaline-earth metals);
2. The lanthanides and actinides;
3. The transition metals;
4. The B-metals.

The chapters on the pre-transition metals (Chapter 20), the lanthanides (Chapter 21), and the B-metals (Chapters 30, 31, and 32) then emphasize, respectively, the application of the simple ionic model, the *atomic* character of 'inner' orbitals, and the effects of cation-ligand polarization or partial covalent bonding. These are further illustrated in the chapters on transition-metal chemistry, where in addition the symmetry of the ligand field (Chapter 24 A) becomes particularly significant.

Within each class all the metals are treated together. The same general pattern is adopted in each case, namely atomic structure, valence, structural chemistry, solid-state chemistry, solution chemistry, and where appropriate spectra and magnetism. This pattern is somewhat modified from class to class. Thus in dealing with the very extensive chemistry of the transition metals the discussion is divided into seven separate chapters. Chapter 23 contains an account of atomic structure and a simple introduction to transition-metal valence. It shows how many of the distinctive features of transition-metal chemistry may be qualitatively interpreted in terms of a simple ionic model and the *atomic* characteristics of the 'inner' $(n-1)d$ electrons. The general chemistry is then discussed largely in terms of divalent metals (Chapter 25), higher-valence metals (Chapter 26), and low-oxidation-state metals especially organometallic compounds (Chapter 27). The discussion of the chemistry in terms of *horizontal* series of the divalent ions from Ca^{2+} to Zn^{2+} (Chapter 25) and of the corresponding trivalent ions (Chapter 26) serves to illustrate in particular the general change from pre-transition-metal to B-metal characteristics. Chapter 27 reflects particularly the recent concentration of interest in the unusual structures and reactivities of the organometallic compounds of the transition metals. The spectroscopic and magnetic properties of transition-metal compounds are considered in Chapter 28, and their kinetics in Chapter 29. While the predictions of ligand-field theory (Chapter 24) are a feature of all the transition-metal chapters, they are examined in most detail in Chapter 28 where the theory has its most powerful application.

A comparison between the different classes of metals is afforded by the discussions of qualitative analysis and occurrence in Chapter 34: a general link between them is also provided by the simple related discussions of valence and Oxidation State Diagrams in the earlier chapters.

As in Vol. I the material has been arranged deliberately so that the book may be used by readers at different stages of sophistication. Thus a general introduction to metal chemistry can be obtained by using only about half this volume: Chapters 20, 21, 23, 24 A, 25, 26, 30, 31, and 32 are recommended as a basis for such an approach.

A number of problems are given at the end of each chapter, but, because of the manner in which the book has been written, it should also be a most useful general exercise for students to consider all the facets in the chemistry of an individual element. Some guidance for this may be found in the Element Index.

We wish to thank authors and publishers for permission to reproduce diagrams in both volumes: in each case the source has been acknowledged in the text.

C. S. G. P.

R. J. P. W.

Merton College
Wadham College
Oxford

CONTENTS

PART III

METALS

19 · Metals and Alloys

19.1. Introduction

Most elements are metals. This volume is concerned with their chemistry. It is convenient at the outset to distinguish two kinds of combination into which metal atoms can enter. In the first, metal atoms are either combined with identical atoms to give the metallic elements or they are combined with other metal atoms to give alloys. This will be the subject-matter of this chapter. In the second, metal atoms are combined with non-metal atoms, particularly those of markedly greater electronegativity. In this combination the metals may be regarded to a first approximation as existing as ions, and demonstrating that electropositive character which is the *chemical* hallmark of a metal. This will be the subject-matter of most of the remaining chapters in this volume. Intermediate kinds of combination are also possible, as in many metallic borides, carbides, silicides, arsenides, etc. These have already been treated in Part II. Since the discussions of the two kinds of combination tend to be quite distinct, those who so wish may pass over this chapter and start directly at Chapter 20.

The first kind of combination has already been considered in some detail in Part I. In Chapter 3 the binding energies of all the metals were treated in outline. For our purposes these are the most significant properties of metals, and we shall therefore consider them in more detail in this chapter. Many of the physical properties of metals were discussed in Chapter 6 on the band model, where metals were characterized by the possession of incompletely filled bands of valence electrons. The thermodynamics of alloy formation was a central theme of Chapter 8.

The physics and chemistry of metals is a subject of immense practical importance. It is commonly regarded as a science of its own, the science of metals or metallurgy, and many textbooks of inorganic chemistry hardly touch upon the properties of metals at all. The boundary between chemistry and metallurgy is hard to define: as between so many sciences little is to be gained by setting up artificial distinctions. We shall, however, concentrate on those aspects of metals which are of most interest to chemists, and deliberately avoid any extensive discussion of such topics as phase relations, grain and surface phenomena, and mechanical properties in general.

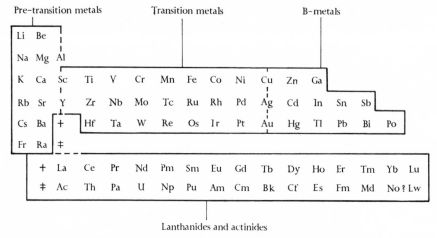

Fig. 19.1. The classification of metals used throughout this book.

CLASSIFICATION OF METALS

The metals may be divided into four main classes (Fig. 19.1):

(1) The pre-transition metals. These occur in Group Iᴀ and IIᴀ of the Periodic Table, and for a number of purposes it is also convenient to include with these the Group III metals, Al, Sc, and Y.

(2) The lanthanides and actinides.

(3) The transition metals. These occur from Group IIIᴀ to Group Iʙ, although transitional character is not very marked in Sc, Y, and La, while the metals of Group Iʙ also show B-metal character.

(4) The B metals. These occur from Group Iʙ onwards into the non-metals.

The chemistry of the pre-transition metals is largely dominated by their outermost s electrons, which are readily removed to form ions of noble-gas electron structures. In the metallic state these electrons occupy essentially s electron bands in the Group Iᴀ metals, but in Group IIᴀ the overlapping np and $(n-1)d$ bands play a very important role. These metals and their alloys one with another will be discussed in section 19.2. The lanthanides are characterized by the building up of an inner $(n-2)f$ electron sub-shell, which to a first approximation is chemically inert in the M^{3+} and more highly charged ions. Both in their general chemistry and in their metallic properties, they behave therefore very largely as metals with a constant number (3) of valence electrons. An $(n-2)f$ electron sub-shell is also built up in the actinide elements, but the electrons are now much more prone to take part in chemical bonding. The lanthanide and actinide metals are discussed in section 19.3. The transition metals have many similarities with the actinide metals. Their inner $(n-1)d$ sub-shells are appreciably involved in bonding, particularly at the beginning of each series, and in general in the second and third transition series more readily than in the first. In the transition metals themselves (section 19.4) the atomic d orbitals are transformed into a metallic d electron band, while in the lanthanides the corresponding f orbitals are best regarded as essentially located on individual atoms. The d sub-shell closes with the elements of Group IB, but it may still be broken into so that Cu, Au, and to a lesser extent Ag, exhibit characteristics of transition-metal chemistry. The B metals are discussed in section 19.5, where their similarity to the non-metals is brought out particularly in the metal structures, most of which are not the regular close-packed (f.c.c., c.p.h., and b.c.c.) structures normally found with the other metals.

BINDING ENERGIES AND RELATED PROPERTIES

This classification of metals will also be used in the following chapters, and it will be one of the objects of this chapter to bring out those features of the metals themselves which are reflected in their general chemistry. One of these is the binding energy of the metal. This is of prime importance because, in most of their compounds, metal atoms have been split away from one another. It is also of interest because there is a useful rough correlation between chemical valence and binding energies. In other words *electrons and orbitals which are of value in binding atoms to atoms of a different kind are also generally important in binding atoms to their own kind.* Many physical properties of metals are related to their binding energies. Thus there is a general though approximate correlation between binding energy and boiling-point, melting-point, hardness, compressibility, and coefficient of expansion.

The relation between binding energy and boiling-point is illustrated in Table 19.I. It will be seen that the ratio of the latent heat of evaporation to the absolute boiling-point (the entropy of vaporization, Trouton's constant) is approximately constant for a wide range of metals, and particularly so when allowance has been made for the contributions to the entropy from the population of low-lying quantum levels available for the gaseous atoms.

The values for Li, Na, and K are unusually low as their vapours are known to contain a considerable proportion of diatomic molecules.

TABLE 19.I. *The relation between latent heats of vaporization and the boiling-points of metals*

Metal	Heat of sublimation to atoms at 25 °C (kcal/ g atom)	Latent heat of vaporization at the boiling-point (kcal/ g atom)	Boiling-point (°K)	Trouton's constant (e.u.)	Allowance† for gas atom quantum levels (e.u.)	Corrected Trouton's constant (e.u.)
Li	38·6	35·3	1702	20·8	1·4	19·4
Na	25·9	21·3	1163	18·3	1·4	16·9
K	21·4	18·5	1039	17·9	1·4	16·5
Be	77·9	70·4	2750	25·6	0	25·6
Mg	35·6	30·8	1390	22·1	0	22·1
Ca	42·2	35·8	1765	20·2	0	20·2
Ba	41·7	36·1	1910	18·9	0	18·9
Al	78·0	70·7	2740	25·8	3·5	22·3
Ti	112·6	102·5	3525	28·7	5·5	23·2
Zr	146·0	139	4700	29·6	3·9	25·7
V	122·8	110	3625	31·2	5·8	25·4
Ta	186·8	180	5700	31·5	2·8	28·7
Cr	94·9	81·3	2938	27·7	3·9	23·8
Mo	157·5	142	5100	27·8	3·6	24·2
Mn	66·7	52·5	2309	22·7	3·6	19·1
Fe	99·6	84·2	3150	26·8	5·1	21·7
Co	101·6	91·4	3150	29·0	4·7	24·3
Ni	102·8	89·6	3175	28·2	5·4	22·8
Pt	134·9	121·7	4105	29·6	4·3	25·3
Cu	80·5	72·0	2820	25·5	1·4	24·1
Ag	68·4	61·0	2450	24·9	1·4	23·5
Au	90·5	82·0	3223	25·4	1·4	24·0
Zn	31·2	27·6	1181	23·4	0	23·4
Cd	26·8	23·9	1038	23·0	0	23·0
Hg	14·7	14·1	630	22·3	0	22·3
Ga	66·5	61·4	2523	24·3	1·7	22·6
In	59·1	55·5	2348	23·6	1·4	22·2
Tl	43·2	39·7	1733	22·9	1·4	21·5
Sn	72·0	69·4	2960	23·5	0	23·5
Pb	46·8	42·9	2020	21·3	0	21·3

Average (excluding alkali metals which give some diatomic vapour molecules) 23·1

Data for this table have been taken mainly from Elliott and Gleiser, *Thermochemistry for Steelmaking*, Addison-Wesley, Reading, Mass., 1960.

† The allowance for the gas-atom quantum-level contributions have been taken from Kelley, *U.S. Bureau of Mines, Bulletin* 477, 1948. Thus for sodium, only the lowest electronic state of the atom needs to be considered. This has a degeneracy of 2, so that the allowance is $R \ln 2 = 1·4$ e.u.

The process of melting is less akin to atomization than is boiling, and melting-points are usually much more structure-sensitive.

STRUCTURES

Polymorphism is commonly found among metals, and for one metal there is in general very little difference in energy between one structure and another. Thus iron crystallizes in the b.c.c. structure (α) up to 1184 °K, when it changes to the f.c.c. structure (γ) with an energy of transition of

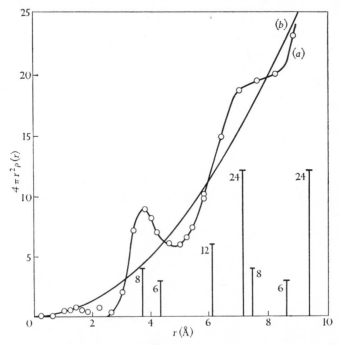

FIG. 19.2. The structure of liquid sodium. (a) Radial distribution of atoms ($4\pi r^2 \rho(r)$ where $\rho(r)$ is the atom density at distance r) as obtained from X-ray diffraction studies. (b) Curve for radial distribution which would be obtained if density were constant. The vertical lines give the numbers of atoms at various distances in crystalline sodium (after Barrett).

0·22 kcal/g atom. At 1665 °K it changes back again to the b.c.c. form (δ) with an energy of transition of 0·27 kcal/g atom. (The term β-iron was used for the f.c.c. structure above the Curie point, 1042 °K, when ferromagnetism disappears without any atomic rearrangement, but this form of iron is now called paramagnetic α-iron.) Iron melts at 1809 °K with a latent heat of fusion of 3·70 kcal/g atom, and boils at 3150 °K with a latent heat of evaporation at the boiling-point of 84·18 kcal/g atom. The heat of sublimation to atoms at 298 °K has been estimated as 99·6 kcal/g atom. While the changes in the solid metal are of immense practical significance, they are much less important in the ordinary chemistry of iron.

Interatomic distances usually vary only slightly from one form to another. Such distances reflect in part the 'true' atomic radii, and in part the strength of metallic binding. Relatively little is known about the structures of liquid metals, but a generally useful picture regards them as 'broken down' or blurred derivatives of the crystalline state. From X-ray diffraction measurements it is possible to construct a radial distribution curve for a liquid metal, an example of which is shown in Fig. 19.2. For most metals, the innermost peak occurs at a distance close to that for the shortest interatomic distance in the solid. Some data on liquid structure are summarized in Table 19.II.

TABLE 19.II. *Structures of the liquid phases of the elements (after Barrett)*

Element	Tempera-ture	Coordination number and nearest atom distance (Å)	
		In liquid	In crystal
Aluminum	700 °C	10–11 at 2·96	12 at 2·86
Argon	84 °K	10–11 at 3·79	12 at 3·84
Bismuth	340 °C	5 at 3·32	3 at 3·10, 3 at 3·47
Cadmium	350 °C	8 at 3·06	6 at 2·98, 6 at 3·29
Chlorine	25 °C	1 at 2·01	1 at 2·02
Gallium	20 °C	11 at 2·77	1 at 2·44
Germanium	1000 °C	8 at 2·70	4 at 2·45
Gold	1100 °C	11 at 2·86	12 at 2·88
Indium	165 °C	8½ at 3·30	4 at 3·24, 8 at 3·36
	165 °C	8 at 3·17, 4 at 3·88	
Lead	375 °C	8 at 3·40, 4 at 4·37	12 at 3·50
Lithium	200 °C	10 at 3·24	8 at 3·03
Mercury	20 °C	8 at 3·0	6 at 3·00, 6 at 3·47, 6 at 4·59
Nitrogen	89 °K	1 at 1·3	
Oxygen	89 °K	1 at 1·3	
Phosphorus:			
Liquid yellow	48 °C	3 at 2·25	
Amorphous red and black	20–50 °C	3 at 2·28	2 at 2·17, 1 at 2·20
Potassium	70 °C	8 at 4·64	8 at 4·63
Sodium	100 °C	8 at 3·83	8 at 3·72
Sulphur	20 °C	2 at 2·08	2 at 2·04
	225 °C	1·7 at 2·07	
Thallium	375 °C	8 at 3·30, 4 at 4·22	6 at 3·41, 6 at 3·46
Tin	280 °C	11 at 3·20	4 at 3·02, 2 at 3·18
Zinc	460 °C	11 at 2·94	6 at 2·66, 6 at 2·91

OPTICAL, ELECTRICAL, AND MAGNETIC PROPERTIES

All metals absorb and reflect light strongly, these processes being associated with energy changes in the electron bands. The appearance of a metal is very much influenced by the thin film of oxide with which it is usually covered. A clean metallic iron surface is much brighter than the iron surface normally encountered. An artificially thickened aluminium oxide film may be dyed to produce a variety of very bright surface colours. The colours of copper and gold will be discussed in section 19.5. The incompletely-filled electron bands make metals good conductors of heat and electricity: an electrical conductivity which falls with rise of temperature (see Fig. 19.3) is the *physical* hallmark of a metal.

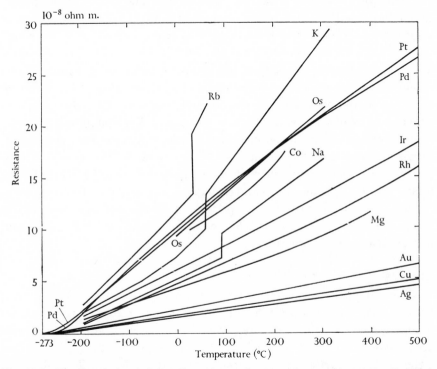

FIG. 19.3. The electrical resistivity of metals as a function of temperature (after Guertler).

When a substance is placed in a magnetic field, a force is exerted on it. The ratio of the force or intensity of magnetization to the field inducing it is called the susceptibility, χ. There are three main types of magnetic behaviour:

(1) Diamagnetism, in which χ is small and negative, so that substances are weakly repelled by the field. Diamagnetism is present in all substances. It is largely a phenomenon in which individual atoms act independently,

so that the diamagnetism of compounds can normally be computed from individual atomic parameters with a few constitutive corrections.

(2) Paramagnetism, in which χ is fairly small and positive, so that substances are attracted by a magnetic field. Where present it usually swamps the diamagnetism. It is again commonly a phenomenon in which individual atoms act independently, but in metals the important contributions are often from the collective energy bands.

(3) Ferromagnetism, in which χ is large and positive, so that substances are strongly attracted. Examples include metallic iron, cobalt, nickel, gadolinium, and various alloys such as Cu_2MnAl. Ferromagnetism is associated with co-operative interactions between individual atoms which tend to align their electron spins parallel to one another. In antiferromagnetic substances atoms tend to align so as to cancel out each other's magnetic moment. Ferromagnetism and antiferromagnetism diminish with rise of temperature and are normally replaced by paramagnetism above a critical temperature (Curie point and Néel point respectively) which is characteristic of the substance. In most compounds the magnetically-significant metallic ions are too far apart for ferromagnetic or antiferromagnetic behaviour, and such compounds are said to be 'magnetically dilute'. However, some oxides and carbides, for example, are ferromagnetic.

The periodicity of magnetic properties among the metals is brought out in Fig. 19.4. In general A metals are paramagnetic, while B metals and non-metals are diamagnetic.

ALLOYS

Alloys are phases formed from two or more metals. They may be divided broadly into two types, (1) substitutional, where different metal atoms occupy somewhat equivalent sites, and (2) interstitial, where smaller atoms are inserted into 'holes' in the structure of the larger atoms. Interstitial structures are particularly common in carbides, nitrides, hydrides, etc. Substitutional-type alloys are in general restricted by three factors—atomic sizes, electron/atom ratios, and electronegativity differences. Primary solubility of one atom in the lattice of another is small if the difference in atomic radii is greater than 15 per cent. Electron/atom ratio effects have already been considered in Chapter 6. The greater the difference in electronegativity between two atoms, the greater their tendency to form a compound rather than an alloy. In general like dissolves like, and unlike forms compounds with unlike. For this reason alloys formed between metals of the same class are treated in the section devoted to this class, while alloys between different classes of metals are treated in section 19.6. Many of the reactions of metals will be dealt with in later chapters, but as an example of these reactions the general problem of metallic corrosion is discussed very briefly in section 19.7. Like so much else in this chapter, this is a very large

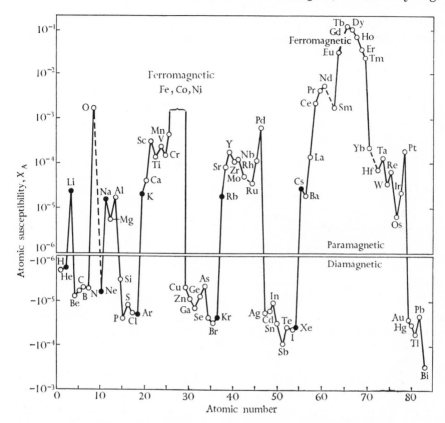

FIG. 19.4. Magnetic properties of the elements. Atomic susceptibilities at 0 °C.

problem of immense industrial importance, of which we can do no more than give an outline.

19.2. Pre-transition metals

THE METALS

For the most part the metals of this class are highly reactive and therefore of little metallurgical interest. Very important exceptions are provided by magnesium alloys and aluminium, whose surfaces are protected by stable oxide films, and which are used on an enormous scale where light metals are required. The alkali metals are of considerable theoretical interest because of the relative simplicity of their energy-band structures. They were referred to frequently in Chapter 6 on this account.

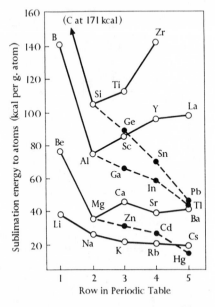

FIG. 19.5. The binding energies of the pre-transition metals and of some related elements.

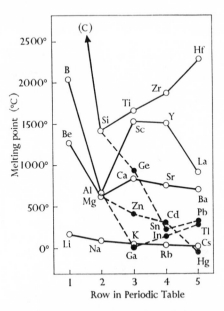

FIG. 19.6. The melting-points of the pre-transition metals and of some related elements.

The interatomic binding in Group II is associated with an overlap of the s and p bands (contrast helium), and the relatively low binding energies of Mg and Al may be a result of the relatively high $s \to p$ promotion energy in the atoms of the second row of the Periodic Table (see Chapter 18). The $(n-1)d$ bands are of considerable importance in scandium, yttrium, and lanthanum, are probably important in calcium, strontium, and barium, and may even play a role in the heavier alkali metals such as Rb and Cs.

The metallic binding energies (heats of atomization at 25 °C) are plotted in Fig. 19.5, together with some values from corresponding B Groups and from Group IV for comparison. The melting-points of the same elements are plotted in Fig. 19.6, and it will be seen that there is a general correlation between Figs. 19.5 and 19.6, which breaks down, however, on points of detail. As stated above melting-points are a good deal more structure-sensitive than boiling-points.

The metallic radii are plotted in Fig. 19.7. In each Group there is a general increase in size with increase in atomic number. The breaks between K and Rb, and between Ca and Sr, may be associated with the appearance of the first transition series (see Chapter 18), and similar breaks would be expected between Cs and Fr, and between Ba and Ra, associated

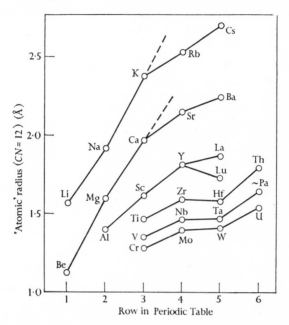

Fig. 19.7. Atomic radii for the metals of Groups IA to VIA.

with the appearance of the lanthanide series. The lanthanide contraction is clearly shown between La and Lu, and in the remarkably similar radii of Zr and Hf, Nb and Ta, Mo and W, respectively. The general contraction with increasing Group number in any row of the Periodic Table is in part due to the increase of effective nuclear charge, which will reduce the size of the free atom, and in part due to the increase of binding energy as more electrons (and to some extent more effective orbitals) are used to bond the metal atoms to one another. The alkali metals are examples of what are known as 'open' metals: the interatomic distances are so large that there can be little overlap between individual alkali *ions* in the cloud of valence electrons. Many of the properties of these metals may therefore be interpreted in terms of the properties of the metallic 'free'-electron cloud.

ALLOYS

The formation of alloys between one pre-transition metal and another is limited by differences in atomic size. Thus immiscible liquids are formed in the Li—Na, Li—K, Li—Rb, and Li—Cs systems, while continuous solid solutions are formed only in the K—Rb, K—Cs, and Rb—Cs systems.

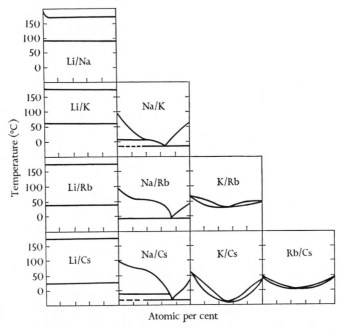

Fig. 19.8. Phase diagrams for the binary alloys of the alkali metals. Each diagram shows how the melting points of the pure metals change on adding a second metal (from Böhm and Klemm, *Z. anorg. Chem.*, 1940, **243**, 69).

This is illustrated by the phase diagrams reproduced in Fig. 19.8, and is in conformity with the percentage size increases of Li to Na (22 per cent), Na to K (24 per cent), K to Rb (6 per cent), K to Cs (14 per cent), and Rb to Cs (7 per cent) (see also Fig. 19.6). A rather analogous situation develops in Group I$_B$: the Cu—Ag phase diagram is similar to that for Na—K, the Ag—Au to that for K—Rb, and the Cu—Au to that for K—Cs. The highly electropositive character of the alkali metals also limits their formation of solid solutions as distinct from metallic compounds. A continuous range of solid solutions can of course occur (see Chapter 8) only if, over its whole extent, the plot of the free energy of mixing against mole fraction is convex towards the mole fraction axis. Compound formation will tend to produce regions of mole fraction where the free energy will be unusually low.

A chart of elements whose solubility in magnesium is known is given in Fig. 19.9, and a similar chart for aluminium is given later in Fig. 19.27 (section 19.6). In both charts the importance of atomic size and electronegativity is stressed.† The N(E)/E (band-model) curve for aluminium

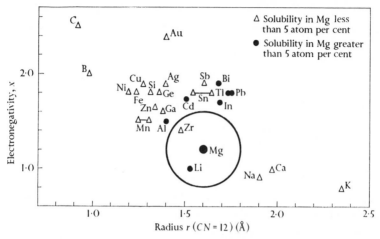

Fɪɢ. 19.9. Solubility of elements in magnesium (after Darken and Gurry).

appears to rise to a narrow peak in the region of three electrons per atom, and it has been suggested that this is one of the reasons why the solubility of most elements in aluminium is particularly restricted. If this is so we have a clear instance of the third limiting factor in metal–metal solubility, the electron/atom ratio.

SOLUTIONS OF METALS IN LIQUID AMMONIA

All the alkali and alkaline-earth metals other than beryllium dissolve to some extent in ammonia, amines, ethers, alcohols, and even oxygen-free water to form blue paramagnetic solutions. Blue solutions are also formed when the metals are dissolved in molten salts, hydroxides, and amides. At high concentrations such solutions have many metallic properties, and have been considered as examples of an expanded metal containing units such as $Na(NH_3)_6$, the electrons moving in expanded orbitals which include the ammonia molecules. From such solutions metallic solids such as $Ca(NH_3)_6$ may be isolated. At lower concentrations the properties of these solutions become more 'salt-like', the metal ions carrying about one-seventh of the

† Too much quantitative significance should not be attached to the electronegativity scale in these diagrams; see Hume–Rothery, 'Some Electron Theories of Alloys', *Metallurgist*, 1964, **3**, 11.

electric current. The conductivity passes through a minimum. The dilute metal solutions have two intense absorption maxima, one in the infra-red about 7000 cm^{-1} and one in the visible about 15,000 cm^{-1}. The infra-red band is associated with the paramagnetic species present and is the only one to appear in very dilute solutions. It has been suggested that this band is due to a solvated-electron anion, and that the expanded metal first breaks down mainly to dimer units $Na_2(NH_3)_n$ which then break down further to Na ions and electrons in cavities of the solvent. Dimer units are probably responsible for the 15,000 cm^{-1} band. These metal-ammonia solutions are of great importance as reducing agents, especially in organic chemistry.

19.3. Lanthanides and actinides

THE METALS

The properties of the lanthanide metals, particularly their magnetic properties, strongly suggest that for the most part they can be regarded as elements contributing three valence electrons per atom to the metallic bands, while the remaining 4f electrons are essentially located on individual atoms and fairly well shielded from the influence of neighbouring atoms. In the actinides, however, the number of electrons in the metallic bands appears to be much more variable, and, as in their chemistry, they show a variable valence which links their properties somewhat with those expected of a transition series.

This distinction is brought out by the various physical properties plotted in Fig. 19.10. Relatively small changes are found along the lanthanide series, while there are quite marked changes in the actinide series. The most clear-cut anomalies in the lanthanides are provided by Eu and Yb, which behave much as would be expected of divalent metals. These are also the lanthanide metals which most readily form divalent ions in their compounds, these ions having half-filled and filled 4f sub-shells respectively. The transition-metal character of the actinide metals is most marked in the early members of the series; again this behaviour is paralleled in the general chemistry. The actinide metals are notable for their very numerous allotropic forms.

The electrical resistivities of the lanthanide metals are higher than those for any other close-packed metals. Bridgman has shown that under high pressures the lanthanides undergo a number of transitions which are only revealed by measurements of electrical resistivity. These appear to be associated with a transfer of electrons between 'atomic' orbitals and the conduction band, and if this is so they should be of considerable theoretical

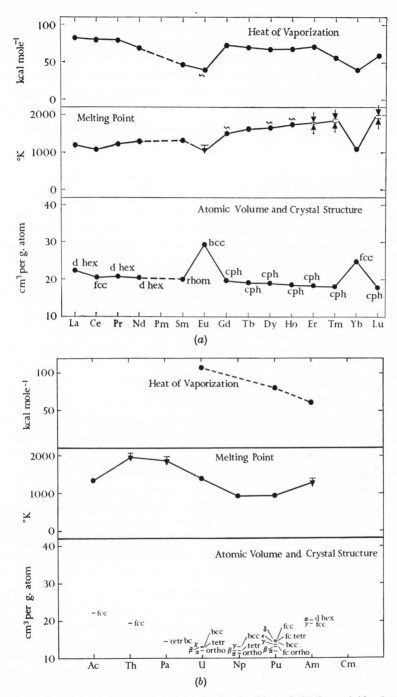

Fig. 19.10. Some physical properties of (a) the lanthanide and (b) the actinide elements (after Seaborg and Katz, eds., *The Actinide Elements*, McGraw-Hill, New York, 1954).

interest. The metals are appreciably paramagnetic. Yttrium which is sometimes included with the lanthanides is only mildly so. Gadolinium is strongly ferromagnetic below 16 °C. Dysprosium is strongly ferromagnetic below -168 °C, and exhibits a remarkable magnetic anisotropy, very much stronger magnetic fields being required to produce saturation along one crystal axis than another. Antiferromagnetic behaviour is also found.

ALLOYS

The lanthanide metals readily form alloys with one another, but apart from this they will form extensive solutions or intermetallic compounds only with the later actinides. The actinide metals—at least from thorium to americium—are not soluble in one another to any great extent.

A particularly interesting lanthanide alloy is 'mischmetall', with 50 per cent Ce, 25 per cent La, and the rest mostly Nd and Pr. This alloy is added to partly purified iron when it preferentially removes elements such as C, O, S, N, and P into the slag as lanthanide compounds. Mischmetall is also used in cigarette-lighter flints as it is pyrophoric.

19.4. Transition metals

ELECTRONIC STRUCTURES

Our understanding of the electronic structure of the transition metals is very far from complete, but a useful general picture may be developed in terms of the band theory. The s and d orbitals of the isolated atoms broaden out into bands in the metallic crystals, e.g. Fig. 19.11. It is convenient to distinguish between an s band (which will involve in its higher regions a fair amount of p character as well) and a predominantly d band. The s band is relatively broad in the crystal, as there is considerable overlap between the s orbitals of the metal atoms. It will have a low density of energy levels in so far as it is derived from an atomic s orbital which holds only two electrons per atom. On the other hand the d band will be broad at the beginning of the transition series, but will contract as the d electrons are drawn into the atomic cores across the transition series. At copper, for example, where the d band is full with ten electrons per atom, the d band width has been estimated as 3·5 eV while the occupied region of the s band probably extends over about 7 eV, the depth of the d band below the Fermi surface (i.e. below the highest occupied s levels) being about 2·3 eV. The d band is able to hold ten electrons per atom, so that the density of levels is very much greater than in the s band.

The band theory naturally emphasizes the collective nature of the valence electrons. It is also possible to treat the transition metals on a localized-electron picture, in which the movement of d electrons into atomic cores may be partly described by regarding some of the d electrons as essentially atomic while the rest contribute to bonding. Pauling, on

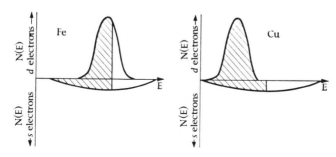

FIG. 19.11. Band structures for iron and copper (schematic).

the basis of magnetic moments, has thus drawn up a bonding scheme in which the five d orbitals are split into about two non-bonding (atomic) orbitals and about three bonding orbitals. This particular approach cannot be easily summarized. For details see Pauling, *The Nature of the Chemical Bond*, 3rd ed., Cornell University Press, Ithaca, 1960. It has also been suggested by Griffith and Orgel that in the body-centred cubic metals, two of the d orbitals (d_{z^2} and $d_{x^2-y^2}$) would be non-bonding as they have zero amplitudes along all the nearest-neighbour directions. Thus b.c.c. iron is ferromagnetic with a saturation moment corresponding to two unpaired electrons, and this would be interpreted in terms of two electrons with parallel spins, one in each of the non-bonding d orbitals. Both the Pauling view and that of Griffith and Orgel fit in well with the neutron-diffraction data which reveal a moment corresponding to about two atomic electrons per atom.

All these treatments are alike in attributing a strong bonding contribution from d electrons at the beginning of a transition series, where the s and d electrons are energetically similar, and a weaker contribution from the d electrons in the later members of each series. On the band-theory this weakening of d bonding is discussed in terms of a narrowing of the d band, and on the localized electron theories in terms of an increasing occupation by electrons of non-bonding or atomic d orbitals.

BINDING ENERGIES

The heats of sublimation of the metals in the three transition series are plotted in Fig. 19.12 which has already appeared in Chapter 3. A number of simple properties are related to the binding energies, as will be seen by inspection of Figs. 19.13 to 19.16 which show the corresponding melting-points, compressibilities, coefficients of expansion, and atomic diameters

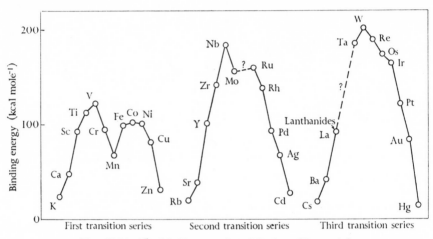

Fig. 19.12. The binding energies of the transition metals.

of the metal atoms. An exact correspondence between all these figures should not be expected, as other factors will be operating in addition to the overall binding energy in determining the various properties. Thus the low compressibilities of Cu and Au, as compared with, say, Ti and Hf, must in part be due to the strong repulsion between the closed d sub-shells, which would result from compressing the Ib metals. Again the atomic diameters reflect the general isolated-atom contraction along a transition series as well as changes in binding energy.

At the beginning of each transition series, the binding energies rise steadily with increasing numbers of electrons. This type of behaviour has already been commented on in Chapter 3, and suggests that it might be reasonable to suppose that all the 'valence' electrons (i.e. $3d$ and $4s$ in the first transition series) are here contributing to metal binding. The steady rise in binding energies ceases after Group Va in the first and second transition series, and after Group VIa in the third transition series. The normal chemical valences of the metals similarly change at these points. Thus in its compounds Cr is most stable in the trivalent state, while Mo and W are

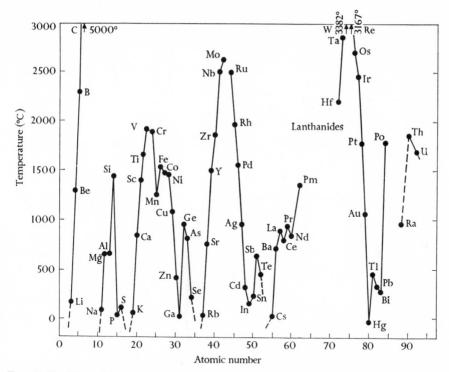

FIG. 19.13. The melting-points of the transition metals (after Hume-Rothery and Coles).

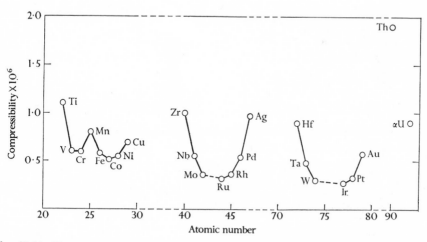

FIG. 19.14. The compressibilities of the transition metals (after Hume-Rothery and Coles).

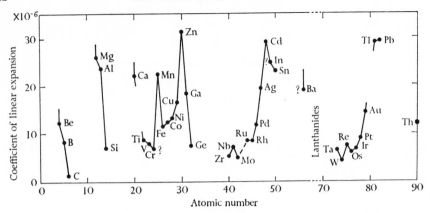

FIG. 19.15. The coefficients of expansion of the transition metals (after Hume-Rothery and Coles).

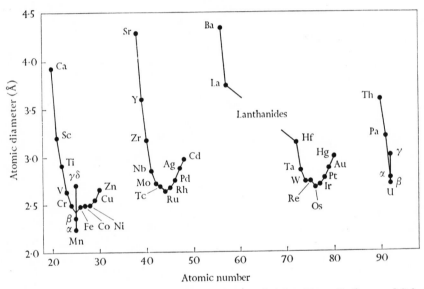

FIG. 19.16. The atomic diameters of the transition metals (after Hume-Rothery and Coles).

most stable in the Group valence of 6. In the chemistry of the elements following V, the Group valence state is either strongly oxidizing (Cr and Mn) or non-existent (Fe, Co, and Ni).

ELECTRICAL CONDUCTIVITY

The electrical conductivities for the metals of the first transition series are plotted in Fig. 19.17. Resistance arises from the thermal vibrations of the lattice, and the consequent scattering of the electrons. Correction

factors for this effect may be deduced from the theory of specific heats, so
that the conductivities may be compared at constant lattice vibration.
The relative conductivities thus obtained are shown by the lower line in
Fig. 19.17. In comparison with, for example, K, Ca, or Zn, the conductivities of the main transition metals are now much reduced because of

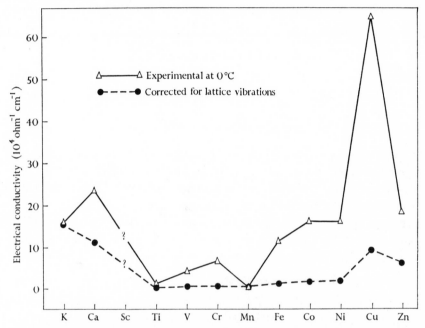

FIG. 19.17. The electrical conductivities for the metals of the first transition series.
The ordinate scale refers only to the experimental values.

their stronger binding energies in the metallic crystals. These low corrected
conductivities of the transition metals are due to the small mean free paths
of their s electrons. Irregularities in the metal can lead to s electrons
jumping into the d band, and it can be shown that the probability of this
happening will depend upon the number of vacant quantum levels in the
d band in the same range of energy. This probability will be high because
of the very high density of energy levels in the d band.

THERMAL PROPERTIES

The transition metals are also good conductors of heat. On the free-
electron theory it is predicted that there should be a direct relation between
the thermal, k, and electrical, σ, conductivities, the Wiedemann–Franz ratio.
The Lorenz number, $k/\sigma T$, has the theoretical value of $2\cdot45 \times 10^{-8}$ watt ohm

deg^{-2}. In this connexion the transition metals (as well as non-transition metals such as Cd, Sn, and Pb) are reasonably represented by the free-electron theory (Table 19.III). The contribution of the electrons to the specific heat of a metal is relatively low, for an appreciable effect can be expected only from the electrons at the top of the band. These electrons can be raised to vacant levels by the small amounts of thermal energy.

TABLE 19.III. *The Lorenz number for various metals*
$(10^{-8}$ *watt ohm deg*$^{-2})$

	273 °K	373 °K		273 °K	373 °K
Mo	2·61	2·79	Cu	2·23	2·33
W	3·04	3·20	Ag	2·31	2·37
Ir	2·49	2·49	Au	2·35	2·40
Pt	2·51	2·60			

The experimental values, which can be estimated most reliably from low-temperature data, are higher than those for non-transition metals, which is a consequence of the relatively high density of levels (d and s) at the top of the Fermi sea. Values for the three transition series are given (lower curve) in Fig. 19.18. Simple free-electron calculations for electrons in an s band suggest that the electronic contribution would be of the order of $10^{-4}T$ cal mole^{-1} deg^{-1}.

MAGNETISM

All transition metals exhibit weak paramagnetic behaviour, at high temperatures. At low temperatures this may be swamped by ferromagnetism, as in iron, cobalt, and nickel below their Curie temperatures, or by antiferromagnetism. An unfilled electron band will give rise to paramagnetism. In the absence of an applied field, the band will contain very nearly equal numbers of electrons with each spin (Fig. 19.19 (a)). On application of a magnetic field, electrons of one spin will be lowered in energy while those of opposite spin will be raised in energy. There is, therefore, a redistribution of electrons to give a net excess of electron spins in line with the applied field (Fig. 19.19 (b)). The effect will be related to the density of energy levels at the top of the band, so that some correlation between atomic susceptibilities and electronic specific heats might be expected, as is shown in Fig. 19.18.

Isolated transition-metal ions with incompleted d sub-shells can also give rise to strong paramagnetism as a result of the magnetic ordering of their otherwise randomly oriented magnetic moments. This is very commonly observed in the compounds of transition metals, where the paramagnetic susceptibilities are much greater (about a hundredfold) than in the metals. It would appear that in all transition *metals* the overlap of d orbitals is

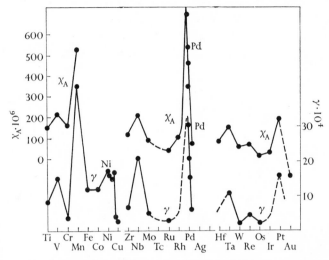

FIG. 19.18. A comparison of the magnetic susceptibilities per atom (upper curve, left-hand scale) and the electronic specific heats, cal degree⁻¹ atom⁻¹ (lower curve, right-hand scale), of the transition metals (after Caterall, *J. Proc. Inst. Chem. Gt. Br.*, 1960, **110**, 319).

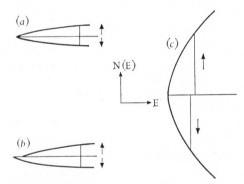

FIG. 19.19. Schematic band structures for paramagnetic ((*a*) and (*b*)) and ferromagnetic ((*c*)) metals. The arrows indicate electron spins. See text for further details.

sufficiently strong to prevent individual ions from showing completely random magnetic behaviour. The same type of restriction, however, may not apply to the *f* orbitals of the lanthanide series, and the relatively high paramagnetic moments, particularly of the later lanthanide metals (see Fig. 19.4), may be associated with contributions from individual ions.

As the d band is drawn into the atomic cores towards the end of the first transition series, the phenomenon of ferromagnetism appears. There has been considerable theoretical speculation about the origin of ferro-magnetism. It certainly seems to be associated with a high ratio of atomic radius to radius of the d sub-shell, and with a correspondingly high density

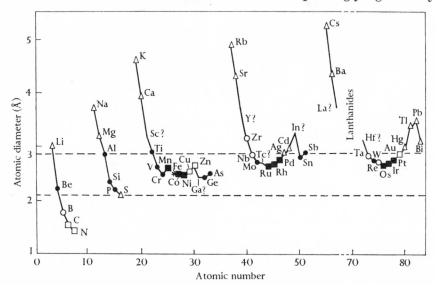

Fig. 19.20. Atomic diameters of elements with favourable size-factor for iron. The dotted lines cut off the diameters which are within 15 per cent of the atomic diameter of iron. The triangles represent elements whose solubilities in iron are very small. The other symbols distinguish different kinds of binary alloy. For further details see Hume-Rothery and Raynor from whom this diagram is reproduced.

of energy levels in the d band. In terms of the band structure it may be crudely pictured as a spontaneous occupation of electron levels with electrons of parallel spin (Fig. 19.19 (c)), just as with *degenerate* levels in the lowest energy states of atoms and molecules. In terms of the individual ions it can be interpreted in wave-mechanical language as a co-operative aligning of individual spins resulting from a positive exchange integral. Antiferromagnetism would then arise when this integral was negative.

Ferromagnetic substances commonly exhibit a *domain* structure, in which each domain is permanently magnetized. The direction of magnetization can, however, be different in different domains so that the material as a whole may appear to be unmagnetized. On application of an external magnetic field the favourably oriented domains grow at the expense of the others.

ALLOYS

In the absence of any satisfactory theory of the pure transition metals, it is only natural that our understanding of their alloys should be on a very qualitative level. Solid solutions in transition alloys are limited by the usual size-factor (see Fig. 19.20), by electron/atom ratios, and by the

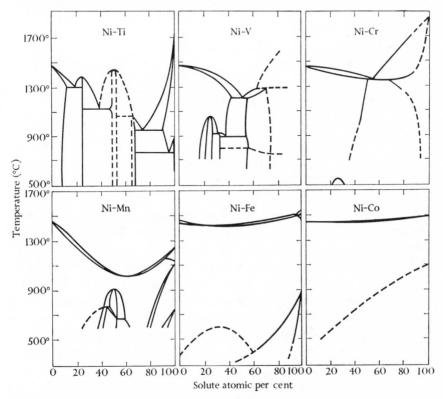

FIG. 19.21. Binary phase diagrams for nickel and other elements of the first transition series (after Hume-Rothery and Coles).

tendency to form compounds rather than solutions with the electronegative elements. There are among the transition metals themselves a large number of atoms of similar size, as will be seen by reference to Fig. 19.16, and this is particularly marked among the middle members of the second and third transition series, where the effect of the lanthanide contraction is to bring the two series close to one another in sizes. Solid solutions in the c.p.h. modifications of transition metals are much more restricted than in either the f.c.c. or b.c.c. forms. Superlattices are formed in transition-metal alloys to a much greater extent than would be expected from differences in size and electronegativity (e.g. in the Fe–Co and Fe–Ni systems), but the general tendency for ordered structures to become more stable with increase of the size-factor effect is still clear. This is shown by the equilibrium diagrams of Fig. 19.21, for Ni with all other metals from Ti to Co,

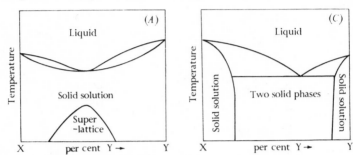

FIG. 19.22. Types of phase diagram common for components X and Y, both of which are transition metals. Very frequently the eutectic diagram (C) is broken up into a large number of phases (see Smithells).

in which there is a change to unstable superlattices (disordered on heating to relatively low temperatures) from intermetallic compounds (ordered up to the melting-point).

The changes in the interaction between two transition metals can be described simply in terms of the two phase diagrams of Fig. 19.22. In case (A) there is complete miscibility in the solid state, but this is broken at lower temperatures: the metals X and Y are rather similar. In case (C) the phase diagram contains a eutectic. If the mutual solid solution regions do not extend beyond about 20 per cent then X and Y are considerably dissimilar. Intermediate behaviour between (A) and (C) will be represented by more extensive solid solution and this will be classified as (B) behaviour. It must be understood that the area ('two solid phases') between the two regions of mutual miscibility of Fig. 19.22 (C) is usually broken up into a large number of different phases (see Chapter 8).

Table 19.IV classifies the phase diagrams of a large number of binary transition-metal systems. The alloys in Table 19.IV (a) are formed between two metals of the first transition series. The restrictions of solid solution are not related to size, but are more clearly dependent on the changing electronegativity. The alloys of first series metals with the elements of one transition-metal Group are compared in Table 19.IV (b). Group similarities are very strongly marked. The metals of the first series differ from those of the second and third series more than the latter differ from each other.

TABLE 19.IV. *The character of binary phase diagrams. The diagrams are divided into three classes, A, B, and C (see text)*

(a) *Alloys of two metals from the first transition series*

	Ti	V	Cr	Mn	Fe	Co	Ni	Cu	Zn
Ti	..	A	A	C	C	C	C	C	C
Cr	A	A	..	C	A	B	C	C	C
Fe	C	A	A	A	..	A	A	C	C
Ni	C	C	C	A	A	A	..	A	B

(b) *Alloys of two metals, one from the first transition series*

	Cr	Mo	W
Cr	..	A	A
Co	B	B?	C
Ni	C	B?	B

	Ni	Pd	Pt
Cr	C	C	C
Co	A	A	A
Ni	..	A	A

(c) *Alloys of two metals from the second or third transition metal series*

Class A	Class B	Class C
Zr—Nb, Mo—W	Zr—Au	Zr—Mo
Ru—Pt, Os—Pt	W—Pt	Zr—W
Rh—Pt, Ir—Pt	Pt—Ag	Zr—Ag
Pd—Pt, Pd—Ag		
Pd—Au, Pt—Au		

Thus Mo and W give a phase diagram corresponding to almost ideal solution behaviour. Table 19.IV (c) shows that the solution of two metals from the second or third series is again restricted by electronegativity considerations. Compared with other transition metals Ni, Pd, and Pt are relatively soluble in B metals such as Cu, Ag, and Au.

As an illustration of the continuous change in physical properties with electron concentration in transition-metal series, Fig. 19.23 plots magnetic susceptibility per atom against electron concentration. The importance of electron concentration per atom here outweighs electronegativity or size-factor differences for the majority of systems. However, if two of the metals are somewhat dissimilar, e.g. Ni/Mn, Co/Cr, other factors than electron concentration affect physical properties. For a further discussion of the importance of the electron concentration principle in these alloys see Hume-Rothery 'A Note on the Intermetallic Chemistry of the Later Transition Elements', *J. Less-Common Metals*, 1964, **7**, 152.

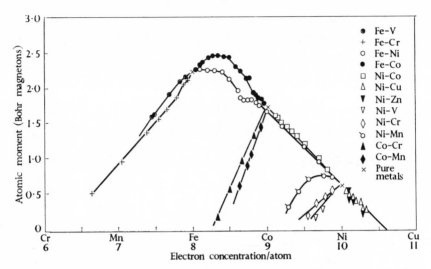

Fig. 19.23. Magnetic susceptibilities of a series of binary alloys of transition metals (after Hume-Rothery and Coles).

19.5. B metals

BINDING

Many of the properties of the B metals and their alloys have been treated in previous sections of this chapter or in Part I. Their binding energies (excluding those of I B) are plotted in Fig. 19.5, and the corresponding melting-points in Fig. 19.6. Their boiling-points are plotted in Fig. 19.24, together with those of the typical and non-metallic elements for comparison. There are three general Group patterns. (1) In Group I, Cu, Ag, and Au have much higher boiling-points than do Li and Na. This pattern is also found in other related properties such as binding energy and melting-point, as may be seen from various figures in the previous section. In fact Cu, Ag, and Au exhibit in these ways their positions at the ends of the three transition series, where the $(n-1)d$ electrons still play a role in interatomic bonding. (2) Down Groups II, III, and IV there is a fairly steady fall in boiling-point associated with the general fall in interatomic binding. The solids all have structures with continuous three-dimensional chemical binding, and to a reasonable approximation the liquids boil to give atomic vapours. (3) In the remaining Groups the boiling-points rise steadily with increase in atomic weight. This is in part due to increased van der Waals' interaction (e.g. the noble gases), and in part due to those increased chemical interactions between molecules which are associated with the change from molecular structures (e.g. N_2) to structures which are essentially metallic (e.g. Bi). The relation between heats of atomization and boiling-points is now completely invalid.

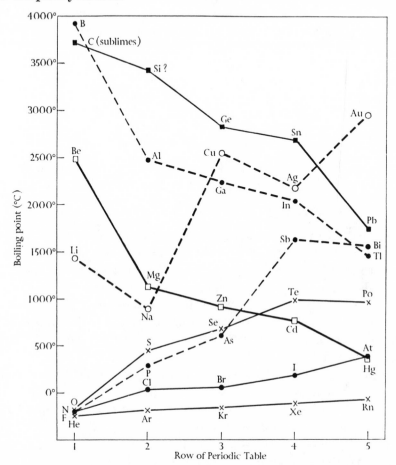

FIG. 19.24. Boiling-points of the B metals together with boiling-points of some typical and non-metallic elements for comparison of Group relations.

COLOUR

The occurrence of filled d bands near to the electron energy surface provides an explanation for the colours of metallic copper, silver, and gold. The bands for copper and silver are shown schematically in Fig. 19.25. X-ray data indicate that the top of the d band is about 2·3 eV below the Fermi surface (s–p band) in copper, and about 4 eV below in silver. Electrons from the copper d band can therefore be excited to the s–p band by green, blue, or violet light, but not by the red end of the spectrum. Electrons from the silver d band can only be correspondingly excited by ultra-violet radiation. This distinction between copper and silver is in complete accord with the details of atomic structure which will be discussed in section 23.2, for the $4d$ electrons in the silver atom are held more firmly than are the

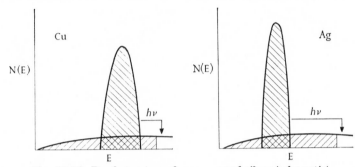

FIG. 19.25. Band structures for copper and silver (schematic).

$3d$ electrons in the copper atom. It is also in accord with the general chemistry of the two elements, for the $(n-1)d$ sub-shell is easily broken in copper to give Cu(II) compounds, but is only broken with difficulty in silver, whose chemistry is predominantly that of Ag(I). Solution of zinc atoms in copper metal will increase the electron/atom ratio, so that the s–p band is occupied to higher levels. The absorption peak moves to lower wavelengths and the colour of the alloys changes from the orange-red of copper to the yellow of brass.

The absorption peak for gold occurs at slightly shorter wavelengths than that for copper, but at longer wavelengths than that for silver. It is again reasonable to associate the yellow colour of gold with excitation of electrons from the $(n-1)d$ band to the s–p band. The atomic structures (section 23.2) show that, following the introduction of the lanthanide series of elements, the $6s$ (and $6p$) electrons are relatively stabilized, while the $5d$ appear to be somewhat destabilized. Gold does not therefore have the properties expected by an extrapolation from copper and silver, but in many respects has affinities with copper. This is also brought out in the chemistry of gold, where Au(III) is a normal valence state.

STRUCTURES

The structures of the B metals are of considerable interest as they form a link between the typical close-packed and related metal structures of the A metals, and the individual structures of the non-metals, in many of which each atom has $8-N$ near neighbours, where N is the Group number.

In fact, following Hume-Rothery and Raynor, the elements may be divided roughly into three structural classes as in Fig. 19.26. The numbers of near neighbours and the interatomic distances in the B elements, and the structures of the non-metals have already been discussed in Chapter 6. Copper, silver, and gold have normal close-packed (f.c.c.) structures. Zinc

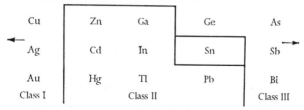

FIG. 19.26. The structural classification of metals suggested by Hume-Rothery and Raynor.

and cadmium crystallize in distorted c.p.h. structures, and mercury in a rhombohedral (distorted-cubic) structure: in each case an atom has 6 nearest and 6 next-nearest neighbours, so that it would appear to be attempting to conform to both the normal metallic close-packing rule with 12 near neighbours and the $8-N$ rule with 6 near neighbours. Ga has a rather complex structure with 1 nearest neighbour. This could be an 'inert-pair' (i.e. inert s^2 electron pair) effect, and may well be associated with the unusually low melting-point of gallium. The structures of indium and thallium are only slightly distorted from regular close-packing, while lead is f.c.c. These metals are, however, included among the elements of structural class II, because they have rather large interatomic distances, which have also been interpreted in terms of the 'inert-pair' effect. In metallic tin each atom has 4 nearest neighbours which form a very flattened tetrahedron around it, with 2 next-nearest neighbours a little further away. These irregular structures are reflected in anisotropic properties, e.g. the magnetism of single crystals of Zn, Cd, Hg, Tl, Sn, Sb, and Bi, or the electrical resistivities quoted in Table 19.v.

TABLE 19.v. *Electrical resistivities of metals at room temperature* (10^{-6} *ohm cm units), parallel and perpendicular to the principal crystal axis*

	Zn	Cd	Hg (−45·5 °C)	Sn	Bi
Parallel	6·0	8·4	17·8	13·1	143
Perpendicular	5·8	6·9	23·5	9·1	109

ALLOYS

The alloys formed between the B metals have already been discussed in Chapter 6 in connexion with the Hume-Rothery rules (electron/atom ratios), and to some extent in Chapter 8 in connexion with the relation between free-energy changes and phase diagrams.

19.6. Alloys between metals in different classes

SOLID SOLUTIONS

Solid-solution of one metal in another of the same class and the same Group of the Periodic Table is restricted by size rather than by electronegativity differences. Thus the phase diagrams for the IA metals show no evidence for the stabilization of phases of intermediate composition. There are no maxima in Fig. 19.8. The phase diagrams for two IB metals are similar. In much the same way, size factors appear to limit the solution of IA, IIA, and IIIA metals in one another. Slight positive deviations in the melting-point curves are found for IB, IIB, and IIIB metals and the phase diagrams themselves become very complex. This complexity can be accounted for in terms of the filling of the electron bands (see Chapters 6 and 8). This must cause the free energy of alloy formation to change irregularly with composition and hence give rise to the formation of two or more phase systems. There are then two kinds of alloy phase in these diagrams. One is directly related to the parent metal structures and is a disordered (though not strictly random) solution of A in B or B in A, and the second is an intermediate phase on the composition diagram which cannot be *directly* related structurally to either parent metal. It is the second type of alloy which is *directly* related to a compound (see Chapter 8).

When alloys are formed between metals of different classes, much grosser deviations from the ideal free energies of mixing occur, because of a partial transfer of electrons from one kind of atom to another. The degree of transfer is roughly related to the electronegativity difference between the atoms. This strong variation of free energy with composition must restrict the solubility of one metal in another, as can be seen from the relationship between phase-diagrams and free-energy/composition plots. Thus the alloys between metals of different classes are usually of the intermediate-phase type and not of the random-solid-solution type.

The biggest electronegativity difference between A metals and B metals of the same Group is in Group I. Here very little mutual solubility is found. In Group II the electronegativity difference between the lighter metals, beryllium and magnesium, and such metals as zinc and cadmium is slight, so that this factor does not limit solubility. However, the zinc atom is

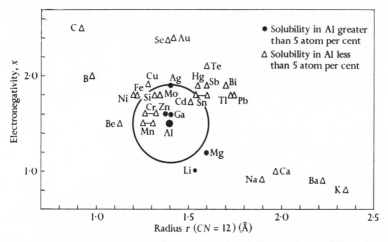

Fig. 19.27. Solubility of elements in aluminium (after Darken and Gurry).

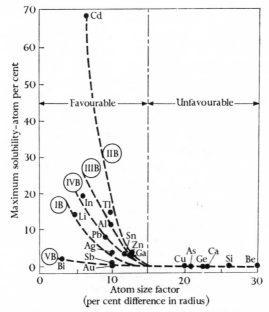

Fig. 19.28. Solubility in magnesium of metals from different B Groups (after Darken and Gurry).

much smaller than the magnesium atom and only cadmium dissolves readily in magnesium. Of other B metals it is again the larger atoms, lead, indium, and thallium, which dissolve readily in magnesium (Fig. 19.28).

The combination of the effects of size and electronegativity difference on solubility is also seen in Fig. 19.9. As the metals become more electronegative their solubility in magnesium decreases. Fig. 19.27 shows that

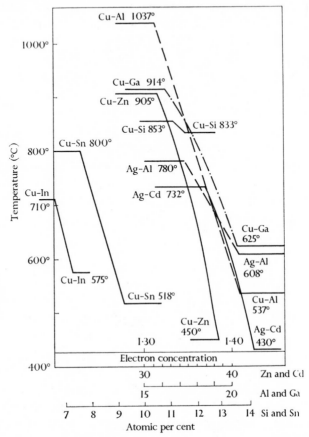

FIG. 19.29. Solubility of different elements in copper as a function of temperature. Horizontal lines show the limits of temperature over which the systems can be studied. The abscissa is plotted in electron concentration per atom, each atom supplying its valence electrons, but underneath this scale the usual atomic per cent scales of the phase diagrams are given (after Hume-Rothery).

a similar situation is observed with aluminium, size and electronegativity differences largely controlling the solubility picture.

Since the preceding discussion has been centred on alloys formed between metals of the same Group, the importance of the electron-atom ratio has been effectively excluded. However, it is illustrated by the data for magnesium alloys given in Fig. 19.28. Another example is provided by the formation of Cu—Al alloys where the limiting composition of the alloy phase occurs at the electron/atom ratio of 1·35/1·0, the same as that for Cu—Zn and Cu—Ga. This is shown in Fig. 19.29.

With the exception of the alloys of Mn or Ni with copper, solid solutions of transition metals in other metals are generally limited. In their effect on the phase boundaries otherwise controlled by electron/atom ratios, the electron contributions of the transition metal are low, as is shown by the data in Table 19.VI for ternary alloys involving a transition metal and either Cu—Zn or Cu—Al. Manganese contributes approximately two electrons per atom, which leaves essentially a half-filled d sub-shell. Apart from the case of Ni in the Cu—Al—Ni alloy, Fe, Co, and Ni contribute very approximately the number of $4s$ electrons per atom which they are thought to contribute to the binding in their own metal crystals. There is some evidence to suggest that transition metals may show variable valence in alloys, much as in their chemical compounds. In such a situation the electron-atom rules are difficult to operate.

TABLE 19.VI. *Electron contributions as judged by the effect on phase changes $\alpha \to \alpha+\beta$ and $\alpha+\beta \to \beta$ in ternary alloys*

	Cu—Zn		Cu—Al	
	$\alpha/\alpha+\beta$	$\alpha+\beta/\beta$	$\alpha/\alpha+\beta$	$\alpha+\beta/\beta$
Mn	1·83	1·83	1·91	1·93
Fe	1·0	1·0	1·1	0·9
Co	0·8	0·8	0·9	..
Ni	0·61	0·61	1·75	0·02

There are thus three factors limiting mutual solution—size, electronegativity, and the number of valence electrons per atom. These restrictions apply to alloys between metals of the same class and between metals in the different classes. A word of caution is necessary, however, on the use of electronegativity scales. The Pauling electronegativities used in Figs. 19.9 and 19.27 are derived from compounds of the metals with elements such as oxygen. The degree to which this scale may be misleading is shown by Fig. 19.30 for solid solutions in silver. Copper, silver, and gold are all of very high electronegativity in chemical compounds, but judging from their general behaviour in alloys their electronegativities in the zero oxidation state should be considerably reduced relative to other elements. Fig. 19.30 also shows that Al and Mg are the only pre-transition metals to dissolve in Ag to a similar extent to the B metals, Zn, Ga, In, and Sn. This is in keeping with size and the modified electronegativity restrictions.

From this review of *solubility*, a fairly clear pattern emerges. We turn next to those alloys which are most closely and in fact continuously related to compounds. These alloys, which may be stable phases over either a small or a wide range of composition, are immiscible with the pure components. We shall be concerned with the way in which electronegativity

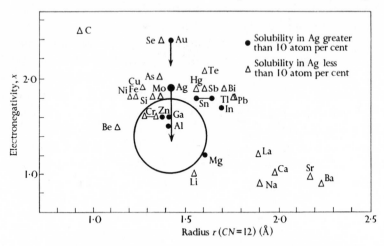

Fɪɢ. 19.30. Solubility of elements in silver (after Darken and Gurry).

differences affect these phases. Many are formed with a considerable evolution of heat and a considerable volume change. The magnitudes of these two changes are closely related.

HEATS OF FORMATION AND INTERATOMIC DISTANCES

The Pauling electronegativity is based upon the heats of formation of AB from A and B, and is therefore related to the difference in heat contents

$$\frac{H_A + H_B}{2} - H_{AB}.$$

A similar quantity, with which the heat of formation can be correlated, is the percentage volume contraction

$$100\{(V_A + V_B) - V_{AB}\}/(V_A + V_B).$$

The plot of these quantities against one another is shown in Fig. 19.31. The general correlation between interatomic distance and the stability of homonuclear assemblies has already been stressed in Chapter 3. Here there is a close correlation between interatomic distance *changes* and the energy *changes* on formation of compounds from homonuclear assemblies.

Compound formation allows the electrons to see on the average an increased nuclear charge and there is a resultant contraction in interatomic distances. This contraction is accompanied by a transfer of charge so that the relative sizes of two atoms, or in the extreme case, of two ions, is a function of the

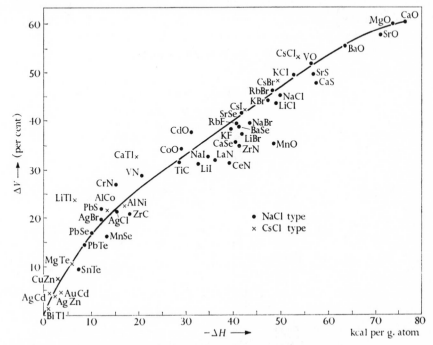

FIG. 19.31. The relationship between the heat of formation of a compound and the volume contraction expressed as a percentage of the sum of the volumes of the component elements in solid phases (after Kubaschewski and Evans, *Metallurgical Thermochemistry*, Pergamon Press, London, 1956).

electronegativity differences. Thus the atomic radii used in earlier figures may in no way represent the sizes of the atoms in alloys where there are big differences in electronegativity.

INTERMETALLIC COMPOUNDS

In Fig. 19.31 there is a *continuous* relationship between alloys, e.g. BiTl, and ionic compounds, e.g. CaO. Moreover, both the NaCl and CsCl structures occur along the whole series of compounds. However, from the changes in electrical conductivity and other physical properties along the series, it is clear that there is a change from metals to salts. There is a concomitant change in the way in which electrons are distributed on the atoms

AB, and thus there is a slow change in the 'sizes' to be associated with atomic centres. Table 19.vii shows that the molecular volume in a number of I_A/V_B compounds lies closer to the sum of ionic volumes than to the sum of atomic volumes. However, the contraction has probably come about through a change to a *partial* rather than to a complete ionic character. It would be very difficult to explain the high electrical conductivity of many of these alloys on an ionic model alone. Thus K_3Sb (see Chapter 17) although not a metal is quite a good semiconductor.

TABLE 19.vii. *Molecular volumes, ml/g mole*

	Exptl	Sum of atomic volumes	Calc. for ions
Li_3N	27	61	25
Li_3P	36	61	41
Li_3As	40	61	43
Li_3Sb	48	66	49
Li_3Bi	46	69	63
Na_3P	57	81	55
Na_3As	61	81	60
Na_3Sb	72	86	66
Na_3Bi	75	89	80
K_3As	90	143	88
K_3Sb	102	148	94
K_3Bi	110	151	108
Rb_3Sb	114	177	106
Rb_3Bi	109	180	120
Cs_3Sb	116	216	124
Cs_3Bi	121	219	138

The underlined compounds have typically metallic structures related to that of Fe_3Al. Li_3N has a simple hexagonal structure and the others have the Na_3As structure.

Atomic-size factors still appear, however, to control the formation of many phases. Thus there is a series of so-called Laves phases which have little in common except structure. Some examples are given in Table 19.viii. It has been pointed out that the ratio of *atomic* size is approximately constant in this series of compounds, but more extensive data suggest that size factors alone do not limit the occurrence of Laves phases.

An interesting set of compounds between metals of different classes are the Zintl compounds formed between pre-transition and B metals. The heats of formation of two series of these compounds from Group I and II of the pre-transition metals respectively are plotted in Fig. 19.32. In both halves of the figure the electronegativity differences in the compounds

TABLE 19.VIII. *Compounds which crystallize in a Laves phase structure (after Hume-Rothery and Raynor)*

MgCu$_2$ type		MgZn$_2$ type		MgNi$_2$ type	
AgBe$_2$	NbCo$_2$	BaMg$_2$	TaCr$_2$	HfCr$_2$	
BiAu$_2$	NbCr$_2$	CaAg$_2$	TaFe$_2$	HfMn$_2$	
CaAl$_2$	PbAu$_2$	CaCd$_2$	TaMn$_2$	HfMo$_2$	
CeAl$_2$	PrNi$_2$	CaLi$_2$	TiCr$_2$	ReBe$_2$	
CeCo$_2$	TaCo$_2$	CaMg$_2$	TiFe$_2$	FeB$_2$	
CeFe$_2$	TaCr$_2$	CrBe$_2$	TiMn$_2$	MoBe$_2$	⎫
CeMg$_2$	TiBe$_2$	FeBe$_2$	UNi$_2$	NbCo$_2$	⎬ with excess
CeNi$_2$	TiCo$_2$	HfFe$_2$	VBe$_2$	TaCo$_2$	⎬ of the second
GdFe$_2$	TiCr$_2$	KNa$_2$	WBe$_2$	TiCo$_2$	⎬ component
GdMn$_2$	UAl$_2$	MnBe$_2$	WFe$_2$	WBe$_2$	⎬
HfCo$_2$	UCo$_2$	MoBe$_2$	ZrCr$_2$	ZrFe$_2$	⎭
HfFe$_2$	UFe$_2$	MoFe$_2$	ZrIr$_2$		
HfMo$_2$	UMn$_2$	NbFe$_2$	ZrMn$_2$		
HfV$_2$	ZrCo$_2$	NbMn$_2$	ZrRe$_2$		
HfW$_2$	ZrCr$_2$	ReBe$_2$	ZrRu$_2$		
KBi$_2$	ZrFe$_2$	SrMg$_2$	ZrOs$_2$		
LaAl$_2$	ZrMo$_2$	TaCo$_2$	ZrV$_2$		
LaMg$_2$	ZrV$_2$				
LaNi$_2$	ZrW$_2$				
NaAu$_2$					

increase from left to right, but only roughly from bottom to top. Magnesium and, in some respects, lithium are not very different in electronegativity from lead, thallium, cadmium, indium, zinc, and tin. Many of these metals are quite soluble in magnesium, as was shown in Fig. 19.9. With the larger and more electropositive metals, such as sodium, potassium, calcium, and barium, the compounds formed change in character and become more salt-like. Thus although potassium and antimony are metals, they are not soluble in one another and KSb and K$_3$Sb are only semiconductors with an activation energy of some 0·25 eV for conduction.

Transition metals also form alloys with metals from other classes. The alloys with B metals, which conform to a somewhat modified set of Hume-Rothery rules, have already been mentioned. With the more extreme B metals such as tellurium a closer approximation to usual valence rules is found. Transition-metal selenides and tellurides are discussed in Chapter 16. Alloys of transition and pre-transition metals are limited by the large differences in size which restrict mutual solubility, and by the rather small differences in electronegativity which do not lead to very stable intermediate phases. However, for aluminium, beryllium, and to some extent magnesium there is only a small difference in size, and many transition-metal alloys are found.

Alloys of the lanthanide and actinide metals are common especially with transition metals, B metals, beryllium, and aluminium. For example, solid solutions are formed by uranium with some metals early in the first and second transition series. This group of elements is followed in the

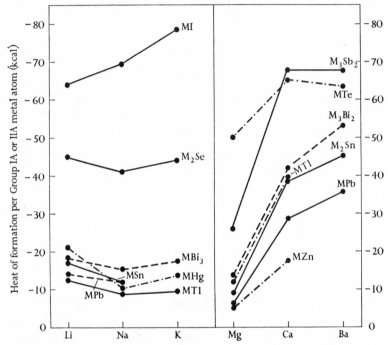

FIG. 19.32. Heats of formation of alloys. The series of alkali iodides is included as an example of ionic compounds.

Periodic Table by a group which form neither solid solutions nor intermetallic compounds, and then, toward the end of the transition series and extending into the B metals, there is a series of elements which give intermetallic compounds with uranium. It is very difficult to understand these rapidly-changing alloy properties through such a gradually-modified series of elements. Size factors would appear to be quite favourable and electronegativity differences are only large with the B metals. The formation of alloys of the actinides could be of very great practical value, as there are many limitations to the use of actinides in reactors which arise from the character of the metals themselves.

19.7. Corrosion

With the exception of Au and possibly Pt, all metals form oxides with negative free energies of formation from the elements. Ag_2O is only just stable at room temperature ($\Delta H_f^\circ = -7\cdot3$, $T\Delta S_f^\circ = -4\cdot7$, kcal mole^{-1}), and unstable at temperatures where the reaction rate is appreciable, although oxygen dissolves as atoms (obeying Henry's law) in molten silver. The thermodynamic data, therefore, show that nearly all the metals should be converted spontaneously into their oxides on exposure to air. In practice the rate of oxidation is often slow, and upon this fact depends the industrial importance of the various metals.

The alkali and alkaline-earth metals all form oxides for which the volume per metal atom is less than the atomic volume of the metal from which it is formed. For these metals the oxidation product cannot fill the volume previously occupied by the metal, and any oxide layer formed is porous, so that oxidation proceeds rapidly with a linear law of growth. Other metals have an oxide which occupies a larger volume than the metal which it replaces, so that a protective surface layer of oxide may be formed. At the beginning of the oxidation the overall rate of reaction will be controlled by the rates of the reactions at the metal/oxide and oxide/oxygen inter-faces. However, as the reaction proceeds and a thicker layer is built up, diffusion through the oxide layer becomes the rate-controlling process. Sometimes the oxidation layer may be complex; thus iron in certain circumstances has an oxidation product which consists of three successive layers, FeO, Fe_2O_3, and Fe_3O_4, with the oxygen-rich layer on the outside. The protection of metals by coherent oxide films is deliberately brought about in the process of anodizing, e.g. of titanium. The most dangerous wastage of metals is normally due to a combination of corrosion (chemical or electrochemical action) with erosion by mechanical agencies, e.g. bending and cracking, which removes the obstructive layer of corrosion product.

Most metallic oxides, with the exception of the oxides of the alkali metals, the alkaline-earth metals, and thallium, are sparingly soluble in water, so that most oxide layers still act as a protection against attack when moisture is present or when the metal is actually immersed in water. It may, however, happen that solution will lead to the production of the oxide a little way away from the metal, so that much of the protective action is lost. Thus if iron is allowed to rust in pure water to which there is only a limited supply of oxygen, iron(II) hydroxide is produced in solution, but may be oxidized to the insoluble hydrated iron(III) oxide some distance away from the iron. The production of the corrosion product at a distance may also be assisted by electrochemical action. If a piece of copper and iron are joined together and put in salt solution, the iron tends to dissolve as Fe^{2+} ions, while oxygen is converted to OH^- at the copper surface where the *overvoltage* is much less. Similar electrochemical effects may be brought about by irregularities in the surface of one metal, with consequent increase in the corrosion rate. In galvanized iron, part of the protective action of the zinc rests with its tendency to become the anode with respect to any exposed iron.

It was at one time thought that the presence of CO_2 was necessary to initiate the corrosion of iron in natural waters or in the atmosphere, but this does not appear to be so. In hard waters CO_2 tends to dissolve any $CaCO_3$ which has been precipitated on the iron and thus acts as a protective coating. Appreciable concentrations of CO_2 make the solution acid, which in itself accelerates the oxidation reaction. The form of corrosion product can often be very complex: the following formulae have been given for the main constituents of copper patina formed (1) inland and (2) near the sea.

$$(1) \quad \left[Cu \left\{ \begin{matrix} HO \\ HO \end{matrix} \right\rangle Cu \right\}_3 \right] SO_4 \qquad (2) \quad \left[Cu \left\{ \begin{matrix} HO \\ HO \end{matrix} \right\rangle Cu \right\}_3 \right] Cl_2$$

In nearly neutral solutions, the principal cathodic reaction for oxidation is

$$\tfrac{1}{2}O_2 + H_2O + 2e^- \rightarrow 2OH^-,$$

the corresponding anodic reaction being

$$M \rightarrow M^{n+} + ne^-.$$

In acid solutions an alternative cathodic reaction is provided by

$$2H^+ + 2e^- = H_2,$$

and the tendency for this to occur will be largely governed by the position of the metal in the electrochemical series and by the overvoltage of the metal for hydrogen evolution. Many of the transition metals are more electropositive than hydrogen (e.g. Cr, Mn, Fe, Co, and Ni), but for those that are less (e.g. Cu, Ag, Pd, Pt, Au, Ir, Rh, and Os) considerable action is only possible when complex ions are formed (e.g. cyanides), or when the acid acts as an oxidizing agent (e.g. HNO_3 on Cu, oxidizing acids on Os). On the other hand a number of trivalent metals (e.g. Fe, Cr, and Al) are surprisingly resistant to strong nitric acid. This is due to the formation of an oxide coating, and it has been suggested that the effect is tied up with the *slow* rate of solution of sesquioxides. Thus at lower nitric acid concentrations, iron, which can be produced in the more soluble iron(II) state, is readily attacked, but aluminium which has no divalent compounds is only slowly attacked.

Problems

1. The band model is the most important model in this chapter, while the ionic model will be the most important in the chapters which follow. Why should this be so?

2. Explain why it is that stoicheiometry is of little concern in this chapter, but is a dominant theme in the other chapters of Part III.

3. In the substances discussed in this chapter the atoms commonly have very high coordination numbers, while they have in general lower coordination numbers in the substances discussed in the later chapters of Part III, and even lower coordination numbers in the substances discussed in Part II. Comment on these distinctions and their underlying causes.

4. Why is it that the lattice spacings for a metal are largely independent of the crystal structure adopted?

5. Ductility is a characteristic property of metals. Metals may be hardened by various forms of cold-working (hammering, drawing, etc.) or by the formation of alloys (e.g. steel). Comment.

6. The paramagnetism of salts is commonly very temperature-dependent, but that of many metals is relatively independent of temperature. Can you suggest a possible reason for this difference?

7. On the free-electron theory (see Chapter 6), the average Fermi energy is three-fifths of the maximum Fermi energy. By means of the Virial Theorem (Chapter 1), show that the work function of a metal may be estimated as being equal to the sum of the metal sublimation energy and its ionization potentials (for valence electrons) divided by three times the number of its valence electrons. Test this relation for the metals Li (2·4), K (2·2), Cs (1·9), Ag (4·3), Ca (2·8), and Al (4·3). The experimental work functions (volts) are given in parentheses in each case.

8. Comment in detail on the pattern of binding energies plotted in Fig. 19.5. How may the pattern be related to atomic structures?

9. The following compressibility values (10^{-6} cm^2 kg^{-1}) have been given by Spedding for the lanthanide metals:

La 3·9; Ce 4·7, Pr 3·7, Nd 3·0, Pm ?, Sm 3·5, Eu 6·99, Gd 2·5, Tb 2·45, Dy 2·6, Ho 2·5, Er 2·5, Tm 2·6, Yb 7·5, Lu 2·3.

How may the variations along the series be interpreted?

10. Compare the sequences of binding energies, melting-points, atomic volumes, etc., in the three transition series and in the lanthanide and actinide series. How may these changes be reflected in the chemistry of all these elements?

11. The atomic diameters (Fig. 19.16) are very similar in the second and third transition series (e.g. Zr 3·19, Hf 3·17 Å) and greater than the atomic diameters in the first transition series (e.g. Ti 2·93 Å). Why is this so?

12. What general changes will one expect to find in the properties of the metals on passing from Cr to Mo to Nd to W to U? In what ways are these changes reflected in the chemistry of the metals?

13. Show that the ratio of the atomic radius to the radius of the density maximum of the d electron (for values see Chapter 2) is high for the ferromagnetic elements Fe, Co, and Ni.

14. Can you suggest a reason why no metals of the second and third transition series are ferromagnetic?

15. Draw correlations between the differences in the metallic properties of K and Cu and differences in their chemical properties.

16. What properties of the metals help to make Cu and Ag more noble metals than Zn and Cd?

17. The γ-brass structure is found for the following alloys:

$$Cu_5Zn_8, \ Cu_9Al_4, \ Cu_{31}Sn_8, \ Ni_5Zn_{21}.$$

Comment. (See also Chapter 6.)

18. The maximum solubility in copper of zinc is 38·5 atomic per cent, of aluminium is 20·5 per cent, of germanium is 12·0 per cent, of cadmium is 1·5 per cent, of indium is 11 per cent, and of lead is 0·01–0·02 per cent. Comment.

19. From a knowledge of their properties as atoms (Chapter 2) and as metals (this chapter), what would you expect to be the main chemical differences between the four classes of metals: pre-transition; lanthanides and actinides; transition; B metals?

20. Explain why a non-protective oxide film should increase in thickness at an approximately linear rate, while with a protective film the thickness increases at a rate approximately proportional to the square root of the time.

21. An electrical cell is set up with two compartments each containing clean iron electrodes in a common air-free KCl solution. When oxygen is

bubbled around one electrode, the other electrode is found to corrode, and a current flows in the wire connecting the two electrodes. The oxygenated solution becomes alkaline, while Fe^{2+} ions are produced in the other compartment. Comment on and produce an explanation for these observations.

22. Suggest explanations for the following reported observations. A piece of metallic sodium was found to be substantially unaltered after immersion in liquid bromine. A copper wire was transformed into a hollow copper oxide tube by oxidation at high temperature. Iron objects have been excavated after 4000 years and found to have a skin of rust only 1 mm thick.

Bibliography

C. S. BARRETT, *Structure of Metals*, 2nd ed., McGraw-Hill, New York, 1952.

P. A. BECK (ed.), *Electronic Structure and Alloy Chemistry of the Transition Elements*, Interscience, New York, 1963.

R. COLLONGUES, Les Composés Non-Stoechiométriques a Caractère métallique, Phases Intermétalliques, *Tenth Solvay Conference*, ed. R. Stoops, p. 83, Brussels, 1956.

L. S. DARKEN and R. W. GURRY, *Physical Chemistry of Metals*, Metallurgy and Metallurgical Engineering Series, McGraw-Hill, New York, 1953.

H. J. EMELÉUS and J. S. ANDERSON, *Modern Aspects of Inorganic Chemistry*, 3rd ed., Routledge & Kegan Paul, London, 1960.

U. R. EVANS, *An Introduction to Metallic Corrosion*, 2nd ed., Arnold, London, 1963.

W. HUME-ROTHERY, *Atomic Theory for Students of Metallurgy*, 3rd ed., Institute of Metals, London, 1960.

W. HUME-ROTHERY and B. R. COLES, 'The Transition Metals and their Alloys', *Phil. Mag. Suppl.* 1954, **3**, 149.

W. HUME-ROTHERY and G. V. RAYNOR, *The Structure of Metals and Alloys*, 4th ed., Institute of Metals, London, 1962.

W. KLEMM, 'Metalloids and their Compounds with the Alkali Metals', *Proc. Chem. Soc.*, 1958, 329.

C. J. SMITHELLS, *Metals Reference Book*, 3rd ed., Butterworths, London, 1962.

B. M. TRAPNELL, 'Specificity in Catalysis by Metals', *Quart. Rev. Chem. Soc.*, 1954, **8**, 404.

20 · The Pre-transition Metals

20.1. Introduction

EMPHASIS OF CHAPTER

This chapter is primarily concerned with the chemistry of the alkali and alkaline-earth metals as exhibited in their most ionic compounds and in aqueous solution. It is also concerned with the related chemistry of Mg, Sc, Y, and La, and to a lesser extent of Be and Al. It does not set out to give a properly balanced account of any of these elements. Certain aspects are almost entirely excluded, and the reader is referred to other parts of the book for a discussion of these, e.g. to Chapter 19 for the metals and their alloys, to Chapter 11 for hydrides, to Chapter 17 for nitrides, carbides, etc., and to Chapter 33 for organometallic compounds.

This bias has been taken deliberately in order to illustrate the application of the ionic model in those circumstances where it is most appropriate and most effective. As we have stressed already, the ionic model, for all its failings, is the only model which leads directly to precise quantitative predictions. We shall therefore use it quite generally as a basis for the discussion of metal chemistry. Elsewhere, most notably in the chapters on the transition-metals and the B metals, it will become necessary to focus attention on the very considerable deviations from the ionic model, but here such deviations will not be considered in any detail, even though they may often be of considerable significance. The reader is asked to bear this bias in mind as he reads this chapter, and to recall the caveats on the ionic model which were put up in the second part of Chapter 5. He should also be aware that we shall tend to overlook a number of the subtleties of the ionic model discussed in the first part of Chapter 5.

ENERGIES AND THE IONIC MODEL

It may be convenient at this stage to recall certain features of the simple ionic model, although these have already been discussed in detail in Chapter 5. In Fig. 20.1 various ionic binding energies are plotted as functions of interionic distance or ionic radius. The first series of energies (top left

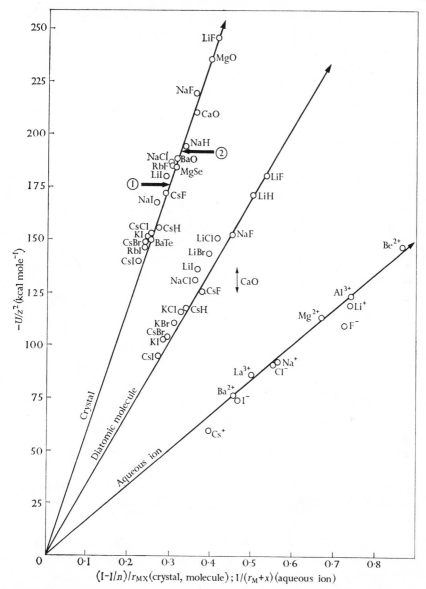

FIG. 20.1. Ionic binding energy (crystal and diatomic molecule) as a function of interatomic distance, r_{MX}, and ionic hydration energy as a function of effective ionic radius ($r_M + x$). Abscissa units are reciprocal Å. The lines are theoretical and the points experimental.

in Fig. 20.1) are lattice energies (divided by z^2 where z is the ionic charge) for salts crystallizing in the 6:6 (NaCl) structure. The corresponding distance function is $(1-1/n)/$(shortest interionic distance), where n is the repulsion exponent. The lattice-energy equation (Chapter 5) then predicts that all the points should lie on the straight line of slope NAe^2, where N is Avogadro's number, A is the Madelung constant (1.75), and e the electronic charge. This line is drawn at the left-hand side of Fig. 20.1 and is seen to

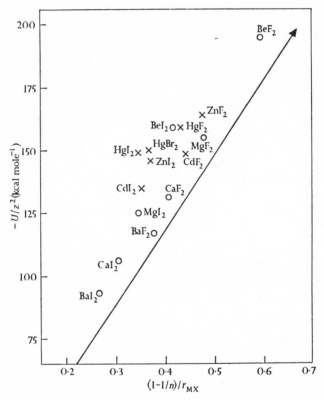

Fig. 20.2. Ionic binding energies of some MX_2 gas molecules as a function of interatomic distance. Abscissa units are reciprocal Å. The straight line is the theoretical ionic one for linear molecules.

be in remarkably good agreement with the experimental values. The second series of energies (middle of Fig. 20.1) are for the dissociation of diatomic molecules (again divided by z^2) to give the corresponding ions, e.g.

$$NaCl(\text{diatomic}) \rightarrow Na^+ + Cl^-.$$

The distance function is the same as for the crystal lattice energies, except that the interionic distances are smaller as would be expected on the basis of the discussion in Chapter 5. The corresponding straight line (central line in Fig. 20.1) predicted by the ionic model now has a slope of Ne^2, for the Madelung constant is 1. Again quite good agreement is obtained between experiment and theory. However, the agreement is less good for the triatomic molecules (assumed to be linear although some are bent) plotted in Fig. 20.2 (theoretical slope now $0.875Ne^2$), deviations taking place in the same direction as with the B metals although in general they are not so large. Strikingly large deviations are also found for species of higher charge, e.g. $Ca^{2+}O^{2-}$. Here we see an illustration of the breakdown of the simple ionic model. The third series of energies in Fig. 20.1 (bottom right) are 'absolute' ionic hydration energies (see Chapter 5) for which the appropriate radius function is $1/(r_M+x)$, where $x = 0.85$ Å for a cation and is zero for an anion. The theoretical line predicted by the Born equation is given at the bottom right of Fig. 20.1, and is seen to give a reasonable fit with the experimental values.

OUTLINE OF THE CHAPTER

Since the ionic model is naturally related to the properties of ions, it will first be necessary to see how each ion may be formed from the corresponding metal. The major energy involved will be that required to ionize the atom, although the sublimation energy of the metal (Chapters 3 and 19) will also be significant. Section 20.2 is therefore concerned with the details of atomic structure, and it also discusses the sizes of the metal ions, as these will be most important in the application of the ionic model. Section 20.3 treats the problem of what valence the ions will show, i.e. which values of z will be stable and which will not. This problem could be tackled in a number of ways, e.g. for ions in crystals, ions in simple gaseous molecules, or for ions in aqueous solution. We have chosen to pay most attention to the last of these, as this produces a treatment, albeit somewhat empirical, which can be most readily extended to other metal ions in later chapters. The basis of the argument may be seen from Fig. 20.1. Hydration energies increase approximately with z^2. However, the energy of ionization of s electrons of the same principal quantum number, n (or of those $(n-1)d$ electrons which are energetically similar), increases less rapidly with z (Chapter 2), so that in general, if it is worth pulling out one electron, it is worth pulling out all electrons back to the noble-gas shell. In the next series of elements, the lanthanides (Chapter 21), where we become concerned with the non-penetrating $4f$ electrons, this kind of argument no longer holds.

Questions of structure and of related physical properties are taken up in section 20.4. As was stressed in the latter part of Chapter 5, structural features often demonstrate most clearly departures from the ionic model, and it will prove convenient at this stage to have a reminder of these departures. Boiling-points, and to a lesser extent melting-points, will be directly related to differences such as those represented in Fig. 20.1 between crystals and simple gaseous molecules. In general for ionic substances, these differences will increase with increase of lattice energy. Compare thus the sequence of melting-points CsI 621°, NaCl 801°, LiF 850°, BaO 1925°, CaO 2600°, and MgO 2770° C (sublimes) with the top-left side of Fig. 20.1.

The thermochemistry and the reactions of ionic solids are discussed in section 20.5, which is therefore also much concerned with lattice energies. Thus a double decomposition of the type

$$CsF + LiI \rightarrow CsI + LiF$$

will be expected, for it brings the smaller ions together and hence increases the total lattice energy. This may be easily seen from Fig. 20.1 by comparing the midpoint of the line joining CsF to LiI (arrow 1) with the midpoint of the line joining CsI to LiF (arrow 2). Solubility relations are taken up in section 20.6. As was shown in Chapter 7, the detailed treatment of the solubility of salts in water is a fairly complex matter, in which either energy or entropy effects can play the dominant role. Many of the energy considerations may be interpreted in terms of the two outermost lines of Fig. 20.1. Somewhat similar considerations are involved in complex-ion equilibria which form the subject matter of section 20.7. Finally in section 20.8 there is a brief discussion of the non-ionic compounds and of the so-called 'diagonal relationship'.

20.2. Atoms and ions

IONIZATION POTENTIALS

In Fig. 20.3 the ionization potentials for the valence electrons of the alkali-metal atoms (top line) are compared with the ionization potentials for electrons with the same quantum numbers in the excited hydrogen atoms (lowest line). Thus for K the difference between the two lines represents the energy (3·49 eV) by which the $4s$ electron is stabilized as a consequence of its penetration through the inner electron shells towards the nucleus. The nuclear charge does not increase down the series in a completely regular pattern, and this is reflected in slight irregularities in the otherwise steady decrease of ionization potential.

From H to Li the nuclear charge increases by 2 and this increase is not completely shielded from the $2s$ electron by the completed $1s^2$ shell. Similarly the removal of the 3s electron from the excited state of B, $1s^2\,2s^2\,3s^1$, requires 3·34 eV representing a penetration energy of 1·83 eV as compared with 1·99 eV for the 2s in Li. However, the removal of the 3s electron from Na requires 5·14 eV, or a penetration energy of 3·63 eV associated with the nuclear charge of 11. Thus the changeover from building up beyond a 2-electron shell to building up beyond an 8-electron shell places the ionization potential of Na higher than expected by an extrapolation from H to Li. Similarly the introduction of the 18-electron shell, and the consequent increase of 18 in nuclear charge between K and Rb, raises the 5s energy above the value expected by an extrapolation from Na and K. The ionization potential of Fr is expected to lie high by comparison with a Rb—Cs extrapolation. At the time of writing this value is not known.

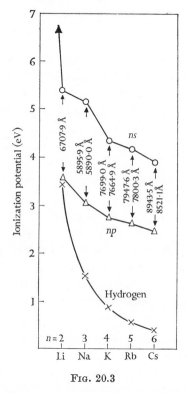

Fig. 20.3

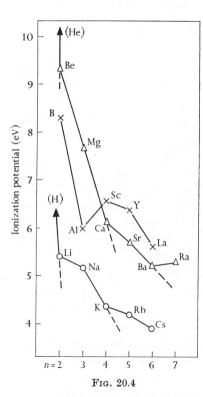

Fig. 20.4

Fig. 20.3. First ionization potentials of alkali metals (top-line), compared with those from hydrogen ns orbitals (bottom-line). The middle line gives the ionization energies from np orbitals of excited metal atoms. The spectroscopic transitions, $np \leftrightarrow ns$, are indicated.

Fig. 20.4. A comparison of first ionization potentials for the typical and A atoms of Groups I, II, and III.

Also plotted in Fig. 20.3 (middle line) are the ionization potentials for np electrons in the excited atoms (e.g. Na $1s^2 2s^2 2p^6 3p^1$) of the alkali metals. For the 2p electron in Li the penetration stabilization is very small. In all cases the np electron is less stabilized by penetration than is the ns. This observation should be compared with those on the $3d$ electron in K or the $4f$ in Rb (Chapter 2). The differences in energy between the upper and middle lines of Fig. 20.3 correspond to the Principal lines in the alkali-metal emission spectra. These are seen as doublets because spin-orbit interactions split the atomic p states. The irregular sequence of wavelengths is related to the irregular pattern of nuclear-charge build-up already discussed. The colours observed are represented below.

Violet	Indigo	Blue	Green	Yellow	Orange	Red
	$(n+1)p \to ns$				$np \to ns$	
KRb	Cs			Na	Li	KRbCs

The $(n+1)p \to ns$ change is also represented for K, Rb, and Cs, as these correspond to the colours normally used for their identification by flame spectra: the K red doublet is just on the limit of visibility, where the eye is very insensitive. At the temperature of a Bunsen flame, the extent of the $(n+1)p$ excitation in K will be considerably less than the np excitation in Na, so that the K flame test is of much lower sensitivity than is that of Na. All these atomic emissions can be used in the quantitative determination of the alkali metals with a flame photometer which has a wide range of detection from the ultra-violet into the infra-red.

Although the patterns of ionization potentials in Groups IA and IIA are similar, there is an important difference, which may be seen by close inspection of Fig. 20.4. Between Li and Be the ionization potential increases by 73 per cent, but the percentage increase from Group I to Group II falls down the series as the effect of penetration becomes relatively more important than that of the increase of charge external to inner electron shells. The increases are for Na to Mg 49 per cent, for K to Ca 41 per cent, for Rb to Sr 36 per cent, and for Cs to Ba 34 per cent. The biggest change in ionization potential down Group II occurs between Be and Mg. This is reflected in a large change in chemical character: magnesium is much more electropositive than beryllium. The second ionization potentials of B and Al are concerned with the removal of s electrons and are, as expected, greater than the second ionization potentials of Be and Mg. The first ionization potentials are, however, concerned with the removal of the less-penetrating p electrons and are even lower than the first ionization potentials of Be and Mg, despite the increases of nuclear charge. The relatively easy removal of the single p electron is related to the occasional appearance of monovalence in Al, e.g. AlF, AlCl, AlBr, AlI and probably Al_2O, Al_2S, and Al_2Se, although such species are only stable at high temperatures. Monovalence is even more marked in Ga, In, and especially Tl, where it is often described in terms of an 'inert-pair' (i.e. inert ns^2 pair) effect. The ionization potentials of Sc, Y, and La are more comparable with those of the alkali metals and the alkaline-earth metals, for they are again concerned with the removal of an s electron, here to leave the singly-charged ions with the configuration $(n-1)d^1\ ns^1$ outside the respective noble-gas atomic cores.

SIZES OF IONS

Ions in the gas phase do not have a 'size', but an ion size is required in applying the ionic model. We shall use the Pauling crystal radii as given in Chapter 5. We shall also make the assumption that these radii remain substantially constant in different chemical environments. This is a reasonably good approximation for the ions considered in this chapter, and most of the small deviations can be accounted for by refinements of the simple ionic model. It is, however, no longer true for transition-metal and B-metal ions.

These radii are plotted in Fig. 20.5 for the ions of typical and A metals of the early Groups in the Periodic Table. There is an increase in ionic size down any Group, but superimposed on this are irregularities analogous to those found in the ionization potentials. Thus the increase of 18 in the nuclear charge between K and Rb leads to a rather greater similarity in their ionic radii, and indeed in much of their chemistry, than would have been expected by extrapolation from Li^+, Na^+, and K^+. In the same way the increase of 32 in the nuclear charge brings together Cs^+ and Fr^+, Ba^{2+} and Ra^{2+}, and La^{3+} and Ac^{3+}. The similarity of radii is even more marked between Y^{3+} and Lu^{3+}, and between Zr^{4+} and Hf^{4+}. The separation of the latter pair of elements is, as a result, extremely difficult. (Ca^{2+} (0·99 Å) and Cd^{2+} (0·97 Å) have almost identical ionic radii too, but the increase in ionization potential from Ca to Cd is sufficient to give the Cd^{2+} ion a much increased affinity for polarizable ligands, so that Ca and Cd are easily separated. This type of distinction will be discussed more fully in section 31.3.)

Increase of *external* charge produces a marked reduction in ionic size, e.g. $K^+ > Ca^{2+} > Sc^{3+} > Ti^{4+}$. As a consequence ions such as Na^+ and Ca^{2+} are similar in size and can replace each other in ionic lattices, provided the charge effect is suitably balanced elsewhere in the lattice. A special case of this replacement is found in naturally-occurring silicates, where the more highly charged ions have usually been concentrated in the early stages of crystallization. Thus Na^+ ions are found in the later crystallization of Ca^{2+} minerals, and Ba^{2+} in early deposits of K^+ minerals.

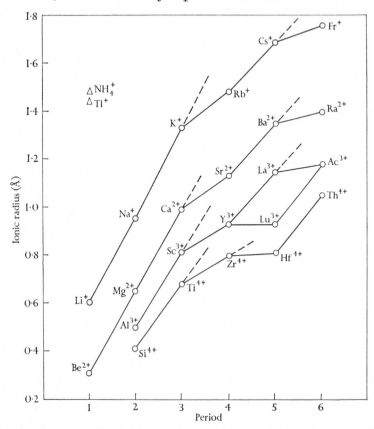

FIG. 20.5. The ionic radii for the typical and A atoms of Groups I, II, III, and IV.

20.3. Ionic valence

In the formation of their ionic compounds, the pre-transition elements all follow a simple rule; they strip off their outer electrons until they attain the *electron configuration* of the preceding noble gas. This is in marked contrast to the lanthanide elements with which we shall be concerned in the next chapter; these elements lose electrons to give almost invariably a constant ionic *charge*. The actinide and the transition metals fall between these two extremes. The B metals are somewhat analogous to the pre-transition metals in that they may be regarded as stripping off their outer electrons to leave either a noble-gas core plus a completed d sub-shell (Group valence), or a noble-gas core plus both a completed d sub-shell and a completed s sub-shell (inert-pair effect).

OXIDATION STATE DIAGRAMS. CALCULATION PROCEDURE

It is convenient to have some semi-quantitative method by which all these valence states may be related to the atomic structures of the elements. We choose to do this by estimating, with a rather simple ionic model, the Oxidation State Diagrams (see Chapter 9) for the various metals. In this way we link our discussion of metal chemistry with that of the non-metals, where frequent use is made of such diagrams.

The estimated Oxidation State Diagram is obtained in the following way. The energy required to convert the metal into the appropriate metal ions and electrons is called the *Ionization Energy*. It is very largely a sum of ionization potentials although it also includes the sublimation energy. This energy is compensated by the energy, called the *Chemical Energy*, released on placing the ion into a chemical environment. (If the environment is a crystal then the Chemical Energy is the calculated lattice energy plus the energy of the process in which the required number of anions z are formed, for example

$$z(\tfrac{1}{2}Cl_2 + e^- \rightarrow Cl^-).$$

The difference in magnitude between the Chemical Energy and the Ionization Energy may then be compared directly with the heat of formation of the crystal from its elements. Examples of such calculations will be found at the end of this section.)

For a conventional Oxidation State Diagram the chemical environment is taken as an aqueous solution. The required hydration energy of the metal ion is given approximately by

$$- \frac{7 \cdot 3 z^2}{r + 0 \cdot 85} \text{ eV},$$

in which z is the charge and r the Pauling crystal radius of the ion (in Å). The arguments in favour of using this formula have already been discussed in Chapter 5 (n.b. $7 \cdot 3$ eV $\equiv 167$ kcal). Since electrode potentials are normally related to that of the H^+/H_2 couple, the electrons must be combined with hydrogen ions, for which process the estimated energy release is $4 \cdot 7$ eV per g equivalent of electrons. (The ionization potential of H is $13 \cdot 60$ eV, half the dissociation energy of H_2 is $2 \cdot 24$ eV and the 'absolute' hydration energy of H^+ is $-11 \cdot 18$ eV (-257 kcal).) Combining the two terms, the Chemical Energy is

$$-\frac{7 \cdot 3z^2}{r+0 \cdot 85} - 4 \cdot 7z \text{ eV.}$$

The net energy, Chemical Energy+Ionization Energy, is approximately equivalent to the *free* energy of the reaction

$$M(metal)+zH^+(aq.) = M^{z+}(aq.)+\tfrac{1}{2}zH_2$$

so that these estimated energies compare directly with volt equivalents. The error in this approximation is quite small, compared with the overall accuracy of the calculations: a proper allowance for the entropy changes alters the respective total energies by $-0 \cdot 3$ volts for K^+, $-0 \cdot 1$ volts for Ca^{2+}, $-0 \cdot 4$ volts for MnO_2, and $+0 \cdot 3$ volts for Fe^{3+}.

For a number of ions there are no values of crystal radii. In such cases we shall use the radii of ions of the same charge taken from adjacent positions in the Periodic Table. Thus Ca^+ will be regarded as having the same radius as K^+, and Ca^{3+} as having the same radius as Sc^{3+}. While this may not be strictly justified, it is probably the best that can be done. In order to be consistent, we shall also use the Pauling radii for transition-metal ions and for Cu^+, Ag^+, and Au^+, although somewhat better results would have been obtained using experimental radii taken from oxide structures.

OXIDATION STATE DIAGRAMS. CALCULATED RESULTS

Table 20.I gives as an example some calculations made for calcium (sublimation energy of the metal $2 \cdot 00$ eV, ionization potentials $6 \cdot 11$, $11 \cdot 87$, and $51 \cdot 21$ eV for the removal of the first three electrons).

TABLE 20.I. *Volt equivalent values for calcium ions of different charge*

Ion	Ionic radius (Å)	Chemical Energy (eV)	Ioniza- tion Energy (eV)	Volt equivalent	
				Esti- mated	Experi- mental
Ca^+(aq.)	$1 \cdot 33$ (K^+)	$-8 \cdot 0$	$+8 \cdot 1$	$+0 \cdot 1$	..
Ca^{2+}(aq.)	$0 \cdot 99$	$-25 \cdot 3$	$+20 \cdot 0$	$-5 \cdot 3$	$-5 \cdot 7$
Ca^{3+}(aq.)	$0 \cdot 81$ (Sc^{3+})	$-48 \cdot 1$	$+71 \cdot 2$	$+23 \cdot 1$	..

The experimental volt equivalent for Ca^{2+}(aq.) is, see Chapter 9, the electrode potential for Ca^{2+}/Ca ($-2 \cdot 87$ volts) multiplied by the charge on the ion (2). These results are also plotted in Fig. 20.6, to give an estimated Oxidation State Diagram for calcium. The diagram shows that Ca^+(aq.) should disproportionate into Ca(metal) and Ca^{2+}(aq.), and that the couple Ca^{3+}(aq.)/Ca should be an extremely powerful oxidizing agent, with an

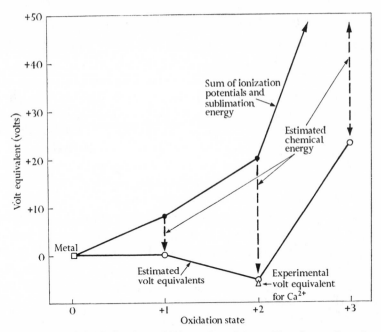

Fig. 20.6. Estimated Oxidation State Diagram for calcium. (Data here refer only to acid solution, $a_H = 1$, and, as in *all* other Oxidation State Diagrams given in this book, are for 25 °C.)

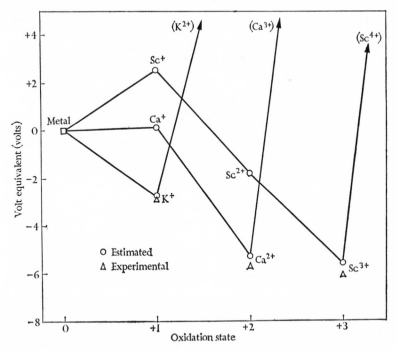

Fig. 20.7. Estimated ($\bigcirc$) and experimental ($\triangle$) Oxidation State Diagram for K, Ca, and Sc.

electrode potential of about $+7 \cdot 7$ volts (i.e. 23/3). This potential is far higher than that of O_2/H_2O ($+1 \cdot 2$ volts) or even of F_2/F^- ($+2 \cdot 9$ volts). In Fig. 20.7, the estimated Oxidation State Diagrams for K, Ca, and Sc are shown together. It will be seen that in each case breaking into the noble-gas core involves such a large ionization potential increase that the ions K^{2+}, Ca^{3+}, and Sc^{4+} would all be too powerfully oxidizing to exist in contact with water. The volt equivalent for K^{2+} is estimated as $+11 \cdot 8$ eV, and for Sc^{4+} as $+26 \cdot 9$ eV. The low oxidation states of scandium, Sc^+ and Sc^{2+}, should be unstable to disproportionation, e.g. in Fig. 20.7 the Sc^+/Sc couple is more oxidizing than the Sc^{3+}/Sc^+ couple.

The results of similar calculation for the metals of IA, IIA, and IIIA and for Zr are summarized in Table 20.II in the form of electrode potentials, i.e. volt equivalents divided in each case by ion charge. The predicted stability of the Group valence is again the main feature, but the table brings out several other features of pre-transition valence states. Thus, in view of the preparation of XeF_2, the estimated electrode potential of Cs^{2+} is of some interest. This is only $+3 \cdot 6$ volts, which is not very much greater than the redox potential of F_2/F^- ($+2 \cdot 9$ volts). A Cs^{2+} compound could perhaps be made.

TABLE 20.II. *Estimated electrode potentials* M^{z+}(aq.)/M *with experimental values in parentheses* (*volts*)

z equals	1	2	3	4
Li	$-2 \cdot 7$ $(-3 \cdot 1)$	$+24 \cdot 0$		
Na	$-2 \cdot 5$ $(-2 \cdot 7)$	$+12 \cdot 4$		
K	$-2 \cdot 8$ $(-2 \cdot 9)$	$+5 \cdot 9$		
Rb	$-2 \cdot 7$ $(-2 \cdot 9)$	$+4 \cdot 3$		
Cs	$-2 \cdot 9$ $(-2 \cdot 9)$	$+3 \cdot 6$		
Be	$+3 \cdot 0$	$-1 \cdot 9$ $(-1 \cdot 9)$	$+36 \cdot 0$	
Mg	$+0 \cdot 4$	$-2 \cdot 3$ $(-2 \cdot 4)$	$+17 \cdot 2$	
Ca	$+0 \cdot 1$	$-2 \cdot 7$ $(-2 \cdot 9)$	$+7 \cdot 7$	
Sr	$-0 \cdot 4$	$-2 \cdot 8$ $(-2 \cdot 9)$	?	
Ba	$-0 \cdot 6$	$-2 \cdot 8$ $(-2 \cdot 9)$	?	
B	$+4 \cdot 7$	$+2 \cdot 5$	$+0 \cdot 3$	$+50 \cdot 3$
Al	$+0 \cdot 4$	$-0 \cdot 4$	$-2 \cdot 1$ $(-1 \cdot 7)$	$+20 \cdot 4$
Sc	$+2 \cdot 5$	$-1 \cdot 0$	$-1 \cdot 9$ $(-2 \cdot 1)$	$+6 \cdot 7$
Y	$+3 \cdot 1$	$-0 \cdot 5$	$-2 \cdot 5$ $(-2 \cdot 4)$	?
La	$+2 \cdot 2$	$-0 \cdot 7$	$-2 \cdot 2$ $(-2 \cdot 5)$	?
Zr	$+5 \cdot 2$	$+1 \cdot 1$	$-0 \cdot 6$	$-1 \cdot 5$ $(-1 \cdot 5)$

Lower oxidation states such as Al^+ are not thermodynamically stable in water. However, the observed electrode *reactions* of A metals are not governed by the Oxidation State Diagrams. Thus Al^+ and Mg^+ are thought to be the main immediate products of electrolysis using metal anodes. The low-valence cations then react with water evolving hydrogen, but as this reaction is slower than the electrode process extremely reducing conditions exist in the vicinity of the electrodes. No prediction of the path of reaction or of the time taken for the most stable chemical species to be formed can be obtained from Oxidation State Diagrams.

LATTICE ENERGIES

Entirely equivalent arguments may be based on a consideration of lattice energies. We illustrate the case of CaF crystal. The Ca^+ ion is formed endothermally ($+187$ kcal or $+8 \cdot 11$ eV per g ion) from Ca metal, while the F^- ion is formed exothermally ($-64 \cdot 5$ kcal per g ion) from F_2 gas. The heat of formation of CaF may therefore be estimated as -69 kcal mole^{-1} on the assumption that its lattice energy will be very similar to that of KF ($-191 \cdot 5$ kcal mole^{-1} from a Born–Haber cycle). Now the heat of formation of CaF_2 is -290 kcal mole^{-1} (calculated on ionic model, -296 kcal mole^{-1}), so that the disproportionation reaction

$$2CaF \rightarrow Ca + CaF_2$$

would be expected to be highly favoured with an estimated heat of reaction of -152 kcal mole^{-1}. Table 20.III gives some similar calculated heats of

TABLE 20.III. *Estimated heats of formation for some hypothetical compounds on the ionic model* (kcal mole^{-1}) (*after Waddington*)

M	MF	MCl	M_2O
He	$+255$	$+303$	$+660$
Ne	$+208$	$+246$	$+589$
Ar	$+100$	$+130$	$+382$
Kr	$+68$	$+97$	$+320$
Xe	$+39$	$+62$	$+316$
Be	-14	$+34$	$+122$
Mg	-68	-30	$+36$
Ca	-69	-38	$+44$
Sr	-78	-49	$+28$
Ba	-73	-50	$+31$

M	MF_2	MCl_2	MO
Li	..	$+1061$	$+1037$
Na	$+403$	$+513$	$+522$
K	$+104$	$+204$	$+243$
Rb	$+39$	$+131$	$+188$
Cs	-30	$+51$	$+123$

formation, and Table 20.IV corresponding heats of disproportionation reactions.

TABLE 20.IV. *Estimated heats of the disproportionation reaction* $2MX \rightarrow M + MX_2$ *(kcal mole^{-1}) (after Waddington)*

M	MF	MCl
Mg	−148	−93
Ca	−152	−114
Sr	−134	−100
Ba	−140	−106

20.4. Structures and physical properties of ionic solids

STRUCTURES

The structures and many of the physical properties of ionic solids have already been discussed in Part I. Simple radius-ratio considerations suggest that there would be a changeover, from low to high coordination number around a metal ion, with increase in size of this ion or decrease in size of the anion. This is generally found, although as we have already seen the actual pattern of structures can be more complex. Some of these complexities find reasonable explanations in terms of simple refinements of the ionic model. Thus the retention of the 6:6 structure in KF, RbF, and CsF, although the cation/anion ratios are appropriate to an 8:8 structure, is readily accounted for when proper allowance is made for the effect of coordination number on ionic radii (see Chapter 5). Most of the heavier halides of Group IA also give rise to the expected crystal structures, though a change from 8:8 to 6:6 coordination can sometimes be brought about by change of pressure or temperature, or by the growing of crystals on seeds of a non-preferred crystalline modification. This shows that different crystal structures are not of very different energy. The crystal structure of LiI (NaCl) is not in accord with the radius-ratio considerations, but the greatest deviations from ionic behaviour are expected with such a combination of cation and anion.

The structures of the oxides (M_2O, antifluorite; MO_2, CaC_2 or pyrites; but Cs_2O, layer) and sulphides of Group IA, their lattice energies, and their interionic distances are also much in accord with the expectation of the ionic model. The packing of more complex anions is possibly governed by the geometry of the anion, but an examination of these structures does not lead us to suppose that the ionic model, properly employed, would not account for their occurrence.

The fluorides of Group IIA also crystallize in structures which conform rather well with radius-ratio arguments. BeF_2 (Pauling univalent radius ratio 0·32) has the 4:2 cristobalite structure, MgF_2 (ratio 0·60) the 6:3 rutile structure, while CaF_2 (ratio 0·87), SrF_2, and BaF_2 adopt the 8:4 fluorite structure. That covalence may be of greater importance in the gas phase is shown by the bent structures of CaF_2, SrF_2 ($SrCl_2$ and $BaCl_2$), BaF_2 (Wharton, Berg, and Klemperer, *J. Chem. Phys.*, 1964, **40**, 3471). In Group IIIA, the changes of coordination number in the fluorides require a more sophisticated explanation. BF_3 forms a molecular lattice with a boron coordination number of 3. AlF_3 has a structure with 3 F-atoms at 1·70 Å from the Al and another 3 at 1·89 Å. Sc in ScF_3 probably has 6 equivalent neighbours, but YF_3 has a crystal structure in which the metal is surrounded by 8 almost equidistant nearest-neighbour fluorine atoms with 1 fluorine atom more distant. In the tysonite structure of LaF_3 each La^{3+} ion has 5 nearest fluorine neighbours at 2·36 Å with 6 more at 2·70 Å. Only ScF_3 could be said to conform to ionic-model expectations. In all three Groups a change from fluorides to chlorides, bromides, and especially to iodides leads generally to a smaller coordination number of the metal and a greater tendency to form molecular, chain, and layer structures (Table 20.v). A similar distinction has been noted between oxides and sulphides.

TABLE 20.V. *Some chloride structures*

LiCl (6:6)	$BeCl_2$ (chain)	BCl_3 (molecular)	CCl_4 (molecular)
NaCl (6:6)	$MgCl_2$ (layer)	$AlCl_3$† (layer)	$SiCl_4$ (molecular)
KCl (6:6)	$CaCl_2$ (deformed rutile)	$ScCl_3$ (layer)	$TiCl_4$ (molecular)

† Al_2Br_6 (molecular)

Table 20.VI suggests that it is also quite impossible to predict the change in structure of dihalides down Group IIA on ionic grounds alone. The irregularities probably require a consideration of covalent bonding. On the basis of ion size, the divalent lanthanide ions, Eu^{2+} and Sm^{2+} should be like Sr^{2+} or possibly Ca^{2+}. In fact they differ from both these IIA cations in their halide structures. Again it seems to be necessary to postulate more specific interactions than those considered in the simple ionic model.

TABLE 20.VI. *Crystal structures of some dihalides (after Wells)*

	Ca	Sr	Ba	Eu	Sm	Pb
Fluoride	F	F	F	F	..	F or P
Chloride	C	F	P	P	P	P
Bromide	C	S	P	S	S	P
Iodide	CdI_2	..	P	..	..	CdI_2

F = CaF_2, 8-coordinate; C = $CaCl_2$, deformed rutile with 2 nearest neighbours and 4 more distant; CdI_2 = 6-coordinate, layer lattice; S = $SrBr_2$, 9-coordinate, 5 nearest neighbours only; P = $PbCl_2$, 9-coordinate.

Most of the salts of complex anions have crystal structures in which the cation–anion distances are those expected from ionic radii. However, the geometry of the crystals is frequently controlled by hydrogen bonding, e.g. in $LiClO_4,3H_2O$; $CaSO_4,2H_2O$; and alums. A similar situation is found in the ammonium salts and most of the differences between the structural chemistry of the ammonium ion and the rubidium ion are due to hydrogen-bonding, e.g. NH_4F has a 4:4 lattice.

BOILING-POINTS AND MELTING-POINTS

The lattice energies of the IA salts and the heats of dissociation of their diatomic molecules to ions have been shown to be in agreement with the ionic model (Fig. 20.1). At first sight the boiling-points and melting-points do not form a simple pattern: thus the values for the lithium salts lie lower than those of the corresponding sodium salts in Figs. 20.8 (*a*) and 20.9 (*a*). The values can be very largely rationalized (Figs. 20.8 (*b*) and 20.9 (*b*)) while retaining the ionic model (Pauling, p. 527) if anion-anion repulsion is taken into consideration. On account of this repulsion in the lithium *salts*, the Li—X distance is always considerably longer than its ionic radius would have indicated. Therefore although the lattice energy is that expected on the basis of the Li—X distance, it is relatively low compared with that of the LiX molecule where the Li—X distance is not affected by anion/anion repulsion. It is also probable that, for example, in LiI vapour there will be some polarization of the iodide anion. The fact that melting-points show the same sequences as boiling-points indicates that melting is accompanied by a drop in average coordination number.

As the structures of Groups IIA and IIIA compounds are not in accord with the expectations of the ionic model, their physical properties will be expected to be irregular. This is especially true of melting-points and boiling-points (Fig. 20.10), for the lower coordination in the liquid and the vapour is bound to lead to a greater contribution from covalence. In

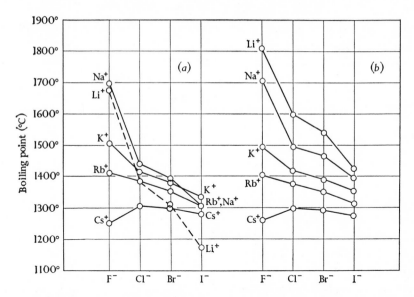

FIG. 20.8. Boiling-points of the alkali halides. (a) Experimental. (b) Corrected for the radius-ratio effect (after Pauling.)

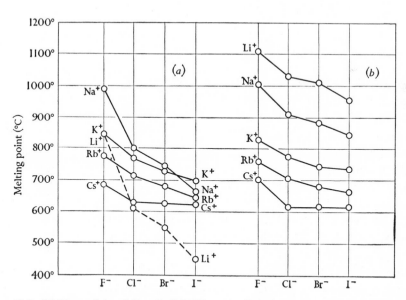

FIG. 20.9. Melting-points of the alkali halides. (a) Experimental. (b) Corrected for the radius-ratio effect (after Pauling).

Group III, BI_3 has a higher melting-point than all other boron halides, but both in Group IIIA and Group IIA the order for the heavier cations is $F^- > Cl^- > Br^- > I^-$ as in Group IA. Presumably, as the lattice type changes from a simple, ionic, close-packed structure to a layer and then to a molecular lattice, polarizability terms take over from coulombic terms in dominating melting-points.

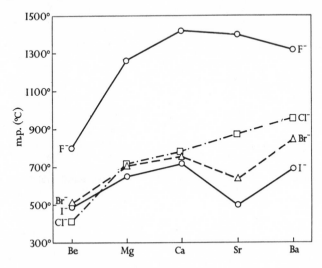

FIG. 20.10. The melting-points of the halides of Be, Mg, Ca, Sr, and Ba.

OTHER PHYSICAL PROPERTIES

In Group IA physical properties of salts such as compressibility are still best understood in terms of the ionic model. Table 20.VII shows the systematic change of compressibility (and coefficient of expansion) with interatomic distance and n. It is, of course, the repulsive term B/r^n which is largely dominant in controlling these physical properties for a lattice of a given charge type. Increase of charge decreases compressibility and also increases hardness (Table 20.VIII). Although physical properties of ionic melts, including surface tension, are in good agreement with ionic theory, properties of the solids such as their breaking strength agree very poorly. This lack of agreement has been attributed to faults in the crystals.

In later Groups, when the crystal structures are no longer those expected on an ionic model, physical properties are very different from those of typical salts. The Group III halides such as BCl_3 and $AlBr_3$ are more like organic cystals in that they have, for example, relatively low hardnesses.

Layer lattices are anisotropic, behaving more like ionic crystals in the planes of the layers and more like organic crystals perpendicular to these planes.

TABLE 20.VII. *Some mechanical properties of the alkali-metal halides*

Salt	Interatomic distance (Å)	n	Coefficient of linear thermal expansion $(10^{-6}/°K)$	Volume compressibility $(10^{-12} cm^2 dyne^{-1})$
LiF	2·01	6·0	32	1·43
LiI	3·03	8·5	58	5·30
NaF	2·31	7·0	32	2·06
NaCl	2·81	8·0	40	3·97
NaBr	2·98	8·5	43	4·75
NaI	3·23	9·5	48	6·21
RbF	2·82	8·5	..	3·66
RbI	3·66	11·0	43	9·00
CsF	3·01	9·5	..	4·25
CsI	3·96	12·0	47	7·83

CsI has the CsCl structure while all the other halides have the NaCl structure.

TABLE 20.VIII. *Some hardness values. Mohs' scale (diamond = 10)*

NaF	3·2	LiBr	2·5	BeO	9·0	CaO	4·5
MgO	6·5	MgSe	3·5	MgO	6·5	CaS	4·0
ScN	7–8			CaO	4·5	CaSe	3·2
TiC	8–9			SrO	3·5	CaTe	2·9
				BaO	3·3		

All compounds except BeO (zinc blende) crystallize in the NaCl structure.

LATTICE DEFECTS

In Chapter 5 two common defects in ionic crystals were described—the Frenkel defect and the Schottky defect. The first arises from the movement of an ion into an interstitial site from a lattice site: the second is a vacancy which may be compensated by the addition of an ion at the surface of the crystal. At any temperature other than absolute zero there will always be defects of both kinds at equilibrium. Schottky defects are less energetically unfavourable and are present in greater numbers. However, in any real crystal there will also be kinetically-stable defects trapped during crystal growth. Diffusion of defects occurs moderately readily and can be followed by using radioactive tracers. Its mechanism involves the jump of lattice ions to unoccupied sites. In alkali-metal halides the cations diffuse more readily than the anions, and at low temperatures the cations usually carry most of the current in an applied electrical field. The activation energy for this ionic conduction is high, 20–40 kcal. The number of mobile ions is dependent on the number of Schottky defects.

Apart from defects arising in pure crystals, defects can be incorporated by the deliberate introduction of foreign ions, e.g. Ca^{2+} into NaCl. Each Ca^{2+} is equivalent to two Na^+ ions and so one Na^+ vacancy must be introduced. In more complex ionic crystals defects are often the initial sites of chemical reactions such as the decomposition of the anion.

If an alkali-halide crystal is heated in the presence of the alkali-metal vapour then the crystal becomes strongly coloured due to the uptake of metal atoms. The colour is due to a quite sharp absorption band, called an F-band (from the German—Farbzentrenbande). The colour is dependent only on the crystal, LiCl (yellow), NaCl (red), KCl (mauve), CsCl (blue-violet), and either Na or K produces the same colour in KCl. Colour can also be produced by X-ray irradiation of alkali-halide crystals. The theory of these colours is that an electron is released from the metal atom and occupies a vacancy (Fig. 20.11). The low-lying excited states are the quantum states of the electron in this somewhat peculiar potential-energy well.

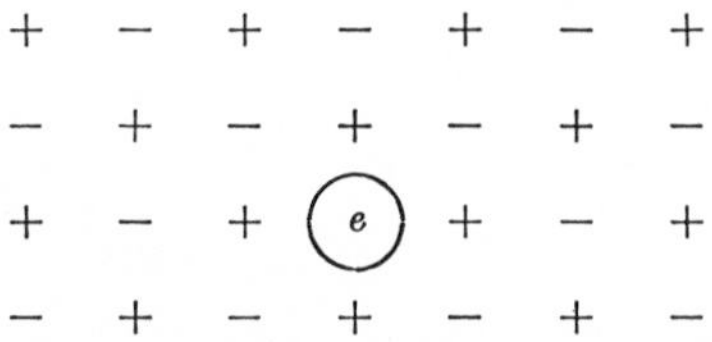

$$+ \quad - \quad + \quad - \quad + \quad - \quad +$$
$$- \quad + \quad - \quad + \quad - \quad + \quad -$$
$$+ \quad - \quad + \quad \textcircled{e} \quad + \quad - \quad +$$
$$- \quad + \quad - \quad + \quad - \quad + \quad -$$

FIG. 20.11. An electron in a vacancy in an alkali-halide crystal.

The coloured crystals are photo-conductors. If a single crystal is subjected to an applied voltage the F-centres can be seen to migrate through the crystal toward the anode. This is a visual demonstration of the movement of current carriers—here electrons. Most stoicheiometric Group Ia and IIa compounds are certainly insulators, but the anomalous Cs_2O, which has a layer lattice and is reported to be coloured, may well be an intrinsic semiconductor.

20.5. Thermochemistry and the reactions of ionic solids

PREPARATION OF METALS

The metals of this chapter are the most electropositive elements in the Periodic Table, and they therefore form salts of considerable thermo-dynamic stability. Since these salts are also good electrical conductors in the fused state, electrolysis is generally the preferred method for the production of the metals. The fused chlorides are most commonly used, but hydroxides (e.g. Na), and cyanides (e.g. Rb and Cs) have also been employed, while Al is produced on a vast scale by the electrolytic reduction of Al_2O_3 (purified bauxite) dissolved in cryolite, Na_3AlF_6. In some cases the metal tends to form a fog which makes it difficult to separate it from the melt. Examples are K, Rb, Cs, and especially Ba. K may also be produced by such reactions as

$$2KF + CaC_2 \rightarrow 2K{\uparrow} + CaF_2 + 2C,$$
or
$$2K_2SiO_3 + Si + 3CaO \rightarrow 4K{\uparrow} + 3CaSiO_3,$$

which are essentially reduction with Ca and Si respectively. Rb and Cs have been made by reduction of their hydroxides or carbonates with Al or Mg, and Ba by reduction of its oxide with Al. A commercial method has been developed for the high-temperature reduction of MgO with carbon. In the laboratory many of the alkali and alkaline-earth metals may be made conveniently by the thermal decomposition of their azides.

The free metals are in general very reactive, but Mg alloys and Al are protected by the formation of very stable surface films of oxide. These metals can therefore be used in an oxygen-containing atmosphere, and, because of their lightness, have very considerable industrial application.

HEATS OF FORMATION

The ease with which a free gaseous ion is formed from the solid metal increases steadily down each of the Groups IA, IIA, and IIIA. At the same time the ionic sizes increase and therefore the lattice energies decrease. As a result of the balance of these two opposing trends, there is often relatively little change in the heats of formation (for constant anion) down any of these Groups, in marked contrast (see Chapter 12) to the pattern of behaviour down a non-metal Group. With small anions the lattice-energy changes become dominant, and there is a fall in the numerical values down a Group (e.g. MF in Fig. 20.12). This fall becomes more marked with anions of higher charge (e.g. $\frac{1}{2}M_2O$ in Fig. 20.12). With large anions the trend is reversed (e.g. compare MF, MCl, MBr, and MI in Fig. 20.12). Some deviations from these general observations are found with small cations and large oxyanions, which to some extent must behave as multipoles rather than as simple charged species. Similarly while the ammonium salts in general fit quite well to the pattern of the Rb salts (Pauling radii NH_4^+ = Rb^+ = 1·48 Å), NH_4F is markedly more stable than might have been expected on simple spherical-cation considerations. This deviation is reflected in the structure of NH_4F which has $4:4$ rather than $6:6$ coordination; the $4:4$ structure allows each F^- to be placed near one of the positively-charged H atoms of an NH_4^+ ion, the total structure being similar to that of ice.

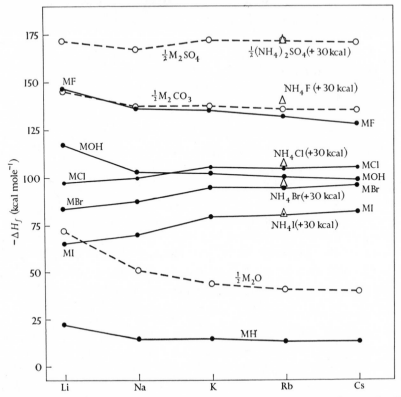

Fig. 20.12. The heats of formation of a number of salts of the Group I$_A$ metals. NH_4^+ values are also included, but for comparative purposes are plotted 30 kcal high (i.e. $-\Delta H_f$ of $NH_4I = 48$ kcal mole^{-1}).

These relative changes in heats of formation down an early A-Group may be further illustrated as in Fig. 20.13, by plotting the differences in heats of formation for corresponding Ba and Mg salts as a function of anion radius. The increasing stability of the Mg relative to the Ba salts with decrease of anion size or increase of anion charge is brought out clearly. This follows qualitatively the expectations of the simple ionic model. The agreement with its quantitative prediction is only very approximate, which, in part at least, is the result of attempting to estimate a relatively small energy from the difference between two large lattice energies. Essentially similar considerations apply to the differences in the heats of forma-

tion of Ba and K salts, which are plotted in Fig. 20.14. Figs. 20.13 and
20.14 may be usefully compared with the thermochemical fluoride/chloride
(Chapter 12), oxide/chloride (Chapter 13), and oxide/sulphide (Chapter 16)
plots. Also marked in both Fig. 20.13 and Fig. 20.14 are two horizontal

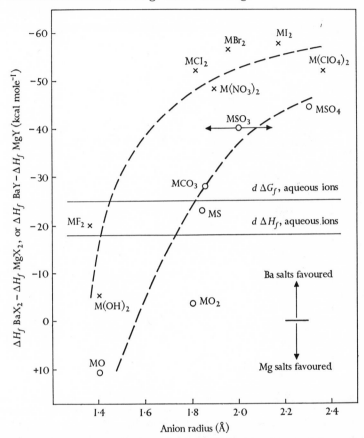

FIG. 20.13. The effect of anion radius on the relative heats of formation of
barium and magnesium salts. The two horizontal lines give the differences between
the heats and between the free energies of formation of the two hydrated ions.

lines corresponding to the differences in the heats and free energies of
formation of the aqueous metal ions from their respective metals. These
lines will be of some significance in our discussion of solubility in the
following section.

CHANGE OF ION SIZE

Many of the simple reactions of ionic solids can be interpreted in terms
of lattice-energy effects, and hence in terms of ionic charges and ionic radii.

Thus the ionic model predicts that with decrease in the size of an anion, there will be a greater increase of lattice energy the smaller and the more highly charged the cation with which the anion is combined. The decomposition of such salts as carbonates, nitrates, sulphates, peroxides, and

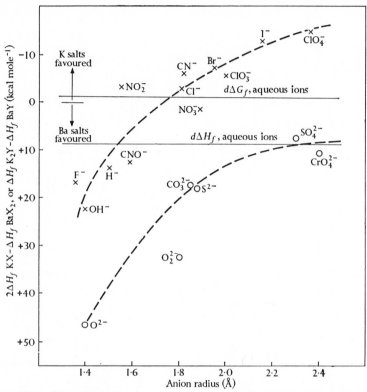

FIG. 20.14. The effect of anion radius on the relative heats of formation of potassium and barium salts. The two horizontal lines give the differences between the heats and between the free energies of formation of the two hydrated ions.

hydroxides to oxides and of polyhalides to halides should therefore take place more readily with the lighter metals of a Periodic Group, or on going from a low-valence cation to one of similar size but greater charge (e.g. from Na^+ to Ca^{2+} to Y^{3+}). The decomposition of the carbonates of divalent cations has already been shown to conform to this pattern (Chapter 7). The effects of charge are seen in the series formed by Na_2CO_3 (equilibrium pressure 6·2 mm of CO_2 at 1000 °C), $CaCO_3$ (equilibrium pressure 760 mm of CO_2 at 900 °C), and the lanthanide carbonates (all lose CO_2 very readily on heating). As an example of the reverse type of reaction, burning the alkali metals in excess of oxygen gives Li_2O, Na_2O_2, KO_2, RbO_2, and CsO_2.

In Group II, Ba is the only metal which forms a peroxide on heating in air. The reaction has been used in the industrial preparation of O_2 and H_2O_2.

Similar considerations will apply to the change in size of a cation. Complex cations such as hydrates and ammines are most stable with large anions. Thus NaF and NaCl are anhydrous, NaBr forms a dihydrate with the release of 4·6 kcal mole^{-1}, while the formation of $NaI,2H_2O$ releases 5·6 kcal mole^{-1}. The stability of ammines also tends to fall off in passing from iodide to chloride. The halides of Group IIIA except the fluorides are very heavily hydrated. An extension of these ideas to oxysalts can be misleading, however, if the anions are treated as simple spherical ions, for oxyanion salts are often not hydrated when the salts of smaller halide ions are. $NaClO_4$, $NaIO_3$, $NaClO_3$, $NaClO_2$, and NaClO are not hydrated while NaBr is. This could be due to the influence of the multipole character of oxyanions. Hydration tends to increase with diminution in the cation size. $BeCl_2,4H_2O$ is said not to lose water even when stood over P_2O_5, although this observation does not seem to be in agreement with the available thermodynamic data.

It follows from the stability of lattices of large cations with large anions that the larger alkali-metal cations can be used in the preparation of crystalline compounds containing these anions. Thus ICl_4^- is better prepared as a caesium than as a potassium salt. Larger cations permit the preparation of larger stable complex anions: thus cations such as NEt_4^+ and the pyridinium ion have been used to crystallize I_9^-, just as cations such as $[Co(NH_3)_6]^{3+}$ have been used to obtain such unusual complexes as $[CuCl_5]^{3-}$.

By way of contrast, the smaller cations often form compounds with the smallest and most highly charged anions available. As well as forming nitrides rather than azides, oxides rather than peroxides, and carbides rather than acetylides, lithium, and, increasingly, beryllium and aluminium give rise to basic salts in which they are combined with the oxide anion. A well-known example is basic beryllium acetate, $Be_4O(acetate)_6$. The ultimate extension of this behaviour is the acidic ionization of the hydroxides, e.g. to form beryllates, aluminates, and borates.

DOUBLE DECOMPOSITIONS

The ionic model is also of value in predicting the direction of double-decomposition reactions such as

$$LiI+NaF \rightarrow LiF+NaI$$
$$BCl_3+AlF_3 \rightarrow BF_3+AlCl_3$$
$$2NaF+CaCl_2 \rightarrow 2NaCl+CaF_2 \quad (r_{Na^+}, 0.95 \text{ Å} \approx r_{Ca^{2+}}, 0.99 \text{ Å}).$$

In general the smaller cation (anion) tends to combine with the smaller and more highly charged anion (cation). The multipole character of oxyanions especially noted in relation to smaller cations such as Li^+ (see above) can lead to some slight anomalies, e.g. both KCl and LiCl will give exothermic double decomposition reactions with $NaNO_3$ ($r_{Cl^-} = 1\cdot81$ Å; thermochemical radius of $NO_3^- = 1\cdot89$ Å, which would suggest a preference by NO_3^- for the larger cation in the exchange).

$$\Delta H \text{ (kcal mole}^{-1})$$

$NaNO_3 + KCl \rightarrow KNO_3 + NaCl$	-11
$NaNO_3 + LiCl \rightarrow LiNO_3 + NaCl$	-19

When there is an appreciable contribution from covalent bonding or strong London forces (see Chapter 5) then the ionic model can give a completely false picture. Thus the reactions

$$AgF + KCl \rightarrow AgCl + KF$$
$$HgF_2 + 2KCl \rightarrow HgCl_2 + 2KF$$

take place as shown, although K^+ is a larger ion than either Ag^+ or Hg^{2+}, and has a smaller charge than Hg^{2+}. The importance of covalent terms in exchange reactions becomes particularly marked for transition-metal ions (e.g. Chapter 25) and B-metal ions (e.g. Chapter 31).

Double-decomposition reactions between ionic crystals are not often studied directly by inorganic chemists. Their consequences are clearly seen, however, in the geological occurrence of the elements (Chapter 34 B), and in reactions which take place through the medium of a suitable solvent, usually water. In the latter case the formation of hydrated salts and hydrated ions in solution can make very significant alterations to the overall reaction (see following section). Thus the differing variations with temperature of the solubility in water of NaCl, $NaNO_3$, KCl, and KNO_3 are used in the normal laboratory preparation of KNO_3.

The similar effects of small size and high charge often lead to a certain similarity in the chemistry of elements related diagonally to one another in the Periodic Table. Thus elements with insoluble fluorides occur along the line Li—Ca—lanthanides, and the amphoteric line of oxides (Chapter 14) passes through Be, Al, and Ti.

20.6. Solid-solution equilibria

THE INTERPRETATION OF SOLUTION EQUILIBRIA

We wish to understand equilibria such as the solubility of salts and the formation of complex ions. These equilibria can be expressed in terms of differences in standard free energy between the species on the two sides of reaction equations such as

$$MX(\text{crystal}) \rightleftharpoons M^+(\text{aq.}) + X^-(\text{aq.}),$$

or
$$MX(\text{complex})(\text{aq.}) \rightleftharpoons M^+(\text{aq.}) + X^-(\text{aq.}).$$

On change from one cation to another, these free-energy differences frequently show *small* but *systematic* changes. At first sight, the *heat* of the reaction would appear to be related directly to the internal-energy changes, and hence to the binding-energy models. However, as we have shown in Chapter 7, this assumption may be incorrect, for the temperature dependence of the heat of reaction itself is known to be large in systems involving ionic solutions. The heat change measured at a given temperature may be quite different from the heat change at absolute zero, which alone can be compared with the internal energies of the constituent atoms and ions of the reaction. Thus, when the experimental data show but small free-energy differences along series the interpretation of these differences can be exceedingly difficult. It is a task for the future to discover, for example, the extent of hydration of the ionic species involved and the variation of this with temperature. Here we shall often be content with correlations between free-energy changes and changes of radii and charge, for, assuming that the ionic model is applicable, they should show how simple electrostatic effects influence equilibria.

Some details concerning the thermodynamic factors affecting the solubility of ionic crystals have been given in Chapter 7. The calculation of the absolute solubility of an *anhydrous* salt such as MgO, from a consideration of lattice energies and absolute free energies of hydration, could however be wrong by a factor of some 10^{10}. This may seem a ridiculously large error, but it must be remembered that solubility is related through $RT \ln(\text{solubility})$ to the difference between two very large free energies, i.e. that of the salt lattice (~ 500 kcal) and that of hydration of the cation and anion (~ 500 kcal). The error in determining such a difference is not likely to be much less than some 10 kcal. This means that we can only expect to understand the orders of the solubilities in series of salts but not the absolute magnitude of any one solubility. The picture is made the more complex as interest centres not so much on the *anhydrous* salts as on the particular *hydrated* salts which come out of a solution. If a stable hydrated salt appears then it must be more insoluble than the corresponding anhydrous salt. It is not possible to calculate even the lattice energy of hydrated salts with any great degree of accuracy. Because of these diffi-culties of proceeding from a theoretical consideration of ionic lattices and of hydrated ions in solution to an understanding of solubility, solubility trends will be tackled empirically by looking for relationships between solubilities on altering the sizes and the charges on the cations and the anions.

HYDRATION

The hydration energies of the pre-transition cations may be predicted with reasonable accuracy. This does not mean that a structure can be given to the hydrates. It is probable that for the ions under considera-tion there are a number of differently-hydrated forms in thermodynamic equilibrium in aqueous solutions. However, ions of high $z^2/r_{effective}$ are clearly heavily hydrated, and the variation of both the heat and entropy of hydration is understandable on an ionic model (Chapters 5 and 7). The hydration of crystalline salts, Table 20.IX, is therefore the more surprising for it contains some rather remarkable sequences. In the table the salts of the weak-acid anions are separated from those of the strong-acid anions. For the latter it is generally true that the cation of higher $z^2/r_{effective}$ is the more highly hydrated, e.g. Li > Na > K, Mg > Ca > Ba, Al > La, and Al > Mg > Na. This is as might be expected for H^+ is a cation of high $z^2/r_{effective}$. On the other hand, amongst the salts of the weak-acid anions hydration is much less common, and it is just as frequently the cations of low as of high $z^2/r_{effective}$ which are hydrated. The form of the salt which comes out of solution is clearly a property not of the cation or anion alone but of the particular combination of anion and cation. This is perhaps not so clear in Group IA where the dependence on cation is dominant. Thus hardly any hydrated salts of rubidium and caesium are known, whereas about 25 per cent of potassium salts are hydrated and about 75 per cent of sodium and lithium salts obtained from solution are hydrates. Elsewhere it appears that hydration generally leads to an im-provement in the matching of anion and cation size and is therefore strongly anion-dependent.

The high affinity for water of certain anhydrous salts is used in drying agents. Calcium chloride and magnesium perchlorate are examples of strong-acid salts, and sodium silicate and carbonate of weak-acid salts. Some salts also 'solvate' with other donors such as amines, alcohols, and ethers. The reverse process, efflorescence, is the basis of cement hardening and perhaps of bone development.

TABLE 20.IX. *Hydration of IA, IIA, and IIIA salts*

Anion	Li^+	Na^+	K^+	Rb^+	Cs^+	Be^{2+}	Mg^{2+}	Ca^{2+}	Sr^{2+}	Ba^{2+}	Al^{3+}	Sc^{3+}	Y^{3+}	La^{3+}
OH^-	1	1	2	0?	0?	0	0	0	8, 2, 1	8, 1	0?	0?	0?	0?
F^-	0	0	2	$1\frac{1}{2}$	$1\frac{1}{2}$	0	0	0	0	0	1	0	?	0
CO_3^{2-}	0	10	$1\frac{1}{2}$	0	0	4	1–5	1–6	0	0	?	?	?	?
Oxalate	0	0	1	0	1	3	2	0	1–3	1–3	?	$2\frac{1}{2}$	$4\frac{1}{2}$	$4\frac{1}{2}$
Formate	1	0–2	0	$\frac{1}{2}$	1	(0)	2	0	2	0	?	?	?	?
Acetate	2	3	$1\frac{1}{2}$	0	0	?	4	2	1–4	1–3	?	?	4	$1\frac{1}{2}$
Cl^-	1	0	0	0	0	4	4–12	1–6	1–6	2	>6	?	6	2
Br^-	2	2	0	0	0	4	4–10	6	2–6	1–2	?	?	?	?
I^-	3	2	0	0	0	?	6–10	6	1–6	1–8	?	?	?	?
SO_4^{2-}	1	0–10	0	0	0	4	1–12	0–2	0	0	$4\frac{1}{2}$	$2\frac{1}{2}$	8	$4\frac{1}{2}$
NO_3^-	3	0	0	0	0	4	2–9	2–4	4	0	9	?	?	6
ClO_4^-	3	1	0	0	0	4	2–6	0	2–4	1–3	9	?	?	?
ClO_3^-	1–3 ?	0	0	0	0	?	4–6	2	3?	1	?	?	?	?

The numbers refer to the numbers of moles of water per mole of salt in the forms stable at room temperature and under normal atmospheric conditions. Weak-acid anions are considered in the upper half and strong-acid anions in the lower half of the table.

TABLE 20.X. Solubilities in water at $\sim 25\,^{\circ}C$ (moles litre^{-1})

Anion	Li$^+$	Na$^+$	K$^+$	Rb$^+$	Cs$^+$	Be^{2+}	Mg^{2+}	Ca^{2+}	Sr^{2+}	Ba^{2+}	Al^{3+}	Sc^{3+}	Y^{3+}	La^{3+}
OH$^-$	5·6	27·0	20·0	19	25	$1·3\times10^{-5}$	$3·2\times10^{-4}$	$1·8\times10^{-2}$	$8·6\times10^{-2}$	0·27	less than 10^{-4}			
F$^-$	0·05	1·0	17	12	24	5·5	$1·9\times10^{-3}$	$3·1\times10^{-4}$	$9·3\times10^{-4}$	$1·2\times10^{-2}$	less than 10^{-3}			
CO$_3^{2-}$	0·2	2·0	8·1	9·6	8·0		$1·3\times10^{-4}$	$6·2\times10^{-5}$	$3·9\times10^{-5}$	$4·4\times10^{-5}$	not stable			
Oxalate	0·7	0·3	2·0	1·5	1·6	3·4	$2·7\times10^{-3}$	$6·7\times10^{-6}$	$2·4\times10^{-4}$	$5·0\times10^{-4}$	less than 10^{-2}			
Formate	8	15	40	very high	very high		0·71	1·3	0·53	1·4	fairly soluble			
Acetate	5	6	29	very high	very high		4·5	2·2	2·0	2·9	fairly soluble			
Cl$^-$	19·0	6·0	4·6	7·5	11·0	large	5·7	7·3	3·5	1·8	2·0	3·0		
Br$^-$	18·8	9·0	5·5	6·5	6·0	large	5·5	7·0	4·0	3·5	>5·0	2·5		
I$^-$	12·4	12·3	9·0	7·0	3·0	large	5·0	7·0	5·3	5·3	>5·0			
SO$_4^{2-}$	3·2	4·3	0·6	1·8	5·0	4·0	3·0	$7·8\times10^{-3}$	$6·2\times10^{-4}$	$9·5\times10^{-6}$	1·0	0·6	0·2	0·04
NO$_3^-$	10·5	11·0	3·0	3·6	1·0	8·2	5·1	7·4	3·3	0·35	2·0			0·2
ClO$_4^-$	5·7	16·0	0·1	0·07	0·09	7·1	4·5	7·9	10·8	5·9	2·0		5·0	0·2
ClO$_3^-$	48·0	10·0	0·6	0·3	0·3		7·7	9·7	6·9	1·1	2·0			

SOLUBILITY

Solubilities for several series of salts are given in Table 20.x. Although the solubilities change by several powers of ten in many of the series, in others the change is very slight. At room temperature every tenfold change in solubility corresponds, for a 1:1 salt, to a change of only 1·4 kcal in free energy. It is surprising that any generalizations should appear amongst these small energy differences, but the table shows that the following rough rules hold.

(1) Cations of small $z^2/r_{\text{effective}}$ give the more insoluble salts with anions of small $z^2/r_{\text{effective}}$. These are usually the anions of strong acids.

(2) Cations of large $z^2/r_{\text{effective}}$ give the more insoluble salts with anions of large $z^2/r_{\text{effective}}$. These are usually the anions of weak acids.

Thus solubility down a Group is anion-dependent in much the same way as the hydration of the salt obtained from aqueous solution is anion-dependent.

These solubility relations may also be discussed in terms of Figs. 20.13 and 20.14. In both figures horizontal lines have been drawn equivalent to the difference in the free energies of formation of the two salts (e.g. BaX_2 and MgX_2 in Fig. 20.13, and $2KX$ and BaX_2 in Fig. 20.14) in aqueous solution, *provided* that there is no complex-ion formation between cations and anions. The points plotted on these figures are for differences in *heats* of formation of the solid salts, but to quite a reasonable approximation they also give the differences in the free energies of formation of these salts. This means that the solubility-product ratios are related approximately to the positions of the points plotted with respect to the horizontal free-energy line. Thus in Fig. 20.13 points lying above the line will correspond to anions whose Ba salts are more insoluble than their Mg salts, and points below the line to anions whose Mg salts are more insoluble than their Ba salts. Similarly points lying above the line in Fig. 20.14 correspond to anions whose K salts are more insoluble, and those below the line to anions whose Ba salts are more insoluble. These considerations apply strictly only for the unhydrated salts, but there is also some general correlation for the hydrated salts. For the unhydrated salts rough quantitative estimates of solubility ratios may be made. Thus from Fig. 20.14 the ratio

$$\frac{\text{Solubility product for } BaSO_4}{\text{Solubility product for } K_2SO_4} = \frac{(\text{Solubility of } BaSO_4)^2}{(\text{Solubility of } K_2SO_4)^3}$$

(mole litre^{-1} units), would be estimated as 10^{-6} from the relation

$$-\Delta G°_{\text{solution}} = RT \ln(\text{Solubility product})$$

or $\quad\quad \log_{10}(\text{Solubility ratio}) = -8·5/1·38$

where 8·5 kcal is the energy by which the SO_4^{2-} point in Fig. 20.14 lies below the $d\Delta G_f$ aqueous ion line. The experimental value in this case for the same ratio is 10^{-7}. If one of the salts being compared in this way is hydrated when in equilibrium with its aqueous solution while the other is not, then its observed solubility must be less than that estimated for the unhydrated salt. Salts whose aqueous solutions show considerable complex-ion formation will be more soluble than estimated.

It is also a general rule that hydrated salts are soluble. These various rules again show that that matching of anion and cation size is a very important factor affecting solubility. Many examples of the rules are put to analytical use. Thus amongst small cations aluminium and magnesium can be precipitated as hydroxides and, after easy dehydration, weighed as oxides. The method is unsuitable for actinium and barium. Lithium can be precipitated as a phosphate, oxalate, carbonate, or hydroxide and this similarity with magnesium is part of the diagonal relationship between these elements. The corresponding salts of potassium are quite soluble but those of aluminium are very insoluble. On the other hand barium and strontium, but not beryllium and magnesium, can be precipitated as sulphates; potassium but not sodium can be determined as its perchlorate, and the nitrates of caesium, barium, and lanthanum are sufficiently insoluble to make these salts useful in fractional recrystallization. Sulphate, nitrate, and perchlorate are strong-acid anions. Qualitative analysis reagents also illustrate the rules, e.g. sodium tetraphenylborate and hexachloroplatinate(IV) are reagents for potassium. Although the above rules serve as useful generalizations there are also many irregularities, many of which can be understood qualitatively in terms of the ionic model. Thus the solubilities of the chlorides go through a minimum at KCl and the solubilities of the perchlorates go through a maximum at $NaClO_4$. These irregularities are also used in analytical and separation methods: a common method for separating calcium from magnesium depends upon the greater insolubility of calcium oxalate.

The occurrence and distribution of the elements in the mineral and living parts of the earth are partly controlled by solubility factors and partly by complex-ion formation in the living systems. In fact living things find it easier to obtain potassium than sodium as sodium is more firmly held in silicates.

20.7. Complex ions

The most striking difference between the pre-transition cations and those of both the transition series and the B subgroups is that they do *not* form stable complexes with a very wide range of ligands in aqueous solution. For example, complexes with such neutral molecules as ethers, thio-ethers, ammonia, and pyridine, and with the large polarizable anions such as chloride, bromide, iodide, and cyanide are only present in relatively concentrated solutions. The complexes with *small* anions are, however, quite strong. This illustrates the great significance of electrostatic energies in pre-transition metal complexes: water has a high dipole moment. The stability sequences with small anions, e.g. fluoride and hydroxide, follow the $z^2/r_{\text{effective}}$ orders:

$$\text{Li}^+ > \text{Na}^+ > \text{K}^+, \quad \text{Mg}^{2+} > \text{Ca}^{2+} > \text{Sr}^{2+}, \quad \text{Al}^{3+} > \text{Sc}^{3+} > \text{La}^{3+},$$

and
$$\text{Ti}^{4+} > \text{Sc}^{3+} > \text{Ca}^{2+} > \text{K}^+,$$

see Tables 20.XI and 20.XIV. (N.B. $\Delta G° = -RT \ln K$.) Other anions for which these orders appear to hold approximately are phosphate, acetate, carbonate, and in fact many weak-acid oxy-anions. The orders are changed occasionally as a result of steric hindrance around smaller cations when the anion is multidentate (see below). The high stability of the proton complexes with these same weak-acid anions implies that the proton behaves like a pre-transition cation in aqueous solution. Masking of the proton in solution (increasing the pH) is achieved by adding weak-acid anions—e.g. buffering anions such as acetate, borate, and phosphate—and masking of pre-transition metal cations is achieved by adding fluoride, citrate, or tartrate.

TABLE 20.XI. *Stability of some complexes of the pre-transition metals,* $\log K_1$ *(mole^{-1} litres), in aqueous solution at 25 °C*

Ligand	Li$^+$	Na$^+$	K$^+$	Rb$^+$	Cs$^+$
OH$^-$	$-0\cdot1$	$-0\cdot7$	← very small →		
P$_2$O$_7^{4-}$	$3\cdot1$	$2\cdot4$	$2\cdot3$	..	$2\cdot3$
EDTA^{4-}	$2\cdot8$	$1\cdot7$	$0\cdot0$	..	..
Cl$^-$	← very small →		..	$-0\cdot8$	$-0\cdot4$
NO$_3^-$	..	$-0\cdot6$	$-0\cdot2$	..	..
SO$_4^{2-}$	$0\cdot6$	$0\cdot7$	$1\cdot0$	..	..

Ligand	Mg^{2+}	Ca^{2+}	Sr^{2+}	Ba^{2+}
OH$^-$	$2\cdot6$	$1\cdot4$	..	$0\cdot6$
F$^-$	$1\cdot8$	$1\cdot0$	..	$<0\cdot5$
polyphosphate	$3\cdot2$	$3\cdot0$	$2\cdot8$	$3\cdot0$
NO$_3^-$	$0\cdot0$	$0\cdot3$	..	$0\cdot9$
SO$_4^{2-}$	$2\cdot2$	$2\cdot3$	..	..

Ligand	Al^{3+}	Sc^{3+}	Y^{3+}	La^{3+}
OH$^-$	$9\cdot0$	$9\cdot0$	$7\cdot0$	$5\cdot0$
F$^-$	$7\cdot0$	$7\cdot1$	..	$3\cdot5$
Cl$^-$	no complexes			$\sim0\cdot1$
SO$_4^{2-}$	..	..	$3\cdot45$	$3\cdot6$
NO$_3^-$	no complexes			$-0\cdot3$

The constants in this table are very sensitive to ionic strength and temperature; see *Stability Constants of Metal Ion Complexes* compiled by L. G. Sillén and A. E. Martell, Special Publication No. 17, Chemical Society, London, 1964.

The similarity between the reactions of the proton and those of certain pre-transition cations is brought out again in their reactions with strong-acid anions such as chloride and nitrate. Cations such as Li^+ and Mg^{2+}, which, like the proton, are small when unhydrated but large when hydrated, do not form complexes with these anions. Weak complexes are formed by the cations, such as Cs^+ and Ba^{2+}, which are relatively large for unhydrated cations but relatively small for hydrated cations. The stability sequences with large, strong-acid anions, e.g. NO_3^- and SO_4^{2-} are

$$K^+ > Na^+ > Li^+, Ba^{2+} > Sr^{2+} > Ca^{2+} > Mg^{2+}, \text{ and } La^{3+} > Al^{3+},$$

the reverse of the orders given for the weak-acid anions. As mentioned above only steric factors appear to be capable of changing these orders. For example, increasing complexity of the ligands can lead to inversion of the usual weak-acid order so that $Ca^{2+} > Mg^{2+}$ (Table 20.XII). The selectivity of action in the formation of complexes is thus very like the selectivity just discussed in the solubility of salts.

TABLE 20.XII. *Stability constants*, $\log K_1$ *(mole^{-1} litres), of complexes of the alkaline-earth ions at* $\sim 25\,°C$

Ligand	Mg^{2+}	Ca^{2+}	Sr^{2+}	Ba^{2+}
Oxalate	3·43	3·00	2·54	2·33
Malonate	2·85	2·49	..	1·71
Succinate	2·15	2·00	..	1·70
Malate	2·52	2·66	..	2·19
Acetate	1·05	1·00	0·97	0·93
Propionate	1·08	1·04	0·97	0·88
Butyrate	1·07	1·05	0·90	0·84
β-Hydroxybutyrate	1·14	1·14	1·01	0·97
Glycine	3·44	1·43	..	0·77
Alanine	1·96	1·24	..	0·77
Glycylglycine	1·06	1·24	..	..
Tartrate	1·36	1·80	1·65	1·62

Note. See footnote to Table 20.XI.

THERMODYNAMIC DATA

For the complexes of ethylenediaminetetraacetate, $EDTA^{4-}$ (Table 20.XI and Table 20.XIII), the stability orders are

$$IIIA > IIA > IA, \text{ and } Li^+ > Na^+ > K^+, \text{ but } Ca^{2+} > Mg^{2+} \simeq Sr^{2+} > Ba^{2+}$$

and
$$(Sc^{3+}) > Lu^{3+} > Y^{3+} > Al^{3+} > La^{3+}.$$

These orders show that the higher the charge the more stable is the complex, but that at constant charge it is only in Group IA that the smallest cation gives the most stable complex. For series of ions of the same charge type the complex of the smallest ion (bold type) becomes less stable relative to the other ions the higher the charge.

TABLE 20.XIII. *Thermodynamic functions for the formation of some* $EDTA^{4-}$ *complexes* ($kcal\ mole^{-1}$). (*Data for* Mg^{2+} *to* Al^{3+} *are at 20 °C and for* Y^{3+} *to* Lu^{3+} *are at 25 °C.*)

	$\Delta G°$	$\Delta H°$	$T\Delta S°$
Mg^{2+}	−11·65	+3·14	14·79
Ca^{2+}	−14·34	−6·45	7·89
Sr^{2+}	−11·57	−4·11	7·46
Ba^{2+}	−10·40	−4·83	5·57
Al^{3+}	−21·60	+12·58	34·18
Y^{3+}	−23·70	−0·59	23·11
La^{3+}	−20·72	−2·93	17·79
Lu^{3+}	−26·11	−2·51	23·60

Inspection of the heat and entropy data (Table 20.XIII) shows that this peculiarity is caused by the heat terms. The entropy terms on complex formation are almost invariably large and favourable to complex formation. The $\Delta S°$ orders are

$$Mg^{2+} > Ca^{2+} > Sr^{2+} > Ba^{2+} \quad \text{and} \quad Al^{3+} > Y^{3+} > La^{3+}.$$

These orders are expected from the theory of ionic entropies discussed in Chapter 5, assuming that the hydration sphere of a cation is largely lost on combination with an anion. It is this loss of hydration, or increased random motion of the water molecules, which is the main factor in the entropy change for reactions between oppositely charged ions, and is often the sole cause of the stability of pre-transition cation complexes (Table 20.XIV). In the absence of steric hindrance there is sometimes a good direct relationship between stability constants and hydration entropies, e.g. with dibenzoylmethane (Fig. 20.15).

In the EDTA complexes the heat terms (often opposed to complex formation (Table 20.XIII)) most favour complex-formation in the sequences

$$Ca^{2+} > Ba^{2+} > Sr^{2+} \gg Mg^{2+} \quad \text{and} \quad La^{3+} > Y^{3+} \gg Al^{3+}.$$

The magnitude of the changes is greater in the last sequence. It is the large *endothermic* heat terms which reduce the stability of the magnesium and aluminium complexes. The *decrease* in the favourability of the heat term with *decrease* in size can be explained as a consequence of the steric difficulty of packing all the six groups of $EDTA^{4-}$, four carboxylates and two amines, around the smaller ions as compared with the relative ease of packing water molecules about these ions. Other series of complexes give rise to similar thermodynamic data, Table 20.XIV. A feature of this table is that it is $\Delta H°$ which stabilizes complexes of low charge and large size while it is $\Delta S°$ which stabilizes complexes of high charge and small size. Limited data suggest that this generalization may be extended to Group IA.

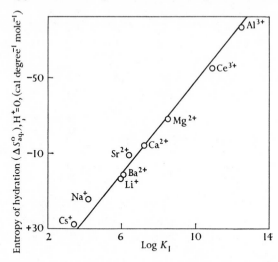

FIG. 20.15. The relationship between the entropies of cation hydration (relative to H^+) and the logarithms of the stability constants for the $1:1$ complexes with dibenzoylmethane.

TABLE 20.XIV. *Thermodynamic functions for the formation of some complex ions (kcal mole^{-1}) at 25 °C*

Complex	$\Delta G°$	$\Delta H°$	$T\Delta S°$
$Mg^{2+}OH^-$	-3.5	..	..
$Ca^{2+}OH^-$	-1.9	$+1.2$	$+3.1$
$Sr^{2+}OH^-$	-1.1	$+1.2$	$+2.3$
$Ba^{2+}OH^-$	-0.9	$+1.8$	$+2.7$
$Mg^{2+}F^-$	-1.7	$+4.0$	$+5.7$
$Mg^{2+}CH_3CO_2^-$	-1.7	-1.5	$+0.2$
$Ca^{2+}CH_3CO_2^-$	-1.7	$+0.9$	$+2.6$
$Mg^{2+}CH_2(CO_2^-)_2$	-4.0	$+3.2$	$+7.2$
$Mg^{2+}HCO_2^-$	-1.9	-1.8	$+0.1$
$Ca^{2+}HCO_2^-$	-1.9	$+1.0$	$+2.9$
$Mg^{2+}SO_4^{2-}$	-3.2	$+4.5$	$+7.7$
$Ca^{2+}SO_4^{2-}$	-3.2	$+1.6$	$+4.8$
$Ba^{2+}S_2O_3^{2-}$	-3.1	$+2.6$	$+5.7$
$Mg^{2+}(NH_3)_2$	-0.3	-1.2	-0.9
$Al^{3+}F^-$	-8.9	$+1.1$	$+10.0$
$Sc^{3+}F^-$	-8.5	$+0.4$	$+8.9$
$La^{3+}CH_2(CO_2^-)_2$	-6.7	$+4.8$	$+11.5$
$La^{3+}SO_4^{2-}$	-5.3	$+2.5$	$+7.8$
$Ce^{3+}SO_4^{2-}$	-4.6	$+4.7$	$+9.3$
$La^{3+}NO_3^-$	$+0.4$	$+1.7$	$+1.3$
$La^{3+}Cl^-$	$+0.2$	-1.4	-1.6

It is large unfavourable $\Delta H°$ terms too which lower the stability of the complexes of strong oxyacid anions with small cations. A few cases, the magnesium formates and acetates and $La^{3+}Cl^-$, for example, are exceptions to these generalizations. In some of these cases the magnitude of the entropy terms suggests that the water molecules around the cations are *not* displaced by the anions and the molecular association is as *ion-pairs* rather than as complexes. These data serve to stress how the analysis of heat and entropy terms may lead to incorrect inferences about the causes of complex-ion stability as a result of the complications introduced by hydration. As suggested in Chapter 7 it can be that in these circumstances $\Delta G°$ is a better guide than $\Delta H°$ to the fundamental property, ΔH_0, i.e. at absolute zero.

From these observations the somewhat general conclusion can be drawn that in aqueous solution complexes of any cation, A-metal, B-metal, or transition-metal, will be very weak, or will not form, with neutral ligands or anions of strong acids unless the heat terms are made more favourable than would be predicted by the ionic model. This occurs in both the transition-metal and B-metal series as is discussed later.

In non-aqueous media of lower dielectric constant, by way of contrast, the pre-transition cations are capable of forming complexes of considerable stability with many ligands. This is in no way surprising for the Debye–Hückel theory of strong electrolytes, as extended by Bjerrum to include formation of ion-pairs, shows that $M/10$ solutions of mono-monovalent salts must be considerably associated when the dielectric constant of the solvent drops below about 40. The theory is based on a simple electrostatic interaction. Thus in alcohol solutions alkali-metal cations form strong complexes with such ligands as sulphate and salicylate. With lithium the geometry of the complexes is thought to be tetrahedral, but the coordination number is probably higher than 4 in both sodium and potassium complexes.

PRACTICAL APPLICATIONS OF COMPLEX FORMATION

Analytical use can be made of the formation of complexes by cations of charge greater than one. Thus all the higher-valence cations can be determined by complexometric titration with EDTA. The end-point of the titration may be observed by the displacement of a coordinated indicator, e.g. Eriochrome Black T, from the cation by EDTA which is more strongly bound. This method has made the determination of the hardness of water a simple and rapid procedure. Water softening itself is achieved by sodium salts of silicates, zeolites, or phosphates (e.g. 'hexasodium hexaphosphate') which combine preferentially with calcium and magnesium. The zeolites can be regenerated in the sodium form by washing with strong brine solutions. Another water softener is the polystyrene sulphonate ion-exchanger, which has a higher affinity for calcium and magnesium than for the proton. Such exchangers are used to prepare conductivity water as they will also absorb alkali-metal cations. The same material is used in the fractionation of the lanthanide cations by ion-exchange chromatography (Chapter 21).

The interaction between the sulphonate group of a simple organic sulphonate, such as methyl sulphonate and calcium or magnesium ions is quite small. However, when detergents which are based on long-chain alkyl sulphonates are used in hard water it is still necessary to add a water softener to prevent combination of the detergent with these cations. The same is true when using traditional soaps which are long-chain alkyl carboxylates. This shows that the soap, or detergent, micelle has a greater affinity for the cations than the simple anions. In fact the old method of determining the hardness of water, using the amount of soap required to give a permanent lather, was a measure of calcium and magnesium content. The water softeners are still stronger complexing agents for the cations by virtue of the many coordinating groups which they possess, i.e. they are chelating agents.

The ability of the larger pre-transition cations to combine with hydroxyl groups (see Table 20.xii) is used in colorimetric reagents, e.g. sodium rhodizonate for barium and strontium and alizarin for beryllium and aluminium. It is also of practical value in mordant dyeing. On the other hand, the combination of calcium and strontium with saccharates is only a nuisance in the sugar industry, where fine control of crystallization conditions is required.

Group Ia cations are not readily extracted from water into organic solvents, but the differences between the solubilities of calcium, strontium, and barium nitrates or chlorides in absolute ethyl alcohol have been utilized in an analytical fractionation method. In paper chromatography even mixtures of alkali-metal cations can be fractionated by elution with hydrochloric acid solutions in organic solvents such as alcohols and ketones, but the water content of the partition systems is deliberately kept low. The more highly charged cations such as magnesium and aluminium can also be extracted from water into, say, chloroform with conventional organic reagents such as 8-hydroxyquinoline. Extraction occurs at a lower pH the higher the z^2/r ratio of the cation. The method can be extended to Group IVa cations. A typical reagent for the extraction and separation of Zr^{4+}

and Hf^{4+} is thenoyl-trifluoro-acetylacetone. These two cations can also be separated by paper chromatography using their differential formation of fluoride complexes.

BIOLOGICAL SIGNIFICANCE OF COMPLEX FORMATION

The I_A and II_A cations are particularly and specifically important in biological systems. Sodium and potassium are the most common cations in biological fluids. Their total concentration is very similar to that in sea water, but the compartments of a biological system, and indeed many simple cells and even mitochondria have the ability to concentrate potassium at the expense of sodium. For example in the plasma of many mammals the ratio of the potassium to sodium ion concentration is about 1:30. In red-blood cells the ratio is reversed to 7:1 in mammals such as man, rabbits, rats, and horses, but has the value of about 1:15 for cats and dogs. It clearly requires expenditure of work both to establish and to maintain such concentration gradients, and biologists have postulated 'sodium pumps' to explain these phenomena. Metabolism of organic substrates here provides the necessary energy to transport sodium or potassium against a concentration gradient. Such pumps require a selective interaction between mobile organic ligands which can penetrate a cell wall —a thermodynamic 'mechanism', or else a set of ion-exchange sites in the cell wall which in some way regulate mobility of the cations—a kinetic mechanism. The most remarkable use of these differential cation concentration gradients has been developed in the nerve cells. A nerve cell shows a potential gradient across its membrane when in the resting state. The potential can be related to that of the potassium concentration cell across the membrane. When the nerve cell is activated by the release of chemicals (often acetyl-choline) near its end-plate, the membrane potential is discharged and the discharge continues to run along the length of the nerve, thus transmitting an electrical pulse from one part of the body to another. This action is not understood. It is a problem of immense importance and needs the attention of some inorganic chemists.

Magnesium and calcium have a similarly important role to play in biological reactions. As was explained in Chapter 17, a biological system obtains energy from the oxidation of organic substrates or from the action of light on its photo-absorbing pigments, and then stores this physical energy mainly by converting it to the chemical energy of pyrophosphate links. This phosphate polymerization is catalysed by magnesium in some cases and by calcium in others. However, when magnesium is the catalyst calcium is often an inhibitor. The stored pyrophosphate, adenosine triphosphate, is degraded with the gain of useful work in many processes. One of these is the hydrolysis reaction in muscle which is triggered by nerve pulses and is controlled by the calcium-ion concentration. Calcium-ion liberation is an essential feature of muscle contraction. In biological systems sugar phosphates are also plentiful, and it would appear that catalysis of their reactions is usually restricted by calcium, and aided by magnesium. The calcium/magnesium antagonism is thought to be one way in which metabolic control is maintained. It could well be that it is selectivity based on hydroxyl groups of the sugar which produces the differential effects both of Ca^{2+} and Mg^{2+} (Table 20.XII) and of K^+ and Na^+.

Magnesium and calcium are important elsewhere in biological systems. The main pigment for the absorption of light is chlorophyll, a magnesium complex of a ligand somewhat like a tetra-pyrrole. Calcium occurs generally in the bone as a phosphate. Very little is as yet understood about changes in the structure of bone materials on ageing, or about the mechanism of the incorporation of magnesium into chlorophyll. Here again there must be intriguing problems for the inorganic chemist.

20.8. The covalent model and the diagonal relationship

In all the previous sections the chemistry of the pre-transition metals has been treated in terms of the ionic model. This model is remarkably satisfactory so long as the electronegativity differences between the pre-transition elements and their partners are large. At the other end of the scale are the compounds with elements of similar electronegativity. These are the alloys formed between different pre-transition metals and described in section 19.2. The bonding in them is probably best treated by band theory. The combination of the pre-transition metals with elements of slightly greater electronegativity, e.g. B metals such as lead and tin, will result in a type of binding somewhere between that represented by the two models. This binding has been called semi-ionic. A number of compounds of this kind, such as some Zintl phases, have been described in Chapter 8 and section 19.6. At somewhat greater electronegativity differences there are groups of compounds which are rather poor electrical conductors and are either simple molecules or polymerized chains, rings, or layers, e.g. BeH_2. It is with the elements of such intermediate electronegativity, C and H for example, that covalent character (as opposed to both metallic or ionic character) is most apparent.

The most non-metallic elements in any Group are those in the first row of the Periodic Table. They show the greatest deviation from the behaviour expected of simple cations and have the greatest number of apparently covalent compounds with the more electronegative elements. Organo-lithium compounds are more stable and less reactive than the other organometallic compounds in Group Iₐ. Beryllium oxide could even be thought of as a giant covalent lattice: its structure, zinc blende, is the same as that of carborundum, SiC. Boron in a wide range of compounds with hydrogen, carbon, and nitrogen does not behave in the least like an ion. Boron shows non-ionic character even in its halides, of which many are cage structures, e.g. B_4Cl_4 and B_8Cl_8. The non-metal character is again apparent in the volatile and molecular, though polymerized, heavy halides and the polymerized hydrides and dimerized methyl of aluminium.

TABLE 20.XV. *References to the more covalent chemistry of pre-transition metals*

Hydrides	Chapter 11
Methyls and other organometallic compounds	Chapter 33
Nitrides, carbides, and borides	Chapter 17
Phosphides, arsenides, and antimonides	Chapter 17
Alloys	Chapters 8 and 19

Many of these compounds have been discussed in sections earlier in the book under the non-metals and Table 20.xv collects together some cross references. It seems reasonably clear that as the charge to size ratio of a cation increases, both across periods and towards the top of a Group, the compounds of pre-transition elements become increasingly covalent. Because it is a combination of position in a Group and position in a period that brings about this change, diagonal resemblances between elements appear within the pre-transition metal Groups.

THE DIAGONAL RELATIONSHIP

In some aspects of their chemistry, there is a similarity between the first member of Group I, lithium, and principally magnesium in Group II, and between the first member of Group II, beryllium, and principally aluminium in Group III.

Li   Be   B   C

Na   Mg   Al   Si   P

Thus the amphoteric lines discussed in Chapter 14 are both an example and an extension of this so-called diagonal relationship. The chemical similarities have often been exaggerated. We shall consider only the nature and extent of the relationship between Li and Mg, leaving it as an exercise to the reader to consider the relationships between Be and Al, and between B and Si.

(1) Lithium salts with large anions in general and large oxyanions in particular are relatively unstable. This instability is noted not only in the decomposition of say the azide, peroxide, and carbonate, but also in the heavy hydration of salts such as the sulphate. The corresponding salts of beryllium and magnesium tend to be more unstable, those of barium less so.

(2) The insoluble salts of lithium are formed from the weak-acid anions, oxalate, fluoride, hydroxide, carbonate, and phosphate, while the more soluble salts are those of the strong-acid anions. Other Group IA cations form their less soluble salts with either both weak-acid and strong-acid anions or only with the latter, although these could hardly be called insoluble. Magnesium is very similar to lithium in these respects. Both differ considerably from calcium, e.g. in the sulphates, and also from beryllium which, due to the strength of its complexes, has a different pattern of solubility behaviour with anions.

(3) Lithium forms weak complexes in aqueous solution but they are considerably stronger than those of other IA cations. The complexes of magnesium are much stronger again than those of lithium (which are more nearly like those of barium in stability), but both cations form complexes with a similar series of weak-acid anions. Beryllium forms such strong complexes, e.g. with hydroxide, fluoride, and acetate, as to be comparable with aluminium and the cations of Group IIIA, rather than with magnesium or lithium.

(4) Lithium aryls and alkyls, which are quite soluble in organic solvents, may be used in place of organomagnesium compounds in synthetic organic chemistry. In passing we note the similar functions of the chlorides of boron, aluminium, and beryllium in Friedel–Crafts' reactions.

(5) Lithium compounds, e.g. the halides, are often of higher volatility than the corresponding compounds of other IA metals. Beryllium and magnesium but not barium halides are also quite volatile. A diagonal relationship of volatility is particularly noticeable between B and Si.

The fact that this kind of diagonal relationship does not extend to a similarity between, for example, C and P suggests that its interpretation should be sought in terms of the ionic model, i.e. in terms of z and r. No simple function of these is however of general applicability in this connexion.

Problems

1. The following are the energies (eV) required to remove the given electrons from Cs atoms to leave in each case the Xe core:

$$6s\ 3·89,\ 6p\ 2·46,\ 6d\ 1·08,\ 6f\ 0·38,\ 6g\ 0·38,\ 6h\ 0·38.$$

Compare these energies with that required to remove the corresponding electrons from the appropriate H atoms, and comment on the comparisons. Show that the change $6p$–$6s$ corresponds to a wavelength just at the red limit of the visible spectrum.

2. Comment on the following series of ionization potentials (eV):

	I	II	III	IV	V
Na	5·14	47·29	71·65	98·88	138·37
Mg	7·64	15·03	80·12	109·29	141·23
Al	5·98	18·82	28·44	119·96	153·77
Si	8·15	16·34	33·46	45·13	166·73

3. Comment on the sequence of wavelengths (Li to Cs) marked in Fig. 20.3.

4. Comment on the following heats of formation ($-\Delta H_f$ in kcal mole^{-1} at 25 °C):

B_2O_3 306·1

Al_2O_3 400·0 Al_2S_3 172·9 Al_2Se_3 129·0 Al_2Te_3 78·0

Sc_2O_3 (410·0)

Y_2O_3 425·0

La_2O_3 430·5

5. From Fig. 20.4 predict a value for the (as yet undetermined) first ionization potentials of Fr and Ac.

6. The ionization process Y^* ($5s^25p^1$) to Y^{+*} ($5s^2$) may be estimated as 5·02 eV. Comment on this value in the light of Fig. 20.4.

7. Calculate the Oxidation State Diagram for the elements Na, Mg, Al, and Si following the procedure outlined in section 20.3. Are there any noticeable differences between Al and Sc (Fig. 20.7)? Comment upon the values for silicon in relation to its known stable valence states. Why is carbon so different from silicon in its chemical behaviour?

8. Show how large values for metal sublimation energies are important in destabilizing low-valence states. Check by calculation some of the values given in Tables 20.II and 20.III.

9. Comment on the following series of standard electrode potentials:

Li $-3·05$, Na $-2·71$, K $-2·93$, Rb $-2·93$, Cs $-2·92$;

Be $-1·85$, Mg $-2·37$, Ca $-2·87$, Sr $-2·89$, Ba $-2·90$ volts.

10. By means of approximate lattice-energy calculations show that the following species would not be expected to exist under normal laboratory conditions: Ba^+, Na^{2+}, Al^{2+}.

11. Suggest an explanation for the observation that while aluminium chloride is dimeric in the vapour state, BCl_3 is monomeric.

12. Comment on the following series of melting-points:

$$Li_2O\ 1430°,\ BeO\ 2530°,\ B_2O_3\ 450°;$$

$$Na_2O\ 920°,\ MgO\ 2800°,\ Al_2O_3,\ 2030°,\ SiO_2\ 1713°;$$

$$Cs_2O\ (490°),\ BaO\ 1925°,\ La_2O_3\ 2320°,\ HfO_2\ 2790\ °C.$$

13. Account for the fact that, on heating, CO_2 is lost with increasing ease in the following series:

$$K_2CO_3 < CaCO_3 < Sc_2(CO_3)_3.$$

14. Cs polyhalides are more stable to heat than are the polyhalides of Rb (e.g. decomposition pressure of 1 atmosphere at 147·5 °C for $CsBr_3$, at 105·5° for $RbBr_3$, at 124° for $CsClBr_2$, and 81° for $RbClBr_2$). What explanation may be offered for this observation? Give some examples of related phenomena.

15. In Fig. 20.13 both $M(NO_3)_2$ and $M(ClO_4)_2$ lie somewhat below the upper broken line. Can you suggest a possible reason for this?

16. Using ionic radii and appropriate values of the repulsive exponent n, calculate the difference expected on an ionic model in the heats of formation of $BaSO_4$ and $MgSO_4$. (The heats of formation of the gas ions from the metals may be taken as $+392$ and $+558$ kcal mole^{-1} for Ba^{2+} and Mg^{2+} respectively.) Compare your result with the experimental value plotted in Fig. 20.13.

Using Figs. 20.13 and 20.14 estimate the heats of the reactions

$$Mg(ClO_4)_2 + BaO \rightarrow MgO + Ba(ClO_4)_2$$
$$Ba(ClO_4)_2 + K_2O \rightarrow BaO + 2KClO_4$$
$$Mg(ClO_4)_2 + K_2O \rightarrow MgO + 2KClO_4$$

Comment on your results.

17. The following are the temperatures at which a water vapour pressure of 10 mm is produced by the following compounds:

$$Mg(OH)_2\ 300°,\ Ca(OH)_2\ 390°,\ Sr(OH)_2\ 466°,\ Ba(OH)_2\ 700\ °C.$$

Comment on these figures, and account for the apparent anomaly that Mg salts are in general better drying agents than those of Ba.

18. Why may not $NaNO_3$ be used instead of KNO_3 in gunpowder?

19. The oxides of Be, Al, and Ti are amphoteric, while the fluorides of Li, Ca, and the lanthanides are insoluble in water. Comment.

20. Draw correlations between Figs. 20.13 and 20.14 and the data given in Table 20.x.

21. When a salt is dissolved in water the increase in volume (between solution and pure solvent) is referred to as the apparent volume of the dissolved salt. By making certain assumptions, it is possible to split this volume into that occupied by the cation and that occupied by the anion. The following values (in cubic angstroms for 25 °C) have been derived for the alkali, alkaline-earth, and silver ions:

$$Li^+ -5 \cdot 7, \ Na^+ -6 \cdot 6, \ K^+ +10 \cdot 3, \ Rb^+ +18 \cdot 7, \ Cs^+ +30 \cdot 9;$$
$$Mg^{2+} -44 \cdot 0, \ Ca^{2+} -36 \cdot 3, \ Sr^{2+} -37 \cdot 8, \ Ba^{2+} -28 \cdot 8;$$
$$Ag^+ -10.$$

Comment.

22. What explanation can you offer for the following complex stability sequences: (1) mono-fluoride $Mg^{2+} > Ca^{2+} > Sr^{2+} > Ba^{2+}$; (2) sulphonated polystyrene (a cation-exchange resin) $Ba^{2+} > Sr^{2+} > Ca^{2+} > Mg^{2+}$; (3) mono-acetate $Mg^{2+} > Ca^{2+} > Sr^{2+} > Ba^{2+}$; (4) tartrate $Ca^{2+} > Sr^{2+} > Ba^{2+} > Mg^{2+}$.

23. In general it is found that the activity coefficients for aqueous solutions of alkali-metal salts increase from Li to Cs for weak-acid anions, but tend to decrease from Li to Cs for strong-acid anions. What explanations may be offered for these observations?

24. Redox-potential measurements show that, while Ba is a thermo-dynamically more powerful reducing agent than Ca in acid solution, in alkaline solution Ca is more powerful than Ba. Suggest an explanation.

25. The following are the ionic conductances of the aqueous ions (at 18 °C and infinite dilution): Li 33·5, Na 43·5, K 64·6, Rb 67·5, Cs 68 ohm^{-1}. Comment.

26. Account for the following so-called peculiarities of Li chemistry as compared with the chemistries of the other alkali metals:

(a) The metal is relatively inert, hard, and high melting.

(b) It has the most stable hydride.

(c) The carbonate, higher oxides, etc., are relatively unstable.

(d) The fluoride, carbonate, and phosphate are relatively insoluble in water.

(e) It combines relatively readily with carbon and nitrogen atoms.

(f) Its alkyl compounds have low melting-points and are soluble in hydrocarbons.

27. The following general changes are observed in the alkaline-earth series:

(a) The hydroxides get less soluble in water.

(b) The salts become more soluble in organic solvents.

(c) The cations become more strongly hydrated.

(d) Basic salts are formed more readily.

(e) Carbonates and peroxides become more stable to heat.

(f) Sulphates and chromates become less soluble in water.

In each case point out the direction of the change in the series and suggest why it is as it is.

28. The heaviest alkali metal, element 87, is called francium. What properties would you expect it to have?

29. The temperatures at which the ammines of $CaCl_2$, $SrCl_2$, and $BaCl_2$ are in equilibrium with 100 mm partial pressure of NH_3 are 105°, 72°, and 12 °C. Comment.

30. Do the following figures give any idea of the coordination number of the beryllium cation?

	Liquid NH_3	$BeCl_2,12NH_3$	$BeCl_2,6NH_3$	$BeCl_2,4NH_3$
Temperature	−50°	−50°	−50°	+156°
Pressure (mm)	306	168	90	6

What might an isotherm, plotting pressure of NH_3 over $BeCl_2,xNH_3$ versus composition (x), look like? Would you expect a similar plot for magnesium ammine salts?

31. What factors contribute to the order of stability of malate complexes $Al^{3+} > Mg^{2+} > Na^+$ and $Ca^{2+} \geqslant Mg^{2+} > Ba^{2+}$?

32. The coordination number of Li^+ and Be^{2+} in complexes with such ligands as salicylate is 4. Discuss this in the light of radius-ratio considerations.

33. Tartaric acid gives a precipitate with K^+ (and NH_4^+) but not with Na^+. What explanation can you offer for this selective reaction of a weak-acid anion? (See Table 20.XII.)

Bibliography

L. BREWER and E. BRACKETT, 'The Dissociation Energy of Gaseous Alkali Halides', *Chem. Rev.*, 1961, **61**, 425.

G. E. DARWIN and J. H. BUDDERY, 'Beryllium', *Metallurgy of Rarer Metals, No. 7* Butterworths, London, 1960.

C. W. DAVIES, *Ion Association*, Butterworths, London, 1962.

E. J. HARRIS, *Transport and Accumulation in Biological Systems*, Butterworths, London, 1956.

E. K. HYDE, 'Astatine and Francium', *J. Chem. Educ.*, 1959, **36**, 15.

D. S. LAIDLER, *Lithium and its Compounds*, Royal Institute of Chemistry Monograph No. 6, 1957.

G. H. NANCOLLAS, 'Thermodynamics of Ion Association in Aqueous Solution', *Quart. Rev. Chem. Soc.*, 1960, **14**, 402.

L. PAULING, *The Nature of the Chemical Bond*, 3rd ed., Cornell University Press, 1960.

M. C. R. SYMONS and W. T. DOYLE, 'Colour Centres in Alkali Halide Crystals', *Quart. Rev. Chem. Soc.*, 1960, **14**, 62.

T. C. WADDINGTON, Lattice Energies and their Significance in Inorganic Chemistry, *Advances in Inorganic Chemistry and Radiochemistry*, vol. 1, ed. H. J. Emeléus and A. G. Sharpe, Academic Press, New York, 1959.

21 · The Lanthanide Elements

21.1. Introduction

The fifteen elements (Table 21.i) which follow barium in the Periodic Table are conveniently treated immediately after the pre-transition elements and before the actinide and transition elements, as in this sequence the core electrons become increasingly more important. In describing the pre-transition elements, we have had little occasion to mention the underlying core of $(n-1)s^2$ and $(n-1)p^6$ electrons, where n is the principal quantum number of the valence shell. The $(n-2)f$ electrons, which are being added to the core in the lanthanide series, lie much nearer in energy to the valence electrons and they do have some influence on chemical properties. The fact that the f electrons of the *atoms* are not very different in energy from the valence electrons, s and d, can be seen from the variation in the configurations of the atomic ground states in Table 21.i. However,

TABLE 21.I. *Probable ground-state electron configurations and ionization potentials of the lanthanide atoms*

Atom	Symbol	Ground state			First ionization
		4f	5d	6s	potential (eV)
Lanthanum	La	0	1	2	5·61
Cerium	Ce	1	1	2	5·60
Praseodymium	Pr	3		2	5·48
Neodymium	Nd	4		2	5·5
Promethium	Pm	5		2	..
Samarium	Sm	6		2	5·6
Europium	Eu	7		2	5·67
Gadolinium	Gd	7	1	2	6·16
Terbium	Tb	9		2	5·98
Dysprosium	Dy	10		2	..
Holmium	Ho	11		2	..
Erbium	Er	12		2	6·08
Thulium	Tm	13		2	5·81
Ytterbium	Yb	14		2	6·22
Lutetium	Lu	14	1	2	6·15
		4d	5s		
Yttrium†	Y	0	1	2	6·38

† Although Y is not a lanthanide, its chemistry is in many ways very similar to that of a lanthanide and is therefore referred to in this chapter at various points.

as is shown in the next section, with increasing ionization of the atom the f electrons behave more and more as part of the core and, so far as most chemical environments are concerned, do so completely when the lanthanide atom has a charge of $+3$. This means that throughout the series of elements the number of 'valence' electrons is roughly constant. It is this feature of the lanthanides that dominates their chemistry. Again the added $4f$ electrons so screen the valence electrons that the $6s$ and $5d$ orbitals hardly change in energy through the series. This is shown in Table 21.I by the almost constant value of the first ionization potentials. As a consequence, the trivalent lanthanides are all extremely similar in their general chemistry. In the pre-transition series, by way of contrast, increase of atomic number within a period results in a regular increase in the number of valence electrons, e.g. Na, Mg, and Al. These electrons are in the ns and np orbitals. In transition series there are regular changes in the stability of different valence states. The elements can, however, also be compared in one valence, but, in contrast to the lanthanides, it is found that there are very marked chemical changes, e.g. from Ca^{2+} to Zn^{2+}, which may be largely attributed to the considerable changes in the energy of the $(n-1)d$, ns, and np orbitals.

Along the lanthanide series then, there are, in general, relatively small changes in chemical properties. One illustration has already been given in discussing the metals themselves. In section 19.3 it was shown that the changes in binding energy and other physical properties of the lanthanide elements are for the most part rather small and irregular. A further example is given in Fig. 21.1. The pattern can be rationalized if it is assumed that each of the lanthanide atoms contributes three electrons to the metallic bonding, except for Eu and Yb which only contribute two so as to leave behind half-filled and filled $4f$ sub-shells respectively. The general contraction along the series is a reflection of the decreasing size of the core with increase of nuclear charge, rather than of a general increase in binding energy (see Chapter 3 or Fig. 19.10(a)).

As already mentioned, the lanthanides show a remarkably constant valence of three in most of their ionic compounds. This implies that, whereas the chemical energy of combination is sufficiently great to exceed the ionization energy to the trivalent state, it is usually insufficient to permit further ionization. It will be shown that two factors bring about this situation. (1) The ionization energy of $4f$ electrons increases rapidly with the charge on the central atom. This problem is discussed in more detail in the next section. (2) The $4f$ orbitals are so contracted at high charge that they do not overlap with the neighbouring atoms or ions. This combination of circumstances means that a high-valence state becomes unstable because the gain in chemical energy has fallen below the increase in ionization energy. The two elements which most readily show a higher-

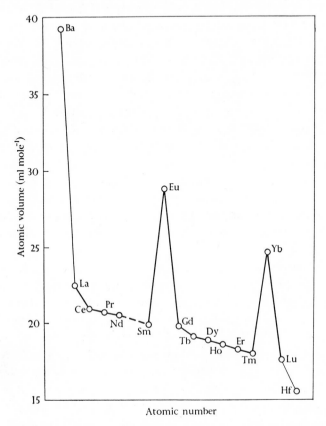

FIG. 21.1. Changes in atomic volume with atomic number in the lanthanide elements.

valence state of four are cerium and terbium, but Ce(IV) and Tb(IV) are very powerful oxidizing agents. At the other extreme the two elements, europium and ytterbium, which are extraordinary in the physical properties of their metals have moderately stable divalent states.

The lanthanides have two features in common with the actinide and transition-metal series: (1) a systematic gradation of property from one element to the next, which may be broken at the half-filled, and at the completely-filled, sub-shell; (2) a variable valence, which in the lanthanides is a very minor effect, but which becomes a major effect in the actinide and transition elements where the core becomes more exposed and therefore sensitive to the environment.

21.2. f, d, and s electrons

THE EFFECTIVE PRINCIPAL QUANTUM NUMBER

In a hydrogen-like atom or ion which contains a nucleus of charge Z and only one electron, the energy of combination of the electron and nucleus is given by the relation

$$E = -13 \cdot 6 Z^2/n^2 \text{ eV},$$

where n is the principal quantum number of the electron. This follows from wave-mechanical theory and is found to hold in spectroscopic practice.

In other atoms and ions we may take as a first approximation a picture in which there is an outer electron and a nucleus of charge Z_0, equal to the nuclear charge minus the charges on the other inner electrons, i.e. Z_0 is the external charge on the *atom* plus one. If the outer electron were wholly outside the inner electrons then the situation would again be hydrogen-like, and the ionization potential would be given by the above equation with Z_0 instead of Z. In practice this is not so, and the outer electron to some extent penetrates through the inner electrons and comes under the influence of an effective charge greater than Z_0 (Chapter 2). Alternatively the expression

$$E = -13 \cdot 6 Z_0^2/n_e^2 \text{ eV}$$

can be used, where the effective principal quantum number n_e measures the deviation from hydrogen-like behaviour. For completely non-penetrating electrons $n_e = n$, while for strongly-penetrating electrons n_e becomes much less than n. The n_e values for various electrons added to the argon core in the isoelectronic series of ions K^+, Ca^{2+}, Sc^{3+}, Ti^{4+}, V^{5+}, and Cr^{6+} are plotted in Fig. 21.2. For K^+ the n_e value of the $3d$ electron ($2 \cdot 85$) is only a little different from n (3), but for the succeeding ions this value drops a little showing that the $3d$ orbitals are now being pulled somewhat into the $3s^2 3p^6$ shell. For the $4s$ (and to a lesser extent the $4p$) electron, however, n_e for K^+ ($4s = 1 \cdot 77$) is very different from n (4). In the succeeding ions this n_e rises because the external charge effect becomes relatively more important with respect to penetration through the inner shells. From Sc^{3+} onwards, an electron is bound more firmly into a $3d$ orbital than into a $4s$ orbital. Chapter 2 considers this change in a slightly different way; compare also section 23.2. Our immediate concern is with an essentially analogous comparison between the $4f$ and $6s$ orbitals which becomes of great chemical significance in the elements following Cs.

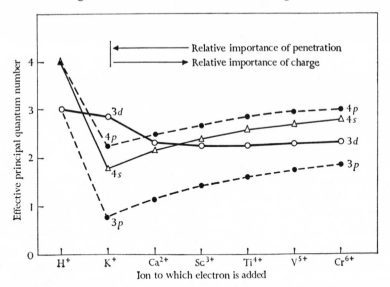

FIG. 21.2. Effective principal quantum numbers for $3p$, $3d$, $4s$, and $4p$ electrons.

THE LANTHANIDES AND n_e

Figure 21.3 gives the n_e values for various electrons added to the ions Cs$^+$, Ba^{2+}, La^{3+}, and Ce^{4+}, each of which has the xenon atomic core. Although unfortunately the data are less complete than they were for Fig. 21.2, it will be seen that the distinctions found between $3d$ and $4s$ there reappear here between the $4f$ and the $6s$, but are now much more marked. The $4f$ electron, which hardly penetrates in Cs, is not only sensitive to the increasing charge external to the xenon core, but is also strongly pulled into that core from Cs$^+$ to Ce^{4+}. This 'disappearance into the inner core' which occurs with $4f$ electrons in highly-charged lanthanide atoms leads to the remarkable overall simplicity in the chemistry of the lanthanides as compared with the elements of the first transition series. It is therefore particularly convenient to discuss them first, and then to look in the transition series for similar patterns of chemical behaviour.

The normal atomic configuration for the uncharged (Cs) and singly-charged (Ba$^+$) species is thus $4s^1$, for the doubly-charged species (La^{2+}) is $5d^1$, and for the triply-charged species (Ce^{3+}) is $4f^1$. Clearly increase in charge stabilizes $4f$ rather than $5d$ rather than $6s$. Now this discussion can be extended to an individual lanthanide in different charged states.

Unfortunately there is relatively little quantitative spectroscopic information for the lanthanides. From such as there is, however, it seems that for each member of the lanthanide series the same rough pattern applies as is found in the isoelectronic series Cs to Ce^{3+}, except that the $4f$ electrons

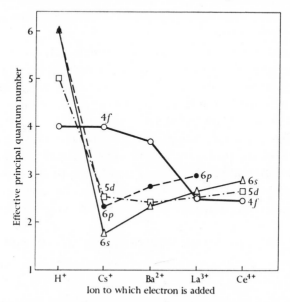

Fig. 21.3. Effective principal quantum numbers for $4f$, $5d$, $6s$, and $6p$ electrons.

(which do not, of course, adequately shield one another) get relatively more stable until the $4f^8$ configuration is reached, when one electron has to be put into an *f* orbital which is already occupied. This electron is relatively easily removed, but 'doubled' $4f$ electrons again become more stable as nuclear charge increases further in the second half of the lanthanide series.

The general ionization pattern would appear to be that the first electrons to be removed are the two $6s$ electrons, then either a $5d$ or a $4f$ relatively close in energy to a $6s$ electron, while the fourth electron removed is a $4f$. The energy pattern with respect to the removal of the first three electrons is therefore somewhat similar to that of Sc and Y, so that all elements will ionize relatively readily to the trivalent state. The fourth electron to be removed is a $4f$ electron at a Z_0 of 4. The ionization energy required is now considerably greater than that which would have been required for removal of another *d* electron (as, e.g., in Zr and Hf). Thus the ionization potential to the $+4$ state is very high, and this energy largely prevents $+4$ from being a common valence state of the lanthanides. This situation is also a result of the lack of f orbital overlap already discussed. The peculiar behaviour of the $4f$ electrons as compared with the $6s$ (and to a lesser extent the $5d$) arises from their extreme sensitivity to external charge (or Z_0).

21.3. Valence states

The valences of the lanthanides in their simple salts are shown in Table 21.II. The periodic behaviour of the valences corresponds to the approach to the half-full and the completely-full f-electron sub-shell. Thus immediately following lanthanum and gadolinium there are elements showing 4-valence, while immediately before gadolinium and lutetium there are divalent elements. The formation of high and low valence states for a somewhat wider range of elements near the half-filled and completely-filled f sub-shell is possible in fused salts. The general reasons for 4-valence and 2-valence are immediately apparent—the $4f$ electrons can be more readily ionized at cerium and terbium and less easily removed at europium and ytterbium.

TABLE 21.II. *'Ionic' valence states of the lanthanides*

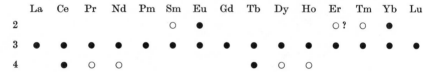

	La	Ce	Pr	Nd	Pm	Sm	Eu	Gd	Tb	Dy	Ho	Er	Tm	Yb	Lu
2						○	●					○?	○	●	
3	●	●	●	●	●	●	●	●	●	●	●	●	●	●	●
4		●	○	○					●	○	○				

The most common valence states are represented by full circles and the less common by open circles.

ESTIMATED OXIDATION STATE DIAGRAM

We shall now attempt to put our valence-state arguments on some quantitative basis, using again the simple ionic hydration model used in discussing the valence states of the pre-transition metals (section 20.3). Here unfortunately there are few reliable ionization-potential data, but just sufficient are available to outline the main trends. Use will still be made of Pauling ionic radii, although a slightly better fit with the experimental electrode potentials is in fact obtained if experimental radii are taken from oxide structures. In view of the overall approximations, it does not, however, seem worth while to complicate the simple and consistent pattern of the argument. We assume that the radii of La^+ and Ce^+ are equal to the radius of Cs^+, and that the radii of La^{2+} and Ce^{2+} are equal to the radius of Ba^{2+}. Since Eu^{2+} has a radius almost identical with Sr^{2+}

(as a result of the lanthanide contraction), we assume Eu^+ to have a radius equal to Rb^+.

The estimated Oxidation State Diagram for La is given in Fig. 21.4 (compare Sc in Fig. 20.7). The outstanding feature is the predicted stability of only the La^{3+} ion, as is found experimentally. The fourth ionization

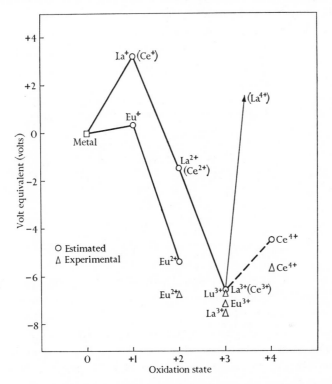

FIG. 21.4. Estimated (o) and experimental (△) Oxidation State Diagram for some lanthanide elements.

potential of La is not known, but we have supposed that this will be high as it involves the breaking open of the Xe core, and have therefore estimated that the volt equivalent for La^{4+} will be high as it is for Sc^{4+}. This is indicated by the arrow in the diagram. There is no reliable second ionization potential for Ce, but since the first and third ionization potentials are similar to those for La it has been assumed in plotting Fig. 21.4 that the Oxidation State Diagram for Ce^+, Ce^{2+}, and Ce^{3+} is much the same as for La. For Ce, however, the fourth ionization potential is known to be 36·72 eV and an estimated point can be given on the diagram for Ce^{4+}, assuming Ce^{3+} has the same volt equivalent as La^{3+}. Similarly the estimated volt equivalents for Eu^+ and Eu^{2+} can be given as the first and second ionization potentials of Eu are known.

SOME EXPERIMENTAL DATA

Some experimental values are also plotted in Fig. 21.4, and it will be seen that they agree approximately with the estimated values. This suggests that the estimates may not be too far out for the other ions which are not known experimentally. The general pattern of Fig. 21.4 using both estimated and experimental values together may now be used in an attempt to get a more complete picture.

TABLE 21.III. *Electrode potentials for the trivalent lanthanide ions*

	4f electrons	E°. M^{3+}_{aq}/M (volts)		4f electrons	E°. M^{3+}_{aq}/M (volts)
La	0	−2·52	Dy	9	−2·35
Ce	1	−2·48	Ho	10	−2·32
Pr	2	−2·47	Er	11	−2·30
Nd	3	−2·44	Tm	12	−2·28
Pm	4	−2·42	Yb	13	−2·27
Sm	5	−2·41	Lu	14	−2·25
Eu	6	−2·41			
Gd	7	−2·40	(Y	0	−2·37)
Tb	8	−2·39			

Trivalent ions. The experimental values (Table 21.III) show that there is only a small change for the electrode potential M^{3+}/M right across the whole lanthanide series (e.g. La −2·5, Gd −2·4, Lu −2·3 volts). Since the nuclear charge increases along the series the ionization potentials may well rise somewhat, but this possible rise must be almost exactly balanced by a combination of the changes in metallic binding energy and the increases in hydration energy associated with the lanthanide contraction. In view of the magnitudes of some of the energies involved, it is really rather curious that the balance should remain so similar along the whole series.

Tetravalent ions. While Sc^{4+} and presumably La^{4+} would be far too strongly oxidizing to exist in normal chemical circumstances, Ce^{4+} does exist in aqueous solution as a strong oxidizing agent. The Ce^{4+}/Ce^{3+} potential is about $+1·7$ volts in perchloric acid solutions, but is reduced to $+1·4$ volts in sulphuric acid solutions, due to preferential complexing of the Ce^{4+} ion with sulphate. Acid cerium(IV) sulphate solutions are used in volumetric analysis, and are remarkably stable considering that the O_2/H_2O potential is $+1·2$ volts. Unlike permanganate oxidations, Ce(IV) oxidations may be carried out quantitatively in the presence of HCl,

although the Cl_2/HCl potential is $+1\cdot4$ volts in acid solution. The production of Ce^{4+} involves the removal of the single $4f$ electron to leave the
Xe core. Removal of one of the two $4f$ electrons from the Pr^{3+} ion is clearly
harder. The Pr^{4+}/Pr^{3+} potential is about $+2\cdot9$ volts and the couple
liberates oxygen from aqueous solutions. The change from cerium to
praseodymium demonstrates the increasing stability of the $4f$ electrons with
increase of nuclear charge. There is no value for the Nd^{4+}/Nd^{3+} potential,
but it is presumably even more strongly oxidizing. Tb, Dy, and Ho are
also capable of showing 4-valence, although with increasing difficulty.
Again there are no electrode-potential or ionization-potential data but
we can see the expected similarity with Ce, Pr, and Nd. With Tb^{4+}, Dy^{4+},
or Ho^{4+} the last electron will have been removed from an orbital containing
two $4f$ electrons. The mutual repulsion of two electrons in the same orbital
is enough to counterbalance the general increase in stability of a $4f$ orbital
which has taken place between Ce and Gd.

Divalent ions. As with Sc^{2+}, La^{2+} and presumably most of the divalent
lanthanide ions will be unstable with respect to disproportionation into the
metal and the trivalent ion. This is clearly shown by the estimated value
for La^{2+} in Fig. 21.4. However at Eu^{2+} the divalent state is stable to
disproportionation. The estimated values for Eu^+ and Eu^{2+} are seen to
lie below La^+ and La^{2+}, there being two reasons for this. (1) The binding
energy of europium metal is about 2 eV less than that of lanthanum. This
distinction we have associated with the divalence of Eu in europium metal.
(2) The smaller sizes of the Eu ions will produce a further $1\cdot5$ eV difference
in the estimated values for La^{2+} and Eu^{2+}.

This change between La and Eu may well be a gradual one, and indeed
Sm is also found as the divalent ion, though this is less stable than Eu^{2+}.
The removal of $4f$ electrons at a given charge presumably gets steadily
harder from La to Eu, and the consequences of this are seen in the marked
difference in slope for the M^{3+}/M^{2+} couple (estimated for La, estimated
and experimental for Eu). The Eu^{3+}/Eu^{2+} couple (potential $-0\cdot4$ volts)
is mildly reducing (Eu^{2+} may be prepared from Eu^{3+} solutions by reduction
with Zn (Zn^{2+}/Zn $-0\cdot8$ volts), so that Eu^{3+} is still the state normally found.

Although there are no estimated or experimental values for Gd^{2+}, it is
expected to be distinctly unstable, the main reason being that the ion
contains one electron more than the half-filled $4f$ sub-shell. This electron
could only be accommodated as a $4f$ electron if it went into an orbital
already occupied by another electron. The position with Gd is therefore
somewhat reminiscent of that for La, and divalence does not become a

stable state again until the f orbitals have been even further stabilized by increase of nuclear charge (Er?, Tm?, and Yb; experimental Yb^{3+}/Yb^{2+} $-1 \cdot 15$ volts).

21.4. Trivalent ions

IONIC SIZE

The sizes of the ions as measured in their oxides are illustrated in Fig. 21.5. The contraction is most rapid early in the series and there is a definite

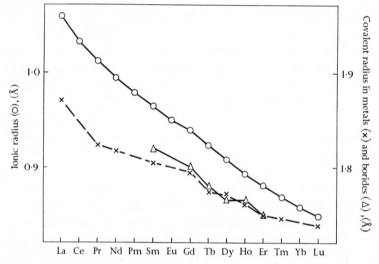

FIG. 21.5. Ionic radii of lanthanides in oxides (o) and covalent radii of lanthanides in metals (×) and borides (△).

though small break in the slope after gadolinium. This double-humped pattern is observed in all the salts of the lanthanides and is not dissimilar from that in the metals themselves.

Such a regular pattern of size must owe its origin to the property of the underlying core of $4f$ electrons. There are two possible explanations, neither of which is really satisfactory. The first suggests that the variation is due to crystal-field effects (see Chapter 24) superimposed upon a general core contraction. The essential feature of this theory is that the f electrons can align themselves so as to avoid the directions pointing towards the surrounding anions. This alignment is not possible when there are seven or fourteen $4f$ electrons, as all possible directions are then equally occupied. Thus, as observed, there should be a more marked contraction for the first three or four lanthanide ions and for the three or four lanthanide ions following Gd^{3+} (with the half-filled $4f$ sub-shell), than for the other ions. The exact form of the curve should be dependent upon the symmetry of the field around the ions. Spectroscopic evidence, however, shows that this crystal-field splitting is very small. Moreover, this theory is not applicable to the metals themselves where a similar change of size with number of f electrons is found.

The second explanation is independent of the symmetry of the field of ligands around the cations. It has two parts: (1) the regularly increasing electron-electron repulsion from 1–7 and from 7–14 electrons in the $4f$ core with a break, an increase, between 7 and 8 electrons; this is superimposed upon the total contraction of the core in the series. (2) A covalent contribution to bonding using $6s$, $6p$, and $5d$ orbitals. It is difficult to assess the covalent term and its effect, but some evidence for it is provided by the nephelauxetic effect, the observation that electron–electron repulsion as measured spectroscopically (section 28.6) appears to depend on the exact chemical environment. Peculiarly the overall contraction is smaller in the metal or the borides than in the oxides, Fig. 21.5. As neither of the available theories is adequate the pattern will be treated merely as an empirical fact.

GENERAL CHANGES ALONG THE LANTHANIDE SERIES

The validity of the ionic model for lanthanide compounds is not open to direct test, for there are insufficient ionization-potential data available to permit the calculation of lattice energies. However, in order to discuss the changes in the chemistry along the series it is necessary to have in mind one model or another, and we shall postulate that the ionic-model predictions for the compounds are approximately correct. This assumption is supported by various pieces of physical evidence. Thus, from electron spin resonance studies, the $4f$ electrons have been shown to spend less than 1 per cent of their time on the fluoride ions in paramagnetic LnF_3.

In the absence of covalence the energy changes along the series are governed by the interionic distances just discussed. The plot of lattice energy against atomic number for all compounds will then be as in Fig. 21.6, upper three curves. The slight curvature and the gradient of the line will depend upon the chemical partner of the lanthanides. The chemistry is then decided by the differences between such plots for the different non-metals. Provided that the differences between two non-metal ligands are big then a continuous and almost linear change in the free energy of the reaction

$$LnL_2 + L_1 \rightarrow LnL_1 + L_2$$

should arise. This is found for the solid reaction

$$LnCl_3 + 3NaOH \rightarrow 3NaCl + Ln(OH)_3, \quad \text{see Table 21.IV};$$

for the solubility products of the hydroxides

$$Ln^{3+} + 3OH^- \rightarrow Ln(OH)_3 \quad \text{in Fig. 21.10};$$

and for the stability constants of the complexes of ethylenediamine-tetracetate in Fig. 21.13. In general where there is a large difference in base strength between the exchanging ligands a regular series is anticipated. This is the basis of most modern separation methods for the lanthanides;

thus elution from strong-acid ion-exchange resins with the weak-acid anion citrate brings out the lanthanides in an order which is the exact reverse of their atomic numbers.

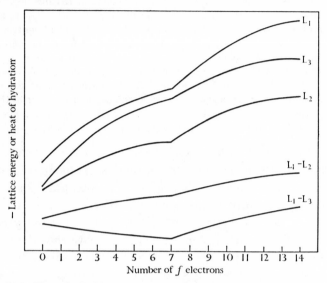

FIG. 21.6. Hypothetical lattice energies (or hydration energies) L_1, L_2, and L_3, showing a regular dependence on atomic number while their differences, e.g. $L_1 - L_2$ and $L_1 - L_3$, may be regular or irregular.

TABLE 21.IV. *Heats or free energies of formation (kcal mole^{-1}) of some lanthanide compounds at 25 °C*

	$-\Delta G_f^\circ$ $M_{(aq.)}^{3+}$	$-\Delta H_f^\circ$ MCl_3	$-\Delta H_f^\circ$ MI_3	Difference in ΔH_f° $(MI_3 - MCl_3)$	$-\Delta G_f^\circ$ $M(OH)_3$
La	174·5	263·6	167·4	96·2	313·2
Ce	171·8	260·3	164·4	95·9	311·6
Pr	170·3	257·8	162·0	95·8	309·7
Nd	168·2	254·3	158·9	95·4	309·3
Pm	167·6	251·9			309·0
Sm	167·0	249·8	153·4	96·4	308·7
Eu	166·5	247·1			308·6
Gd	165·8	245·5	147·6	97·9	308·0
Tb	165·4	241·6†			305·7
Dy	162·8	237·8†	144·5	93·3	305·4
		(234·8)‡		(90·3)	
Ho	160·4	232·8‡	141·7	91·1	304·1
Er	158·8	231·8‡	140·0	91·8	302·8
Tm	157·6	229·5‡	137·8	91·7	302·4
Yb	156·8	228·7‡			301·7
Lu	156·0	227·9‡	133·2	94·7	301·0
Y	164·1	234·8	143·2	91·6	307·1

† Structure change.   ‡ Second structure change.

In those cases where two competing ligands differ only slightly in base strength, the differences in slope, say between L_1 and L_3 in Fig. 21.6, may combine with differences in curvature to produce almost any sequence of free-energy changes. See, for example, the Cl^-/I^- exchange data in Table 21.IV. The following sections will give numerous additional examples. In such cases minor steric factors may well play a dominant influence in the chemistry. In Chapter 20 it has been shown how steric factors can derange orders of melting-points, solubilities, and stability constants even in the compounds of Groups IA and IIA. For this reason the account of lanthanide chemistry will start with the structures and properties in the solid state.

SOLID STRUCTURES AND PROPERTIES

The coordination number of the lanthanides in their solid compounds is curiously variable. Table 21.V gives the structures of the oxides showing how the larger ions can be found in three types of site, two of 7-coordination and one of 6-coordination, while only the 6-coordinate site is found for the smaller and heavier cations. Many of the fluorides crystallize in two forms (Table 21.VI), LaF_3 (5 nearest (2·36 Å) and 6 next-nearest (2·70 Å) neighbours) and YF_3 (8 nearest) $\sim$2·3 Å) and one next-nearest (2·6 Å) neighbours). In the oxyhalides the coordination number is usually 8.

TABLE 21.V. *Structures of lanthanide oxides,* Ln_2O_3

Y	La	Ce	Pr	Nd	Pm	Sm	Eu	Gd	Tb	Dy	Ho	Er	Tm	Yb	Lu
	A	A	A	A	..	A									
		B	B		..	B	B	B		B?					
C		C	C	C	..	C	C	C	C	C	C	C	C	C	C

A is 7-coordinate   B is 7-coordinate   C is 6-coordinate

Where two or more structures are noted, C is the most stable at low temperatures, B at intermediate temperatures, and A at high temperatures.

TABLE 21.VI. *Structures of lanthanide fluorides,* LnF_3

Y	La	Ce	Pr	Nd	Pm	Sm	Eu	Gd	Tb	Dy	Ho	Er	Tm	Yb	Lu
	A	A	A	A	..	A	A				A		A		
B					..	B	B	B	B	B	B	B	B	B	B

A = LaF_3 structure, five nearest neighbours and six next-nearest neighbours.
B = YF_3 structure, eight nearest neighbours and one next-nearest neighbour.

The melting-points of the trivalent halides are plotted in Fig. 21.7. They form a most intriguing series. Reference to the pre-transition series (section 20.4) shows that the melting-point order, in which the fluorides have larger values than the other halides, is as expected. The general order,

$I^- > Br^- > Cl^-$, is unexpected and is related to structural changes. It might also be expected that, with the 3:1 ratio of anion to cation, large cation size would increase the stability of the lattice. This is only true at the beginning of the series and particularly in the chloride, bromide, and

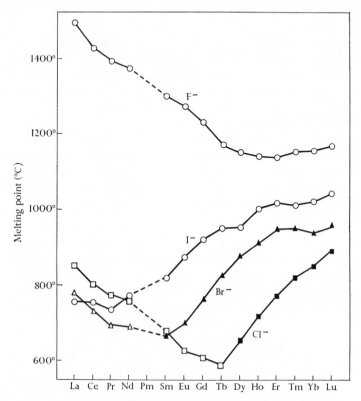

FIG. 21.7. The melting-points of the lanthanide halides, LnX_3.

iodide plots there is a sharp change of slope in the lattice-energy plot (Fig. 21.6). The chloride melting-point falls until a change of structure occurs (Fig. 21.7) from the α- to the β-form. The α-form has the UCl_3 (9-coordinate), the β-form an $AlCl_3$ (6-coordinate) structure. The first three bromides have the UCl_3 structure too, but $NdBr_3$ and $SmBr_3$ have the 8-coordinate $PuBr_3$ layer structure. The first iodide, LaI_3, also has this layer structure and it may well be that all other iodides have this structure too. Although there is no sharp break in the fluoride series, a second structure YF_3 appears to be preferred over LaF_3 after about Gd^{3+}. Thus the initial fall in the melting-points from one lanthanide salt to another also represents a fall in stability of one structure relative to another, while the subsequent rise occurs as the second structure is becoming increasingly stable with respect to the first. Undoubtedly the polarizability of iodide helps to change the absolute order to $I^- > Br^- > Cl^-$. The sequences of melting-points should be compared not only with sequences of observed structures, Tables 21.V and 21.VI, for example, but also with sequences of solubilities and of stability constants.

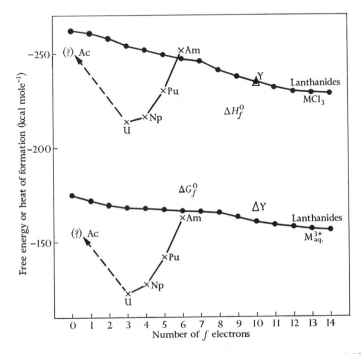

Fig. 21.8. The heats of formation of lanthanide and (for comparison) actinide chlorides, and the free energies of formation of the aquated ions. The Y values are plotted at the same position on the abscissa as Ho, the lanthanide with the same ionic radius.

HEATS OF FORMATION

The plot of heats of formation of chlorides against atomic number (Fig. 21.8) shows a kink in the same region as that seen in the plots of radii (Fig. 21.5). Change of crystal structure along the series has a small but apparently well-defined effect on the increments along the series. The increments are almost equal for the first eight elements but are changing continuously for the last seven. The outstanding feature of these heats of formation is that they are almost exactly the numerical values expected for trivalent pre-transition elements of the correct size. This is illustrated in Fig. 22.6. The $4f$ core plays little or no part in the chemistry of the $+3$ oxidation state. We bring this out below.

HYDRATION

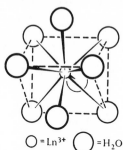

$\bigcirc = Ln^{3+}$ $\bigcirc = H_2O$

FIG. 21.9. The structure of $[Ln(H_2O)_9]^{3+}$.

In the solid state all the lanthanides can give rise to nonahydrates, $Ln(H_2O)_9^{3+}$, or octahydrates $Ln(H_2O)_8^{3+}$. The crystal structure of the nonahydrate is given in Fig. 21.9. Decreasing cation size does not necessarily lead to a decreasing hydration number in the salts. Compare the pre-transition metal cations (section 20.6). Thus in the glycollates the most stable salt is $Ln(glycollate)_3$ for the first eight lanthanide members and $Ln(glycollate)_3,2H_2O$ for the last seven.

The free energies of formation of the hydrated ions are plotted in Fig. 21.8, and show a kink near the ion with the half-filled sub-shell superimposed on a slow general change. The differences between the lanthanides are very slight, and this will be generally so for all their reactions in water. As a consequence the breakdown of ΔG° values into ΔH° and ΔS° may not provide a good lead to the internal-energy differences along the series. This note of warning is sounded in order to remind the reader of the discussion in Chapter 7 on the relationship between ΔG° and ΔH° and ΔH_0, the energy change at absolute zero.

SOLUBILITY OF SALTS

The lanthanide ions are typical of the larger trivalent A-subgroup ions. They form insoluble hydroxides, carbonates, phosphates, fluorides, and oxalates, and soluble nitrates, sulphates, and perchlorates. The soluble salts were used formerly in fractional recrystallization procedures for the separation of the elements. The change in insolubility of the hydroxides is illustrated in Fig. 21.10. As might have been expected the smaller ions are the most insoluble.

For the salts of the weak-acid anions, e.g. OH^- and $[(CH_3)_2PO_4]^-$, solubility generally decreases with decrease of cation size, but for the salts of strong-acid anions, e.g. SO_4^{2-} (Fig. 21.10), the solubility slowly increases with decrease of cation size. With acid anions of intermediate strength irregular orders are obtained. This pattern is similar to that found in the series of pre-transition elements. The reason for the success of fractionation procedures which depend upon competition between weak-

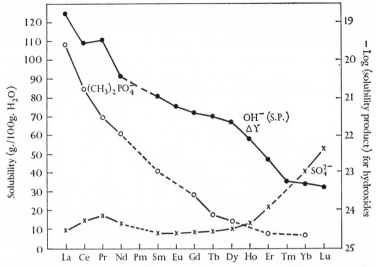

FIG. 21.10. Solubilities of lanthanide sulphates and dimethyl phosphates, and the logarithms of the solubility products of the lanthanide hydroxides; cf. Fig. 21.6.

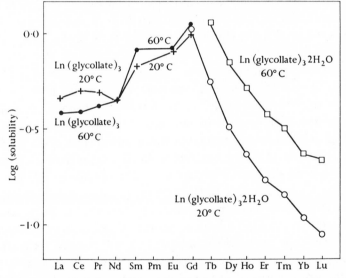

FIG. 21.11. The solubilities (g per 100 g H_2O) of the anhydrous and hydrated forms of the lanthanide glycollates at two temperatures; cf. Fig. 21.6.

acid and strong-acid anions for the lanthanide cations is obvious from these figures and section 21.7.

The solubilities of the glycollates form an interesting series (Fig. 21.11). Whereas the solubility of the salts Ln(glycollate)$_3$ increases regularly with atomic number along the first half of the series, the solubility of the salts Ln(glycollate)$_3$,2H$_2$O decreases regularly along the second half. The consequence of these opposing effects is a maximum in the plot of the solubility of the lanthanide ions in glycollate solutions against atomic number. The solution of the anhydrous salts is slightly endothermic at La but slightly exothermic at Gd. The solution of the dihydrate is endothermic ($\sim +4$ kcal mole^{-1}) roughly independent of the lanthanide. The decreasing solubility in the last series is therefore the result of an increasingly unfavourable entropy of solution as expected on the basis of ionic radii. The first part of the series seems to be dominated by an increasingly favourable internal energy change on solution, which is somewhat surprising in view of the stability-constant changes on formation of glycollate complexes (see the following subsection). Presumably it arises from the increasing difficulty in packing the salt in a lattice as cation size is diminished. This view is in agreement with a change to a more highly hydrated salt at Gd^{3+}. The entropy change on solution is more favourable in the second part of the series and a plot of ΔS^0 against atomic number (as well as of ΔH°) undergoes a sharp break between Gd^{3+} and Tb^{3+}. In cases of changes as complicated as these, detailed knowledge of structure in solution as well as in the solid is required if the equilibria are to be fully understood. This can be illustrated in the following manner.

If we consider any single species Ln(H$_2$O)$_m^{3+}$, the free energy of formation of this species from the gas ions Ln^{3+} will increase with $1/r$, though not linearly since the packing of atoms around Ln^{3+} becomes more difficult the smaller the cation. The increments of these energies with $1/r$ for different ligands will be determined by the nature of the ligands. Three such schematic plots for different environments (H$_2$O)$_m$, (glycollate)$_3$ and (glycollate)$_3$,2H$_2$O are shown in Fig. 21.12. If the more favourable free-energy change resulting from adding Ln(H$_2$O)$_m^{3+}$ to glycollate is computed for each individual lanthanide then a minimum is obtained at Gd. This corresponds to a maximum in the solubility of the salts, Fig. 21.11. Undoubtedly each set of observations on lanthanide equilibria will require a detailed consideration of the steric factors. These are gradually changing along the series and may, as here, affect the actual stoicheiometry of the compounds or complexes formed or may only be seen in trends in ΔS° and ΔH°.

STABILITY OF COMPLEX IONS

Fig. 21.13 shows the variation of stability with atomic number for the lanthanide EDTA complexes. This pattern of stabilities is possibly common

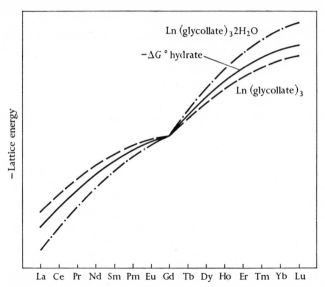

FIG. 21.12. Postulated relationship between lattice energies of anhydrous and hydrated lanthanide glycollates and the free energies of hydration of the constituent ions.

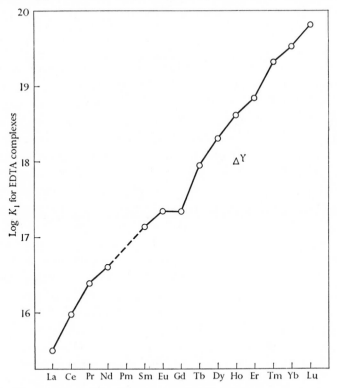

FIG. 21.13. The stability constants of the lanthanide ethylenediaminetetracetate (EDTA) complexes in aqueous solution at 25° C.

to the citrates and acetylacetonates too, but is not followed in the series of complexes of some other polydentate complexing agents, or of malonate, acetate, or glycollate (Fig. 21.14). However, in most of these series there is a general tendency for complex stability to increase with atomic number.

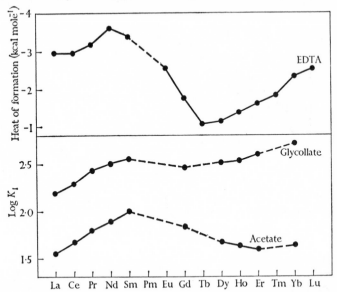

FIG. 21.14. Heats of formation of the EDTA complexes, and stability constants of the glycollate and acetate complexes of the lanthanides.

Thermodynamic measurements have shown this increase to be an effect of the changes of entropy on complex formation (Table 21.VII) and not of enthalpy. In fact $\Delta H°$ often falls with decrease in ion size, and apparently dominates stability orders with mono-, bi-, and tri-dentate ligands where $\Delta S°$ is small, compare Fig. 21.14. The anions in all these complexes are formed from a weak acid, and in all probability such anions displace much of the water of hydration of the lanthanide ions. This dehydration would produce, in theory, an entropy effect of the same size as the experimentally-observed one, though the small changes of $\Delta S°$ from one element to the next are not predictable. The increasingly unfavourable heat change may well be due to steric effects (section 20.7).

The crystal structure of the solid lanthanum EDTA complex shows it to be a trihydrate, $[La(EDTA)(H_2O)_3]^-$, in which the La^{3+} cation is 9-coordinate. As in the solid chlorides, 9-coordination is likely to become of reduced stability at the end of the lanthanide series, as a result of steric hindrance. The structure is also interesting for it shows that the La—O distances are 2·54 Å (O of EDTA) and 2·60 Å (O of H_2O), while the La—N distances are much longer, 2·86 Å. This is an example of the preference of cations in early A subgroups for O rather than N ligands; see section 24.12.

TABLE 21.VII. *Thermodynamic quantities for the formation of lanthanide EDTA chelates in aqueous solution at 25 °C and an ionic strength of* 0·1

Lanthanide ion	$\Delta G°$ (kcal mole^{-1})	$\Delta H°$ (kcal mole^{-1})	$\Delta S°$ (cal deg^{-1} mole^{-1})
La^{3+}	−20·72	−2·93	+59·7
Ce^{3+}	−21·07	−2·94	+60·8
Pr^{3+}	−21·49	−3·20	+61·4
Nd^{3+}	−21·89	−3·62	+61·3
Sm^{3+}	−22·54	−3·35	+64·4
Eu^{3+}	−22·72	−2·56	+67·6
Gd^{3+}	−22·94	−1·73	+71·2
Tb^{3+}	−23·62	−1·11	+75·5
Dy^{3+}	−24·25	−1·21	+77·3
Ho^{3+}	−24·61	−1·36	+78·0
Er^{3+}	−25·06	−1·71	+78·3
Tm^{3+}	−25·44	−1·87	+79·1
Yb^{3+}	−25·91	−2·31	+79·2
Lu^{3+}	−26·11	−2·51	+79·1
Y^{3+}	−23·70	−0·59	+77·5

From Mackay, Powell, and Spedding, *J. Am. Chem. Soc.*, 1962, **84**, 2047.

In series of complexes other than those of EDTA, the changes in $\Delta H°$ are less regular and the degree of hydration of the complexes may be undergoing discontinuous changes. In the series of sulphate complexes there is little to choose between the stability of one lanthanide complex and the next, and if anything the stability decreases with increase of atomic number. Most of the salts and probably the complexes of such strong-acid anions are heavily hydrated. A feature of the complex formation is that it is almost invariably the entropy change which stabilizes the complexes, so that complexes with neutral molecules such as NH_3 are not formed.

CONCLUSION

Comparison with the compounds of other IIIA metals shows that the behaviour patterns of the lanthanides are roughly those expected on the ionic model. A detailed inspection of this hypothesis shows, however, that much remains to be understood. The element, yttrium, gives a trivalent ion of a similar size to holmium. In its chemistry it is remarkably like a lanthanide, but in any given chemical reaction the lanthanide which yttrium most closely resembles changes considerably. Note, for example, the nomadic behaviour of Y in Figs. 21.8, 21.10, and 21.13, and in Tables 21.III, 21.IV, and 21.VII. We leave it as an exercise for the reader to collect the information, and to try to unravel the changing position of yttrium in the series. Is this position just a property of the compressibility of the ionic core (n in the lattice-energy equation), or is it the different relative importance and energies of s, p, d, and f orbitals which constantly change in the lanthanides?

21.5. Other valence states

Sm(II), Eu(II), and Yb(II) are all strong reducing agents, thermodynamically unstable with respect to hydrogen evolution from aqueous solutions (redox potentials M^{3+}/M^{2+}, -1.55, -0.43, and -1.15 volts respectively). Water, however, only oxidizes Eu^{2+} slowly. Eu(II) is stabilized in the solid state, and the sulphates are particularly useful for recovery of these ions. In general the solubilities and crystal structures of their compounds are similar to those of Ca^{2+} and Sr^{2+}, Pauling radii Eu^{2+} 1·12, Sr^{2+} 1·13; Yb^{2+} 1·13, Ca^{2+} 0·99 Å.

Ce(IV) is much the most stable of the 4-valent states, and Ce^{4+} solutions may be used as volumetric oxidizing agents although they are thermodynamically unstable with respect to evolution of oxygen from water ($Ce^{4+}/Ce^{3+} = +1.74$ volts). The Pr^{4+}/Pr^{3+} couple has been estimated as $+2.86$ volts, which makes it similar in oxidizing potential to fluorine. Apart from Ce(IV) compounds the other 4-valent species are almost entirely confined to oxides and fluorides. They may be conveniently stabilized (Pr(IV), Nd(IV), Tb(IV), Dy(IV)) by trapping in a suitable crystal lattice. Similarly the divalent ions may be stabilized by trapping in SrO or in silicate glasses.

HYDRIDES, BORIDES, CARBIDES, NITRIDES, AND SULPHIDES

We have grouped these compounds together as they show considerable deviations from ionic behaviour. The hydrides are described in Chapter 11. They are non-stoicheiometric, of formula MH_n where n lies between 2 and 3. The formulae of the other compounds are (1) MB_4 and MB_6 for the borides—compare CaB_6 but contrast AlB_2; (2) M_3C, M_2C_3, and MC_2 for the carbides—compare BaC_2 but contrast Al_4C_3; (3) MN for the nitrides, compare AlN; and (4) M_2S_3 and MS_2 for the sulphides. For many of these compounds it is very difficult to associate the metal atom with a valence state. Although exact formulae are commonly written, it is probable that the substances exist over small ranges of composition, and there is un-doubtedly much metal–metal bonding. Many of these compounds are darkly coloured and are good semiconductors or even metallic conductors. In all these properties the lanthanide compounds are more like compounds of transition metals than of pre-transition metals. Neutron-diffraction studies have shown, however, that even the sulphides of formula MS have magnetic moments corresponding to the trivalent ion M^{3+}. It has been concluded that the $5d$ orbitals form a narrow band of energies, hardly interacting with the $4f$ orbitals, and that it is this band of d levels, contain-ing about one electron per atom, which gives rise to the deep colours and high conductivity. Probably a similar system of energy levels accounts for the properties of those other lanthanide compounds which are good semi-conductors and in which the lanthanide is *three*-valent by its stoicheiometry. Here, however, the $5d$ *band* will be a series of excited levels of very low population. The contrast with the transition-metal sulphides, MS, is marked in that unpaired electrons in the d orbitals of the transition-metal ions lead to metallic properties only in the compounds of the early elements, e.g. Ti^{2+}. The sulphides of the later elements, e.g. NiS, are semiconductors. Presumably the $5d$ orbitals of the lanthanides are quite strongly exposed to the ligand fields, especially in low-valence states.

21.6. Spectra and magnetic moments of lanthanide ions

SPECTRA

The $4f$ electrons are rather little affected by their chemical environment, because they lie so deep inside the lanthanide ions. This means that the spectroscopic and magnetic properties of these ions, which are largely properties of incompletely-filled $4f$ sub-shells, are closely related to those of the simple gaseous ions. Despite the complexities of lanthanide spectra, there is therefore an essential simplicity in the correlation of the gas-ion and ionic-compound spectra in the lanthanides which is absent elsewhere in the Periodic Table.

Moreover, because the $4f$ electrons do not penetrate close to the atomic nuclei, their spin and orbital angular momenta may be treated approxi-mately by the simple Russell–Saunders coupling, which is not normally useful for electrons in heavy atoms. However, the spin-orbit coupling (Chapter 28) is so large that only the lowest J state is normally occupied. Much of the discussion of atomic structure is directly applicable to the problems of lanthanide spectra and magnetic moments.

The most common type of transition giving rise to lanthanide spectra is that associated with a rearrangement of electrons inside the $4f$ sub-shell, and a corresponding change in the interelectronic repulsion. Such transitions are Laporte forbidden (i.e. forbidden by first-order wave-mechanical treatment) so that the intensity of absorption is weak. The bands are

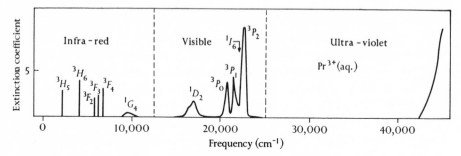

FIG. 21.15. The spectrum of the aqueous Pr^{3+} ion showing the excited states
(after Jørgensen).

narrow and relatively little shifted (nephelauxetic effect, the most conspicuous example being Nd_2O_3 which is pale blue while other Nd^{3+} compounds are pink) or split (ligand field) by changes in the chemical environment. Fig. 21.15 shows the spectrum of the Pr^{3+}(aq.) ion, which has the electron structure (xenon core) $4f^2$. The lowest spectroscopic state will be $^3H_4$ (see problem 21.19 for this and other spectroscopic states of f^2), and the various transitions have been assigned to the excited states as marked on Fig. 21.15. (A further state, ^1S, would be expected to give rise to a band in the ultra-violet.)

It has been observed qualitatively that the colours of the ions from La^{3+} to Gd^{3+} tend to repeat themselves in the sequence Lu^{3+} back to Gd^{3+} (Table 21.VIII). For those ions with 0 or 1 unpaired f electron, there will

TABLE 21.VIII. *Colours of trivalent lanthanide ions*

Colour	Ion	Number of unpaired f electrons	Ion	Colour
Colourless	La^{3+}	0	Lu^{3+}	Colourless
Colourless	Ce^{3+}	1	Yb^{3+}	Colourless
Yellow-green	Pr^{3+}	2	Tm^{3+}	Pale green
Reddish	Nd^{3+}	3	Er^{3+}	Reddish
Pink; yellow	Pm^{3+}	4	Ho^{3+}	Pink; yellow
Yellow	Sm^{3+}	5	Dy^{3+}	Yellow
Pale pink, nearly colourless	Eu^{3+}	6	Tb^{3+}	Pale pink; nearly colourless
Colourless	Gd^{3+}	7	Gd^{3+}	Colourless

be in each case only one spectroscopic state (apart from different J states). This will also be true for those ions with six and seven unpaired f electrons, provided that the overall spin is unaltered (change of spin or multiplicity gives rise to much weaker absorptions than those involving no change of spin), so that we can account for the seven colourless (or nearly colourless) ions. For the remaining ions, it would appear at first sight that there might be some real correlation with the number of unpaired electrons, especially as the spectroscopic states will have the same designations for two ions with the same number of unpaired electrons (e.g. Pr^{3+} and Tm^{3+}, $4f^2$ and $4f^{12}$, which may be checked along the lines of problem 21.19). However, this does not appear to be more than an accident, for the interelectronic repulsions change considerably along the series, so that the spectroscopic states of Tm^{3+} are spread out with respect to those of Pr^{3+} by a factor of about 2. Thus the green of Pr^{3+} arises from an energy gap between the states ^1D and ^3P (see Fig. 21.15), while for Tm^{3+} the 'green gap' lies between ^3F and ^1G.

Laporte-allowed bands have been observed for Ce^{3+}, Tb^{3+}, Sm^{2+}, Eu^{2+}, and Yb^{2+}. These bands are not so weak in intensity as those we have just been discussing, for they correspond to a change f^n to $f^{n-1}d$, which is not Laporte forbidden. They are also broader since the $5d$ electron produced will interact considerably with the chemical environment. Thus the energy difference between $4f$ and $5d$ levels is about 19 per cent smaller in the Ce^{3+}(aq.) ion than in the Ce^{3+}(gas) ion, and some 28 per cent lower in complexes of ethylenediaminetetracetate, citrate, chloride, etc. (the nephelauxetic effect; see Chapter 28). It is of interest to note that in Ce^{3+} the excitation from $4f$ to $5d$ would be expected to be easier than in any other trivalent ion in the first half of the lanthanide series, and that after the half-filled f subshell this excitation should also become relatively easy again at Tb^{3+}, since the f electron promoted will come from f^8, i.e. from an orbital containing two f electrons (both transitions are however in the ultra-violet). In the divalent ions, as we have already noted, the distinction between f and d will be less marked than in the trivalent ions. The Sm^{2+} transitions are of lower energy than the Eu^{2+} transitions in keeping with the steady increase in stability of a $4f$ as against a $5d$ electron across each half of the lanthanide series.

The yellow colour of the Ce^{4+} ion is attributable to charge transfer of an electron from a ligand to the f orbitals of Ce. Some compounds of 3-valent ions with reducing anions are also coloured yellow due to electron transfer from the anion, e.g. Eu^{3+}. Many lanthanide nitrides and sulphides are also very deeply coloured. This may be treated on a charge-transfer model or perhaps better in terms of delocalized electron bands.

MAGNETIC MOMENTS

The paramagnetic moments of the tripositive lanthanide ions are plotted in Fig. 21.16. The upper curve is that calculated by Van Vleck. Both spin and orbital angular momenta contribute to the total magnetic moment, and the general shape of the curve arises from the fact that with sub-shells less

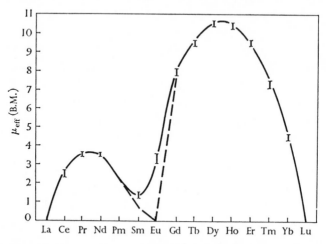

FIG. 21.16. The paramagnetic moments of the lanthanide ions at 300 °K ——— and at absolute zero — — — — —.

than half-filled the lowest J state occurs when these two momenta work in opposition, while with sub-shells more than half-filled when they work together. Gd^{3+} has the spin-only value, approximately $\sqrt{\{7 \times (7+1)\}}$ B.M., since with one electron in each of the seven f orbitals the net orbital contribution will be zero. Eu^{3+} with six unpaired electrons ($S = 6 \times \frac{1}{2} = 3$) and an orbital-angular-momentum contribution 3 (one *hole* equals one electron in counting orbital-angular-momentum contributions; again see problem 21.19) will have zero magnetic moment in its ground state. At low temperatures this is found experimentally. At normal temperatures, excited J states of Eu^{3+} are also occupied, as is the case with Sm^{3+}. The excellent correlation with atomic theory is a further confirmation of the largely atomic nature of the $4f$ electrons in lanthanide ions. When we come to consider d electrons in transition-metal ions, this is no longer true, although as a first rough approximation (see section 24.2) the magnetic moments may then be calculated using the spin-only formula, assuming that all the orbital contribution has been quenched by the chemical environment of the transition-metal ion.

21.7. Separation procedures

Because of the very great chemical similarity between successive trivalent lanthanide ions, their separation has proved to be a matter of some difficulty. In certain cases it is, of course, possible to effect valence changes. Thus Ce(III) may be selectively oxidized and removed by crystallization or solvent extraction, and Eu(III) may be separated from mixtures in which it is present in only trace quantities by addition of zinc dust, barium chloride, and sulphuric acid. The europium is then recovered by oxidizing the mixed barium-europium(II) sulphate precipitate. Europium, samarium, and ytterbium can be removed from mixtures with metal amalgams.

Much of the classical work on the separation of the lanthanides was carried out by laborious fractional-crystallization methods which often involved hundreds of crystallizations. The method is most effective at the lanthanum end of the series where the solubility differences are most pronounced, and the double ammonium nitrate method is still of value in the separation of lanthanum itself.

Greater selective separation in one stage may be obtained by the use of solvent extraction, and this method can also be adapted readily to continuous and repeated operation. Thus in the extraction from aqueous nitric acid solutions by tri-n-butyl phosphate (TBP), the equilibrium

$$Ln^{3+}(aq.) + 3NO_3^- (aq.) + 3TBP(org.) \rightleftharpoons Ln(NO_3)_3(TBP)_3(org.)$$

is established. The extent of extraction increases with decrease in ionic radius, the ratio between adjacent lanthanides (separation factor) being on the average about 1·5. With di-(2-ethylhexyl)phosphoric acid as a complexing agent the separation factor may be increased to 2·5.

ION EXCHANGE

Solvent-extraction procedures are being used increasingly, but still the most generally effective procedure is ion-exchange chromatography. A typical ion-exchanger is a sulphonated polystyrene resin. This behaves as an insoluble acid, the protons of which (from the strong-acid SO_3H groups) are able to exchange with metal ions in an aqueous solution.

$$M^{3+} + 3HR_{(solid)} \rightleftharpoons MR_{3(solid)} + 3H^+$$

For a strong-acid ion-exchanger, the equilibrium lies more to the right with the more basic lanthanide ions, i.e. the larger *unhydrated* cations at the lanthanum end. In general, differences between successive lanthanides are rather small, but these may be considerably enhanced by the use of a *weak*-acid complexing agent such as citrate, ethylenediaminetetracetate, or alpha-hydroxybutyrate in the aqueous solution. In fact the differences in complexing ability are usually more significant than the differences in the exchange behaviour.

The cation exchanger is packed into a column, the mixed lanthanide ions placed at the top of the column and eluted through the column with the appropriate aqueous complexing solution. The rate of movement of a given lanthanide ion will be directly proportional to its distribution coefficient, D:

$$D = \frac{\text{concentration of lanthanide ion in solution}}{\text{concentration of lanthanide ion in resin}}.$$

In practice, concentration peaks are obtained corresponding to the various distribution coefficients as is illustrated in Fig. 22.11, the smaller and more highly complexed ions at the lutetium end of the series emerging from the column first. Individual lanthanides therefore emerge under controlled conditions at characteristic retention times, so that any general identification technique (e.g. radioactivity in the case of lanthanides recovered from fission products) may be used. In the other methods of separation a highly selective identification technique must be employed, of which spectrophotometry is the most generally useful, because of the sharp lanthanide bands. Not only does the retention time serve to identify a known ion, but the method has been used (see section 22.7) for the identification of new elements. It will be seen from Fig. 22.11 that the ions are not quite evenly spaced in the elution sequence, and in particular that Eu^{3+} and Gd^{3+} are close together, while Gd^{3+} and Tb^{3+} are relatively far apart. This is a reflection of the break in the stability-constant curve; compare Fig. 21.13.

It is possible to scale up the ion-exchange separation; pure lanthanides (99·99 per cent) can thus be obtained in kilogram quantities. In such separations the concentrations are usually such that individual lanthanide ions compete with one another for places in the ion-exchange resin, and the chromatographic theory is somewhat more complicated than that outlined above. Like all chromatographic processes, the ion-exchange method may also be regarded as effectively a continuous and automatic repetition of an inherently rather inefficient one-stage process. It is thus in many ways analogous to fractional crystallization or repeated solvent extraction. In each process every attempt is made to make the one-stage separation factor as large as possible. In solvent extraction an extractant is used which is as selective as possible for the weaker bases (hence in part the increased efficiency of the dialkyl-phosphate over the nitrate extraction), just as in the ion-exchange process a strong-acid exchanger is used in company with a weak-acid complexing agent.

Problems

1. Explain, in terms of what we know about atomic structure, how it comes about that in the whole sequence of lanthanide elements trivalence is strongly predominant.

2. Successive ionization potentials for s and p electrons increase approximately in proportion to z: successive ionization potentials for $4f$ electrons increase more nearly as z^2: chemical energies (hydration and lattice) increase roughly as z^2. Comment on the relevance of these observations to the valences exhibited by the pre-transition and the lanthanide elements.

3. Suppose that in the future a number of new trans-uranium elements are discovered in which it is clear that $5g$ electrons are playing a corresponding role to the $4f$ electrons of the lanthanides or the $3d$ electrons of the first transition series. What might be the general chemical characteristics of these elements?

4. Account for the fact that the chemistries of Nb and Ta are very similar but distinct from that of V.

5. Comment on the series of standard potentials, M^{3+}/M, for the lanthanide elements as given in Table 21.III.

6. Most of the lanthanide complexes are with oxygen-containing ligands (e.g. acetylacetone, citric acid, EDTA, dibenzoylmethane). Comment.

7. The variation of stability constant with atomic number for the complexes of the lanthanides with many ligands similar to $EDTA^{4-}$, e.g. with nitriloacetate, $N(CH_2CO_2^-)_3$, does not increase regularly with atomic number. What explanations can be offered?

8. Why is it a reasonable prediction that chloride complexes will hardly alter in stability from La^{3+} to Lu^{3+}, while citrate complexes will become more stable?

9. What factors derange a monotonic sequence for the solubility of the lanthanide nitrates?

10. Account for the different rate of change of solubility with cation for the two anions OH^- and $(CH_3)_2PO_4^-$ (Fig. 21.10).

11. What factors affect the slopes and absolute magnitudes of the plots in Fig. 21.12?

12. Use Fig. 21.11 to estimate the heats of solution of the lanthanide glycollates. Why is such an estimate likely to be unreliable? (See Chapter 7.)

13. What is the origin of the high entropy terms in Table 21.VII?

14. A number of lanthanide minerals (e.g. monazite) are usually deficient in Eu, which is found among Ca minerals. Comment.

15. Europium(II) hydroxide is soluble in water, but the carbonate and sulphate are not. Comment.

16. Outline the main features expected for the chemistry of Eu^{2+} from your knowledge of the chemistry of Ba^{2+} and Ca^{2+}.

17. Use the ionic model to predict differences in chemistry between Ce^{4+} and Ce^{3+}.

18. Comment on the following values for the standard potential of the Ce^{4+}/Ce^{3+} couple (volts):

$+1{\cdot}28$ (in $2M$ HCl), $+1{\cdot}44$ ($1M$ H_2SO_4), $+1{\cdot}61$ ($1M$ HNO_3), $+1{\cdot}70$ ($1M$ $HClO_4$).

19. Derive the spectroscopic states for two f electrons (Pr^{3+}) according to the following simplified procedure (Russell–Saunders coupling). Write down seven orbitals with m_l values (orbital angular momentum in a given direction) of 3, 2, 1, 0, −1, −2, −3. Allot the two electrons to these orbitals in every possible way, remembering that with parallel spins (triplet states) two electrons cannot be in the same orbital, but that with opposed spins (singlet states) they can be either in the same or different orbitals. In each case add the m_l values for each electron to give M_L. Collect all the triplet M_L values, and show that they may be grouped into three sets ^3H (5, 4, 3, 2, 1, 0, −1, −2, −3, −4, −5), ^3F (3, 2, 1, 0, −1, −2, −3), and ^3P (1, 0, −1). Similarly derive the singlet states (see section 21.6).

Show that the same states arise when there are twelve f electrons, i.e. Pr^{3+} and Tm^{3+} will have the same notation for their states.

Using a similar procedure derive the spectroscopic states for two p electrons and compare with Chapter 1.

What are the limitations of this procedure?

20. Calculate the magnetic moments of Fig. 21.16 using the equations given in section 24.2.

21. In the ion-exchange separations of the lanthanide ions, e.g. Fig. 22.11, the ions are not evenly spaced in the elution sequence. How may this unevenness be accounted for?

22. How would changes of pH affect the separation of lanthanides achieved by elution with citrate from a sulphonated polystyrene column?

Bibliography

L. B. ASPREY and B. B. CUNNINGHAM, Unusual Oxidation States of some Actinide and Lanthanide Elements, *Progress in Inorganic Chemistry*, vol. 2, ed. F. A. Cotton, Interscience, New York, 1960.

I. GRENTHE, 'Thermodynamic Properties of Rare Earth Complexes, IV. Discussion of Factors of Importance in Complex Formation in Aqueous Solution', *Acta Chem. Scand.*, 1964, **18**, 293.

C. K. JØRGENSEN, *Absorption Spectra and Chemical Bonding in Complexes*, Pergamon Press, Oxford, 1962.

E. V. KLEBER (ed.), *Rare Earth Research*, Macmillan, New York, 1961.

T. MOELLER, D. F. MARTIN, L. C. THOMPSON, R. FERRÚS, G. R. FEISTEL, and W. J. RANDALL, 'The Coordination Chemistry of Yttrium and the Rare Earth Metal Ions', *Chem. Rev.*, 1965, **65**, 1.

J. F. NACHMAN and C. E. LUNDIN (eds.), *Rare Earth Research*, Gordon and Breach, New York, 1962.

T. MOELLER, *The Chemistry of the Lanthanides*, Reinhold, New York, 1963.

C. E. MOORE, 'Atomic Spectra of the Rare Earths', *Appl. Optics*, 1963, **2**, 665.

F. H. SPEDDING, 'Rare Earths', *International Science and Technology*, April 1962, p. 39.

F. H. SPEDDING and A. H. DAANE (eds.), *The Rare Earths*, Wiley, New York, 1961.

N. E. TOPP, *Chemistry of the Rare-Earth Elements*, Elsevier, Amsterdam, 1965.

R. C. VICKERY, *Analytical Chemistry of the Rare Earths*, Pergamon Press, Oxford, 1961.

R. C. VICKERY, *Chemistry of Yttrium and Scandium*, Pergamon Press, London, 1960.

K. S. VORRES (ed.), *Rare Earth Research*, Gordon and Breach, New York, 1964.

D. M. YOST, H. RUSSELL, and C. S. GARNER, *The Rare-Earth Elements and their Compounds*, Wiley, New York, 1947.

22 · The Actinide Elements

22.1. Introduction

The elements from atomic number 89 are listed in Table 22.1. It has proved extremely difficult to investigate the chemistry of many of them, as, except for actinium, thorium, and uranium, they do not occur in nature in significant amounts. All the others have been made artificially. Those close to uranium have been obtained in greater than gram quantities, but the heavier the actinide, the smaller the quantity of material that has been available. Apart from the precautions against radioactivity which have been necessary, our knowledge of the chemistry of uranium, neptunium, and plutonium has been built up using experimental methods not greatly different from those used in studying familiar elements. The next three elements, americium, curium, and berkelium, have been studied on the microgram and semi-microgram scale while the later elements have been studied by tracer methods, often working with only very small numbers of atoms. It is not appropriate to detail here the extremely refined methods which have been used in this work, for which the interested reader is referred elsewhere (see the bibliography at the end of the chapter).

TABLE 22.1. *The actinides*

Element	Symbol	Atomic number	Probable electron configuration of the atom	Ionic radius (Pauling) of trivalent ion (Å)
Actinium	Ac	89	$6d^1 7s^2$	1·18
Thorium	Th	90	$6d^2 7s^2$	1·14
Protactinium	Pa	91	$5f^2 6d^1 7s^2$	1·12
Uranium	U	92	$5f^3 6d^1 7s^2$	1·11
Neptunium	Np	93	$5f^4 6d^1 7s^2$	1·09
Plutonium	Pu	94	$5f^6 7s^2$	1·07
Americium	Am	95	$5f^7 7s^2$	1·06
Curium	Cm	96	$5f^7 6d^1 7s^2$	
Berkelium	Bk	97	$5f^8 6d^1 7s^2$	
Californium	Cf	98	$5f^{10} 7s^2$	
Einsteinium	Es	99	$5f^{11} 7s^2$	
Fermium	Fm	100	$5f^{12} 7s^2$	
Mendelevium	Md	101	$5f^{13} 7s^2$	
Nobelium ?	No ?	102	$5f^{14} 7s^2$	
Lawrencium	Lw	103	$5f^{14} 6d^1 7s^2$	

From the time of Bohr's treatment of the Periodic Table, it had been recognized that following actinium there should be either a new 'outer' transition series (corresponding to the filling of the $6d$ sub-shell) followed by a new lanthanide or 'inner' transition series (corresponding to the filling of the $5f$ sub-shell), or a new lanthanide series followed by a new transition series. From that time until 1940 only the chemistries of the three elements, thorium, protactinium, and uranium, were well established. These elements were placed in Groups IVA, VA, and VIA of the Periodic Table, as though they represented the beginning of a new transition series, rather than of a new lanthanide series. The chemical and physical properties of these elements do not support this assumption, but neither do they obviously lead to the *simple* classification of the elements as members of a second lanthanide series. However, when the later elements in the series (now up to element 103) had been prepared and studied in reasonable detail, it was found that they were more closely akin to the lanthanides, and particularly so from element 96 onwards.

In order to show the changing character of the actinides, we shall first compare their atomic structures and valence states with those of the lanthanides, and then go on to describe their chemistry. The electron configurations in the ground states of the actinide atoms (Table 22.1) already show that there is less distinction between d and f electrons than was observed in the lanthanides (Table 21.1).

22.2. $5f$ electrons

Just as in the lanthanides where the primary concern was with a comparison between the binding energies of $4f$, $5d$, and $6s$ electrons, so now concern centres on a similar comparison between $5f$, $6d$, and $7s$ electrons. The essential points are the same in the two series. The least-penetrating f orbitals become rapidly stabilized with increase of effective nuclear charge outside the noble-gas core, either with increasing atomic number and constant ionic charge (Fig. 22.1) or with increasing charge at constant atomic number. However, since the $5f$ electron is partly penetrating (its effective principal quantum number n_e has already decreased to about 4 in Ce^{3+} and Hg^+, atomic species for which there are reliable data), these effects are less marked than with the $4f$ electrons. An exactly similar distinction between $4d$ and $3d$ electrons in the second and first transition series has been noted in Chapter 2. In Fig. 22.2 the energy required to remove a $5f$ or a $6d$ electron is compared with that required to remove a $7s$ electron from ions, each of which contains one electron outside the noble-gas (radon) structure. It will be seen that for the ions with positive charges greater than

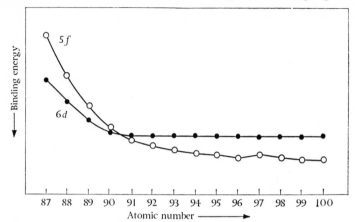

FIG. 22.1. Relative energies of 5f and 6d electrons in the actinide atoms (schematic) (after Katz and Seaborg).

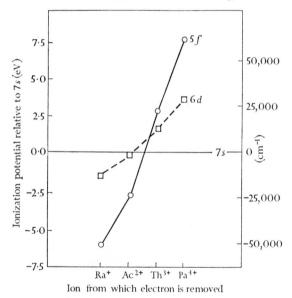

FIG. 22.2. *Ionization* energies of 5f and 6d electrons relative to the 7s electrons for an iso-electronic series of the first few actinides.

three the 5f electrons are much the most stable, but that for the $+3$ ion the distinction between 5f and 6d is not very great (9000 cm^{-1}). In fact Th behaves chemically very much as if it were a straightforward tetravalent transition element like Hf. However, by the time U^{3+} is reached, the energy difference between the electron configurations $5f^n$ and $5f^{n-1}6d$ has risen to 26,000 cm⁻¹, and it rises still further in Np^{3+} (33,000 cm⁻¹) and Pu^{3+} (40,000 cm⁻¹). The major difference between the actinides and the lanthanides is the more gradual change of all the energies with charge and atomic number.

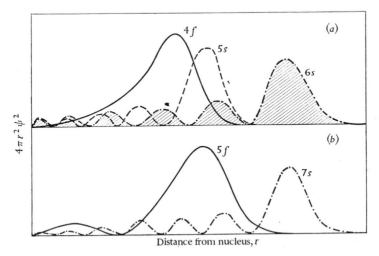

Fig. 22.3. The radial distribution functions of (*a*) the 4*f*, 5*s*, and 6*s* electrons of the lanthanides and (*b*) the 5*f* and 7*s* electrons of the actinides (schematic).

ORBITAL OVERLAP POSSIBILITIES

In the next section chemical valence will be discussed in the light of the electronic structures of the actinide atoms. Before the problem can be tackled, the radial distribution function of the *f* as opposed to the relevant *s* orbital must be studied. Fig. 22.3 gives a rather naïve and impressionistic graph of the two functions for both the lanthanides and the actinides. (Not only is the 4*f* sub-shell of the lanthanides well inside the 6*s* valence sub-shell, but, as information from the X-ray spectra of the atoms suggests, it is also well inside the 5*s* sub-shell—especially towards the end of the series. There can be no question in lanthanide compounds of a considerable overlap between the 4*f* orbitals and the surrounding ligand field. In fact the possibility of such an overlap was ignored altogether in the last chapter. The situation is less clear at the beginning of the actinide series: the 5*f* orbitals are, to some extent, penetrating orbitals, and it is to be expected that they will be more diffuse at the outside of the atom (Fig. 22.3 (*b*)).

In confirmation of this, an examination of the spectra of the ions of this series shows that the neighbouring ligands around a central cation do affect the spectrum somewhat. This is known as a ligand-field effect, the theory of which will be considered in detail in Chapter 24. The variation in the ligand-field effect, however, is small, and probably never contributes more than 1–2 kcal to the energy. For this reason the overlap of $5f$ orbitals with neighbouring atoms will not be given much weight except in a few cases, e.g. in oxocations and in low-valence states of early actinides.

Many of these comparative comments about the $5f$ orbitals of the actinides have been illustrated in section 19.3, where the metallic elements were considered. There it was seen that the binding energy of the *early* elements in the series definitely indicates that atomic f electrons become involved in the binding. Later in the series this involvement apparently disappears, and the $5f$ electrons behave more like the $4f$ electrons as observed in the lanthanide series.

The effects of the $6d$ orbitals also need to be considered. These orbitals are not of great significance in the trivalent state, and the $5d$ orbitals have been virtually ignored in discussing the lanthanides. However, higher charges on the central atom cause contraction of the d orbitals and must make them important in binding. The oxocations occur at the beginning of all three transition series in high-valence state compounds only, and it could be that d orbitals are the cause of their formation there and play an important role in the higher valence states of the actinides.

Finally there is the problem of the core size. As in the lanthanide ions, contraction is most rapid over the first three or four ions in both the 3-valent and 4-valent series, and there is presumably a break at the cations with the half-filled $5f$ sub-shell.

22.3. Valence states

The well-established valence states of the actinides are shown in Table 22.II. The common states of the first five elements after actinium in the series are from 4 to 6, but from americium onwards the 3-valent state becomes dominant. Table 22.III illustrates the pattern of the known oxides. In this respect therefore the beginning of the series is like a transition-metal series, but the later part is like the lanthanide series. It seems probable that the chemistry of the elements after curium is largely limited to 3 valence, making a simple parallel with the chemistry of the 3-valent lanthanides.

The Oxidation State Diagram of the actinide elements in different valence states is given in Fig. 22.4. The VE values or potentials are all valid for

TABLE 22.II. *Valence states of the actinides*

	Ac	Th	Pa	U	Np	Pu	Am	Cm	Bk	Cf	Es	Fm	Md	No
2		○?												
3	●	○	○	○	○	◑	●	●	●	●	●	●	●	●
4		●	○?	●	●	●	◑	○	◑					
5			●	○	●	◑	◑							
6			●	●	◑	◑								

The most important states are marked with closed circles, the least important with open circles.

TABLE 22.III. *Ideal formulae of important oxides*

Valence							
2	ThO	PaO	UO	NpO	PuO	AmO	
3					Pu_2O_3	Am_2O_3	Cm_2O_3
4	ThO_2	PaO_2	UO_2	NpO_2	PuO_2	AmO_2	
5		Pa_2O_5					
6			UO_3				

There are also mixed-valence phases of composition $(PaO_{2.3})$, U_4O_9, U_3O_8, and Np_3O_8. These are similar to such phases as Fe_3O_4.

solutions in $1\cdot0\,M$ perchloric acid. In such a solution the species should be as nearly comparable as is possible, for the perchlorate anion has the least tendency of any anion to bind cations and the hydroxide concentration is kept low by the acidity. The higher the pH of the solution the more the higher-valence states will be favoured since they exist as oxocations, MO_2^{n+}, which can be written formally as equivalent to $M(OH)_4^{n+}$.

The consequences of the variation in stability of the metallic elements is illustrated by the changes of the M^{3+}/Metal potentials which become more positive (less negative) from actinium to uranium and then fall again to americium. Electrode potentials in the lanthanides become steadily more positive with increase of atomic number. The actinide series may perhaps follow this type of progression for the elements after curium.

The $M(IV)/M(III)$ potential increases with atomic number so that americium(IV) is a powerful oxidizing agent, more so than cerium(IV), while plutonium, neptunium, and uranium(IV) are less powerful. Uranium(III) is in fact a strong reducing agent. Of the higher valence states, all except those of uranium are strongly oxidizing. The potentials of the three plutonium couples are so close together that equilibrium mixtures of all four oxidation states can occur in the same solution. While UO_2^+ disproportionates, NpO_2^+ and AmO_2^+ are comparatively stable. Because of the variety of fairly stable oxidation states it is difficult to study the chemistry

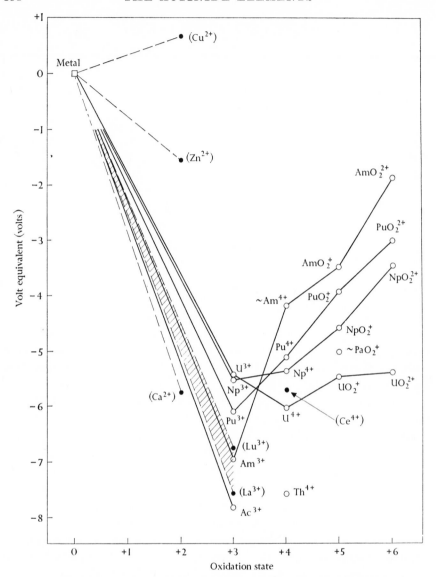

FIG. 22.4. Experimental Oxidation State Diagram for the actinides.

of many of them, although fortunately the rate at which equilibrium is set up in aqueous solution is generally quite slow; see, for example, Fig. 22.5. The slowness of these reactions may perhaps be associated with the poor overlap of ligand orbitals with the 5f orbitals.

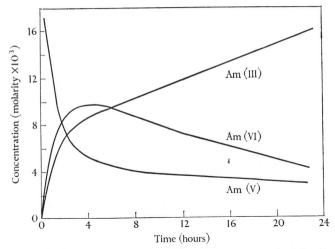

FIG. 22.5. Disproportionation *et seq.* of AmO_2^+ in $6M$ $HClO_4$ at 25 °C (after Penneman and Asprey, *Proc. Intern. Conf. Peaceful Uses Atomic Energy*, Geneva, 1957, **7**, 355).

22.4. The 3-valent state

Different lines of evidence, some of which have been quoted above, suggest that the actinides should be regarded essentially as a $5f$ series similar to the $4f$ lanthanide series. In the general chemistry of these elements, therefore, it will be most useful to compare the properties of the trivalent compounds with the corresponding properties of the trivalent lanthanide compounds. The halides provide a convenient starting point.

LaF_3, AcF_3, UF_3, NpF_3, PuF_3, and AmF_3 are isomorphous as are the corresponding chlorides. In the chloride structure, UCl_3, the coordination of the central cation is 9: this could arise from the utilization of d^5sp^3 hybrid orbitals. The lanthanide hydroxides have a similar structure, but insufficient is known of the actinide hydroxides for a comparison to be made. A change in structure-type takes place along several series of lanthanide and actinide halides (see section 21.4). For the bromides there is a change from the 9-coordinated UCl_3 structure (Ac, U, and Np) to 8-coordination for β-$NpBr_3$, $PuBr_3$, and $AmBr_3$. All the trivalent actinide iodides from UI_3 onwards have the latter structure (cf. Fig. 21.7). The melting-points of these halides would be of interest, but at present they are unknown. Other isomorphous series (Table 22.IV) include the trioxides M_2O_3 (not known in uranium and neptunium) and the complex fluorides, $NaMF_4$.

Despite the very close structural similarity between the lanthanide and actinide series, there are differences in the magnetic moments of their

TABLE 22.IV. *Isostructural compounds* (*3-valent*)

Compound	Structure type	Ac	U	Np	Pu	Am	La	Nd
MF₃	LaF₃	√	√	√	√	√	√	√
MOF	CaF₂	√			√	√	√	√
NaMF₄	Na₂ThF₆†				√		√	√
MCl₃	UCl₃	√	√	√	√	√	√	√
MOCl	PbClF	√			√	√	√	√
MBr₃(I)	UCl₃	√	√	√			√	
MBr₃(II)	PuBr₃			√	√	√		√
M₂O₃	La₂O₃	√			√	√	√	√
M₂S₃(I)	Sb₂S₃		√	√				
M₂S₃(II)	Ce₂S₃	√			√	√	√	

† ABF₄ compounds isostructural with Na₂ThF₆ arise through the ability of A and B to occupy either the Na or Th positions. The formula of the compounds should be written $A_{3/2}B_{3/2}F_6$ (see Wells, *Structural Inorganic Chemistry*, 3rd ed., Oxford, 1962).

compounds which cannot be explained in terms of the general change to jj as opposed to LS couplings (section 22.6). They imply that in the actinides there is some interaction between the f electrons and the surrounding field which was of little consequence in the lanthanides. In order to demonstrate this clearly studies have been made on magnetically-dilute samples of the actinide ions. For example, dilute solid solutions of the actinide halides have been made in non-magnetic lanthanide halides, e.g. $LaCl_3$, with which they are isostructural. These studies show that the magnetic moment per actinide atom increases with dilution, and therefore that there is a reduction in cation–cation interaction with increasing separation of the actinide ions. The cation–cation interaction is greater in sulphides than in chlorides; for example, there is evidence that U_2S_3 is a good semiconductor. Electrical conductivity appears to depend on the degree to which the inner d or f orbitals are exposed. Increases in the intensity of charge-transfer bands in trivalent halides generally parallel increases in electrical conductivity. The extinction coefficients (see section 28.2) are lanthanides—10^2, actinides —10^3, and transition-metals—10^{3-4}.

HEATS OF FORMATION

The heats of formation of actinide compounds are not very different from those of lanthanide or pre-transition metals of comparable ionic radius (Fig. 22.6). However, it is noticeable in the figure that the heats of formation have lower numerical values in the region between actinium and americium. This reflects the high heats of sublimation of the metal lattices to atoms. The fact that there is no compensating high heat of formation of the salt lattice from atoms implies that only at low charge do the $5f$ orbitals and electrons contribute significantly to chemical bonding. At charge $+3$ the f orbitals are too contracted to be of much importance. Fig. 22.6 also shows how the effects are magnified in transition-metal and B-metal series.

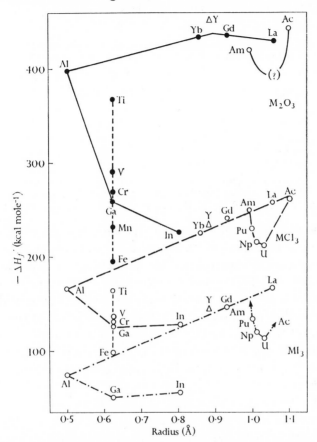

FIG. 22.6. Heats of formation of compounds of trivalent metals as a function of the ionic radius observed in oxides. Radii for transition-metal ions are put equal, see Fig. 26.1.

Apart from structural and thermochemical similarities, the general chemistry of the 3-valent compounds of the actinides also closely parallels that of the lanthanides. Nitrates, perchlorates, and sulphates are soluble while hydroxides, fluorides, and carbonates are insoluble. In solution the similarities between the two series are also very strong. Perhaps the best way in which this has been demonstrated is in the elution of complex citrates or ethylenediaminetetracetates from cation-exchange columns (section 22.7). The actinide EDTA complexes are somewhat more stable than the corresponding lanthanide complexes. A similar difference on increase of ionic size has been noted between Mg^{2+} and Ca^{2+}. The effect shows itself in the heat term, and has been attributed to a decrease in steric hindrance. The thermodynamic data for some actinide complexes are given in Table 22.v.

TABLE 22.v. *Thermodynamic data for the formation of some* EDTA *complexes in aqueous solution at* 25 °C *and an ionic strength of* 0·1 (*after Fuger and Cunningham, J. Inorg. Nucl. Chem.*, 1965, **27**, 1079)

Complex	$\Delta G°$ (kcal mole^{-1})	$\Delta H°$ (kcal mole^{-1})	$\Delta S°$ (cal deg^{-1} mole^{-1})
[Pu EDTA]$^-$	−24·65	−4·23	+68·6
[Am EDTA]$^-$	−24·78	−4·67	+67·4
[La EDTA]$^-$	−21·67	−1·15	+68·8

Note that it is the low heat term in the lanthanides that causes their lower stability. The La values differ from those given in Table 21.vii. This is an illustration of the discordant values commonly reported for the thermodynamic data of complexes in solution.

As in the lanthanide series, the cations can also form complexes with strong-acid anions such as sulphate, chloride, and nitrate. The stability of these complexes is not expected to show any great dependence upon atomic number. Within the limits of existing data, the only easily detectable effect is that of the ion size: there is no obvious ligand-field effect.

The next section deals with the higher valence states of the actinides. Fig. 22.7 shows that the stability of the states as measured by the heats of formation does not increase rapidly after 3-valence except perhaps in the fluorides. Thus in uranium the higher states become increasingly stable in the sequence $I^- < Br^- < Cl^- < F^-$, and $S^{2-} < O^{2-}$. Comparison with the data for plutonium or americium shows that the heat of formation of the 4-valent state is not very dependent on atomic number for oxide or fluoride, in contrast with the heats of formation of the 6-valent fluorides. The fall-off in stability must be due to the effect of the increasing nuclear charge on the 5f orbitals.

22.5. Other valence states

THE 4-VALENT STATE

The prevalence of the 4-valent compounds of the actinides led to the suggestion that the series be called a thoride series. The 4-valent state is one of the most stable not only in thorium and uranium but also as far as americium, and it is possible to prepare 4-valent compounds up to berkelium.

In this valence state there is evidence for bonding which is not of a simple ionic kind. For example, in the isostructural halides MCl_4 of Th, Np, and U, specific directional forces must be operating in the crystals. There are four short metal-chlorine bonds (nearly in a plane), and a large number of

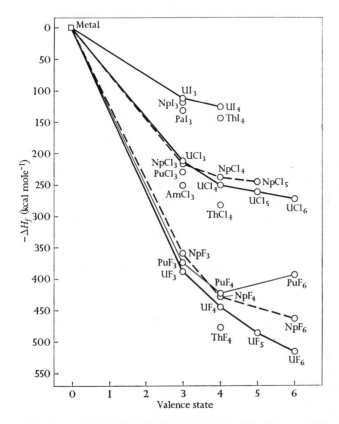

FIG. 22.7. Heats of formation for halogen compounds of the actinides in different valence states, compare Fig. 22.4.

similar but more distant bonds. In the complex ions $M_2Cl_9^-$ (U, Np, and Th) the unit is presumably like $W_2Cl_9^{3-}$, in which there are two equivalent metal atoms, but $W_2Cl_9^{3-}$ has a distorted structure due to M—M bonding which is probably absent in the actinide compounds. The structural peculiarities may be a consequence of the exposed $5f$ or $6d$ orbitals.

In solution the M^{4+} ions form many complexes, mostly with anionic ligands. As in the series of trivalent ions the radii of M^{4+} fall towards the heavier members, but the stabilities of their complexes show little change, at least in so far as the complexes of strong-acid anions are concerned; see Table 22.VI.

TABLE 22.VI. *Stability constants for* M^{4+} *complexes* ($mole^{-1}$ $litre$)

	Th^{4+}	U^{4+}	Np^{4+}	Pu^{4+}
HSO_4^-	2000	2000	2000	2000
NO_3^-	3·0	..	..	4·0
Cl^-	1·0	4·0	..	2·0

The values are very sensitive to ionic strength and rounded numbers are quoted for closely similar conditions in aqueous solution at 25 °C.

5-VALENT AND 6-VALENT STATES

Although there are a number of other compounds of these valence states, the majority are of the type MO_2X and MO_2X_2. Interest naturally centres around the nature of the oxocations MO_2^{n+}, for it has been shown that MO_2^+ and MO_2^{2+} exist as ions both in solution and in solids, e.g. in NpO_2Cl and UO_2Cl_2. The 5-valent compounds are not readily studied, but the 6-valent MO_2^{2+} ions are common to the four elements from U to Am. From force-constant measurements, it is concluded that the strongest bonding in the series of MO_2^{2+} ions is at UO_2^{2+}. Structure studies of the MO_2^{n+} unit have shown it to be linear, but it is capable of coordinating with a great variety of other groups in exceptional geometries. The simple solids UO_2F_2 and $Ca.(UO_2).O_2$ contain UO_2^{2+} ions with U—O distances of approximately 1·75–2·00 Å. At a greater distance there are 6 F^- or O^{2-} ions in a flattened octahedron around the central ion. However, in $Ba.(UO_2).O_2$ the structure unit is $(UO_2)^{2+}$ with only four O^{2-} units around it. 5-coordination of UO_2^{2+} is found in $K_3.(UO_2).F_5$. Compounds containing MoO_2^{2+}, PuO_2^{2+}, and AmO_2^{2+} are often isostructural with uranium compounds, so that it appears that the $5f$ electrons play but an insignificant structural role. The same point is brought out by the structural similarity between $K_3U(IV)F_7$, $K_3.(UO_2).F_5$, and $(NH_4)_3ZrF_7$.

In many ways the MO_2^{n+} ions of the actinides behave like small pre-transition metal ions of high z^2/r (where z is the charge and r the radius) but of relatively low electron affinity compared with transition-metal or B-metal ions of the same size and charge. It is thus not possible to account for the stability or the selectivity of their complex formation on the basis of the formal charge on the ions: the properties of uranyl, to take a specific example, are similar to those of a pre-transition cation of the same size but of charge approaching +4. Another way of putting this is to say that UO_2^{2+} behaves like a divalent ion of very small radius, e.g. Be^{2+}, although the U–ligand distances are large. This is brought out in Fig. 22.8

by the high stability of the fluoride, sulphate, and hydroxide complexes of UO_2^{2+} as compared with Cu^{2+}. The cations also form nitrate, acetate, and many other oxyanion complexes, compare Be^{2+}. However, they do not easily form complexes with nitrogen or sulphur bases, e.g. dipyridyl or ethylenediamine, unless these bases are bound in organic compounds already containing oxyanions, e.g. 8-hydroxyquinolinate. The oxocations

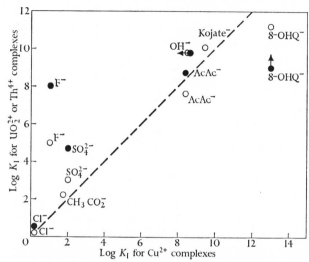

FIG. 22.8. The stability constants for Th^{4+}, ●, and UO_2^{2+}, ○, complexes as a function of those for Cu^{2+}. Data are for aqueous solution and 25 °C. The dotted line is at 45°.

of transition-metals do not behave in quite the same way (Chapter 26) but highly-charged cations, e.g. Th^{4+}, are rather similar. The peculiarities of the actinide oxocations could arise from their stereochemistry as well as from their relatively low electron affinity.

The 5-valent and 6-valent ions form a variety of complexes. The extraction of the 6-valent complexes into organic solvents is of analytical importance. The easy change of valence in the actinide series makes separation less of a problem than it is in the lanthanide series. Thus the analytical and preparative methods in the actinide series differ greatly from those in the lanthanides. Furthermore, volatile species are more readily obtained. Thus UF_6 is used in the isotopic enrichment of ^{235}U by gas-phase diffusion.

The formation of nitrato, sulphate, and carboxylato complexes of high coordination number by these small cations of high effective (or actual) positive charge is probably a consequence of the anion geometries. Nitrate, sulphate, and carboxylate as well as such anions as phosphate, carbonate, silicate, and borate have short oxygen–oxygen distances of the order of 2·2–2·3 Å. By chelating a central cation a fair number of such pairs of oxygens can be accommodated around a small cation to give a high electro-static stabilization. The radius of oxygen in water is about 1·35 Å, so that the smallest cation around which an octahedron of water molecules can be packed without considerable oxygen–oxygen repulsion must be of radius 0·6 Å. In oxide lattices the following cations are smaller than this: Be^{2+}, Al^{3+}, transition-metals in the first transition series with charge greater than 3, transition-metals in the second and third transition series with charge equal to or greater than 4. For higher coordination, e.g. 8, the permitted cation radius is some 5 to 10 per cent larger. It is expected that sulphate, nitrate, etc., will be preferred to water by most 4-valent cations. Clearly the argument must be restricted to essentially ionic situations, for covalent bonding will lead to a preference for oxygen atoms which are more polarizable than those present in the strong-acid anions.

HYDRIDES, NITRIDES, AND CARBIDES

Some non-stoicheiometric compounds of the actinides will be described first as they are most nearly related to the trivalent compounds. While transition metals with more than a half-filled d sub-shell form but weakly stable pure hydrides, all the lanthanides form stable hydrides with a stoicheiometry slightly different from MH_3. The known hydrides of the actinides are

$$ThH_2 \qquad\qquad\qquad\qquad PuH_2 \quad AmH_2$$
$$ThH_{3-4} \quad PaH_3 \quad UH_3 \quad NpH_{3\cdot7} \quad PuH_3 \quad AmH_{3-4}$$

They are black non-stoicheiometric solids. They are formed exothermically from the elements, e.g. PuH_2, $\Delta H_f = -37\cdot4$ kcal mole^{-1}, and they react rapidly with water or acids. Presumably the later actinides will also form hydrides similar to the lanthanide hydrides.

Several nitrides have been prepared:

$$Th_3N_4 \qquad\qquad\qquad UN \quad NpN \quad PuN$$
$$U_2N_3$$
$$PaN_2(?) \qquad UN_2$$

UN is somewhat like tungsten nitride. It is a refractory substance, strongly exothermic ($\Delta H_f = -80$ kcal mole^{-1}), stable in moist air, and does not decompose at 1300 °C. Plutonium nitride, on the other hand, is attacked by weak mineral acids and moist air, and is unstable at 1200°. The pattern of change along the series is characteristic of the change from a transition-metal to a lanthanide series of compounds. A similar change occurs in the carbides.

ThC	UC	NpC	PuC
	U_2C_3	Np_2C_3	Pu_2C_3
ThC_2	UC_2	NpC_2	

ThC_2 and UC_2 are refractory carbides of melting-point, 2655° and 2425 °C respectively. They are not attacked by moist air at 1000 °C. They too are black exothermic compounds and good electrical conductors. The numerous borides are similar and not unlike lanthanide borides. Th, U, Pu, and Np all have at least one silicide of formula MSi_2. Among the lanthanides, only cerium forms such a silicide, and this is assumed to be a 4-valent compound. The actinide and cerium silicides are isomorphous. Here is another indication of the higher valence of the actinides as compared with the lanthanides, although the above compounds are usually non-stoicheiometric and cannot really be discussed satisfactorily in terms of valence states.

22.6. Spectra and magnetic moments

The spectra and the magnetic properties of the actinide ions are even more complicated than those of the lanthanide ions. In part this arises from the breakdown of the simple Russell–Saunders type of coupling, since spin–orbit interaction is no longer subsidiary to spin–spin and orbit–orbit interactions (i.e. jj coupling must now be used). In other words, as well as electron–electron repulsion (see Chapter 1), the relativistic effects, which occur as the somewhat-penetrating $5f$ electrons come into the vicinity of the heavy atomic nuclei, become of major account. In part it arises from the fact that the $5f$ electrons are also nearer the surface of the atom and come under the influence of the chemical environment, although to nothing like the same extent as do the d electrons, with which we shall be primarily concerned in our discussion of the transition series in the chapters immediately following. And in part it arises from the less sharply defined distinctions between $5f$ and $6d$ electrons as compared with $4f$ and $5d$ electrons.

SPECTRA

The most conspicuous difference between the Laporte-forbidden bands in the two series is the intensity, which is about thirty times larger (including the effect of band widths which are about twice as large in the actinides) in the actinides than in the lanthanides. The ligand-field splitting (see Chapter 24) is from two to five times as large in the actinides as in the lanthanides (compare, however, a few hundred cm^{-1} in lanthanides with 20,000 cm^{-1} and 30,000 cm^{-1} for trivalent ions in the first and second transition series respectively), and the nephelauxetic effect (see also Chapter 28) is about twice as large (interelectron repulsions themselves are lower by about 40 per cent). Absorptions accompanied by change of spin

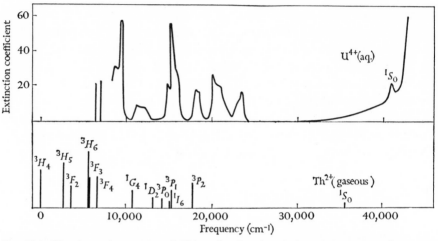

FIG. 22.9. The absorption spectra of $5f^2$ ions showing the relationship between U^{4+}(aq.) and Th^{2+} (gas) (after Jørgensen). The ground state of Th^{2+} ($^3H_4$) is also shown.

become more 'allowed'. Fig. 22.9 gives the absorption spectrum for U^{4+}(aq.) and for gaseous Th^{2+}, both of which are $5f^2$ ions. Precise assignment of bands in terms of the simple atomic levels is probably not possible for the U^{4+}(aq.) ion, because of ligand-field effects. Comparison should be made with Fig. 21.15, Pr^{3+}(aq.) $4f^2$, noting in particular the increased intensity in the actinide ion. Interpretation of the spectra of 5-valent and 6-valent actinide ions is complicated considerably by the effects which the O atoms in MO$_2^+$

TABLE 22.VII. *Colours of actinide ions (from Katz and Seaborg)*

Element	M^{3+}	M^{4+}	MO$_2^+$	MO$_2^{2+}$
Actinium	Colourless	..	..	..
Thorium	..	Colourless	..	..
Protactinium	..	Colourless	(Colourless)	..
Uranium	Red	Green	(Colour unknown)	Yellow
Neptunium	Blue to purple	Yellow-green	Green	Pink to red
Plutonium	Blue to violet	Tan to orange-brown	(Reddish-purple)†	Yellow to pink-orange
Americium	Pink	..	Yellow	Rum-coloured
Curium	Colourless	..	..	..

† Predicted from the absorption spectrum of Pu(V).

and MO_2^{2+} may have on the $5f$ sub-shell. The observed colours of the actinide ions in aqueous solution are given in Table 22.VII.

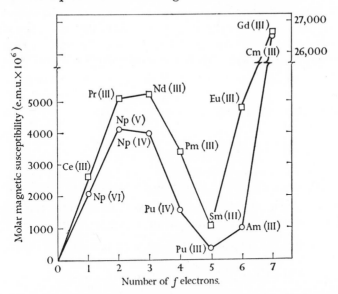

FIG. 22.10. The magnetic susceptibilities of some actinide oxidation states (after Katz and Seaborg).

Laporte-allowed $5f^n$ to $5f^{n-1}6d$ transitions have been observed in Pa^{4+}, U^{3+}, Np^{3+}, and Pu^{3+} compounds. Charge-transfer bands are more readily observed in the actinides than in the lanthanides, for they often occur at quite low energy and are of greater intensity than in the lanthanides. The lower energy is due to the greater oxidizing power of the higher-valence actinides as compared with the trivalent lanthanide ions. The heightened intensity is partly a consequence of the greater overlap of the more exposed $5f$ orbitals.

MAGNETIC PROPERTIES

Fig. 22.10 demonstrates the similarities between the magnetic properties of actinide and lanthanide ions. It will be noted that high-valence states have been chosen for $5f^1$, $5f^2$, $5f^3$, and $5f^4$ ions. There is, for example, some doubt whether the magnetism of U^{4+} (which is less than Np^{5+}, $5f^2$) is better interpreted in terms of $6d^2$ rather than $5f^2$. Again the thorium sulphides are not paramagnetic, although the analogous cerium compounds are paramagnetic to an extent consistent with the presence of unpaired f electrons. This has been attributed to the presence of $6d$ electrons rather than $5f$ electrons in the Th^{4+} compounds. In general the magnetic evidence suggests that in the early part of the actinide series and especially with lower-valence states, the distinction between f and d configurations is not simple, but that with the later actinide elements and especially with higher-valence states, $5f^n$ configurations become the rule. Certainly such a pattern would fit in well with the picture (which we have discussed in sections 21.2 and 22.2), in which the f electrons are very sensitive to the charge external to the core, this effect being more marked with the $4f$ (lanthanide) than with the $5f$ (actinide) electrons.

22.7. Separation problems

The techniques used for the separation of the actinides are essentially similar to those used for the lanthanides, but the possibilities of valence variations are much greater. We may take as an example the isolation of plutonium from uranium and its fission products produced in a nuclear reactor:

$$^{235}U + n \rightarrow \text{fission products} + \sim 2 \cdot 5n + 200 \text{ MeV}$$

$$^{238}U + n \rightarrow {}^{239}U \xrightarrow[23 \cdot 5 \text{ min}]{\beta^-} {}^{239}Np \xrightarrow[2 \cdot 33 \text{ days}]{\beta^-} {}^{239}Pu$$

After 'cooling' for about ten days, the most significant fission species are ruthenium, zirconium, niobium, and the lanthanide elements. The concentrations of these must be reduced by a factor of about 10^6 or 10^7, so that many purification stages are commonly required. A number of procedures have been used which may be roughly classified as precipitation, solvent-extraction, and ion-exchange processes. In each case advantage is taken of the variable valence of Pu, and the corresponding variations in its chemical properties.

In the bismuth-phosphate process, Pu is brought to the 4-valent state with nitrite ion, while uranium remains as uranyl(VI) nitrate. The Pu(IV) is then coprecipitated with $BiPO_4$ (with which, curiously, it is removed more efficiently than is Pu(III), the uranyl(VI) ion being kept in solution by addition of sufficient sulphate ion (as sulphuric acid). The Pu is separated from the $BiPO_4$ by oxidation to soluble Pu(VI) with sodium bismuthate, potassium permanganate, or potassium dichromate. Further precipitation cycles with $BiPO_4$ and LaF_3 carriers follow, until the Pu concentration is sufficiently high for direct precipitation of an insoluble plutonium compound such as plutonium peroxide. The precipitation processes are not very convenient for the recovery of uranium as well as plutonium, but this double object may be achieved with solvent-extraction procedures. In the

Redox process, Pu(VI) and U(VI) are both extracted from aqueous nitrate solutions into methyl *iso*butyl ketone, and the Pu is then stripped from the organic phase by reduction to Pu(III) with a reducing reagent which leaves the U unaffected. In the Purex process Pu(IV) and U(VI) are extracted into tributyl-phosphate (in some inert solvent such as kerosene, because

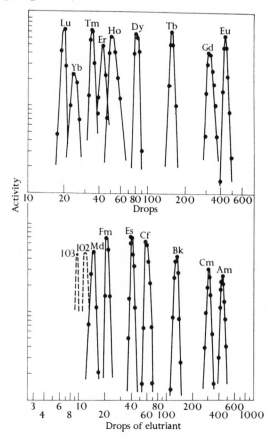

FIG. 22.11. Ion-exchange chromatograms of lanthanides and actinides under comparable conditions. The figure demonstrates the rather greater ease of separation of the actinides (after Katz and Seaborg).

of the high viscosity of tributyl-phosphate and the similarity of its density to water), and again the Pu is removed via reduction to the Pu(III) state.

Ion-exchange methods are used principally for the concentration of species from very dilute solutions, and for the separation of actinide elements one from another and from the lanthanide elements. A direct separation between lanthanides and actinides may be made using the fact that, in high concentrations of hydrochloric acid, the actinide elements form complexes with chloride ions more readily than do the lanthanides. The use of ion-exchange chromatography has been of very considerable assistance in the identification of the trans-uranium elements. As will be seen from Fig. 22.11, the elution behaviour of the actinides is very similar to that of the lanthanides, so that the retention times of new elements, especially in the trivalent state, may be predicted even before they have been produced. From the pattern of redox-potentials (see, e.g., Fig. 22.4) the range of aqueous solution potentials in which the trivalent state should exist may also be predicted. In this way, taking advantage of the radioactivity of these elements to detect their presence, it has been found possible to separate and identify them literally on the scale of a few atoms only. This is perhaps one of the most elegant examples of qualitative analysis in the whole of inorganic chemistry.

The separation of the uranium isotope 235 has attracted a very considerable attention because of its fissionable properties. Successful methods which have been developed include gaseous diffusion of UF_6 through porous membranes, the acceleration and magnetic separation of uranium ions in gigantic mass spectrographs, and thermal diffusion of liquid UF_6. A discussion of these and other isotopic separation methods is, however, outside the scope of this book and the reader is referred elsewhere (e.g. to Glasstone).

Problems

1. In the lanthanide series of elements, which was largely studied by European chemists (europium), one of the early workers was Gadolin (gadolinium). Lanthanide ores were discovered near Ytterby (terbium, etc.) in Sweden. Are there any analogies in the nomenclature of the actinide elements?

2. Why might we expect higher valences to be more common in the actinides than in the lanthanides?

3. Show that the following effective principal quantum numbers (n_e) for Ra^+
$$5f\ 3 \cdot 66, \quad 6d\ 2 \cdot 53, \quad 7s\ 2 \cdot 32$$
are consistent with data plotted in Fig. 22.2.

4. Jørgensen has suggested that, in the gaseous actinide ions and their complexes, the difference in energy between the configurations $5f^n$ and

$5f^{n-1}6d$ (where n is not greater than 7, i.e. up to the half-filled sub-shell) is given by the relation

$$(Z-96)7000 \text{ cm}^{-1}+(Z_0-1)18{,}000 \text{ cm}^{-1},$$

where Z is the atomic number and Z_0 the ionic charge plus one. Compare the results obtained by using this formula with the values given in the text (Fig. 22.2 and the numerical values for M^{3+} ions given in section 22.2).

5. On the basis of our knowledge of the behaviour of f electrons and of the chemistry of the lanthanides and actinides, predict the general trends which we might expect to find in the three transition series ($3d$, $4d$, and $5d$ electrons).

6. From a comparison of Figs. 22.4 and 22.7 estimate approximate values for the (as yet unknown) heats of formation of the following compounds: NpF_5, $NpCl_6$, NpI_4, PuF_5, $PuCl_4$, $PuCl_5$, PuI_3, AmF_3, AmF_4, AmF_5, AmF_6, $AmCl_4$, $AmCl_5$, $AmCl_6$, AmI_3.

7. Comment on the following oxidation potentials for M^{4+}/M^{3+} in $1M$ perchloric acid at 25 °C:

U -0.63, Np $+0.16$, Pu $+0.98$, Am $+2.7$, Bk $(+1.6)$ volts.

8. 0.2130 g of anhydrous uranyl (U(VI)) nitrate were dissolved in 20 ml of $2N$ H_2SO_4 and shaken with zinc amalgam. The resulting solution was titrated with $0.08673N$ permanganate, of which 12.47 ml were required to produce a permanent pink colour. Calculate the valence state to which U(VI) was reduced. (Atomic weights: U, 238.08; O, 16.00; N, 14.01.)

9. Suggest why the equilibrium

$$U(VI)+Fe(II) \rightleftharpoons U(IV)+Fe(III)$$

which lies to the left in aqueous solutions of sulphuric acid, should be driven to the right on the addition of phosphate ion.

10. Which of the combinations of ions of the actinides will readily undergo reactions such as

$$Pu(IV)+Pu(V) \rightarrow Pu(VI)+Pu(III)\,?$$

(See Fig. 22.4.)

11. The oxidation of Pu(IV) to Pu(VI) is fast with Ag^{2+} and HOCl but slow with $KMnO_4$, $KBrO_3$, and H_5IO_6. Can you suggest a reason for this distinction?

12. In general changes in property along the series of trivalent ions of the lanthanides are similar to but smaller than those along the series of the actinides. How can you account for this difference?

13. Many of the oxides of the actinides, e.g. U_3O_8, AmO_2, are non-stoicheiometric, but this is true of few lanthanide oxides. Comment.

14. Comment upon the following melting-point data (°C):

UCl_3	UCl_4	UCl_5	UCl_6
835	590	(327)	179 (decomp.)

UF_3	UF_4	UF_5	UF_6
1140 (decomp.)	960	< 400 (decomp.)	64

15. What problems are raised by the following bond distances (Å)?

	M—O	M—F
$(UO_2)F_2$	1·91 (2)	2·50 (6)
$K(AmO_2)F_2$	1·93 (2)	2·47 (6)
$Mg(UO_2)O_2$	1·93 (2), 2·18 (4)	
$Ca(UO_2)O_2$	1·91 (2), 2·29 (6)	
$K(PuO_2)CO_3$	1·94 (2), 2·55 (6)	

The numbers in parentheses are the number of neighbours at the given distance from the actininide atom, M.

16. In what ways does the general chemistry of UO_2^{2+} differ from that of Mg^{2+}?

17. Comment on the following stability constants for the UO_2^{2+} ion:

	CO_3^{2-}	F^-	Cl^-	Br^-	$CH_3CO_2^-$	NO_3^-
$K_1 = \sim$	10^6	4×10^4	0·8	0·5	240	0·5

18. In what ways may we expect U to depart from the properties expected for eka-W, i.e. from an extrapolation $Cr \rightarrow Mo \rightarrow W \rightarrow U$?

19. The spectroscopic and magnetic properties of the actinide ions are in some ways intermediate between those of the lanthanide and those of the transition-metal ions. Comment and elaborate on this statement.

20. Why is it easier in general to separate actinides than lanthanides?

21. By means of filter-paper attached to drone aircraft very small quantities (about 200 atoms) of element 100 were collected from the atmospheric debris of the 'Mike' thermonuclear explosion, which took place in the Pacific in November 1952. Using a combination of radioactive detection and ion-exchange resins, it was found possible to identify this element which had hitherto been unknown. Suggest how this was done. How (possibly) might this technique be adapted to help in discovering the nature of a nuclear weapon, recently tested in the atmosphere by a foreign power?

Bibliography

L. B. ASPREY and B. B. CUNNINGHAM, Unusual Oxidation States of some Actinide and Lanthanide Elements, *Progress in Inorganic Chemistry*, vol. 2, ed. F. A. Cotton, Interscience, New York, 1960.

A. E. COMYNS, 'The Coordination Chemistry of the Actinides', *Chem. Rev.*, 1960, **60**, 115.

H. G. FRIEDMAN, G. R. CHOPPIN, and D. G. FEUERBACHER, 'The Shapes of *f*-Orbitals', *J. Chem. Educ.* 1964, **41**, 354.

S. GLASSTONE, *Sourcebook on Atomic Energy*, 2nd ed., van Nostrand, New York, 1958.

G. T. SEABORG (ed.), Symposium on the New Elements, *J. Chem. Educ.*, 1959, **36**, 2, and six following papers.

N. HODGE, Fluorides of the Actinide Elements, *Advances in Fluorine Chemistry*, vol. 2, ed. M. Stacey, J. C. Tatlow, and A. G. Sharpe, Butterworths, London, 1961.

C. K. JØRGENSEN, *Absorption Spectra and Chemical Bonding in Complexes*, Pergamon Press, Oxford, 1962.

J. J. KATZ and G. T. SEABORG, *The Chemistry of the Actinide Elements*, Wiley, New York, 1957.

J. J. KATZ and I. SHEFT, Halides of the Actinide Elements, *Advances in Inorganic Chemistry and Radiochemistry*, vol. 2, ed. H. J. Eméleus and A. G. Sharpe, Academic Press, New York, 1960.

C. E. MOORE, 'The Atomic Spectra of the Rare Earths', *Appl. Optics*, 1963, **2**, 665.

L. E. J. ROBERTS, 'The Actinide Oxides', *Quart. Rev. Chem. Soc.*, 1961, **15**, 442.

23 · Transition Metals: Atomic Structure and Valence

23.1. Introduction to transition-metal chemistry

THEMES AND COMPLEXITIES OF TRANSITION-METAL CHEMISTRY

The characteristic features of transition-metal chemistry are exhibited by the elements extending from Group IVA to Group IB in each of the three long periods of the Periodic Table. These features are associated with the distinctive role played by the $(n-1)d$ electrons and orbitals in atoms falling between (1) those in which they are of little chemical significance (Group IIA), or in which they are little distinguished energetically from ns electrons and orbitals (Group IIIA), and (2) those in which they have become part of the atomic core, so that $(n-1)d$ electrons can no longer be pulled out by chemical forces (Group IIB). In a sense then transition-metal chemistry reflects a *transition* of these d orbitals from diffuse excited orbitals to tightly-bound core orbitals.

The chemistry of the transition metals is extremely complex, and we have no one simple model to guide us through its intricacies. In the chemistry of the pre-transition series we were able to concentrate our discussion on the application of the simple ionic model, and in the chemistry of the lanthanides on the core characteristics of the $4f$ orbitals. In the transition series the ionic model is complicated by the non-spherical nature of many transition-metal ions (crystal-field effects), and by the very considerable deviations from ionic character which are brought out particularly in the general *transition* from A-metal to B-metal character which takes place along each of the transition series. Moreover, the relatively non-penetrating $(n-1)d$ electrons vary from valence to core electrons depending on the redox potential of the chemical environment, the nature of the metal, and the nature and position of the ligands or anions with which it is surrounded.

Nevertheless there appear to us to be three main themes in transition-metal chemistry. *Theme* 1 is *the steady transformation of $(n-1)d$ orbitals* *from excited orbitals, through valence orbitals, to core orbitals across each of the three transition series.* This transformation occurs most rapidly in the first transition series, so that high-valence states are relatively more stable in the second and especially the third transition series. (Compare the lanthanide and actinide series.) *Theme 2 is the tendency of transition-metal*

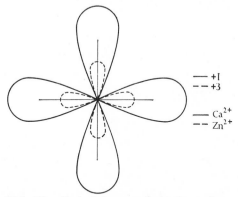

FIG. 23.1. The effect of charge and atomic number on the extension of 3d orbitals (schematic).

cations to form semi-covalent bonds. If this bonding were restricted to the use of the *ns* and *np* cation orbitals, it would be reasonable to expect a fairly steady gradation in properties along such a series as

$$Ca^{2+}, (Sc^{2+}), Ti^{2+}, V^{2+}, Cr^{2+}, Mn^{2+}, Fe^{2+}, Co^{2+}, Ni^{2+}, Cu^{2+}, Zn^{2+}.$$

This simple pattern will, however, be modified considerably by the covalent contributions of the $(n-1)d$ orbitals and electrons. Covalent bonding will depend very markedly on the sizes of the transition-metal orbitals. The general contraction of the d orbitals with atomic number and charge is illustrated schematically in Fig. 23.1. *Theme 3 is the dependence of both ionic and covalent energies on the symmetry of the field provided by the surrounding ligands or ions.*

OUTLINE OF TRANSITION-METAL CHAPTERS

This chapter is concerned with a fairly detailed account of atomic structure (Part A), and of the relation of this to the stability of different valence states, especially those found in aqueous solution (Part B). The discussion follows the same general pattern as the discussions of the valence states of the pre-transition and lanthanide metals. The main emphasis will be on theme 1, although the discrepancies between experimental and predicted Oxidation State Diagrams will draw attention to the importance of the other two themes. The first part of Chapter 24 is largely taken up with the basic theory of the ligand field, that is with theme 3, while in the second part the general significance of theme 2 is explored. The chemistry of the divalent transition-metal ions is described in Chapter 25. The wide occurrence of such ions throughout the transition series makes their comparison most convenient for the illustration of a number of important trends, and especially those trends which are a direct reflection of theme 2. The higher oxidation states are then considered in Chapter 26, where emphasis is laid on the interaction of the three themes, i.e. it is an extension and amplification of the discussion given at the end of this chapter. The chemistry of the transition metals in their low oxidation states is in many ways distinct from that in their higher oxidation states, and requires some more sophisticated theory. It forms the subject-matter of Chapter 27. A brief outline of the spectra and magnetic properties of transition-metal compounds is given in Chapter 24, but a more detailed account is contained in Chapter 28. Theme 3 will be the most significant theme in Chapters 27 and 28. Finally Chapter 29 is an account of the kinetics and mechanism of reactions involving transition-metal ions and compounds. This field of study is in a very early stage of development, and considerable changes are to be expected over the next few years: most of the recent theoretical interpretation has been given in terms of theme 3.

The ordering of the transition-metal chapters has been largely governed by two factors. The first is the necessity of illustrating the three dominant themes. The second is the desire to consider the general and more traditional chemistry before the more exotic. In this way the relationship between transition and non-transition metal chemistry is most clearly exemplified. In some ways the material of Chapters 27, 28, and 29 follows most logically directly after Chapter 24, for many of the most elegant applications of the theory of the ligand field are in spectra and magnetism. However, the relegation of the more normal chemistry to the end of the discussion would give a false balance to transition-metal chemistry. This is particularly undesirable as the recent and intense interest in crystal-field and molecular-orbital theories has naturally tended to overemphasize their relative importance.

VALENCE AND OXIDATION STATE

In the previous chapters the concepts of valence and oxidation state have both been used. In transition-metal chemistry use is also made of both these terms, despite the fact that in some compounds there can be no really clear definition of them. *Valence* is a well-defined quantity when using either the ionic or the simple bond model. In the first model it is the number of charges, independent of sign, which are placed on an atom in a compound: in the second it is the number of single bonds, plus twice the number of double bonds, etc., formed by an element. In certain compounds, valence is easily defined by reference to the appropriate model. For example, $NiCl_2$ contains divalent nickel and OsO_4 contains octavalent osmium. But $Ni(NH_3)_6^{2+}$ does not obviously contain divalent nickel. In order to avoid such problems, the coordination of an atom is deliberately excluded from the valence when the ionic model is appropriate. However, when the covalent model is appropriate, as in a compound such as $Cl_3P{\rightarrow}O$ which can be written with a double bond or a coordinate bond, the distinction becomes valueless. There is now no accepted convention. The coordinate bond can be counted as increasing the valence by two. Thus oxygen is divalent and phosphorus pentavalent in Cl_3PO, but nitrogen is not pentavalent in $R_3N{\rightarrow}BF_3$.

Oxidation state has been defined in Chapter 9. Combining elements are divided such that some, e.g. oxygen and chlorine, add to the oxidation state, and some, e.g. hydrogen, subtract from the oxidation state of the central element with which they are combined. Again positive charge increases, and negative charge decreases the oxidation state. In transition-metal chemistry there is no problem with the oxidation state of such compounds as NiO, H_2CrO_4, $ReCl_6^{2-}$, and $Co(H_2O)_6^{3+}$. In fact problems of definition are not met while discussing compounds in which the charge carried by the ligand can be given a simple formal value. Thus ligands such as NH_3 and H_2O will not affect the oxidation state, while Cl^- adds one and O^{2-} adds two to the oxidation state. Again the convention adopted is that groups such as CO, PF_3, and dipyridyl also do not alter the oxidation state of a central atom to which they are bound. Difficulties then arise only when the charge carried by a ligand is uncertain. Two such cases are NO and H. A metal bound to such ligands may donate or take electrons, giving NO^-, H^-, or NO^+ and H^+ respectively, while in certain compounds NO may act as a neutral ligand. Where the oxidation state cannot be defined without a detailed knowledge of electron structure the term will be avoided.

In general the term valence state will be used in discussing those compounds for which the ionic model provides at least a reasonable approximation, and oxidation state for those (see especially Chapter 27) where it does not.

23.2. Atomic structure

$3d$ AND $4s$ ELECTRONS THROUGHOUT THE PERIODIC TABLE

Fig. 23.2 compares the binding energies of a $3d$ and a $4s$ electron in atoms of steadily increasing atomic number. Until K, neither of these electrons is present in the lowest atomic state, but from spectroscopic data the

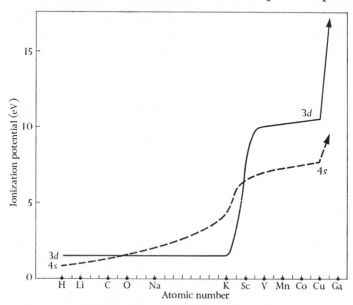

FIG. 23.2. The relative ionization energies of $3d$ and $4s$ orbitals.

energies required to ionize each of these electrons from the excited atomic states can be computed. Thus for Na the ionization processes compared are

$$1s^2\,2s^2 2p^6\,3d^1 \quad \text{and} \quad 1s^2\,2s^2 2p^6\,4s^1 \quad \text{to} \quad 1s^2\,2s^2 2p^6.$$

In the H atom the $3d$ electron is more firmly bound than the $4s$, because of its lower principal quantum number. But since the $3d$ orbital lies almost wholly outside the inner electron shells, its binding energy increases very little from H to K (H, 1·51 eV; K, 1·67 eV). On the other hand the $4s$ electron penetrates to some extent through the inner shells (Chapter 2): this leads to a considerable increase in binding energy, from 0·85 eV in H to 4·34 eV in K. For the elements up to C in the Periodic Table the $3d$ is the more stable orbital, but from N onwards the $4s$ becomes the more stable. Then for the elements which immediately follow K the $3d$ orbital increases in stability very rapidly indeed, so that a second reversal of

relative stability occurs in the first transition series. With Zn, at the end
of the series, the $4s$ electrons are involved in chemical reactions much as
they are in Ca. However, the $3d$ electrons have now become part of an
essentially-inert inner core, although in Ca they are hardly stable enough
to appear on the chemical scene. For the later elements of the Periodic
Table, as is shown by X-ray spectra, the $3d$ orbitals are much more firmly
bound than the $4s$ (e.g. Sr, $3d = 132$ eV; $4s = 34$ eV).

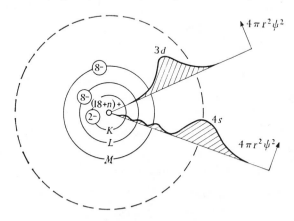

FIG. 23.3. Schematic illustration of the radial distribution functions
for $3d$ and $4s$ orbitals. Note both the penetration and the extension
of the s orbital.

$3d$ AND $4s$ ELECTRONS IN THE FIRST TRANSITION SERIES

The filling up of the $3d$ and the $4s$ orbitals across the first transition series
is a fairly complex process. In Chapter 2 this problem was discussed
generally in relation to the charge external to the inner shells. It will be
necessary at this stage to enter into more detail, and in order to do so it is
convenient to have a rough picture of the radial distributions of the $3d$ and
$4s$ orbitals in the atoms of the first transition series, such as that given in
Fig. 23.3. It must be recognized at the outset that this picture is highly
idealized, as will be a good deal of the following discussion. The electrons
of the K, L, and the incomplete M shell are imagined as forming concentric
rings of electron density. The $4s$ electrons then have a maximum probability on a fourth and outer ring, while the $3d$ electrons are largely concentrated between the M and the outer $4s$ ring. In practice they will lie
relatively further out at the beginning of the transition series, and further
in when the transition series has been completed. The radial distributions
neither of the $3d$ nor of the $4s$ will be as hydrogen-like as depicted.

In Ca the lowest configuration is (Ar core).$4s^2$, and the removal of one of these $4s$ electrons requires (see Fig. 23.2) 1·4 times as much energy as the removal of the $4s$ electron from K. To remove a $3d$ electron from the excited Ca atom, $3d^14s^1$, requires, however, 2·15 times as much energy as is required to remove the $3d$ electron from the excited state of K (Ar core. $3d^1$). If a $3d$ electron lay wholly inside a $4s$ electron this increase would have been nearer fourfold (2^2). In Sc the most stable atomic configuration is $3d^14s^2$. Removal of an s electron (the normal ionization potential) requires only a little more energy (1·5 times the ionization potential of K) than in Ca. This suggests that the $3d$ electron may now be regarded as lying essentially inside the main part of the $4s^2$ orbital. On the other hand, in Sc the binding energy of the $3d$ electron has again risen sharply, and is equal to 4·8 times the energy with which it was held in the excited K atom. In fact removal of this electron from Sc now requires more energy than removal of one of the $4s$, so that the first ionization potential of Sc corresponds to the process

$$3d^14s^2 \text{ to } 3d^14s^1, \text{ rather than } 3d^14s^2 \text{ to } 4s^2.$$

The most stable configuration of Ti is $3d^24s^2$. The energy required to remove the $4s$ electron has again increased only slightly to 1·6 times the ionization potential of K, while the removal of the $3d$ electron now requires 5·95 times as much energy as it did in the excited K atom. The increase in d electron stability between Sc and Ti is again quite large, but, as Fig. 23.2 shows, it is not so pronounced as was the rise from Ca to Sc. The $3d$ electrons tend to shield one another to some extent from the full effects of the increased effective nuclear charge outside the argon core. Thus the general pattern is that a single $3d$ electron will increase in stability very rapidly across the transition series, but that the increase will be much less marked when there is more than one $3d$ electron. Thus Sc does not adopt the configuration $3d^24s^1$ in its most stable state. It is only at Cr that the configuration $3d^{n-1}4s^1$ becomes preferred over $3d^{n-2}4s^2$. The relative energies of the three configurations

$$3d^n, \quad 3d^{n-1}4s^1, \quad \text{and } 3d^{n-2}4s^2$$

are given in Fig. 23.4. After Cr it will be seen that there is a reversion to $3d^{n-2}4s^2$ as the most stable configuration. This is a consequence of the strong repulsion which exists between two d electrons in the same highly-directed space orbital, for in the ground state of the Cr atom each $3d$ orbital is just half-filled. By the time Cu is reached, the $3d^{n-1}4s^1$ configuration has again become the most stable.

The lower part of Fig. 23.4 makes a similar comparison of configurations in the singly-charged ions. It will be observed that, on a relative basis, the configurations with more $3d$ and less $4s$ electrons have been rather strongly stabilized. In the ionization of transition-metal atoms it is, there-

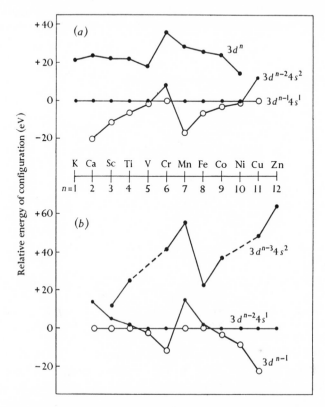

FIG. 23.4. The relative energies of different electron configurations as a function of atomic number for (a) neutral atoms and (b) M^+ ions. In each case the energy of the configuration with one $4s$ electron is arbitrarily taken as zero. Ground states are marked by open circles.

fore, the $4s$ electrons which are removed first and then the $3d$. In the highly-charged transition-metal ions the $3d$ electrons have become very much more stable than the $4s$, as was discussed earlier in Chapter 2. Fig. 23.4 demonstrates, however, that the ionization processes may not always be similar or simple. Thus the first ionization potential of V corresponds to a change from $3d^34s^2$, the most stable configuration of the V atom, to $3d^4$, the most stable configuration of the V^+ ion.

The discussion so far has been concentrated on the difference between the 3d and the 4s electrons in the first transition series. A somewhat similar comparison may be made between the 4d and the 5s electrons in the second transition series, although there will be significant differences, reflecting in particular the lower relative sensitivity of the partly-penetrating 4d electrons to external charge (Chapter 2). In the third transition series

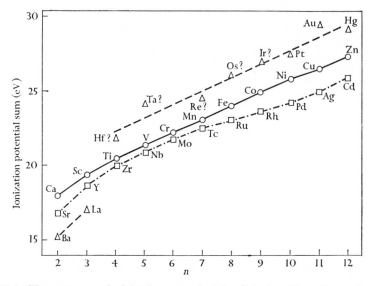

Fig. 23.5. The energy required for the removal of the s^2 electrons from the configuration $d^{n-2}s^2$ as n goes from 2 to 12 in the three transition series.

there is a similar overall relationship between the 5d and the 6s electrons, but there is now a new factor to be taken into account. Between La and Lu the nuclear charge increases by 14, while the 4f electrons enter the inner core.

The separate changes in the ns and $(n-1)d$ binding energies across the three transition series will now be considered.

s ELECTRONS

In Fig. 23.5 are plotted the ionization energies for the removal of the two s electrons from the configurations

$$3d^{n-2}4s^2, \quad 4d^{n-2}5s^2, \quad \text{and} \quad 5d^{n-2}6s^2$$

in the first, second, and third transition series, respectively. Many of the values for the third transition series are only very approximate. For the first transition series all the values correspond to the sum of the first two ionization potentials, except for Cr and Cu where the values plotted are less by the excitation energies $3d^{n-1}4s^1$ to $3d^{n-2}4s^2$. In the second transition series more corrections have to be made to the ionization-potential sums, for $4d^{n-1}5s^1$ is the most stable configuration in the atoms Nb, Mo, Ru, Rh, and Ag, while in Pd it is $4d^{10}$.

In both the first and second transition series there is a gradual increase in the stability of the s electrons across the series, the net result of which is the typical transition from the relatively easy ionization of the IIA metals, Ca and Sr, to the less easy ionization of the IIB metals, Zn and Cd. B-metal character thus tends to increase steadily in the chemistry of the transition elements. In the third transition series the increase in the stability of the $6s^2$ electrons is very marked as a consequence of the nuclear charge increase in the lanthanide series. This increased difficulty of ionization between Ba and Hg is strongly reflected in their comparative chemistry. The order of stability of the s electrons is then third series > first series > second series.

The normal ionization potentials for the atoms of the first transition series are given by the lower broken line in Fig. 23.6. The rather irregular pattern is a consequence of the variety of the ionization processes, e.g. Ti—$3d^24s^2$ to $3d^24s^1$, but V—$3d^34s^2$ to $3d^4$ and Cr—$3d^54s^1$ to $3d^5$, as follows from the relative energies of the configurations plotted in Fig. 23.4. When the ionization potentials of Fig. 23.6 are corrected, where necessary, so as to give a constant change of $3d^{n-2}4s^2$ to $3d^{n-2}4s$, the pattern is more regular. For the continuous line in Fig. 23.6 ionization is taken to the state in which the remaining $4s$ electron has its spin parallel with the majority of the $3d$ electrons (all the $3d$ electrons up to Mn, the half-filled sub-shell), while for the upper broken line its spin is opposed. The rather large differences which can occur as a consequence of spin correlations are thus exemplified by the energy gaps between these two upper lines, and indeed spin-correlation effects are most important within the transition series. Fig. 23.6 also serves to illustrate a rather simple way in which the relative magnitude of spin correlations may be calculated. This starts with the approximate assumption that each pair of electrons with parallel spin may be regarded as contributing a binding 'exchange energy'. This energy arises (Chapter 1) as electron motions are so correlated as to keep electrons out of one another's way, i.e. there is a reduction of *repulsion* between electrons. The total exchange energy is given by a constant, E_{ex}, multiplied by the number of pairs of electrons with parallel spin. Thus of the two spin states considered for Cr $3d^44s^1$, the lower state with all the spins parallel has a total of ten distinct pairs, while the higher state with the $4s$ electron spin opposed to those of the $3d$ will have only six pairs (d_a with d_b, d_c, d_d; d_b with d_c, d_d; d_c with d_d). The difference in energy between the two states, which is the difference between the upper broken line and the continuous line in Fig. 23.6, is then $4E_{ex}$ for Cr. Similarly we expect $5E_{ex}$ for Mn, $4E_{ex}$

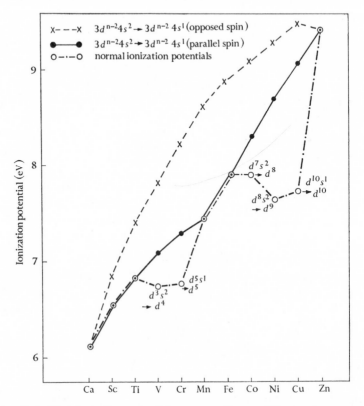

Fig. 23.6. First ionization potentials corresponding to different electron configurations in the atoms and M$^+$ ions of the first transition series.

for Fe, $3E_{ex}$ for V and Co, $2E_{ex}$ for Ti and Ni, $1E_{ex}$ for Sc and Cu, and zero for Ca and Zn. The experimental values fit reasonably well with a value of E_{ex} of 0·25 eV as is shown in Fig. 23.7.

The values of electron–electron repulsions have been calculated considering spin–spin interaction only. Within a configuration d^n both changes of spin and changes of angular momentum are possible. States of different values of L are also of different energy. The total electron–electron repulsion energy of each LS state arising from a d^n configuration can be calculated and expressed in terms of so-called Racah parameters. It is this energy which is responsible for the observed d^n configuration and the difficulty of raising an ion to the configuration most obviously suitable for bond formation. The Racah parameters are particularly convenient for expressing the energy differences between states of the gas ion of maximum multiplicity, for these are multiples of one parameter B only. Differences between other states and the ground state are expressed as sums of mB and nC. For a change from high spin to low spin the repulsion energies are greatest at d^5 for similar reasons to those leading to Fig. 23.7. See Orgel, *An Introduction to Transition-Metal Chemistry*, Methuen, London, 1960.

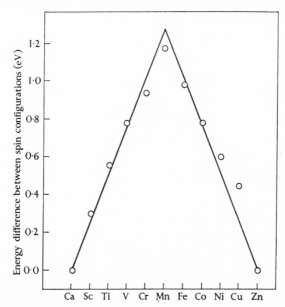

FIG. 23.7. The differences in energy between the (lowest) states in which the $4s$ electron spin is opposed to and the (lowest) states in which it is parallel to the net spin of the $3d$ electrons for the M$^+$ ions $(3d^{n-2}4s^1)$.

d ELECTRONS

The energies required to remove a d electron are compared across the three transition series in Fig. 23.8. For this purpose the change

$$d^{n-1} \quad \text{to} \quad d^{n-2},$$

in which an electron is ionized from the singly-charged transition-metal ion has been used. For many transition metals this is the normal second ionization potential. It will be seen that the binding energy of the d electrons increase steadily across each series, with a distinct break after the half-filled d sub-shell, when the electrons are being taken from orbitals containing two d electrons. The repulsion between two d electrons in the same orbital is particularly marked as a result of the rather highly directed properties of d orbitals. For the larger $4d$ and $5d$ orbitals the break is less pronounced, so that the pairing of electrons into the same orbital is energetically less unfavourable in the second and third transition series than it is

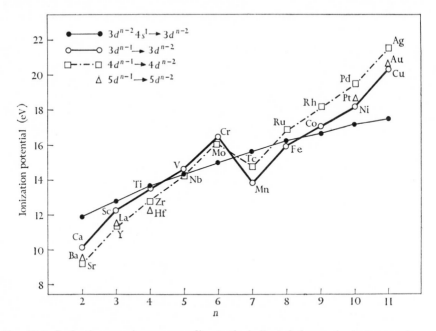

Fig. 23.8. Ionization energies corresponding to the indicated changes in electron configuration. Note the difference between $n = 6$ and $n = 7$ in the spin-pairing energy for the first and second transition series.

in the first. This is an important factor in the formation of spin-paired complexes. In the second half of the second transition series the $4d$ electrons are held more firmly than are the $3d$ in the corresponding members of the first transition series. On the other hand the reverse is true for the s electrons. This provides an explanation for such observations as the ready divalence of Cu as compared with Ag. However, on the formation of high-valence ions the $4d$ electrons will become less stable than the $3d$, as the latter are more sensitive to external charge. Thus in the second transition series both low valence and high valence can be stabilized with respect to the first transition series.

For the third transition series the data are again rather meagre, but there appears to be a relative *lowering* of binding energy of the $5d$ compared with $4d$ as a consequence of the filling up of the lanthanide series. Thus d

electrons are less stable in Hf than in Zr, and in Pt and Au than in Pd and Ag respectively. This effect of the filled $4f$ sub-shell on the $5d$ electrons is confirmed by the study of X-ray spectra. The relative increase of stability of the $4d$ in Pd, and the $6s$ in Pt leads to a curious similarity in the *sum* of the first two ionization potentials of Pd (27·75 eV) and Pt (27·6 eV),

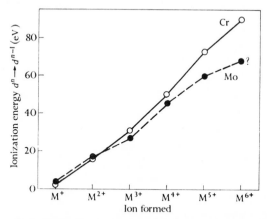

FIG. 23.9. Successive ionization of d electrons in Cr and Mo.

while for Ni the sum is *significantly* less (25·78 eV). There are thus many more similarities between divalent Pd and Pt (section 25.7) than between either of them and divalent Ni.

For comparison, the ionization energies for M^+ to M^{2+} corresponding to the change of configuration

$$3d^{n-2}4s^1 \quad \text{to} \quad 3d^{n-2}$$

(taking the state which has the $4s^1$ electron with its spin parallel to the majority of the d electrons) are also plotted in Fig. 23.8. The relatively greater increase in stability of the $3d$ as against the $4s$ across the first transition series is thus further demonstrated.

Fig. 23.9 shows how charge affects the energy of d electrons. The example given is for the Group VIA elements, Cr and Mo, and the energies are calculated for states of maximum spin. Not only does the energy to remove the d electron increase with charge, but the rate of increase with charge is much faster than that for either s or p electrons (see Chapter 2). Fig. 23.9 also shows that while it is relatively harder to remove the first d electrons of the second element in the Group it is relatively easier to remove the later ones.

SUMMARY

In the rest of this chapter and in Chapters 23 to 29 we shall discuss the chemistry of transition metals. Since one of our objects will be to look for relationships between atomic structure and chemical properties, it is convenient at this point to summarize those features of atomic structure which will be most important in our discussion of transition-metal chemistry.

(1) The binding energies of ns, np, and $(n-1)d$ electrons increase with atomic number across each transition series, except for d electrons immediately following the half-filled sub-shell.

(2) This rate of increase of electron binding energy is greater for $(n-1)d$ than for ns (and also for ns than for np) electrons.

(3) With increase of charge, $(n-1)d$ electrons become more stable relative to ns electrons. The increase of ionization potential with charge is greatest for an element in the first transition series, and is least for one in the third transition series.

(4) Two electron configurations may often be of similar energy for an atom (or ion with low charge), so that the exact configuration need not be of great thermodynamic interest.

(5) Spin-pairing energies decrease from the first to the second and third transition series.

(6) Especially at high charge and at the end of the transition series the contraction of the $(n-1)d$ orbitals may lead to the $(n-1)d$ orbitals and the electrons in them behaving as part of the core.

(7) The radial distribution functions of the ns (and np) electrons are such as to give good overlap with wave functions of neighbouring atoms at all values of atomic number and charge. The effective overlap of $(n-1)d$ electron wave functions, however, will be very dependent upon charge as well as atomic number.

PART B

23.3. Ionic valence in the first transition series

In the discussion of the pre-transition metals, especially section 20.3, it was shown that, in most of their compounds with non-metals, these metals could be considered as losing all their electrons outside the previous noble-gas structure. In general this pattern would seem to be observed whenever groups of outer electrons have essentially the same energy. If it is worth while, in terms of the balance between ionization energy and chemical energy, to pull out one electron, it is worth while to pull out the lot. In the transition elements this pattern of behaviour is also observed in those circumstances where ns and $(n-1)d$ electrons are similar in energy. This will occur at the beginning of each transition series. Thus Sc, Y, and La are uniformly trivalent in their 'ionic' compounds. However, this behaviour will become less common on passing across any transition series since the d electrons become part of the atomic core. Thus Sc(III), Ti(IV), V(V), Cr(VI), and Mn(VII) represent a series of increasing oxidizing power, while there is no evidence for 8-valent Fe, or for any valence state of Cu higher than 3. The distinction between s and $(n-1)d$ at high charge on an atom becomes smaller again on passing from the first transition series to the second and third transition series. The $3d$ electrons are non-penetrating, while the $4d$ and $5d$ are progressively more penetrating. Thus high valences become more stable in the second and especially in the third transition series than they are in the first. This is exactly parallel to the change between the lanthanide and the actinide series. The tendency to pull out electrons to leave behind a constant charge, which was the main characteristic of the lanthanides, is also present in the first transition series. It is less marked, as the sensitivity to increase of charge external to the inner electron shells will be less for the $3d$ than for the $4f$. The divalent state is very stable in the elements following Mn, viz. Fe, Co, Ni, Cu, and Zn. In many ways there is a better parallel between the first transition series and the actinide series, where the *tri*valent state becomes common from about the mid-point, Cm, onwards.

It will be seen that the transition elements show valence characteristics which are, in some ways, intermediate between the simple noble-gas configuration pattern of the pre-transition elements and the simple constant-charge pattern of the lanthanide elements. In addition there is a complication which may be largely neglected in the pre-transition and lanthanide elements, but which will become important here and also in our discussion of B-metal valences. This is that a transition-metal ion cannot be regarded as a simple sphere interacting only electrostatically with its environment. The theory of the ligand field is fairly complex, and is taken up in the next chapter. Before this, however, a simple overall account of transition-metal valence states will be given, starting with the simple ionic hydration model and following the pattern used in the pre-transition and lanthanide series. This approximation is a radical one, but it will help to show the essential link between the atomic structures and the chemistry of the transition elements, before complicating features are introduced.

TABLE 23.I. *Estimation of some volt equivalent (VE) values*

Ion	Ionization energy (sublimation energy + sum of ionization potentials)	'Hydration' energy $\left(-\dfrac{7\cdot3z^2}{r+0\cdot85}-4\cdot7z\right)$	Estimated volt equivalent (Fig. 23.10)	Experimental volt equivalent (Fig. 23.11)
K^+	5·3	−8·1	−2·8	−2·9
Ca^+	8·1	−8·0	+0·1	..
Ca^{2+}	20·0	−25·3	−5·3	−5·7
Sc^+	10·6	−8·2	+2·4	..
Sc^{2+}	23·4	−25·3	−1·9	..
Sc^{3+}	48·1	−53·7	−5·6	−6·2
Ti^+	11·7	−8·3	+3·4	..
Ti^{2+}	25·3	−26·1	−0·8	−3·3
Ti^{3+}	52·8	−54·9	−2·1	−3·6
Ti^{4+}	96·0	−95·1	+0·9	−3·5

(For basis of calculation see section 20.3.)

ESTIMATED OXIDATION STATE DIAGRAM FOR THE FIRST TRANSI-
TION SERIES

The general method of calculation has been described in section 20.3.
Values for ionic radii have again been taken from Pauling, and those for
the monovalent ions between K^+ and Cu^+ have been assumed to fall
steadily across the transition series as do the Pauling radii for M^{2+} and M^{3+}.
Some of the numerical results are given in Table 23.1. Fig. 23.10 gives the
estimated Oxidation State Diagram for the lower oxidation states of the
first transition series. The experimental VE values are plotted in Fig. 23.11.
It will be seen that there is a general overall similarity between the
estimated and experimental plots. The following points may be made by
comparing the two figures.

(1) Across the transition series there is on the whole a gradual decrease
in the stability of any given oxidation state relative to the metal. The most
marked exceptions are Zn^{2+} and Mn^{2+}. The estimated values are based
on the difference between the ionization energy and the chemical or hydration energy. The ionization energy is a sum of ionization potentials, which
rise fairly uniformly along the series, and sublimation energy, which rises
in general to the middle of the series and falls to the end. The chemical
energy rises steadily through the transition series as the ions contract.
Both the ionization potentials and the ionic contraction are, of course,
parallel results of the continuous increase in nuclear charge, but the change
in ionization potential is more marked than the change in the hydration
energy. Thus if we compare Ca^{2+} and Ni^{2+}, the ionization-potential sum
(first plus second ionization potential) rises by 7·8 eV from 17·98 eV, while
the estimated hydration energy only rises by 2·7 eV from 25·3 to 28·0 eV.
In this case the metal binding energy is 2·4 eV greater in Ni than in Ca.
In general as here the dominating factor in all the calculations is the change
in the ionization potentials. The change in hydration energies tends merely
to reduce the general change in ionization potentials, while the sublimation
energy changes are relatively unimportant especially when considering the
higher oxidation states.

(2) The decrease in stability of a given oxidation state is most marked
in general the higher the oxidation state. The higher oxidation states
correspond to removal of a larger number of d electrons, which are becoming
more stable across the series. A relatively simple case is provided by the
M^{3+}/M^{2+} redox couple. We shall discuss this particular couple in much
more detail in sections 26.8 and 26.9.

(3) The 1-valent ionic state is predicted to be unstable in all cases except

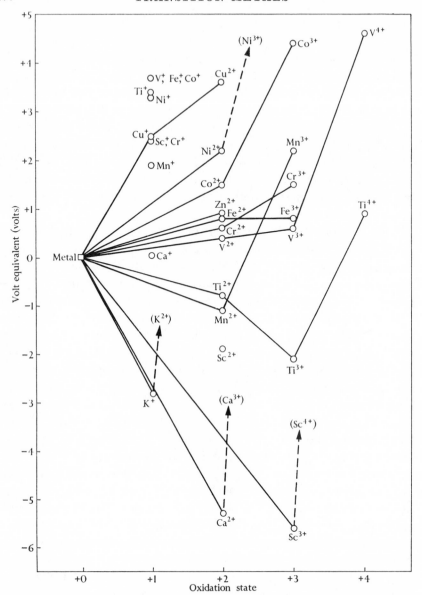

FIG. 23.10. Estimated Oxidation State Diagram for the elements of the first transition
series.

K$^+$. This agrees exactly with the experimental observations: the only
other monovalent ion found is Cu$^+$, which in the absence of complexing
ligands disproportionates into Cu metal and Cu^{2+}. One of the main features

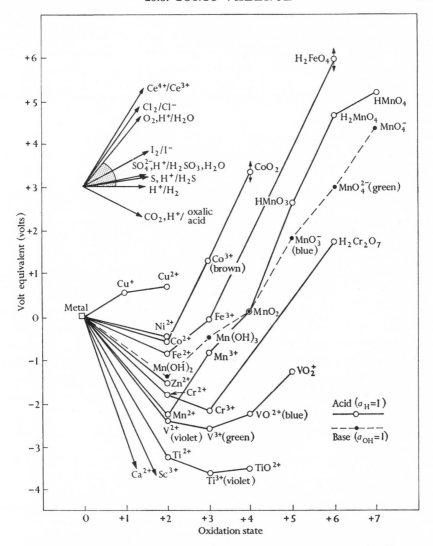

FIG. 23.11. Experimental Oxidation State Diagram for the first transition series. (Although this diagram is plotted with reference to the standard hydrogen couple, the stability of various oxidation states as observed in normal laboratory practice is more closely linked to the values of potentials referred to the standard oxygen couple; see inset, upper left-hand corner.)

militating against monovalent ions is the relatively large sublimation energy for a typical transition metal. This is very significant when both the ionization-potential sum and the hydration energy are low, as they will be for singly-charged ions. Thus the sublimation energy of Fe is 4·30 eV, and its first ionization potential is 7·90 eV. Assuming a radius of 1·07 Å the estimated hydration energy is 8·5 eV, so that the volt equivalent for Fe^+ is estimated as $+3\cdot7$ volts. For Fe^{3+} the sum of the first three ionization potentials has risen to 54·72 eV, and the hydration energy, taking the radius of Fe^{3+} as 0·64 Å, to 58·2 eV. The sublimation energy is now a relatively minor term in the final calculation to give the volt equivalent of Fe^{3+} as $+0\cdot8$ volts.

(4) As stated in (1) the regular trend in the 2-valent ions is broken at Mn^{2+} and Zn^{2+}, which are more stable than would be expected from a simple interpolation or extrapolation. In the estimated plot Mn^{2+} lies about 2 volts too low. This may be attributed in about equal shares to the rather low sublimation energy of Mn, 2·95 eV as against 4·08 eV for Cr and 4·30 eV for Fe, and to the low second ionization potential of Mn, 15·64 as compared with Cr 16·49 eV. Similar considerations account for the case of Zn^{2+}.

(5) The Pauling crystal radii for divalent and trivalent ions of the first transition series decrease fairly steadily across the series, corresponding to the continuous increase in nuclear charge. Somewhat better agreement between experiment and calculation is obtained if radii derived from oxide lattices are used. They show a very rapid contraction at the beginning of the divalent series following Ca^{2+}, but a much smaller effect in the trivalent series following Sc^{3+}. This trend in ionic size may be associated with the ligand-field effects which are discussed in the next chapter, and which must give rise to extra binding energy (chemical energy) in those cases where particularly small radii are found.

TABLE 23.II. *Differences between estimated and experimental volt-equivalent values*

Number of d electrons	0	1	2	3	4	5
Ion	Ca^{2+}	..	Ti^{2+}	V^{2+}	Cr^{2+}	Mn^{2+}
VE (estimated — experimental) volts .	0·4	..	2·5	2·8	2·4	1·2
Ion	Sc^{3+}	Ti^{3+}	V^{3+}	Cr^{3+}	Mn^{3+}	Fe^{3+}
VE (estimated — experimental) volts .	0·6	1·5	3·2	3·7	3·0	0·9

Number of d electrons .	5	6	7	8	9	10
Ion	Mn^{2+}	Fe^{2+}	Co^{2+}	Ni^{2+}	Cu^{2+}	Zn^{2+}
VE (estimated — experimental) volts .	1·2	1·7	2·0	2·7	2·9	2·4
Ion	Fe^{3+}	Co^{3+}	..	..	..	Ga^{3+}
VE (estimated — experimental) volts .	0·9	3·1	..	..	..	2·9

Alternatively the differences between the estimated values (using Pauling radii) and the experimental volt equivalents may be used to *suggest* where such extra binding energy exists. These differences, which are all positive corresponding to a greater experimental hydration energy than estimated, are given in Table 23.II, the main feature of which is the rather large disparity found for d^1, d^2, d^3, and d^4 ions when compared with d^0 and d^5 ions. The significance of this feature will be brought out in the next chapter.

In conclusion it is apparent that the ionic model used provides a reasonable approximate account of the Oxidation State Diagram of the first transition series. The next section will consider Fig. 23.11 in detail, emphasizing its *experimental* significance.

23.4. Experimental Oxidation State Diagram for the first transition series

The experimental Oxidation State Diagram for the elements of the first transition series is given in Fig. 23.11 (see Chapter 9 for a detailed explanation of this type of diagram). All the values are based on the standard hydrogen electrode, and are plotted only for acid solutions ($a_H = 1$), except in the case of manganese where the alkaline solution values ($a_{OH} = 1$) are also given.

Apart from Cu^+ the oxidation state $+1$ is too unstable to be observed in simple compounds. Otherwise the general trend along the series is for decreased ease of oxidation of the metal, or of a lower oxidation state to a higher oxidation state. The immediate consequence of this change is that compounds of the later transition metals provide very powerful oxidizing agents. Thus permanganate will oxidize chromium and its compounds to chromate, chromate will oxidize vanadium and its compounds to vanadate, while vanadate will oxidize titanium and its compounds to titanium dioxide or titanate. The hydrated Co^{3+} ion, ferrates ($Fe(VI)$), and permanganate all evolve oxygen from aqueous solution, although the last only slowly, so that it is commonly employed as a volumetric reagent.

For each of the transition elements from Ti to Co, the plots in Fig. 23.11 are decidedly curved with minima in the $+2$ and $+3$ oxidation states. These states are therefore formed by chemical reaction between the higher and lower oxidation states. Cu^+ is the only example of a simple hydrated monovalent ion, and even this is unstable with respect to disproportionation into Cu^{2+} and Cu metal. The monovalent ions of the other metals are presumably even more unstable with respect to such disproportionation (cf. Fig. 23.10). Cu^+ has, however, strong complexing properties with polarizable ligands (see section 32.2), so that it may be stabilized if these are present. Kinetically-stable low oxidation states of the transition metals, which usually, however, occur mainly in non-aqueous systems, will be described in Chapter 27.

Oxidation State Diagrams are of both analytical and preparative interest. The chemistry of manganese is particularly instructive. Figure 23.11 shows that permanganate will liberate chlorine from hydrochloric acid solutions, although in practice it does so only slowly. Permanganate cannot therefore be used directly to titrate Fe^{2+} produced by the dissolution of iron in HCl. However, by the addition of Mn^{2+} ion, the oxidizing potential of the MnO_4^-, H^+/Mn^{2+}, H_2O couple can be reduced sufficiently to prevent the oxidation of chloride ion. In such circumstances incomplete oxidation of Fe^{2+} ions could occur. The reducing power of the Fe^{3+}/Fe^{2+} couple is therefore increased by the simultaneous addition of phosphate which complexes strongly with the Fe^{3+} ion (Zimmerman–Reinhardt's method). Just as with other elements in their highest oxidation states, e.g. chlorine as perchloric acid, the highest oxidation state of manganese frequently oxidizes only slowly. A well-known example is in the titration of oxalic acid. Examination of the potentials shows that this is thermodynamically a very highly favoured reaction. On the other hand, although I_2/I^- is a much weaker reducing couple, iodides are oxidized virtually instantaneously by permanganate. Manganese(III) sulphate (Mn^{3+}/Mn^{2+}) is an oxidizing agent of very similar potential to permanganate.

Less powerful reagents can be obtained either from the high-valence states of earlier elements or from the lower-valence states of later elements (see Fig. 23.11). Thus dichromate ($Cr_2O_7^{2-}/Cr^{3+}$) is distinctly weaker than permanganate. Potassium dichromate is a primary volumetric standard, and may be used directly for oxidations in chloride media. The oxidizing action of other couples in the series are familiar, e.g. from the reactions which occur in the traditional methods of qualitative analysis. Thus on passing H_2S through an acid solution, vanadates are reduced to the pale blue vanadyl (VO^{2+}) and then further to V^{3+}, chromates to Cr^{3+}, and Fe^{3+} to Fe^{2+}, in each case with the precipitation of sulphur. With a stronger reducing agent (e.g. amalgamated zinc, the Jones Reductor), Ti^{3+} (Ti^{2+} liberates hydrogen rapidly in acid solution), Cr^{2+}, and V^{2+} are quantitatively produced, so that their reoxidation with Fe^{3+} to Ti^{4+}, Cr^{3+}, and V^{4+} can be used for the estimation of these metals in solution. V^{4+} is slowly but quantitatively oxidized with $KMnO_4$ to V^{5+}.

A well-known example of the use of the lowest oxidation states in analysis is the quantitative oxidation of iodide by copper(II)

$$2Cu^{2+} + 4I^- \rightarrow 2CuI + I_2$$

The reaction takes place in the direction of the arrow, despite the fact that (see Fig. 23.11) I_2/I^- is a stronger oxidizing couple than the simple hydrated Cu^{2+}/Cu^+ couple: copper(I) iodide is insoluble.

Each of the couples M^{2+}/metal can clearly function as a reducing agent, although copper is less reducing than H_2. Cu in fact does not dissolve in acids, except to a minute extent, unless the acid is also an oxidizing agent, e.g. nitric acid. While it will dissolve as Cu^+ ion to give a concentration of only about 10^{-9} g ion per litre, addition of reagents which will complex with the Cu^+ ion can lead to ready solution. Thus in the presence of thiourea copper dissolves in normal HCl with a brisk evolution of hydrogen. The rate of dissolution of the metal can be quite slow, partly because of the high binding energy of the metal, but particularly because of the formation of protective films, e.g. of oxides.

As would be expected from Fig. 23.11, Ti^{2+}, V^{2+}, and Cr^{2+} all liberate hydrogen in acidic aqueous solutions. The couple Co^{3+}/Co^{2+}, which normally liberates oxygen, can be made to liberate hydrogen in the presence of cyanide ion, so great is the change of redox potential as a result of the strong complexing of the Co^{3+} ion with cyanide (see section 26.9). The following aquo-ions, in decreasing order of reducing power, have all been used as reducing agents in volumetric analysis: Cr^{2+}, V^{2+}, Ti^{3+}, and Fe^{2+}.

For each metal the lower oxidation states are basic, the oxidation state $+4$ is usually amphoteric, while the higher oxidation states, where they exist, are acidic. Thus the lower oxidation states are relatively more stable in acid solution, the higher oxidation states in alkaline solution. MnO_2 has the same VE value in acid or alkaline solution. The dibasic manganic acid is particularly stabilized in alkaline solution, and titrations with alkaline permanganate may be stopped at this stage or at MnO_2. In the presence of Ba^{2+} ions, which combine with MnO_4^{2-} to give the very insoluble $BaMnO_4$ (compare $BaSO_4$), the alkaline couple MnO_4^-/MnO_4^{2-} becomes an extremely powerful oxidizing agent. The potentials show that oxygen is just not quite powerful enough to oxidize MnO_2 to MnO_4^{2-} at $a_{OH} = 1$, but the reaction goes readily in fused KOH, as in the preparation of $KMnO_4$, when the manganate formed is then disproportionated in acid solution. Mn^{3+} is also unstable with respect to disproportionation, but it may be stabilized by F^- or PO_4^{3-}. Thus K_2MnF_5 may be prepared conveniently by the action of permanganate on Mn^{2+} in acid solution in the presence of fluoride ion.

HEATS OF FORMATION

While the above discussion has been centred on aqueous solution species, analogous results would have been obtained using lattice-energy arguments

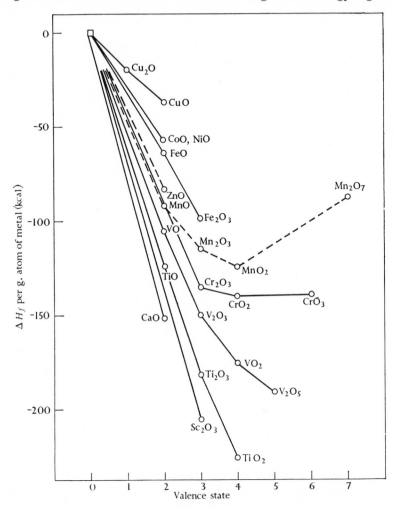

FIG. 23.12. Heats of formation of oxides in different valence states for metals of the first transition series. Broken lines are used for Zn and Mn to emphasize that ZnO and MnO are out of sequence.

to predict and correlate data on heats of formation. The experimental heats of formation of oxides in the first transition series are plotted in Fig. 23.12 in such a manner as to bring out their relationship with the oxidation-potential data plotted in Fig. 23.11.

23.5. A comparison of the three transition series

ATOMIC STRUCTURE AND VALENCE

As already noted, the sensitivity of the d electrons to charge on an atom is much less marked for the partly-penetrating $4d$ and $5d$ orbitals of the second and third transition series than it is for the non-penetrating $3d$ orbitals of the first series. This was illustrated in Fig. 23.9 by the successive ionization potentials for the removal of d electrons. It should therefore be relatively easier to achieve high-valence states in the second, and even more so in the third, transition series than it is in the first. As an illustration of this very general distinction, Table 23.III gives the highest valence states achieved with various non-metals for some typical members of the first and of the third transition series.

TABLE 23.III. *Highest valence states in the first and third transition series*

Transition metal	Fluorides	Chlorides	Iodides	Oxides	Sulphides
V	5	4	3	5	4
Ta	5	5	5	5	5
Cr	5	3	3	6	3
W	6	6	4	6	6
Mn	4	4	2	7	3
Re	7	6	4	7	7
Co	(4)	2	2	(4)	2
Ir	6	4	3	6	6
Ni	(4)	2	2	(4)	2
Pt	6	4	4	4	4

Although the most marked distinction between the first and the second and third transition series is the relative stability of higher-valence states in the latter, it is also possible for very low valence states to be somewhat stabilized in parts of the second transition series as compared with the first. This arises largely as a consequence of the fact that in the uncharged (or singly-charged) atom the d electron is harder to remove in the second transition series. The second ionization potentials of Cu and Ag, for example, are 20·29 and 21·48 eV respectively (in each case d^{10} to d^9). The low-valence states are particularly stable late in the transition series and bigger differences between the lower ionization potentials are found here than earlier in the series.

We shall now illustrate the effects of these ionization potentials upon the estimated Oxidation State Diagrams of the elements in Group IVA.

GROUP IVA AND GROUP VIIA

Estimated and *experimental* volt equivalents for Ti, Zr, and Hf are plotted in Fig. 23.13. There is general agreement between the two sets. The data for Hf, as for all the members of the third transition series, are very sparse, but this Group provides the best opportunity for a comparison.

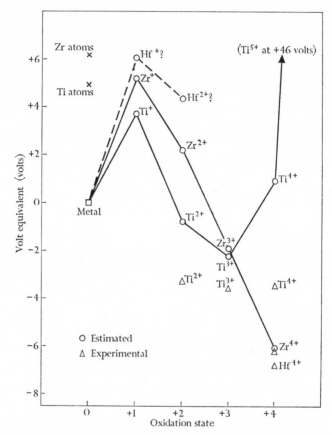

FIG. 23.13. Comparison of the Oxidation State Diagrams for the elements of Group IVA. The lines join estimated values only.

The sublimation energy of Hf is uncertain, and has been assumed equal to that of Zr on the ground that the sublimation energies of Nb and Ta in the next Group are virtually the same. For the first Hf ionization potential 7·8 volts has been taken and for the second 15 volts; both values are quoted as 'estimated'. For Ti and Zr, however, the data are good. Fig. 23.13 should also be compared with Fig. 23.14 which gives the *experimental* data for Mn, Tc, and Re, but for which, unfortunately, good data for making calculations do not exist.

In both figures it will be seen that the lower states are relatively more stable and the higher states relatively less stable in the first transition

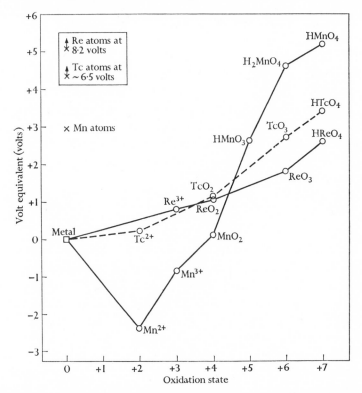

FIG. 23.14. Experimental Oxidation State Diagram for the elements of Group VIIA.

series. In the 1-valent state the extra stability of Ti over Zr in the estimated values arises largely from the higher sublimation energy for Zr. In the 2-valent state the smaller size of the Ti ions also begins to make a substantial contribution. The first and second ionization potentials of Ti and Zr are almost identical. In Hf the higher ionization potentials (first and second) also help to make Hf^+ and Hf^{2+} even more unstable relative to the metal. These high ionization potentials for removal of $6s$ electrons are, of course, associated with the increase of nuclear charge which has taken place in the preceding lanthanide series. For the high-valence states the pattern becomes completely reversed. The differences in the estimated values between Ti and Zr are directly related to the very much sharper increase of ionization potential with charge characteristic of $3d$ as against $4d$ electrons. Thus the fourth ionization potential of Ti is 8·91 volts greater than that for Zr. There are no values for the higher ionization potentials of the third transition series, but it is reasonable to suppose that they rise even less rapidly with charge than they do in the second transition series. In this way the relatively high stability of Hf^{4+} can be understood.

The effect of the metal binding energies may be demonstrated by plotting points for the metallic atoms at oxidation state zero, and at distances above the metal point equivalent to the sublimation energy of the metal. This has been done in Fig. 23.13 for Ti and Zr, and in Fig. 23.14 for Mn, Tc, and Re. In effect metal–metal bonding stabilizes the *zero* oxidation state, and thus makes it easier for low oxidation states to disproportionate. Some metal–metal bonding also occurs in positive oxidation states. In general it would be expected to decrease with increase in the real charge on the metal atoms.

OXIDATION STATE DIAGRAMS FOR THE SECOND AND THIRD TRANSITION SERIES

The experimental Oxidation State Diagrams for the second and third transition series are given in Figs. 23.15 and 23.16 respectively. A comparison between these figures and Fig. 23.11 further emphasizes the general distinctions brought out in Fig. 23.14 for Group VIIA. Along each series there is a general decrease in the electropositive character of the metal, as measured by the ease with which it is oxidized. The second and third series are rather similar to one another and are distinguished from the first by the greater stability of their higher oxidation states. Many of the lower oxidation states of the second and third series do not exist as simple ionic species: this presumably (see Fig. 23.13) is due, in part, to the greater stability of the higher oxidation states and, in part, to the greater binding energies of the metals, i.e. a greater stability of the zero oxidation state. One consequence of this is that the irregularity associated with the half-filled sub-shell (see relative positions of Cr^{2+} and Mn^{2+} in Fig. 23.11) is no longer apparent, although the irregularity associated with the filled d sub-shell still occurs. Thus the regular gradations across the series are broken between Ag and Cd, and to a lesser extent between Au and Hg. This distinction between the second and the third transition series must be attributed to the greater stability of the s electrons in the latter.

The oxides of the second and third transition series are much less acidic than those of the first, so that potentials are less altered on changing from

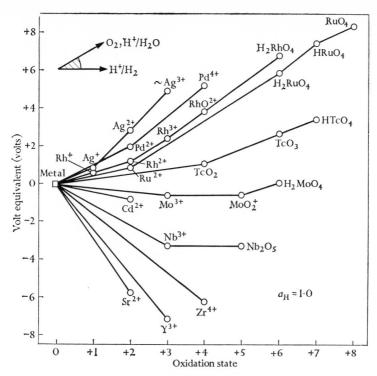

Fig. 23.15. Experimental Oxidation State Diagram for the metals of the second transition series.

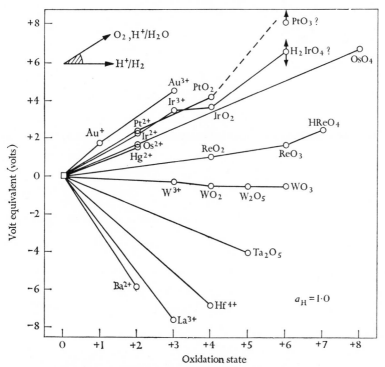

Fig. 23.16. Experimental Oxidation State Diagram for the metals of the third transition series.

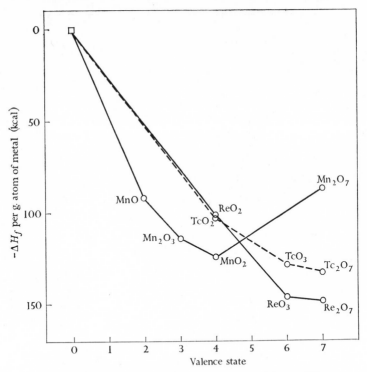

FIG. 23.17. Heats of formation of the oxides of Group VIIA.

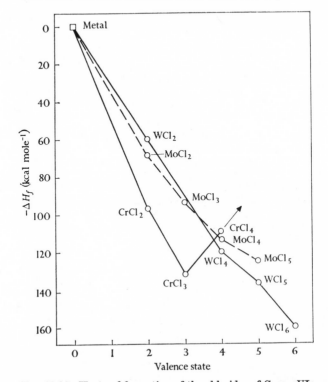

FIG. 23.18. Heats of formation of the chlorides of Group VIA.

acidic to alkaline solutions. The discussion of oxide solutions of the heavy metals is, however, much confused by the considerable polymerization which occurs (see Chapter 14).

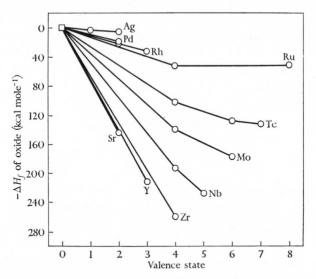

FIG. 23.19. Heats of formation of oxides per gram atom of metal for metals of the second transition series.

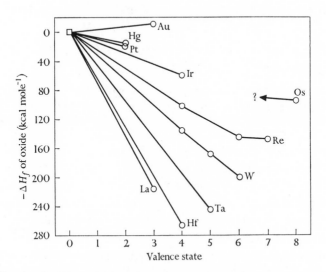

FIG. 23.20. Heats of formation of oxides per gram atom of metal for metals of the third transition series.

HEATS OF FORMATION

Once again the heats of formation illustrate the same general trends as are found in the Oxidation State Diagrams. Heats of formation of Group VIIA oxides (cf. Fig. 23.14) are plotted in Fig. 23.17, and of Group VIA chlorides in Fig. 23.18. The heats of formation of oxides of the second (Fig. 23.19) and third (Fig. 23.20) transition series are also plotted so as to bring out the relationship with the Oxidation State Diagrams (Figs. 23.15 and 23.16 respectively).

The effects of ligands other than water and oxide on redox potentials will be discussed in some detail in Chapter 26, Part B.

Problems

SECTION A

1. Compare and contrast the role of d electrons in the transition series with that of f electrons in the lanthanide and actinide series.

2. Calculate the effective principal quantum numbers (see section 21.2) for ns and $(n-1)d$ electrons in some atoms and ions of elements in the second and third transition series. Comment on your results and their relation to Fig. 21.2. (Data for these calculations are best obtained from Moore, *Atomic Energy Levels*, but there is sufficient information provided in the various figures of this chapter.)

3. Account for the following sequence of first ionization potentials:
$$Zn \gg Fe \simeq Co > Cu > Ni > Mn.$$

4. The action of chlorine on the elements gives $CrCl_3$, $MoCl_5$, WCl_6, UCl_4 (and UCl_5). Comment.

5. How may we account for the fact that while Cu^{2+} is the most stable ion of Cu (at least in normal aqueous solutions), Ag^+ is the most stable ion of Ag?

6. Comment on the following:

(a) The permanganate/manganate couple is very strongly oxidizing in alkaline solutions in the presence of Ba^{2+} ions, even oxidizing iodate to periodate.

(b) Dichromate may be used as a primary volumetric standard but permanganate may not.

(c) If oxygen is prepared by heating solid potassium permanganate, it will usually be found to contain small quantities of CO_2.

(d) $KMnO_4$ is coloured but $KReO_4$ is not.

7. Ferrate(VI) ion is relatively stable in alkaline solution, but decomposes to O_2 and Fe(III) in neutral or acidic solutions. Comment.

8. Copper metal will dissolve in KCN solution with the evolution of hydrogen. When excess KCN solution is added to $CuSO_4$ solution, cyanogen gas is liberated, and the solution remaining will not precipitate CuS on passage of H_2S. Suggest an explanation for these observations.

9. By use of the Oxidation State Diagram (Fig. 23.11) show how Fe^{2+} will only reduce vanadate to the blue VO^{2+}, while metallic Zn will reduce it further via the green V^{3+} state to the deep violet V^{2+}.

10. Compare the potentials for the M^{2+}/M couples from Ti to Cu. Comment on the general trend, and account for any irregularity.

11. Permanganate reacts quantitatively with oxalic acid solution, but the reaction requires warming. With HI it reacts instantaneously and quantitatively to give iodine but not iodate. Comment.

12. Suggest a possible explanation for the occurrence of chromyl chloride and fluoride (CrO_2X_2), but not of chromyl bromide and iodide.

13. Which would you expect to be the most powerful:
    (a) Ti(III), V(II), or Cr(II) as a reducing agent,
    (b) Cr(VI) or Mn(VII) as an oxidizing agent?

14. Comment on the fact that Mn^{2+} is a poorer *oxidizing* agent than either Cr^{2+} or Fe^{2+}.

15. In the preparation of potassium permanganate, K_2MnO_4 is first prepared by fusing MnO_2 with KOH and KNO_3. The solidified green melt is then treated with dilute sulphuric acid to give a solution of $KMnO_4$ and a precipitate of MnO_2. Comment.

16. At 25 °C the potential of the redox couple Cu^+/Cu is $+0\cdot521$ volts in acid solution. Show that in the presence of one atmosphere of hydrogen the concentration of Cu^+ ions in an N solution of a non-oxidizing acid in equilibrium with copper metal should be about 10^{-9} molar.

Estimate the equilibrium constant for the reaction

$$Cu^{2+}+Cu \rightleftharpoons 2Cu^+$$

if the potential of the redox couple Cu^{2+}/Cu is $+0\cdot337$ volts.

17. What are the relative advantages and disadvantages of permanganate and dichromate as volumetric oxidizing agents?

18. Can you provide an explanation for the general trends observed in the Oxidation State Diagram (Fig. 23.11), e.g. from Ca across the first transition series of elements to Zn?

19. Can you account for the general behaviour of the elements of the first transition series as observed in the course of traditional qualitative analysis procedures? (See Chapter 34.)

20. The following are standard potentials for 1 molar sulphuric acid at $25°$: V(IV)/V(III) $+0·35$, I_2/I^- $+0·54$, V(V)/V(IV) $+1·00$, Ce(IV)/Ce(III) $+1·45$, Fe(III) *ortho*-phenanthroline complex/Fe(II) *ortho*-phenanthroline complex $+1·10$ volts. Discuss whether iodine is able to oxidize V(III) ions quantitatively in acid solution. Under what conditions would you expect Fe(II) *o*-phenanthroline to be a suitable indicator for the accurate titration of V(IV) with Ce(IV) solutions?

21. An acid vanadate solution containing $0·01698$ g of V was passed through a column of amalgamated Zn (Jones's reductor) and into an excess of iron(III) alum. The resulting solution was titrated with standard $N/10$ $KMnO_4$ and required 10 ml to produce a permanent pink colour. To what valence state was the V reduced by the Jones's reductor (see e.g. Fig. 23.11), and what do you think is the point of using the Fe^{2+} ion as an intermediate in this procedure? (The atomic weight of V is $50·95$.)

22. The same results as in Question 21 are obtained using a chromate solution containing $0·01300$ g of Cr, and with a molybdate solution containing $0·03198$ g of Mo. With uranium the procedure is slightly changed; the Fe^{2+} ion is not used and the solution after passage through the reductor has a stream of air bubbled through it for a few minutes before titration with permanganate. For a U(VI) solution containing $0·1190$ g of U, 10 ml of $N/10$ $KMnO_4$ are again required, but if the air-bubbling stage is omitted, then somewhat larger and variable amounts of $KMnO_4$ are required. Comment. (Atomic weights: Cr, $52·01$; Mo, $95·95$; U, $238·08$.)

23. Comment on the following sequence of redox potentials, Cr^{3+}/Cr^{2+} $= -0·4$, $Co^{3+}/Co^{2+} = +1·8$, $Rh^{3+}/Rh^{2+} = +1·2$ volts, valid for aqueous acidic solutions at $25°$. What can you say about the possible occurrence of aqueous ions of Mo^{2+} and W^{2+}?

24. Compounds analogous to RuF_6, PtF_6, WCl_6, RuO_4, and OsO_4 do not exist for the corresponding metals of the first transition series. How may this distinction be understood?

25. The action of oxygen on Mn, Tc, and Re gives Mn_3O_4, Tc_2O_7, and

Re_2O_7 respectively. Reaction of Re with fluorine, chlorine, and bromine gives ReF_7, $ReCl_6$, and $ReBr_3$ respectively. Comment.

26. Where would you expect the lower oxides (valence of metal less than 4) of Re and Tc to lie on Fig. 23.17?

27. From Figs. 23.10, 14, and 17 estimate an approximate value for $-\Delta H_f$ for each of the hypothetical oxides Mn_2O, TcO, and Re_2O_3.

28. Platinum is practically as stable in the IV oxidation state as in the II oxidation state and in this respect is very different from palladium. Comment.

29. The best-known oxidation states of molybdenum are III, V, and VI. Compare this observation with the Oxidation State Diagram for chromium.

30. The redox potentials of ReO_4^-/Re and BrO_3^-/Br_2 in acid solution are $+0.36$ and $+1.52$ volts respectively: data for Mn potentials are given in Fig. 23.11. How far does this information fit in with the general trends observed in the Periodic Table down an A Group (i.e. from the first to the third transition series) and between A- and B-Group elements?

SECTION B. (*Experimental*)

Carry out test-tube examinations of the following reactions, noting carefully what you observe. Comment on your observations in relation to Fig. 23.11.

1. Ammonium vanadate solution and HCl.
2. Ammonium vanadate solution, HCl, and Zn.
3. Ammonium vanadate solution, HCl, and KI solution.
4. Potassium chromate solution and HCl.
5. Potassium chromate solution, HCl, and Zn.
6. Potassium chromate solution, HCl, and KI solution.
7. A very little potassium chromate added to molten KOH (in an ignition tube).
8. Potassium chromate solution, NaOH solution, and KI solution.
9. Potassium permanganate solution and HCl.
10. Potassium permanganate solution, dilute H_2SO_4, and KI solution, finally making the solution alkaline.
11. Potassium permanganate, NaOH solution, and KI solution.
12. Potassium permanganate, dilute H_2SO_4, and Cr^{3+} solution.
13. A very little potassium permanganate added to molten KOH (in an ignition tube).
14. Iron(III) chloride solution, HCl, and Zn.

15. Iron(III) chloride solution and KI solution.
16. Iron(III) chloride solution, KI solution, and excess phosphate. (This result should be compared with 15: addition of a little CCl_4 may help.)
17. Copper sulphate solution and Zn.
18. Copper sulphate solution and KI solution.
19. Copper metal and dilute HCl.
20. Copper metal, dilute HCl, and ammonium vanadate solution.

Carry out any further similar experiments which you feel might be of interest.

Bibliography

M. A. CATALAN, F. ROHRLICH, and A. G. SHENSTONE, 'Relations between Low Atomic Configurations in the Long Periods', *Proc. Roy. Soc.* A, 1954, **221**, 421.

W. M. LATIMER, *Oxidation Potentials*, 2nd ed., Prentice-Hall, Englewood Cliffs, New Jersey, 1952.

C. E. MOORE, *Atomic Energy Levels*, Circular of the National Bureau of Standards No. 467, Washington, D.C., 1949 (vol. 1), 1952 (vol. 2), and 1958 (vol. 3).

A. G. SHARPE, *Principles of Oxidation and Reduction*, Monographs for Teachers No. 2, Royal Institute of Chemistry, 1960.

24 · Transition Metals: The Ligand Field

24.1. General introduction

In the chapter on pre-transition elements, a metal ion was considered to be a non-deformable sphere of fixed size. The anions surrounding it were also assumed to be non-deformable and of fixed size. The properties of the compounds could then be reasonably interpreted in terms of ionic charge and ionic radius. Such a description works quite well even for the lanthanides, but it breaks down for transition-metal compounds, and we need to develop some additional theoretical ideas.

In this chapter then we must consider in some detail the interaction between a transition-metal atom or ion and the field produced by the surrounding ions or molecules. Since these may be referred to in general as ligands the problem may be described as that of the Ligand Field. The theoretical study of the nature of this field has developed since about 1930, and especially so far as chemistry is concerned since about 1950, by using at first an ionic model for the effect of field symmetry and field intensity on the energy of the d orbitals of the transition-metal ion, crystal-field theory (a preliminary treatment was given in Chapter 5), and subsequently a treatment of the overlap of the ligand and metal orbitals based on molecular-orbital theory. Since the theoretical discussion is conveniently divided between high-spin and low-spin systems, the spin problem is introduced immediately (section 24.2) albeit in a somewhat superficial manner.

Now the most powerful applications of crystal-field and molecular-orbital theory are in the interpretation of the spectra and magnetic properties of transition-metal compounds (Chapter 28). Crystal-field theory is used particularly in the discussion of the kinetics of transition-metal chemistry (Chapter 29), while molecular-orbital theory is of great value in discussing properties of the organometallic and related compounds (Chapter 27). The theories are significant but less valuable in the discussion of the more traditional chemistry, particularly the thermochemistry, of the transition elements. We have therefore the choice of following the theories with the more complex and least 'chemical' features of transition-metal chemistry in order to illustrate their value most clearly, or alternatively to give the theories immediately before the simple chemistry, in which we must begin at once to point out their limited applicability. We have chosen to take the latter course. *Sufficient basic theoretical ideas will be introduced in this chapter* (1) *to enable us to consider the effects of the ligand field on the chemistry discussed in Chapters 25, 26, 27, and 29, and* (2) *to form an introduction to Chapter 28 where the spectroscopic data lead us to examine in closer detail the real significance of some of the theoretical parameters.*

This chapter is divided into two parts. Part A is concerned with a relatively simple treatment of the symmetry effects of the ligand field surrounding a transition-metal *ion* of defined formal charge. This is discussed both from an electrostatic or crystal field, and from a bond (molecular-orbital or, less satisfactorily, valence-bond) model. Between these extremes it is possible to use crystal-field theory somewhat modified by molecular-orbital considerations. Some authors refer to this combination as 'ligand-field' theory, but we shall not adopt such a convention. Instead the phrase 'ligand field' will be used to cover all interactions between ligands and metal atoms.

The symmetry arguments lead to a number of qualitative conclusions, many of which are identical no matter whether they are expressed in the crystal-field or the molecular-orbital language. All recent calculations suggest, however, that quantitative agreement with experiment cannot be obtained from the crystal-field theory. Molecular-orbital calculations offer a more promising approach but even their validity is still open to question. We shall develop the crystal-field arguments first, partly because they provide a simple introduction to many of the ideas on symmetry and a simple formalism by which the symmetry conclusions may be easily derived, and partly because crystal-field arguments still play a large part in inorganic chemical literature. In a sense the distinctions between the crystal-field and molecular-orbital approaches reflect the more general distinctions between the ionic and the bond models. While much of this book has been written in terms of the ionic model, because of the difficulty of performing calculations with the bond model, it is to be expected that in the future better computational techniques will be developed and that the emphasis will gradually change in favour of the bond model.

The detailed discussion of the extent of covalent bonding will also depend upon the energies and radial extension (i.e. overlap character) of both metal and ligand orbitals, and will thus vary from ligand to ligand, from metal to metal, and from valence state to valence state. These aspects will be discussed in Part B, where, in a final section, the approach to ligand-metal binding starting from *atoms* instead of ions will be described. *For those to whom Part A is essentially new, it is recommended that Part B be passed over at first reading.*

24.2. Spin states and magnetic moments

In *high-spin* ions electrons occupy the $(n-1)d$ orbitals so that the maximum number of electron spins are parallel. All ions with a smaller number of parallel spins are called *low-spin* ions. The distinction between high-spin and low-spin cases is an experimental one. In the older literature, compounds containing the high-spin ions have been called weak-field or ionic, and those containing the low-spin ions strong-field or covalent. These descriptions imply more knowledge of chemical binding than is really justified, and we shall not use them in this way.

The magnetic moment of an ion can be determined either in the solid or solution state by appropriate physical methods (see Selwood). The quantity measured by such methods is the gram magnetic susceptibility of the material, χ_M, which has the temperature dependence

$$\chi_M = \frac{C}{T - \theta_C},$$

the Curie–Weiss Law, where θ_C is called the Curie temperature (or Weiss constant). This formula reflects the effect of random thermal motions in opposing the orientation of the magnetic ions in an applied field. If a value μ is attributed to the magnetic moment of each ion then it is readily shown that

$$C = N\mu^2/3k \quad \text{and} \quad \mu = \sqrt{\left(\frac{3kT\chi_M}{N}\right)}, \quad \text{when } \theta_C \sim 0.$$

The units of μ are now Bohr magnetons, B.M. The experimental μ is interpreted in terms of a model for the electron structure of the compound under examination. For transition-metal compounds the approximation may be used that the magnetic moment arises from electrons in orbitals of the central transition-metal ion only. At first then the problem can be reduced to an atomic one. This approximation is corrected later (Chapter 28). On this basis μ can be calculated to a high degree of accuracy, at least in principle and generally in practice. The total ionic moment depends upon the spins of all the electrons, the orbitals which they occupy, and finally the way in which the spin, s, and angular-momentum, l, contributions of individual electrons are coupled. The simplest formulation is Russell-Saunders coupling (see section 28.3) which describes the magnetic behaviour of the lanthanide cations extremely well. The equations for μ are then

$$\mu = g\sqrt{\{J(J+1)\}},$$

$$g = \left\{1 + \frac{J(J+1)+S(S+1)-L(L+1)}{2J(J+1)}\right\}.$$

However, in transition-metal compounds it is found experimentally that a good *first* approximation to the observed moment is often given by taking $L = 0$ so that $J = S$ and

$$\mu = 2 \cdot 0\sqrt{\{S(S+1)\}}.$$

The success of this formula, which is apparently much simpler than that for Russell-Saunders coupling, is a result of the exposure of the orbital motion of the d electrons to the chemical environment of the central atom. It implies that orbital motions do not contribute to magnetic moments. As a crude analogy we may regard the orbital magnetic properties of the electrons in d orbitals as akin to the magnetic properties of a compass needle mechanically clamped. Just as such a needle would not point north and south because the mechanical force is greater than that produced by the earth's magnetic field, so the electron is unable to move from one m_l orbital to another under an applied magnetic field due to the restrictions of the electrostatic field. A more sophisticated discussion is given in Chapter 28 B. However, no matter what the origin of this particular approximate formula it is valuable as a working guide to the spin state of any central cation in a transition-metal complex. The formula is particularly appropriate in the first row of the transition metals (Table 24.1).

TABLE 24.I. *Experimental magnetic moments and predictions of the 'spin-only' formula*

Cation	Number of unpaired d electrons	$2\sqrt{\{S(S+1)\}}$, (B.M.)	Observed moment (B.M.)
Ti³⁺	1	1·73	1·7–2·0
Ti²⁺, V³⁺,	2	2·83	2·6–2·8
V²⁺, Cr³⁺, Mn⁴⁺	3	3·87	3·7–3·8
Cr²⁺, Mn³⁺	4	4·90	4·0–5·0
Mn²⁺, Fe³⁺	5	5·92	5·8–6·0
Fe²⁺	4	4·90	5·0–5·5
Co²⁺	3	3·87	4·0–5·2
Ni²⁺	2	2·83	2·8–4·0
Cu²⁺	1	1·73	1·7–2·3
Zn²⁺, Ca²⁺	0	0	0
Co³⁺	0	0 (low-spin)	0

It becomes less satisfactory (1) the heavier the element (Chapter 28), (2) the more the environment of an ion resembles that of a free ion (i.e. the weaker the chemical influence of the neighbouring atoms, for it is this influence which 'quenches' the orbital contribution to J), and (3) the greater inter-action there is between the magnetic moments of different magnetic centres.

The number of unpaired electrons in a transition-metal cation may thus be roughly deduced from a single measurement of magnetic susceptibility. By making a series of measurements at different temperatures, and fitting the data into more complex formulae, the spin states can be determined with confidence (see Chapter 28 B).

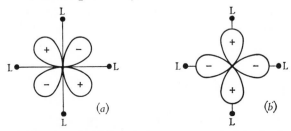

FIG. 24.1. The d_{xy} (a) and the $d_{x^2-y^2}$ (b) orbitals. (Polar diagrams of the wave functions.) Octahedral ligand positions on the x and y axes are marked L. The d_{xz} and d_{yz} orbitals are of the same symmetry, t_{2g}, as d_{xy}, and the d_{z^2} orbital is of the same symmetry, e_g, as the $d_{x^2-y^2}$ orbital. [Group theory distinguishes between d_{xy}, d_{xz}, d_{yz}, which *transform as the irreducible representation* t_{2g}, and $d_{x^2-y^2}$, d_{z^2}, which transform as e_g.]

PART A
SYMMETRY CONSIDERATIONS

24.3. Crystal-field theory: high-spin systems

In this section the effect of field symmetry on the electrostatic energy of *high-spin* cations will be considered. Rather than giving a detailed discussion of many symmetries we shall concentrate upon octahedral, 6-coordination, and tetrahedral, 4-coordination. These are the two site symmetries most frequently observed in compounds. The effect of a *non-spherical* field upon the five degenerate d orbitals of an atom or ion is to *split* them about the baricentre, the centre of gravity of the energy levels (see Fig. 24.3). The way in which the fivefold degeneracy is removed, i.e. the number of degenerate orbitals of one symmetry type produced, depends only on the field symmetry. The energy separation between the orbitals of different symmetry type depends as well upon the field strength.

We shall start the discussion by describing the splitting of d orbitals in an octahedral field of six negative charges placed symmetrically on each of the x, y, and z axes. Fig. 24.1 shows that electrons will then be relatively stabilized in the d_{xy}, d_{xz}, and d_{yz} orbitals, which from here on will be labelled t_{2g}. These orbitals avoid the directions of the octahedral field in contrast with the $d_{x^2-y^2}$ and d_{z^2} orbitals which point directly towards the negative charges and which will be labelled e_g. The t_{2g} and e_g labels refer to symmetry properties, and their significance will become apparent in section 24.6 and in Chapter 28. In the ground state, electrons will occupy the t_{2g} rather than the e_g orbitals. This preferential occupation of d orbitals of one symmetry type rather than another can thus lead to a stabilization of the cation in its environment over that expected for a spherically-symmetrical distribution of the d electrons.† Thus in transition-metal chemistry a new energy term is introduced which is absent in pre-transition-metal chemistry.

Now, as there are three t_{2g} orbitals, the stabilization in *high-spin* systems produced by an octahedral field must be greatest when there are a total of either three or eight d electrons, i.e. when the t_{2g} orbitals are either just half-full or full. Further electrons must then be added to e_g orbitals of lower stability. The removal of electrons from the t_{2g} orbitals can also only result in a reduction in the crystal-field energy. Thus in the 3-electron and 8-electron cases an especially-heightened stability of the cation will be expected in an octahedral field.

For high-spin ground-state arrangements of the d electrons other than d^3, d^5, d^8, and d^{10} the individual t_{2g} or e_g orbitals cannot be occupied equally. This means that the octahedral symmetry of the field cannot be matched exactly by the symmetry of the d electron cloud. A more stable system can then be obtained by distorting the ligand octahedron so that in certain directions the d electrons are less repelled than in others. The directional dependence of the repulsion will obviously be greater for an unequal occupation of the e_g than of the t_{2g} orbitals by electrons. In the former circumstances, d^4 and d^9 cations, the simplest distortions observed are the movement of two ligands, e.g. on the z axis, (1) away and (2) closer to the cation. The resulting fields are both of tetragonal symmetry. Distortions arising in this manner are described as Jahn–Teller effects.

Under the influence of a tetrahedral field (Fig. 24.2) the d orbitals are split into three higher and two lower orbitals of different symmetry type, an inversion of the arrangement in the octahedral field. Just as with three or eight electrons in an octahedral field, so do two or seven electrons occupy

† N.B. All the d electrons are of course repelled by the ligand field so that the bari-centre (Fig. 24.3) is raised. Any *differential* effects which could arise from this repulsion on changing cation or ligand are ignored in crystal-field theory, but are implicit in molecular-orbital treatments.

the split orbitals in a tetrahedral field in only one way. Jahn–Teller type distortions arise, as above, for all high-spin ions except d^2, d^5, d^7, and d^{10}.

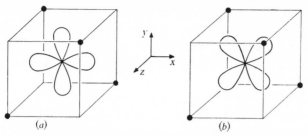

FIG. 24.2. The interaction of (a) the $d_{x^2-y^2}$ orbital and (b) the d_{xy} orbital with four ligands at the corners of a tetrahedron.

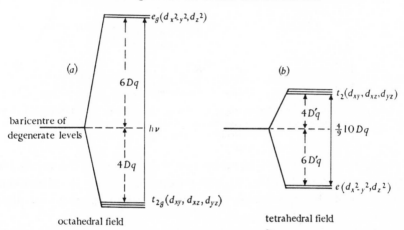

FIG. 24.3. The crystal-field splitting of the d orbital energies in an octahedral and a tetrahedral field.

TABLE 24.II. *Crystal-field stabilization energies for high-spin ions in undistorted octahedral and tetrahedral fields†*

Number of d electrons	1	2	3	4	5	6	7	8	9	10
Stabilization, units of Dq (octahedral field)	4	8	12	6	0	4	8	12	6	0
Stabilization, units of $D'q$ (tetrahedral field)	6	12	8	4	0	6	12	8	4	0

† Contributions from Racah energies have been ignored, here and in Figs. 24.4, 24.5, and 24.6.

If the crystal-field splitting in an octahedral field is $10Dq$, then a t_{2g} orbital must be stabilized to the extent of $4Dq$ and an e_g orbital destabilized by $6Dq$, for two e_g orbitals are equivalent to three t_{2g} orbitals if the baricentre is to be maintained (Fig. 24.3 (a)). The stabilization energies for different numbers of d electrons in high-spin ions in an undistorted octahedral field are therefore given by the first row of Table 24.II. Similar stabilizations in an undistorted tetrahedral field are given by the second row of the table. In the latter field the splitting is less, $10D'q$, and the lower orbitals are each stabilized by $6D'q$ units while the higher orbitals

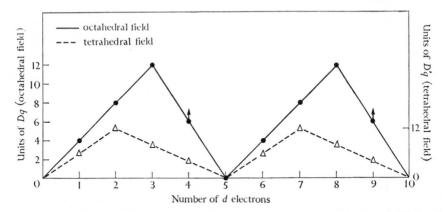

FIG. 24.4. Crystal-field stabilization energies of high-spin d^n ions in octahedral, left-hand scale, and tetrahedral, right-hand scale, fields. Arrows show where distortions will most increase stabilization.

are each destabilized by $4D'q$ units (see Fig. 24.3 (b)). The crystal-field energy is also plotted in Fig. 24.4, the arrows indicating the situations in which Jahn–Teller distortions are likely to lead to the most significant increases in crystal-field energy.

Fig. 24.4 shows that the octahedral field is preferred to the greatest extent by the 3-electron and 8-electron ions. Strong preference for this geometry is also shown by ions with four and nine electrons although the problem is complicated by distortion of the fields. For one, two, six, and seven electrons the tetrahedral arrangement is of more nearly equal stability. Two factors, however, militate against this stereochemistry. (1) Four tetrahedral ligands do not produce the equivalent total field of six octahedral ligands at the same distance. (2) d orbitals do not correspond so neatly with the geometry of a tetrahedral as compared with an octahedral field. As a consequence, a tetrahedral field of four ligands placed at the same distance from the cation as an octahedron of six ligands produces four-ninths of the effective field, i.e. $D'q = \frac{4}{9}Dq$. Some compensation in the tetrahedral field arises from contraction in the metal-ligand distances. Thus it is not possible even on an ionic model to be certain from theoretical considerations which of these two fields will be preferred in the d^1, d^2, d^6, and d^7 ions, for the possible crystal-field energies are very similar. For the d^5 (high-spin) and d^{10} ions the d electrons have no corresponding influence on stereochemistry. Further complications arise if we attempt to consider (1) effects due to the *mixing* of d^n configurations (see section 28.4), when, for example, the stabilization of the d^2 and d^7 ions in an octahedral field is different from that shown in Fig. 24.4; (2) the effect of distortions of the Jahn–Teller type; (3) more complicated field models (section 24.6) which include σ- and π-bonding. For these reasons very close agreement between theory and experiment is not to be expected.

Experimentally (Table 24.III) there is good evidence that the high-spin d^3 and d^8 ions, e.g. Cr^{3+} and Ni^{2+}, show a strong preference for octahedral over other field symmetries. Certainly this preference is stronger than in the case of Co^{2+}, which is often found in tetrahedral symmetry. Cu^{2+} and Cr^{2+} are usually found in tetragonal, distorted octahedral, symmetry. The structural observations thus confirm some general predictions of crystal-field theory for high-spin ions.

It is possible to force a stereochemistry upon a cation. Thus $[CuCl_4]^{2-}$,

TABLE 24.III. *Stereochemistry (high-spin ions)*

Symmetry around cation

Compounds or complexes	Tetrahedral	Octahedral	Tetragonal, four near neighbours	Lower symmetry
Oxides, MO	Zn^{2+}	Mn^{2+}, Fe^{2+}, Co^{2+}, Ni^{2+} *Ti^{2+}, *V^{2+}	Cr^{2+}(?) Cu^{2+}	
Oxides, M_2O_3		Cr^{3+}, Fe^{3+}, Ga^{3+}	Mn^{3+}	*Ti^{3+}(?)
Spinels, $A^{2+}B_2^{3+}O_4$	Mn^{2+}, Co^{2+}, Zn^{2+}, Fe^{3+}	Ni^{2+}, Cr^{3+}	Cu^{2+}(?), Mn^{3+}	
Hydrates, $M(H_2O)_n^{2+}$		Mn^{2+}, Fe^{2+}, Co^{2+}, Ni^{2+} Zn^{2+}	Cr^{2+}, Cu^{2+}	
Hydrates, $M(H_2O)_n^{3+}$		Cr^{3+}, Fe^{3+}	Mn^{3+}	Ti^{3+}(?)
Fluorides, MF_2		Mn^{2+}, Fe^{2+}, Co^{2+}, Ni^{2+} Pd^{2+}	Cu^{2+}	Cr^{2+}
Fluorides, MF_3		V^{3+}, Cr^{3+}	Mn^{3+}	
Chloride complexes	(Fe^{3+}), Ga^{3+}	Cr^{3+}, (Fe^{3+})	Mn^{3+}	
Ammine complexes	Zn^{2+}	Fe^{2+}, Co^{2+}, Ni^{2+} V^{3+}, Cr^{3+}	Cr^{2+}, Cu^{2+} Mn^{3+}	Ti^{3+}(?)

Note. Certain lattice types, e.g. Al_2O_3, undergo some distortion due to straightforward electrostatic repulsion effects. Such distortions have been disregarded. Systems marked * need special consideration due to metal–metal bonding. Systems containing more than one ligand type have been omitted as they will distort for reasons other than those described in section 24.3.

which is normally distorted tetrahedral, becomes square coplanar when crystallized with square coplanar $[Pt(NH_3)_4]^{2+}$. Size and charge effects must also play a large part in the preferential formation of a *tetrahedral* chloride complex $[NiCl_4]^{2-}$ rather than an octahedral complex $[NiCl_6]^{4-}$. Polydentate ligands, may be 'tailored' for a particular stereochemistry: an example is given in Fig. 25.6.

24.4. Crystal-field theory: low-spin systems

The crystal-field energies of low-spin ions in an octahedral field are given in Fig. 24.5. Spin pairing is opposed by the repulsion between two electrons in the same space orbital which we have already examined for the free gas ions in section 23.2. The crystal-field energy gained by a change of spin state must therefore offset the increased electron-electron repulsion in the core. Fig. 24.6 illustrates the problem for the octahedral-field case. The gain in crystal-field energy is a maximum and the total energy gain on changing from high-spin is also greatest for the low-spin d^6 ion. While the crystal-field energies are not very different in the three transition series (their order is first series < second series ⩽ third series), the spin-pairing repulsion energies are much greater in the first than in the other two series (in part because the $4d$ and $5d$ orbitals are larger than the $3d$) and so cause low-spin states to be common in the second and third series. Ions later in all the transition series are more likely to be spin-paired. This follows from simple crystal-field arguments, especially when effects due to distortion are taken into account, see Fig. 24.6.

Just as in high-spin systems, an octahedral distribution of ligands is only stable if each of the t_{2g} and each of the e_g orbitals is equally occupied. Thus the d^6 low-spin system is undistorted in octahedral symmetry. A particularly strong distortion to a tetragonal field, four near neighbours only, is observed in the d^8 low-spin systems (Table 24.iv). As a result, the crystal-field energies calculated for an octahedral field may be considerably too small and some uncertain adjustments are required to Figs. 24.5 and 24.6. The ability of the crystal-field model to predict the stereochemistry of a transition-metal cation is partly restricted by our failure to understand when the distortion energy will be small or large. In high-spin systems the distortion is found (Table 24.iii) to be large for (d^1), d^4, and d^9, and for low-spin systems it is large for d^8, as is reflected in the structures given in Table 24.iv.

In symmetries other than octahedral, one (dodecahedral field, 8-coordination), two (tetrahedral field), or even four (tetragonal field) low-lying

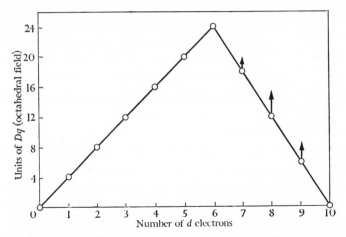

FIG. 24.5. Crystal-field stabilization energies of low-spin d^n ions in an octahedral field. Arrows show where distortions will most increase stabilization.

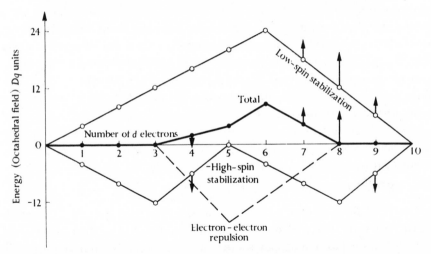

FIG. 24.6. The overall stabilization energy, labelled 'Total', favouring a change from high-spin to low-spin for different d^n ions in the same octahedral field on a crystal-field model. The electron-electron repulsion energy is schematic.

TABLE 24.IV. *Some observed stereochemistries of low-spin ions*

Compound or complex	Octahedral	Tetragonal
MO	. .	Pd^{2+}, Pt^{2+}
M_2O_3	Co^{3+}	Au^{3+}
MO_2	Pt^{4+}	
MCl_2 and chloride complexes of M^{2+}	Ru^{2+}, Os^{2+}	Pd^{2+}, Pt^{2+}
MCl_3, and chloride complexes of M^{3+}	Rh^{3+}, Ir^{3+}	Au^{3+}
MCl_4, and chloride complexes of M^{4+}	Os^{4+}, Ir^{4+}, Pt^{4+}	

orbitals may arise. Examples of *low-spin* ions in the first and last symmetries are $Mo(CN)_8^{4-}$ and $PtCl_4^{2-}$. Still further symmetries are possible, so that a great variety of stabilization energies can arise from crystal-field splittings. Such possibilities make it even more difficult to predict the symmetry of a complex ion from the crystal-field model.

24.5. Spectra and the crystal-field theory

Transition-metal cations are usually coloured. As many of the colours are weak the corresponding excitations must be 'forbidden'. They have been assigned to *d–d* transitions. There are excited electronic states of the d^n configurations not far above their ground states. The differences in energy between the ground and excited states may be expressed in terms of the crystal-field splitting diagrams. We shall consider first the case of one *d* electron. In an octahedral complex, the ground state has the configuration t_{2g}^1 while that of the first excited state is e_g^1. This extremely simple relationship between configurations and spectroscopic states will only arise for the one-electron case, and then only in the absence of distortions from octahedral symmetry. The energy difference between these two states (Fig. 24.3) is $10Dq$, which on the *crystal-field model* is equated with a quantum of energy $h\nu$, observed as a maximum in an absorption spectrum. More complicated relationships between $h\nu$ and $10Dq$ are predicted for many of the *d–d* transitions of d^n systems.

On this basis ligands may be placed in an order of their field 'strength', i.e. in general the order of the energy of the first absorption bands in the octahedral complexes. A major part of the order is

$$CN^- > NO_2^- > \text{dipyridyl} > NH_3 > H_2O \geqslant F^- > Cl^- > Br^- > I^-,$$

a shortened form of the 'spectrochemical series'; see Fig. 24.7. Ligands on the left provide the strongest field and should be the most effective in forcing cations into low-spin states, whereas ligands on the right will usually give high-spin complexes, especially in the first transition series. Although there are exceptions to this correlation between magnetic and spectroscopic properties, there is a large group of examples where it has been shown to be useful (e.g. Table 24.v). In passing it should be noted that, much as predicted by Fig. 24.6, the d^6 cations of the first transition series are most readily forced to low-spin states in complexes while the d^5, d^7, and d^8 resist the change most strongly.

Many cations give rise to more than one *d–d* absorption band. Thus all octahedral complexes of V^{3+} have three bands of moderate intensity in the visible or near ultra-violet, although there are only three high-spin configurations, t_{2g}^2, $t_{2g}^1 e_g^1$, and e_g^2. Using the strong-field approximation, section 28.4, one band can be simply interpreted as $e_g^2 \leftarrow t_{2g}^2$. The reason for the other two bands may be seen by considering the second configuration

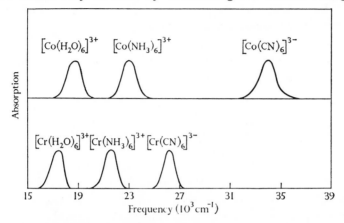

FIG. 24.7. A diagrammatic representation of the positions of the lowest spin-allowed energy bands in the spectra of Co^{3+} and Cr^{3+} complexes.

TABLE 24.V. *High-spin and low-spin complexes in relation to the spectrochemical series*

Cation	Number of d electrons	High-spin complexes	Low-spin complexes
Cr^{2+}	4	H_2O, NH_3	dipyridyl, CN^-
Mn^{2+}	5	The vast majority	CN^-
Fe^{2+}	6	NH_3, H_2O, Cl^-	CN^-, dipyridyl, NO_2^-
Ni^{2+}	8	H_2O, NH_3, F^-, dipyridyl, NO_2^-	CN^-
Fe^{3+}	5	H_2O, F^-, Cl^-	CN^-, dipyridyl
Co^{3+}	6	F^-	all other complexes

with one electron in an e_g and another in a t_{2g} orbital, see Fig. 24.3. It gives rise to two possible *combinations* of the orbital motions of the two electrons, giving two excited states which are different in orbital momentum and hence in their electron–electron repulsion energies. This is simply visualized by considering the one-electron excitations (1) $d_{x^2-y^2} \leftarrow d_{xy}$ and (2) $d_{z^2} \leftarrow d_{xy}$ while the other electron remains in d_{xz}. Thus there are two transitions, and therefore two absorption bands, from the ground state to the configuration $t_{2g}^1 e_g^1$ in the V^{3+} spectrum. In so far as the relative energies of the absorption bands are independent of the ligand-field parameter Dq, they can be used to evaluate the differences in electron–electron repulsion between the two excited states. The methods used are exactly like those employed in evaluating differences in electron–electron repulsion energies between such terms as ^3F and ^3P of the gaseous V^{3+} ion in atomic spectroscopy, and are similarly expressed in units of B, where B is the second Racah parameter. If a change of spin state occurs on excitation then this will also cause a change in electron–electron repulsion, section 23.2, and the total Racah energy change then becomes $mB+nC$. From the positions of the absorption bands in a spectrum, Dq, B, and C can be given values. However, as we shall see in Chapter 28, a fuller appreciation of the procedure which is being used here leads to difficulty in understanding the exact meaning of these quantities.

24.6. Molecular-orbital theory for ions

As was mentioned in the introduction, the effects of the ligand field can be treated either with an electrostatic model or with a covalent one. In the covalent approach the field must be described in terms of ligand wave functions. These will overlap with the $(n-1)d$ orbitals of the central-metal cations, and their interaction will produce bonding and antibonding orbitals. They will also interact with the ns and np orbitals of the cation, but the $(n-1)d$ orbitals will be considered first.

The interaction between these d orbitals and the ligand orbitals will depend both on the symmetry of the ligand arrangement, just as in the electrostatic picture, and the symmetry of the available orbitals of the ligand atoms. Thus in an octahedral field some ligand orbitals will interact with t_{2g} and some with e_g orbitals of the central ion. The exercise of finding the orbitals of different symmetry type (*transformation properties*) which arise in a particular field geometry is a part of *Group Theory*, which is essential for a complete understanding of either crystal-field or molecular-orbital theory. Full treatments are given in the books by Cotton, Phillips, and (at a more advanced level) Ballhausen, listed in the bibliography at the end of this chapter.

For the present purposes the essential feature is the symmetry of ligand-orbital combinations with respect to the cation. Thus the s or p atomic orbitals on six ligand atoms arranged in an octahedron around a cation give rise to a series of combined orbitals of different symmetry (Fig. 24.8). As an aid to clarity we shall give these combined orbitals group-theory labels with capital letters† to distinguish them from the orbitals of the

---

† Capital letters are also used *conventionally* for the symmetry of spectroscopic states, Chapter 28.

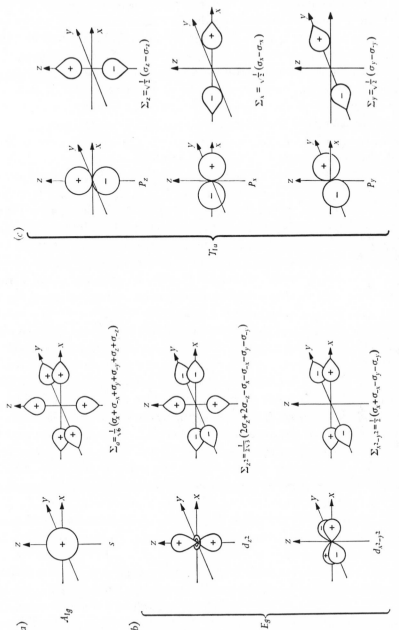

FIG. 24.8. Ligand-orbital combinations in an octahedral field of symmetry types (a) A_{1g}, (b) E_g, and (c) T_{1u} with corresponding metal-ion orbitals on left. Bonding is of σ-symmetry with respect to each cation-ligand axis.

cation and the molecular orbitals resulting from the cation-ligand inter-action. The combinations and therefore the labels will change as the geometry of the ligand field is changed.

The simplest combination of orbitals in an octahedral field is of the kind where all the lobes of the σ orbitals have the same sign for the six ligands, L. There is one such combined orbital from the p orbitals and one from the s orbitals (Fig. 24.8 (a)). Both belong to the symmetry type A_{1g}, A because they are singly-degenerate, 1 because the sign of the combined wave function does not change on rotation about certain axes (see Chapter 28), and g because the combined wave function does not change sign on inversion through the central cation. Alternative combinations of the different σ orbitals of L with alternating signs lead to other combined orbitals of ML_6 of the symmetry type E_g, where E is the symbol for 2-fold degeneracy (Fig. 24.8 (b)). Yet other combined orbitals which can be built from the σ orbitals of L change sign on inversion and are of symmetry type T_{1u} (Fig. 24.8 (c)), where T stands for 3-fold degeneracy, and u for change of sign on inversion. Combination of the π orbitals of the ligands can be built up in a similar manner. Some of these combined orbitals have the symmetry property T_{2g} (octahedral field) as shown in Fig. 24.9. There are many others. Certain combinations of ligand nd orbitals also fall into the types E_g and T_{2g}, but these will not be described.

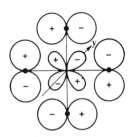

Fig. 24.9. Ligand-orbital combination of symmetry type T_{2g} with corresponding metal-ion orbital. Bonding is of π-symmetry with respect to each cation-ligand axis.

The d orbitals of the central cation can be given symmetry labels of the same kind as those of the combined ligand orbitals. For an octahedron of ligands these d orbitals are of two symmetry types, one is 3-fold degenerate and has the group-theory label t_{2g} (Fig. 24.1 (a)) and the other 2-fold degenerate with the label e_g (Fig. 24.1 (b)). Because the cation is at the *centre* of the complex its individual d orbitals, unlike those of the ligand, can either be described, as earlier, $d_{x^2-y^2}$, d_{xy}, etc., or by the group-theory labels appropriate to the symmetry of the complex. In this way the labels used in section 24.3 arise.

Since ligand orbitals can combine only with orbitals of the central cation of the same symmetry type, the *qualitative* energy diagram of Fig. 24.10 can be produced. The absolute energies of orbitals of different symmetry type will depend upon the strengths of the interactions in ML_n. For most octahedral systems the e_g bonding orbitals lie lowest, the t_{2g} bonding

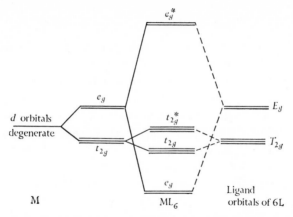

FIG. 24.10. The interaction of the e_g and t_{2g} orbitals of the cation with combinations of orbitals of six octahedral ligands. For clarity the e_g and t_{2g} cation orbitals have first been split as in a weak electrostatic field. The relative positions of the E_g and T_{2g} orbitals will change from case to case.

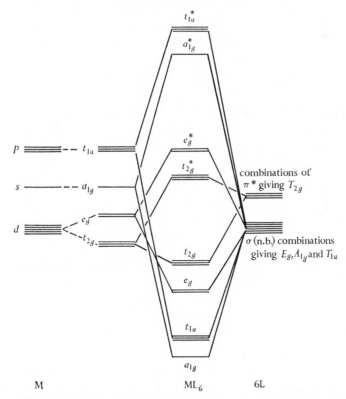

FIG. 24.11. Interaction of the original (i.e. within the ligand) antibonding, π^*, and original non-bonding (n.b.) σ orbitals of six octahedral ligands with the five d, one s, and three p orbitals of a cation. The original bonding π orbitals of the ligand are not represented: these will normally act as π-donors.

orbitals next, the non-bonding orbitals next, the t_{2g}^* antibonding orbitals next, while the e_g^* antibonding orbitals lie highest.

The s and p orbitals of the cation can now be considered. We have just shown how ligand orbitals can combine to give rise to orbitals of A_{1g} and T_{1u} symmetry. These orbitals match the s (a_{1g}) and three p (t_{1u}) orbitals of the cation (Fig. 24.8; see also Chapter 4). If the combinations resulting from s and p cation orbitals are added to Fig. 24.10, the molecular-orbital diagram for an octahedral transition-metal complex, Fig. 24.11, is obtained. The lowest six orbitals are a, $(3\times)t_{1u}$, and $(2\times)e_g$. These are related to the d^2sp^3 hybrid orbitals of the valence-bond approach.

In order to understand the properties of an ion we proceed to consider the filling of the energy levels in the molecular-orbital diagram much as we have done in previous examples (Chapter 3). The electrons involved are both those of the central cation and those of the ligands. The bonding orbitals, a, $(3\times)t_{1u}$ and $(2\times)e_g$, will first be filled by the σ-donor electrons (of the ligands). Some or all of the t_{2g} orbitals may also be filled by π-donor 'ligand' electrons. The filling of these orbitals depends upon the number of electrons in the t_{2g} orbitals of the original cation and ligands, i.e. how many electrons there were in the separated systems. If there are more than enough electrons to fill all these orbitals, then the 'metal' electrons must go into the t_{2g}^* and finally the e_g^* antibonding orbitals. The t_{2g}^* electrons lose energy compared with their initial situation in the isolated cation (but not relative to the averaged energy of *all* the e_g^* and t_{2g}^* levels in the presence of the field).

Before attempting any more detailed description of this bonding, we may observe that molecular-orbital theory has considered some quite new features of the interaction. Firstly, the number of electrons involved has greatly increased because electrons of the ligand have been allowed to interact with the cation nucleus, i.e. the ligand electron cloud is distorted or polarized due to covalence. Secondly e_g orbitals are stabilized most, not t_{2g} orbitals. Thus in an octahedral fluoride or oxide complex, all the electrons in the $2s$ and $2p$ orbitals of the fluoride or oxide anions will be stabilized by interaction with the cation *in the absence of any 'd' electrons*. Putting 'd' electrons into the system adds antibonding electrons first to t_{2g}^* and then to e_g^* orbitals. The addition of these 'd' electrons will cause energy increments, as the number of 'd' electrons increases, in a pattern just like that described on the crystal-field model (Table 24.II). The total stabilization energy will be the amount of stabilization gained by the electrons of the ligands less the amount of destabilization suffered by the d

electrons of the cation. Provided that the first term is constant or a linear function of the atomic number of the cation (as is the electron affinity of s and p orbitals to a good approximation), then the pattern of the increments in the ligand-field energy of the cations will be the same, in Dq units, as was described for the crystal-field model (Figs. 24.4 (high-spin) and 24.5 (low-spin)). Although $10Dq$ may now change from cation to cation the splitting of the t_{2g}^{*} and e_{g}^{*} orbitals can be deduced from spectroscopic measurements in an identical manner to that used in the crystal-field treatment, substituting e_{g}^{*} for e_{g}, and t_{2g} or t_{2g}^{*} (see later) for t_{2g} in section 24.5. Furthermore, from the calculated field strengths of different ligands we may proceed to the discussion of changes of spin state along lines not notably different from those already given for the crystal-field model (section 24.4). Thus provided molecular-orbital effects are small or involve s and p orbital covalence only, the distinction between crystal-field and molecular-orbital theories may not be great. In these circumstances the basic approach of the crystal-field theory can be taken over although the discussion of problems will utilize diagrams such as Fig. 24.10. (As mentioned in the introduction, section 24.1, this approach has been called 'ligand-field theory' by some authors.)

For a series of high-spin octahedral cations, no matter what the exact origin of the splitting between the orbitals of e_{g} and t_{2g} symmetry type, i.e. whether it is that of Fig. 24.1 or of Fig. 24.10, the theories now predict a double hump in the plot of lattice energy against atomic number. Some experimental observations are shown in Fig. 24.12. The predicted plot for a series of low-spin cations is given in Fig. 24.13 (c): there is only a single hump in the plot of lattice energy against atomic number. The plot is compared with the changes in the lanthanide, Fig. 24.13 (a), and high-spin transition-metal series, Fig. 24.13 (b).

Despite this apparent agreement between their predictions, the two theories, crystal-field and molecular-orbital, are only strictly comparable in their discussion of symmetry. Thus there is considerable experimental evidence that the polarization of the ligand electrons by interaction with the d as well as the s and p orbitals (Fig. 24.11) of the central cation does not vary linearly with atomic number, but also leads to a double-humped curve for high-spin ions. This evidence will be described in Part B of this chapter and in Chapter 28.

The difference between the theories will be particularly important for a set of unsaturated (π-acceptor) ligands which in an octahedral field, for example, will provide unfilled T_{2g} combined-ligand orbitals. Hence although the lowest a_{1g}, t_{1u}, and e_g molecular orbitals of the compound will be full, some or all of the t_{2g} molecular orbitals may now be empty. Thus d electrons will first of all go into stabilized t_{2g} molecular orbitals. Expressing this another way we can say electrons of the cation π-bond back on to the

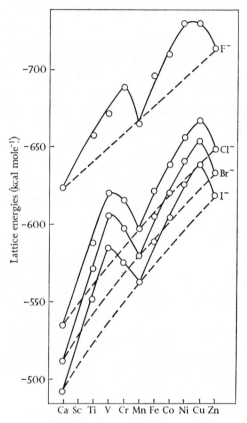

Fig. 24.12. The lattice energies of the divalent metal halides of the first transition series (after Waddington).

ligands. The fewer the $\pi^*(T_{2g})$ electrons of the ligands the more the stabilization of the core electrons. As ligand-field energies now contain different terms for saturated and unsaturated ligands the splitting will depend on the specific nature of the cation/ligand interaction; compare Cr^{3+} and Co^{3+} in Fig. 24.7, noting particularly the positions of the cyanide (unsaturated) complexes. It is obvious that later transition-metal cations, i.e. those with many d electrons, will interact most strongly with unsaturated ligands. We shall develop this aspect in Part B of this chapter

and in Chapters 25 and 26. Unsaturated ligands may not even give rise
to the stereochemistry predicted by the crystal-field model.

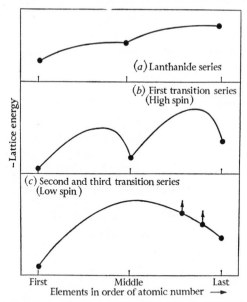

FIG. 24.13. A general comparison of the changes of lattice energy
with atomic number predicted for salts of three series of elements.

STEREOCHEMISTRY AND MOLECULAR-ORBITAL THEORY

We have already pointed out that d^8 (low-spin) and d^9 cations usually
prefer a tetragonal field, and that this experimental observation receives
a ready explanation on crystal-field theory. There are two reasons why
this preference may fail to be generally realized.

(1) The number of ligands bound by a cation can depend on the relative
importance of σ-covalent bonding and electrostatic bonding. Molecular-
orbital theory predicts that the actual structure will depend upon the
symmetry of the orbitals available for bonding and the number of un-
shared lone pairs as well as on the repulsion between the charged atoms
(or the bond electrons). Consider thus the d^8 case. There can be either
4-coordination in a plane when the lone pair of the cation is symmetrical
about the plane in the d_{z^2} orbital (crystal-field model), or 5-coordination
arising from interaction between the d_{z^2} orbital and an sp_z hybrid orbital
to give two orbitals perpendicular to the plane. The lone pair in the latter
situation occupies the sixth octahedral position. A similar argument
applies to the preferred geometry around d^7 (low-spin) and d^9 (high-spin)

cations. Experimentally 5-coordination is in fact observed in $[Ni(CN)_5]^{3-}$, $[Co(CN)_5]^{3-}$, $Fe(CO)_5$, $[CuCl_5]^{3-}$, $[Cu(o\text{-phenan})_2I]^+$, and $[M(DAS)_2 \text{ halide}]^+$ where M is Ni, Pd, or Pt, but the geometry is sometimes that of a square pyramid and sometimes a trigonal bipyramid. The molecular-orbital approach does not indicate clearly when 4- or 5-coordination will be preferred nor which of the possible 5-coordinate geometries is to be expected.

(2) π-bonding can also affect stereochemistry, for example the relative stability of an octahedral and a tetragonally distorted structure. In particular the differences in stereochemistry of dipyridyl and ethylenediamine complexes of Cu^+, Cu^{2+}, and Zn^{2+} are indicative of this effect (Table 24.VI). With unsaturated (π-acceptor) ligands generally there is a stronger tendency toward an octahedral field. For example the d^8 complex $Ni(DAS)_3$ (for the formula of DAS see Table 24.VII) is reported as diamagnetic with the As atoms forming an approximate octahedron around the Ni.

TABLE 24.VI. *Geometry of complex ions*

Cation	Water	Ammonia	Ethylenediamine	Dipyridyl
Cu^+	? linear or tetrahedral	linear	linear	tetrahedral
Cu^{2+}	tetragonal	tetragonal	tetragonal (2 ligands) or octahedral (3 ligands)	5-coordinate (2 ligands) or octahedral (3 ligands)
Zn^{2+}	octahedral	tetrahedral	tetrahedral or octahedral	octahedral

Now most of the above examples have been chosen from the metals at the end of the transition series, where the valences are relatively low. Similar considerations may not apply in higher valences. At the beginning of the transition series there are many cations of valence three or greater. Against the background of radius-ratio considerations and the simple ionic model, it is surprising that these small highly-charged cations are found to have very high coordination numbers. Thus it is known that 8-coordination is common in the compounds of Ti^{3+}, Ti^{4+}, Zr^{4+}, Hf^{4+}, Nb^{4+}, Nb^{5+}, Ta^{5+}, Mo^{4+}, Mo^{5+}, W^{4+}, W^{5+}, and Re^{4+}; 9-coordination is well recognized with the lanthanides and 7-coordination has been found in Mn^{2+} and Fe^{3+} complexes. These results are in no way predictable from the ionic model, with or without crystal-field considerations, but they suggest that the number of empty orbitals of the cation has considerable control over the coordination number. Both valence-bond and molecular-orbital considerations (see below) can lead to the correct geometry. The lower-valence states of the elements early in transition series do not seem to have as strong a tendency to assume high coordination numbers. It is likely that the contraction of the $(n-1)d$ orbitals with increasing charge introduces a strong dependence of coordination number and stereochemistry upon the charge—a result parallel to that observed with the nd orbitals in the second and subsequent rows of non-metals.

24.7. Valence-bond theory

The valence-bond theory has many similarities to the molecular-orbital theory. However, because it is based on the idea of the 2-electron bond, while molecular-orbital theory is initially concerned with a one-electron treatment, it is conventional when using the valence-bond approach to start from the number of totally unoccupied orbitals on a central atom. Thus the zinc cation would be expected to form four tetrahedral bonds because there are four unoccupied orbitals into which electron *pairs* can be donated. The tetrahedral geometry arises from the symmetry properties of the four hybridized orbitals, here $4s4p^3$. A second example would be the hydrated Co^{3+} cation which has been shown to be diamagnetic, i.e. low-spin. The central cation now contains six $3d$ electrons, all paired, so that two $3d$, one $4s$, and three $4p$ orbitals are completely vacant. A coordination number of 6 would therefore be expected and an octahedral stereochemistry resulting from the d^2sp^3 hybridization. This prediction, which also follows from 'low-spin' molecular-orbital theory for this cation, is in agreement with experimental observation. The reasons for the similarity between the theories should be obvious from section 24.6.

Valence-bond theory would further suggest that the coordination number of a metal should be 9, corresponding to d^5sp^3 hybridization, at the beginning of a transition series, where there are no d electrons, and fall by one for every pair of d electrons added until the B metals are reached where it should be 4. The examples in Tables 24.VI and 24.VII show that high coordination is indeed found at the beginning of transition-metal series and lower coordination at the end.

While noting the success of the simple postulates of valence-bond theory at the beginning of transition-metal series, we should also note their frequent failure towards the end. Thus the theory would predict that systems of low-spin with eight electrons would be 5-coordinate. It is more usual for them to be 4-coordinate. Table 24.VIII indicates where 4-coordination (square coplanar) and 5-coordination have been observed. It would appear that it is the neglect of the varying separations in energy between the d, s, and p orbitals, and a resulting over-concentration on the angular parts of wave functions, which has caused difficulty in the application of valence-bond theory. Again the theory is in difficulty in treating systems with odd

TABLE 24.VII. *Stereochemistry of transition metals, high coordination number*

Number of d electrons	Coordination number		
	9	8	7
0	$La(H_2O)_9^{3+}$	$TiCl_4(DAS)_2$	Ln^{3+} oxides
	$La(OH)_3$	$Zr(oxalate)_4$	$[ZrF_7]^{3-}$
	$LaCl_3$	$Th(SO_4)_4^{4-}$	$[NbF_7]^{2-}$
	$[ReH_9]^{2-}$	$[V(O_2)_4]^{3-}$	$[MoF_7]^{-}$
		TaF_8^{3-}	
1 or 2		$Mo(CN)_8^{4-}$	
		$Mo(CN)_8^{3-}$	
		$W(CN)_8^{4-}$	
3 or 4			$[Mo(CO)_2(DAS)_2Br]^{+}$
			$W(CO)_3(DAS)I_2$
			$[Re_3Cl_{12}]^{3-}$
5			$[Mn(EDTA)H_2O]^{2-}$, $[Fe(EDTA)H_2O]^{-}$

Coordinations of 6 and 4 are too general to be listed

DAS is

TABLE 24.VIII

(a) Illustrative list of cations known to give 4-coordinate (square coplanar) complexes

Cr^{2+}	Fe^{2+}	Co^{2+}	Ni^{2+}	Cu^{2+}
4	2	1	0	1
		Rh^{+}	Pd^{2+}	Ag^{2+}
		0	0	1
		Ir^{+}	Pt^{2+}	Au^{3+}
		0	0	0

Beneath each ion is given the number of unpaired electrons in the ion for which the stereochemistry has been observed. Usual ligand atoms are P, S, As, and even C.

(b) Illustrative list of cations known io give 5-coordinate complexes

Al^{3+}, V^{4+}, Cr^{2+}, Mn^{2+}, Fe^{2+}, Co^{2+}, Ni^{2+} Cu^{2+}, Zn^{2+}, Ga^{3+}, Si^{4+}, Ge^{4+}

5-coordination is much more common in the first than in the other transition-metal series.

numbers of electrons, or high-spin systems generally. Here it is presented with the choice of considering either the empty orbitals only, for example sp^3 after the half-filled d sub-shell, or promotion of the unpaired electrons into higher atomic orbitals, e.g. $4p$, in order to release completely empty d orbitals for bonding. For example, the stereochemistry of the Cu^{2+} cation is treated as that of the combination of dsp^2 orbitals, giving a planar geometry, with one electron promoted from the $3d$ orbitals into the empty remaining $4p$ orbital. Spectroscopic evidence is in conflict with this treatment. In fact most cations of high spin in this part of the transition-metal series form octahedral compounds in closer agreement with a simple ionic theory.

Apart from these stereochemical differences between the different approaches, molecular-orbital theory has the general advantage of leading more obviously to a consideration of excited as well as ground states, which means that it is used in the discussion of spectra and in anything more than a simple treatment of magnetism. For these reasons we shall use molecular-orbital rather than valence-bond theory, although in the ultimate stages of refinement these theories must be equivalent. It must, however, be pointed out that valence-bond calculations have sometimes given a better account of electron distributions in ground states than have molecular-orbital calculations. It may well prove to be so for transition-metal compounds too.

PART B

COVALENT AND IONIC BONDING

24.8. Introduction to Part B

Section 24.6 has emphasized the symmetry relations between metal-ion and ligand orbitals which are necessary if covalent bonding is to take place, and in particular has brought out the distinction between σ-bonding and π-bonding orbitals. We now need to consider, so far as we are able, the likely strengths of such bonding. To do this we must pay attention to the energies and sizes of possible bonding orbitals on both metal-ions and ligands, as these will play a dominant role in deciding the bonding effectiveness of orbital interactions. The discussion is divided into three parts which consider respectively: (1) the effects of varying the ligand at constant formal charge on a given metal-ion (section 24.9), (2) the effects of varying the transition-metal ion (or atom) at essentially constant charge and with a constant ligand (section 24.10), and (3) the effects of variations in charge on the mutual interaction of metal ion and ligand (section 24.11).

In each of these sections an attempt will be made to relate the theoretical arguments to such data as there are on the extent of non-ionic bonding in the compounds of transition metals. One general way in which covalent effects are revealed is in the study of stereochemistry, as has already been emphasized in Chapter 5. We therefore consider in section 24.12 some experimental interatomic distances.

In the last two sections we turn to the discussion of bonds which are essentially covalent. Section 24.13 introduces the problem of metal–metal bonding, while in section 24.14 the formation of transition-metal compounds is treated *ab initio* from the bond model, i.e. starting with transition-metal *atoms* rather than transition-metal ions.

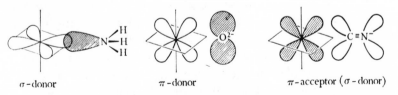

σ-donor   π-donor   π-acceptor (σ-donor)

Fig. 24.14. Pictorial representations of bond formation between d orbitals and the different types of ligand orbitals. Donor orbitals are shaded.

24.9. Ligand polarizability

The following chapter (Chapter 25) on the chemistry of the divalent transition-metal ions is largely an illustration of the variations in cation-ligand interaction with change of ligand and metal ion at constant formal charge on the metal. We here wish to consider the ways in which different ligands may be polarized by transition-metal ions. Ligands may be σ-donors, π-donors, and/or π-acceptors. Ligands that are effective π-acceptors are almost invariably σ-donors as well; they contain unfilled orbitals perpendicular to the direction of the ligand–metal axis and are usually unsaturated molecules or ions (e.g. pyridine, CN^-) or contain atoms with empty nd orbitals, e.g. P and As. The different kinds of bonding interaction are illustrated in Fig. 24.14, while a list of ligands is given in Table 24.ix.

TABLE 24.ix. *Classification of ligands in terms of donor and acceptor characteristics*

σ-donors	NH_3, ethylenediamine, H_2O, R_2O, CH_3^-, H^-
σ- and π-donors	O^{2-}, RO^-, F^-, Cl^-, Br^-, I^-, (RS^-)
π-acceptors	2,2′-dipyridyl, phenanthroline (good σ-donors) R_3P, R_3As, R_2S (moderate σ-donors) CO, RNC, unsaturated organic molecules (poor σ-donors)

The relative bonding effectiveness of different ligands may be estimated in the following ways.

(1) PHYSICAL METHODS

(a) Electron spin (paramagnetic) resonance, ESR (or EPR). At present this is the most powerful of the physical methods. The general procedure will be described in section 28.10. It gives rise to three parameters, g values, spin-orbit coupling constants, ζ, and nuclear hyperfine splitting constants, A, all of which can be related to the percentage of covalent binding. The method has shown that covalence involving d, s, and p orbitals decreases with ligand in the following manner:

$$CN^- > S^{2-} > O^{2-} > NH_3 > H_2O > F^-.$$

Some examples of σ- and π-covalence parameters are given in Table 24.x for Cu^{2+} complexes. The σ- and π-bonding parameters are in the expected order.

TABLE 24.X. *Derived covalence parameters from* ESR *data on* Cu^{2+} *complexes*

Complex	α^2	β^2	Ligand atoms
$[Cu(H_2O)_6]^{2+}$	0·85	~1·0	saturated O
Cu(II)phthalocyanine	0·82	0·59	$\diagdown N$ and $\diagdown N^-$
$[Cu(NH_3)_4]^{2+}$	0·80	~1·0	saturated N
$Cu(II)(CH_3COCHCO^-CH_3)_2$ i.e. bis-acetylacetonate	0·75	0·87	$\diagup C{=}O$ and $\diagup C{-}O^-$
Cu(II)bis-salicylaldoximate	0·76	0·72	$C{-}O^-$ and $C{=}N{-}O^-$
Cu(II)bis-salicylaldiminate	0·76	0·78	$C{-}O^-$ and $C{=}NH$
Cu(II)dithiocarbamate	0·53	(0·85)	$-C{\diagup \diagdown}^{S^-}_{S}$

α^2 is a σ-bond parameter which varies from $\alpha^2 = 0.5$ for 100 per cent covalent to $\alpha^2 = 1.0$ for 100 per cent ionic behaviour. β^2 is a similar parameter for π-bonding in which the ligand acts as acceptor.

(b) Nuclear quadrupole coupling constants give information about the electron density at a given nucleus (Chapter 4). They show, for example, that covalence in palladium and platinum halides in both the 2-valent and 4-valent states increases from chloride to iodide (section 25.7).

(c) The magnitude of the Mössbauer shift (Chapter 5). This is only readily observable with a few nuclei, notably [57]Fe. Table 24.xi shows that the shifts move in the expected manner with change of ligand.

TABLE 24.XI. *Mössbauer shifts, δ, for* Fe(II) *compounds*

Compound	δ (mm sec⁻¹)	Compound	δ (mm sec⁻¹)
$Fe(H_2O)_6SiF_6$	1·42	FeO	1·20
$FeSO_4$	1·42	FeS	0·91
$FeCO_3$	1·38	$[Fe(phenan)_3]^{2+}$ (low-spin)	0·45
$Fe_3(PO_4)_2,8H_2O$	1·38	$[Fe(CN)_6]^{4-}$ (low-spin)	0·03
$Fe(C_2O_4),2H_2O$	1·33	Fe metal	0·0

A small shift represents a highly covalent system.

(*d*) Neutron diffraction, especially with polarized neutrons, permits the calculation of the electron density near a given nucleus. This method is just being developed. Some examples are given in Table 24.XIV in the following section.

(*e*) The study of interatomic distances. This is taken up in section 24.12.

(*f*) Spectroscopic data corresponding to *d–d* transitions. Unfortunately *d–d* transitions are of considerable energy and parameters derived from them relate to differences between the excited and ground states. Thus the study of the ways in which ligands affect the energy of transitions could be misleading. The interpretation of such data and of magnetism will be described later (Chapter 28).

(*g*) From polarizabilities determined from refractive indices. These reflect the ease with which the electron cloud of an ion or molecule is distorted by an electric field. Some values are given in Table 24.XII. The ligand orders are

$$I^- > Br^- > Cl^- > F^- \text{ and } Te^{2-} > Se^{2-} > S^{2-} > O^{2-}.$$

The next few years will undoubtedly see an intensive effort toward the understanding of these physical parameters, and as a consequence we may expect that the ideas of covalence will be put on a more quantitative basis.

TABLE 24.XII. *Polarizabilities of isolated ions from measurements of refractive index* $(10^{-24} cm^3)$

F^-	Cl^-	Br^-	I^-	O^{2-}	S^{2-}	Se^{2-}	Te^{2-}
0·8–1·0	2·9–3·6	4·2–5·0	6·3–7·5	2·7–2·9	7·2–10·2	10·5–11·2	14·0–15·7

(2) CHEMICAL METHODS

(*a*) Some guidance is available from the electronegativity of the ligand atom, which leads to an order of covalence

$$I^- = S^{2-} > Br^- > NH_3 = Cl^- > O^{2-} > F^-.$$

(*b*) Better estimates may be made from differences in the heats of formation of compounds of two metal ions of the same formal charge and of essentially the same radius but of different polarizing power. Thus the

Ca^{2+} and Cd^{2+} ions have almost identical ionic radii ($0 \cdot 99$ Å and $0 \cdot 97$ Å), so that the lattice energies of corresponding Ca and Cd compounds would be virtually the same if the compounds were ionic. If this were so then the difference in the heats of formation would be simply the difference in the heats of formation of Ca^{2+} and Cd^{2+} ions from their metals, i.e. 164 kcal per g atom. In practice the differences are always smaller, e.g. 91 kcal mole^{-1} between CaO and CdO, which may be taken to indicate an appreciable measure of covalent bonding in CdO. The difference is progressively smaller for the sulphides, selenides, and tellurides (75, 50, and 40 kcal mole^{-1}) suggesting that the order of covalence is

$$Te^{2-} > Se^{2-} > S^{2-} > O^{2-}.$$

For a fuller discussion see section 31.3. The application of this method to some transition-metal compounds is given in section 25.3. For the Ca/Cd comparison, the polarizability series is presumably one of σ-donating power only, but with transition-metal ions this method does not distinguish between the various types of interaction.

(c) Differences in the stability constants of complex ions may also be used. This is essentially the same type of approach as (b), but the results are much less clear-cut because of the possibilities of varying ion-solvation energies, which may be reflected in either the heat or the entropy terms or in both. Examples will be found in Chapters 25 and 26.

24.10. Metal orbitals and covalent bonding

The electron structures of the transition-metal ions have already been treated in some detail in Chapter 23. The general pattern of orbital stability may be represented approximately as in Fig. 24.15. The disappearance of the d orbitals into the atomic core is virtually complete at the end of each transition series; the disappearance of the s orbital into the core is reflected in the occurrence of the 'inert-pair' effect in B-metal chemistry; while the disappearance of the p orbitals into the core is more firmly marked by the chemical inertness of the noble gases. In general d orbitals disappear more rapidly in the compounds of the first than in those of the second and third transition series, and s orbitals become relatively more core-like in the third transition series as a consequence of the nuclear charge increase in the lanthanide elements. The occupancy of these orbitals by electrons means that s and p orbitals may be regarded as essentially acceptor orbitals for all transition-metal ions, while d orbitals will only be acceptor in character at the beginning of the transition series and donor in character at the end.

The contribution of an orbital to binding will depend upon its energy and upon its ability to overlap with other orbitals. We have already seen (Chapter 3) that, where orbitals are strongly exposed to a field, σ-covalent binding energies due to interaction with ns and np orbitals may sometimes

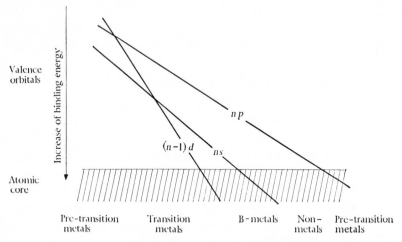

Fig. 24.15. Changes of atomic binding energy of $(n-1)d$, ns, and np electrons with atomic number in a long period of the Periodic Table (schematic). (The radial extension of each orbital decreases with increase of its binding energy.)

be related to atomic ionization potentials. In general it appears that, for σ-bonding using the ns and np orbitals of a transition-metal ion, the extra binding energy above that which might be expected on a simple ionic model is also related to the electron affinity of the orbitals as measured by atomic ionization potentials. See, for example, the increasing lattice energy of Zn^{2+} compounds relative to Ca^{2+} compounds in Fig. 24.12 in the series $I^- > Br^- > Cl^- > F^-$.

The importance of $(n-1)d$ orbital σ-bonding is more difficult to assess. The ionization potentials for these orbitals follow the patterns shown in Fig. 23.8. However, especially toward the end of the first transition series, and more generally at high charge, the $(n-1)d$ orbitals are contracted. The interaction energy between these orbitals and a ligand will not have the same dependence on the electron affinity of the orbital as it has for ns and np orbitals. The percentage occupancy of σ-bonding molecular orbitals by unpaired electrons, but not the energetic importance of the covalence, can be estimated from ESR data (Chapter 28). Some results are given in Table 24.XIII. The unpaired electrons (octahedral field) are in t_{2g} orbitals at the beginning of the transition series and in e_g orbitals at the end of the series, permitting estimations of π-bonding in the former and of σ-bonding in the latter circumstances. In the middle of the series the opposing effects of σ- and π-bonding leads to a measurement only of the *difference* between the occupation of the two types of orbital. Despite these complications the table shows that even in divalent fluorides the unpaired

TABLE 24.XIII. *Occupation of ligand orbitals by unpaired electrons as estimated from ESR measurements (after Hayes and coworkers)*

Electron configuration	Compound into which ion is doped	Ion	% occupation of p_π orbitals	% occupation of p_σ orbitals	
d^3	$KMgF_3$	V^{2+}	4·1		
		Cr^{3+}	4·8		
d^7	$KMgF_3$	Fe^+		2·5	6 near neighbours
		Co^{2+}		2·9	
		Ni^{3+}		9·3	
d^8	$KMgF_3$	Ni^{2+}		4·5	
d^9	LiF	Ni^+		17·0	2 near neighbours
				2·0	4 near neighbours

electrons in d orbitals spend only about 90 per cent of their time on the metal atoms. In these fluorides π-bonding is of considerable importance for ions such as V^{2+}, Cr^{3+}, and Ti^{3+}, while σ-bonding is important for Co^{2+} and Ni^{2+}. At constant charge the covalence contribution increases from Cr^{3+} to Ni^{3+}, but remains roughly constant in the sequence

$$V^{2+} \geqslant Co^{2+} \geqslant Ni^{2+}.$$

However, as the contribution to the *energy* is much smaller from π-bonding this results in greater bond energy in Ni^{2+} than in V^{2+}. Distortions yield very marked increases in covalence too. Thus the Ni^+ (d^9) ion can be obtained in two types of tetragonal field: 4 near and 2 more distant neighbours or 2 near and 4 more distant neighbours. In the second field the ESR measurements indicate that Ni^+–F^- bonds are each 17 per cent covalent, while in the first they are but 2·0 per cent covalent.

Extensive ESR measurements have also been made on oxides and a variety of complex ions. Where comparison has been possible, e.g. in oxides between Mn^{2+}, Fe^{2+}, and Ni^{2+}, or Ti^{3+}, V^{3+}, and Cr^{3+}, there is again evidence that the total covalence, σ and π, does not change greatly along a series of ions of fixed charge. Once again, then, the binding energy will vary with the electron affinity of the orbitals, i.e. in the orders $Cr^{3+} > V^{3+} > Ti^{3+}$ and $Cu^{2+} > Ni^{2+} > Co^{2+} > Fe^{2+} > Mn^{2+}$.

Neutron diffraction provides a more direct method of estimating co-valence than ESR, but it measures the sum of the unpaired electron densities due to σ- and π-bonding rather than their difference. Some results are given in Table 24.XIV. They show that σ-covalence increases rapidly from Mn^{2+} to Ni^{2+}. This would be expected from the increase in the ionization potentials between Mn and Ni atoms.

TABLE 24.XIV. *Covalence effects from neutron-diffraction data*

Ligand orbitals occupied by odd electrons	% occupation			
	MnO or MnF$_2$	NiO	LaCrO$_3$	LaFeO$_3$
% $(\sigma+2\pi)$	3·3	6·0	4·7	10·0
†% (σ)	1·2	6·0	..	5·4
†% (π)	1·0	..	2·3	2·3

† From NMR or ESR and neutron-diffraction experiments.

After Nathans, Will, and Cox, International Conference on Magnetism, Nottingham, 1964.

For any combination of ligands, greater covalence will be expected in the second and third transition series than in the first series, because of the larger $(n-1)d$ orbitals. This is illustrated in section 25.7 for the cations Ni^{2+}, Pd^{2+}, and Pt^{2+}.

Electronegativity values determined from heats of formation of divalent chlorides are given in Table 24.XV. They illustrate the general proposition that covalent *energy* increases along transition-metal series until the d^8 or d^9 cation. Many other thermodynamic properties are in agreement with this proposition; see Chapter 25.

TABLE 24.XV. *Pauling electronegativities as calculated for compounds* MCl$_2$

Ca	Ti	V	Cr	Mn	Fe	Co	Ni	Cu	Zn
1·04	1·5	1·53	1·70	1·60	1·80	1·85	1·90	2·10	1·70
Sr							Pd		Cd
1·05							2·20		1·70
Ba							Pt		Hg
1·05							2·40		2·10

VIBRATION FREQUENCIES

The force constant of a bond can be deduced from vibration spectra (usually infra-red). The constant is generally related to the strength of the bond for closely related molecules. In divalent metal fluorides of the first transition series the largest force constant is found for the Cu^{2+}–F^- stretching vibration. It has been concluded that this bond has the greatest covalent character.

Alternatively it is possible to study the changes in the vibration frequency of a ligand group as the metal atom is changed. For example, changes in the stretching frequency of $>C{=}O$ in salicylaldehyde complexes have been found to be closely related to the stability constants of metal complexes in the order $Pd^{2+} > Cu^{2+} > Ni^{2+} > Mn^{2+} > Mg^{2+}$. Presumably the series is that of covalence in $M—O=C\diagup^{\diagup}_{\diagdown}$.

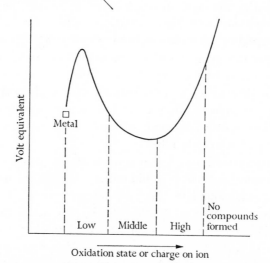

Oxidation state or charge on ion

FIG. 24.16. General pattern of Oxidation State Diagram for a transition metal.

Finally the infra-red frequencies can be used diagnostically to show how a ligand is bound to a cation. Such ligands as NCS^-, SO_3^{2-}, NO_2^-, and $(H_2N)_2CO$ have been studied, and it has been found that whereas Pd^{2+} invariably binds to the more polarizable ligand atom $N > O$; $S > O$; $S > N$, the reverse is true of say Co^{2+} or Cr^{3+}. This is taken as an indication of the more covalent character of the Pd^{2+}-ligand binding.

24.11. Variation of charge on metal-ion

The general relation between charge and stability for a typical transition-metal may be represented by the schematic Oxidation State Diagram shown in Fig. 24.16. This may be usefully compared with Figs. 20.7 and 23.11. Very low *ionic* oxidation states are usually unstable with respect to the metal and higher oxidation states. The singly-charged cation is unstable in all transition series until Group IB. Ions with relatively small charges are particularly unstable at the beginning of the transition series (e.g. Sc^+ and Sc^{2+}), and in the second and especially the third transition series, where, among other factors, the metal binding energies are correspondingly greater than in the first transition series.

This means that the *observable* chemistry of low oxidation states is non-ionic. Hydrates cannot be studied but organometallic compounds can. Thus the chemistry of the low oxidation states is in general very different in character from the chemistry of the medium and high oxidation states. This distinction will be emphasized by using the term *valence* generally for medium- and high-oxidation states. Low-oxidation-state chemistry is treated in a separate chapter, Chapter 27. However, we may note here (1) that the chemistry characteristic of low-oxidation states will tend to occur in the second and third transition series at somewhat higher oxidation states than in the first transition series, and (2) that π-acceptor ligands will be particularly favoured at low charges and towards the end of each transition series when the d orbitals on the metal atoms are both relatively large and relatively filled.

The medium-valence states are in general stable over a range of redox potentials between those which would reduce them to the metal and those which would oxidize them to the high-valence states. In practice this means that they can exist in equilibrium with a whole range of anions and ligands. This characteristic chemistry will tend to occur for *lower*-valence states towards the end of any transition series and for *higher*-valence states in the second and third transition series more than in the first.

High-valence states are almost invariably quite strongly oxidizing, and in general they become more so across each transition series and on passing from the third to the second to the first transition series. In chemical environments, no transition-metal ions are formed in which the charge on the ion is greater than the Group number, i.e. the preceding noble-gas shell is not broken into. The Group-number valence state is not reached in the first transition series after Group VIIA (Mn(VII) is very strongly oxidizing), or in the second and third transition series after Ru and Os respectively, Group VIII. As a result of the oxidizing power, high-valence-state chemistry is severely limited to combinations with anions or ligands which are not readily oxidized. This often means a restriction to oxide and fluoride, and to a smaller extent to sulphide and the heavier-halide chemistry. Usually ligand exchange is slow, and much of the chemistry of the very high oxidation states is similar to the oxide and oxyanion chemistry which has already been discussed in Chapter 14.

We may illustrate these ligand limitations by considering the series of highest valence states shown in iodides, viz.

$$TiI_4/VI_3, CrI_3/MnI_2, FeI_2, CoI_2, NiI_2/CuI,$$

but $$TaI_5?/WI_4, ReI_4, OsI_4, (IrI_3), PtI_4/AuI_3,$$

or the structures of the MS_2 sulphides where the anion may be S^{2-} as in layer structures, or S_2^{2-} (so that the cation is M^{2+}) as in the marcasite or pyrites structures (Table 24.XVI). There would seem to be a curious reversal at Pt, to which we shall refer again in section 26.9.

TABLE 24.XVI. MS_2 *structures*

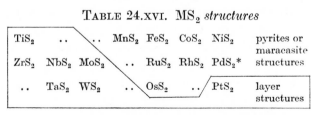

* Variant of the pyrites structure.

In section 24.9 the influence of covalent bonding on metal-ligand interaction was discussed in relation to change of ligand. We should also like to know how this influence will be modified by change of charge, but, as we shall now see, it is by no means an easy matter to reach any very general conclusions. We should perhaps begin by pointing out that the simple ionic model still works quite well with the high-valence-state transition metals in predicting the gross values of hydration and lattice energies. Thus (see Chapter 5) the trivalent ions fit quite well to the $z^2/r_{\text{effective}}$ plot for hydration energies, and (see section 23.5) the redox potential of the Zr^{4+}/Zr couple is predicted with somewhat surprising accuracy by a simple extension of this model. Similarly the lattice energies of the MO_2 oxides with the rutile structure can be estimated quite well on the basis of the formula

$$U = -NAe^2z^2/r(1-1/n),$$

where A is 4·82, the Madelung constant for the rutile structure. Some values are quoted in Table 24.XVII.

TABLE 24.XVII. *Calculated and experimental lattice energies for* MO_2 *oxides with the rutile structure (kcal mole^{-1})*

Oxide	r (exptl) (Å)	Value of n used	Calculated lattice energy	Born–Haber lattice energy
TiO_2	1·96	8	2850	2880
VO_2	1·96	8	2850	3000
CrO_2	1·93	8	2900	3060
(SnO_2)	(2·10)	$(8\frac{1}{2})$	(2690)	(2790)
(PbO_2)	(2·22)	$(9\frac{1}{2})$	(2580)	(2770)

Furthermore, the ionic model would predict that with increasing charge on the metal ion, and with the consequent reduction in size, there should be an increasing preference for smaller and more highly charged anions. This effect is generally observed as has been illustrated by the thermo-chemical comparisons of fluorides and chlorides (Chapter 12), of oxides and chlorides (Chapter 13), and of oxides and sulphides (Chapter 16). We may also note the general greater stability of oxyhalides as against halides with the smaller highly-charged ions, e.g. compare V(V) with Nb(V) or Ta(V). This then is a further factor, in addition to the redox-potential limitations, favouring oxide and fluoride chemistry with high-valence state transition metals. Size arguments based on ionic radii considerations are also useful in predicting many stereochemical configurations. Thus a general change-over from an octahedral to a tetrahedral oxygen coordination would be predicted when the metal-ion radius was reduced to about $0.414 \times 1.40 = 0.58$ Å. This is commonly found as is illustrated by the examples given in Table 24.xviii. Again the ionic model predicts that complexes $[MX_6]^{n-}$ should be unstable for $n > 3$ and, in general, this is observed. Lower-valence cations give rise to tetrahedral anionic complexes.

TABLE 24.XVIII. *Coordination polyhedra in oxides of transition-metal ions with noble-gas configurations (after Dunitz and Orgel, Adv. Inorg. Radio-chemistry, 1960, **2**, 52).*

Ion	Pauling ionic radius (Å)	Coordination	Examples
Hf^{4+}	0.81	Cubic	HfO_2
Zr^{4+}	0.80	Cubic	ZrO_2 ($>1600\,°C$)
		Distorted cubic	ZrO_2, $ZrSiO_4$
		Octahedral	$BaZrO_3$
Ti^{4+}	0.68	Octahedral	TiO_2, $BaTiO_3$ ($>120°$)
		Distorted octahedral	$BaTiO_3$
Ta^{5+}	..	Octahedral	$NaTaO_3$ ($>475°$)
		Distorted octahedral	$NaTaO_3$
Nb^{5+}	0.70	Octahedral	$NaNbO_3$ ($>640°$)
		Distorted octahedral	$FeNb_2O_6$, $NaNbO_3$
W^{6+}	..	Distorted octahedral	WO_3
		Tetrahedral	$CaWO_3$
Mo^{6+}	0.62	Distorted octahedral (square pyramidal + 1 distant)	MoO_3
		Tetrahedral	$CaMoO$
V^{5+}	0.59	Very distorted octahedral (3 near + 3 distant)	VO_2
		Trigonal bipyramid ($+1$ distant)	V_2O_5
		Trigonal pyramid	KVO_3,H_2O
		Tetrahedral	$NaVO_3$
Cr^{6+}	0.52	Tetrahedral ($+2$ distant)	CrO_3
		Tetrahedral	$BaCrO_4$
Mn^{7+}	0.46	Tetrahedral	$KMnO_4$

As an alternative to these regular structures, distorted structures may be produced with decrease of cation size. These are also to be expected on the ionic model, as is the occurrence of ferro-electric effects when ions (e.g. Ti^{4+} in $BaTiO_3$) that are too small for the holes in which they are situated can be drawn to one side by an external electric field.

Despite these apparent justifications for using the ionic model, it is of rather limited application in the high-valence states of transition metals. In part this is due to the lack of ionization-potential data on which to base ionic calculations, but it largely arises from the fact that ionization-potential sums, hydration energies, and lattice energies are now becoming so large that the small differences between them which are of chemical consequence cannot be estimated with any reliability. Thus a mere change in the repulsive component n from 8 to 10 in the lattice-energy calculation for TiO_2 would result in an increase of 83 kcal mole^{-1} in the lattice energy.

Unfortunately the thermochemical data for high-valence states are also very limited, particularly as the possible ligands are themselves often severely limited by redox-potential considerations. However, we may note the sequence given in Table 24.xix, where on the ionic model the differences in the heats of formation of chloride and iodide would have been expected to be numerically greatest with the smallest cation (Ti^{4+} or possibly Pt^{4+}), while exactly the opposite effect is observed.

TABLE 24.xix. *Heats of formation of tetrachlorides and tetraiodides*
(kcal mole^{-1})

	TiX$_4$	ZrX$_4$	ThX$_4$	PtX$_4$
$-\Delta H_f$ MCl$_4$	190·4	231·9	284·5	53·0
$-\Delta H_f$ MI$_4$	101·0	130·0	146·0	10·0
Difference	89·4	101·9	138·5	43·0

At the time of writing (1965) there are insufficient physical data, e.g. ESR, on higher-valence transition-metal complexes to warrant general conclusions. The percentage covalence (Table 24.xiii) is greater in Ni^{3+} than in Ni^{2+} fluorides and oxides. It is also much greater in Fe^{3+} than in Mn^{2+} compounds, Table 24.xiv. It could well be that covalence decreases from zero to two valence and then increases in higher valences. On the other hand the measured percentage covalent character in $[IrCl_6]^{2-}$ is very little different from that in $[CrF_6]^{3-}$. Undoubtedly the energy resulting from this covalence is greater in the iridium compound. Covalence in Pt^{2+} and Pt^{4+} complexes, estimated from nuclear quadrupole coupling constants, increases with charge from some 40 to 60 per cent.

24.12. Interatomic distances

Before the thermodynamic stability of transition-metal compounds can be understood in terms of any model, interatomic distances must also be examined. These distances are related to stability in a complicated way (see Chapters 3 and 5), the interpretation depending very much on the model under consideration.

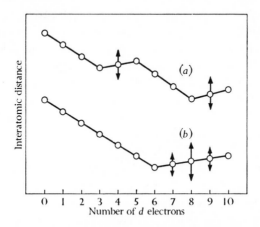

Fig. 24.17. Change of interatomic distance (octahedral field) with atomic number for series of (a) high-spin and (b) low-spin transition-metal compounds as predicted by a simple crystal-field model.

IONIC MODEL

The ionic model predicts that, for a fixed structure and for atoms of fixed charge, the interatomic distances will depend on the repulsive forces. It is these forces which give an ion an effective size. Reference to Chapter 5 shows that they may be expressed in terms of n, the exponent of r in B/r^n. It is difficult to say how the filling of the d sub-shell affects this exponent, but in the lanthanides the sizes of the ions decrease markedly more slowly with atomic number towards the end of the series. There is, too, a small anomaly at the ion with the half-filled f sub-shell. Clearly changes in structure can produce discontinuities in the variation of distance with atomic number and only compounds of the same structure should be compared. Crystal-field theory adds an additional attractive energy to the ionic model. Its magnitude has been given in sections 24.3 to 24.5. The effect of the new energy should be such as to produce a contraction proportional to this energy (Chapter 5 B). Thus the expected plots of distance against atomic number are as in the sketch, Fig. 24.17. The distortions of orbitally-degenerate ground states (Jahn–Teller theorem) lead to deviations of uncertain magnitude especially at d^4, d^9 (high-spin), and d^8 (low-spin) ions.

MOLECULAR-ORBITAL THEORY

Molecular-orbital theory modifies the above account in two ways. (1) σ-bonding will produce an additional energy of covalence roughly proportional to the electron affinity of the cation. This therefore would deepen the troughs in the distance plots. (2) π-donation of cation electrons to the ligand will further accentuate this effect, but π-donation of ligand electrons to the cation will only shorten bond lengths where there are few d electrons, i.e. at the beginning of the series. The effect of σ- and π-bonding is to make M–L distances dependent on the specific M and L under consideration.

Finally, if the covalent interactions are treated in terms of atoms (section 24.14) instead of ions, interatomic distances would be expected to decrease as the number of bonding electrons increased, and then increase as the number of antibonding electrons increased; see also Chapter 3. There would also be an effect of the differences in electronegativity which, for any ligand, decrease along a transition-metal series.

TABLE 24.XX. *Pauling ionic radii in the three transition series* (Å)

Ca^{2+}	0·99			Ni^{2+}	0·72	Zn^{2+}	0·74
Sr^{2+}	1·13			Pd^{2+}	0·86	Cd^{2+}	0·97
Ba^{2+}	1·35	Yb^{2+}	1·13			Hg^{2+}	1·10
Sc^{3+}	0·81			Co^{3+}	0·63	Ga^{3+}	0·62
Y^{3+}	0·93					In^{3+}	0·81
La^{3+}	1·15	Lu^{3+}	0·93			Tl^{3+}	0·95
Ti^{4+}	0·68					Ge^{4+}	0·53
Zr^{4+}	0·80					Sn^{4+}	0·71
Ce^{4+}	1·01	Hf^{4+}	0·81	Pt^{4+}	(0·70)	Pb^{4+}	0·84

INTERATOMIC DISTANCES IN SOLIDS

Table 24.XX shows that even the simplest prediction, that there would be a contraction from the beginning to the end of all three transition series, is incorrect. The contraction in the first series is greater than that in the second series, but there is little or none in the third series, cf. Yb^{2+}, Hg^{2+}; Lu^{3+}, Tl^{3+} and Hf^{4+}, Pb^{4+}. As attractive energies increase in all three series it is a necessary conclusion that the repulsion energy B/r^n must increase along the third series.

The contractions in ions of valence states 2, 3, and 4 in the first transition series are shown in Fig. 24.18 for compounds where the binding is most ionic, e.g. MO, M_2O_3, and K_2MF_6. The overall form of the plots is somewhat similar to that for the lanthanide ions (section 21.4). However, the

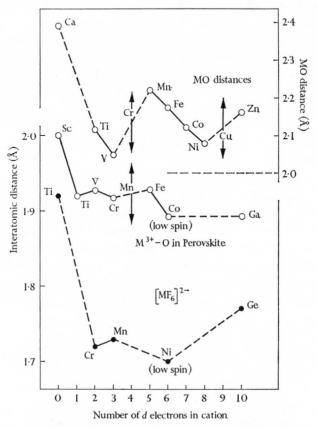

FIG. 24.18. Interatomic distances in MO, perovskite, and K_2MF_6 compounds plotted against the number of $3d$ electrons in the M^{n+} ion.

plots show four differences from those in the lanthanide series. (1) The changes along the divalent series are much larger, and sufficient to make the transition-metal ions smaller in certain cases than B-metal ions, Pauling radii: Ni^{2+} 0·72, Zn^{2+} 0·74; Co^{3+} 0·63, Ga^{3+} 0·62 Å. (2) The line joining Ca^{2+} and Zn^{2+} or Sc^{3+} and Ga^{3+} does not pass very close to the value for the ions Mn^{2+} or Fe^{3+}, the half-filled sub-shell ions. In Fig. 21.5 the line from La^{3+} to Lu^{3+} passes very close to Gd^{3+}. (3) It is clear that there is a much larger change in radius in the first half of the series from Ca^{2+} to

Mn^{2+} than in the second half from Mn^{2+} to Zn^{2+}. (4) The smallest divalent ion in transition-metal oxides is V^{2+}, i.e. an ion before the half-filled sub-shell. The smallest ion in the lanthanide series is the last one.

Some of these features are qualitatively explicable on application of the simple ionic model and crystal-field theory (Fig. 24.17), but in particular the

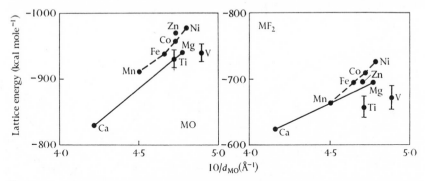

FIG. 24.19. Lattice energies of oxides and fluorides compared with reciprocals of lattice distances in oxides.

small sizes of the early ions in the series are unexpected. The peculiar character of the ion sizes is brought out quantitatively in a plot of lattice energy against the reciprocal of the interatomic distance (Fig. 24.19), which shows that the later transition-metal ions are distinguished from pre-transition metal ions in a different way from the early transition-metal ions. The ionic model could be used to explain the observations by postulating different values of the repulsive exponent, n, across the series, but no evidence is available to show that this is justified. They could also be due to covalent bonding differences, the metal acting as a π-acceptor at the beginning of the series and as a π-donor later. This explanation agrees with the ESR evidence.

The covalent and ionic models lead to different expectations for the changes in M–L distances along the transition series and with the nature of L. Experimental changes are shown in Figs. 24.20 and 24.21; see also Chapter 5B. Nickel(II), d^8, becomes smaller relative to vanadium(II), d^3, in the order $(F^-) \to Cl^- \to Br^- \to I^-$ and in the order $O^{2-} \to S^{2-} \to Se^{2-} \to Te^{2-}$, suggesting that σ-bond covalence increases in importance relative to π-bond covalence in these sequences.

Other factors which affect bond distances are distortions from simple symmetries and changes of spin state. The closest distances in Cu^{2+} complexes are often short compared with those in octahedral Ni^{2+} complexes.

The origin of the distortion can be interpreted in terms of the Jahn–Teller effect even on a purely crystal-field theory, but the valence-bond (dsp^2 hybrids) and molecular-orbital descriptions with their insistence on the importance of covalence are probably more appropriate. 4-coplanar Cu^{2+} complexes are readily obtained.

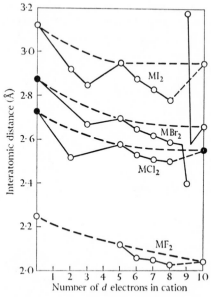

FIG. 24.20. Changes in interatomic distances in some MX_2 compounds of the first transition series. The points marked ● are estimates from ionic radii for 6-fold coordination of the cation.

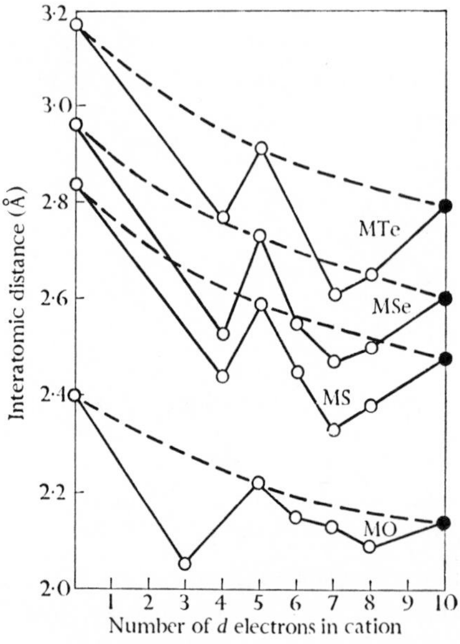

FIG. 24.21. Changes in interatomic distances in some MX compounds of the first transition series. The points marked ● are estimates from ionic radii for 6-fold coordination of the cation.

In low-spin states bond distances are at least 0.1 Å shorter than in high-spin states. Unfortunately data are not available for a long series of comparable low-spin compounds. It is expected that the plots of distance against atomic number for the compounds of the second and third transition series (all low-spin) will go through a single minimum around perhaps the d^8 ions.

METAL-ION LIGAND DISTANCES IN COMPLEXES

A further simple test of the covalent polarization of ligands by cations is provided by interatomic distances in complexes. Covalent polarization will lead to bond-length contractions, and the more polarizable a ligand the greater will be this contraction. Generally nitrogen ligands are more polarizable than oxygen ligands, so that as a transition-metal series is traversed there should be a noticeably greater change in M—N than in M—O bond distances. Some data are collected in Table 24.xxi. In some of the complexes the change in M—N as compared with that in M—O for *the same ligand* is even sufficient to change the bond-length order. In series of complexes, such as the EDTA complexes of the divalent and trivalent cations of the first transition series, the ligand undergoes continuous modification under the influence of the cation. Such observations are extremely important in the interpretation of thermodynamic changes in transition-metal series.

TABLE 24.xxi. M—N *and* M—O *distances in complexes*

Complex	M—N (Å)	M—O (Å)
Mn^{2+} (EDTA)	2·35–2·39	2·21–2·26
Ni^{2+} (EDTA)	2·08–2·13	2·03–2·16
Fe^{3+} (EDTA)	2·30–2·32	2·05
Co^{3+} (EDTA) (low-spin)	1·92	1·88
La^{3+} (EDTA)	2·86	2·54
Cu^{2+} (8-OH-quinolinate)$_2$	1·99	1·95
Pd^{2+} (8-OH-quinolinate)$_2$ (low-spin)	~2·00	2·00
UO_2^{2+} (8-OH quinolinate)$_2$	2·51–2·58	2·25–2·32
Mn^{2+} (pyridoxal alaninate)	2·23	2·08 (phenolate) 2·17 (carboxylate)
Ni^{2+} (salicylaldoximate)$_2$ (low-spin)	1·80	1·90
Cu^{2+} (salicylaldoximate)$_2$	1·90	1·99
Pd^{2+} (salicylaldoximate)$_2$ (low-spin)	1·86	1·94

24.13. Metal–metal bonding

In an NaCl lattice the anions form an octahedron around the cation. The second nearest neighbours of the cation are twelve other cations positioned on the lines drawn from the cation through the mid-points of two octahedral positions. Now these directions are exactly those of the maximum density of the t_{2g} metal orbitals. If the radial extension of these orbitals is great, as it is early in the first transition series, or throughout most of the second and third series, and generally at low charge, strong interaction will occur between the metal t_{2g} orbitals leading to metal–metal bonding. Metal–metal bonding can be detected by magnetic and electrical-conductivity measurements and is also reflected in interatomic distances.

Oxides of metals at the end of the first transition series are in many respects rather like ionic crystals. A study of their absorption spectra strengthens this view. However, the oxides or better still the nitrides and carbides of metals at the beginning of the same series are more properly considered on the band model (Chapter 6) for they are often good metallic conductors. Oxides of these early transition metals change with a lowering of temperature from a metallic type of conductivity to that of a semi-conductor. For compounds with second-row non-metals the ionic model has lost much of its validity, even at the end of the first transition series. For example, in sulphides this change is shown by low magnetic moments, by the structures (e.g. NiAs for sulphides instead of NaCl for oxides), and by the black colour and metallic or good 'semi-metallic' conductivity. The change arises partly from the changed electronegativity difference, partly from a change to low-spin states, and partly from the presence of $3d$ orbitals in atoms like sulphur. These otherwise empty orbitals make a set of bonding orbitals of the complex shown as t_{2g} in Fig. 24.11. The binding of sulphur by the later transition metals (per metal atom) is almost as strong as the binding by the earlier metals. A similar effect has been noticed in the relative heats of formation of nitrides and phosphides (Chapter 17).

The covalent model is even more appropriate in the second and third transition series. At the beginning of the series metal–metal bonding is very commonly found, especially in low-valence compounds where the d orbitals are strongly exposed, but it is also known even in quite high-valence states such as Nb(IV) and Mo(V). Although this effect does increase with less electronegative ligands, e.g. chloride and sulphide, it is also observed here in fluorides and oxides. Spin pairing, which is generally observed in the compounds of the second and third transition series, increases the repulsion between the core electrons which therefore become more exposed. Metal–metal bonds between two different metals have also been observed in low-valence complexes. The most usual combination is between a transition metal and a B-metal atom or ion with an 'inert pair' of electrons, e.g. Hg^0, Sn^{2+}, or Au^-.

24.14. Molecular-orbital theory for atoms

The ionic model considers isolated cations and anions. In the opposite limit all the *atoms* in an assembly are regarded as interacting with one another. This approach is the one adopted in Chapter 6 for the binding of metals, and it is appropriate to return now to this covalent model in order to see if it throws a different light on transition-metal compounds.

We shall use the same approach as that used in Chapter 3. There we saw that if there are n low-energy (good bonding) orbitals belonging to a central atom then the resulting molecular orbitals can stabilize a maximum of $2n$ electrons from ligand or metal atoms. This fact lies behind the so-called 8-electron and 18-electron rules. Thus for a series of transition-metal atoms in compounds of fixed formula, say MX_2, the stability of their compounds might well be expected to increase until there are $2n$ electrons and then fall. As the number of electrons is increased beyond $2n$, the extra electrons must become antibonding. An example helps to make this clear. The heats of formation of the transition *metals* from the transition-metal atoms are plotted in Fig. 19.12. In the third transition series the heats rise to a maximum at Group VI and then fall to Group IIB. This suggests that there are about six orbitals for bonding per metal atom, i.e. five d and one s, and that the three p orbitals are of too high an energy to play a very significant role at low charge. In Fig. 24.22 (b) these heats are plotted in an idealized form as the lower broken line. If, however, the d electrons had served no other purpose than just to fill the core the continuous line would have been expected, much as in the lanthanides. An

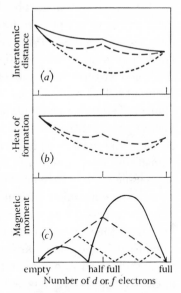

FIG. 24.22. Schematic comparison between (a) interatomic distances (metals or compounds), (b) heats of formation from atoms (metals or compounds), and (c) magnetic moments (compounds) for lanthanides (continuous line), high-spin transition metals (upper broken line), and low-spin transition metals (lower broken line).

intermediate situation is represented by the upper broken line—very much as is observed for the first transition series. This pattern reflects the contraction of the d electrons into the core along the series.

In Chapter 3 we also showed that, parallel to the increase in the excess of bonding electrons over antibonding electrons, there is a decrease in interatomic distance. In the three series of transition metals the plot of interatomic distance against atomic number shows a distinct parallel with that of the heat of sublimation; see Fig. 24.22 (a). The magnetic moments of the metals (Chapter 19) and their compounds (Fig. 24.22 (c)) confirm that the electron configurations are different in the first series from those in the second and third series. Thus it would appear that the d orbitals in the first series (especially after the half-filled sub-shell) behave more like core than valence electrons. Their behaviour is deviating from a model in which there are apparently six bonding orbitals, five d and one s, to one in which there are apparently less than six—in the extreme case just one s. In this respect the metals of the first transition series once again conform more or less to the pattern found in the lanthanide or better still the actinide series of metals (Fig. 19.10). The plots for *compounds* of the first transition series given in Figs. 24.20 and 24.21, and which have been described in terms of a model starting from ions, are also not strikingly different. The resemblance is greater in tellurides than sulphides than oxides. Tellurides are most alloy-like. In fact the deviation from ionic behaviour or lanthanide-like behaviour is very much that expected if the cause of the deviations is covalent binding. The interatomic distances in transition-metal compounds can thus be related to either a pure covalent or an ionic model. By considering the heats of formation of the compounds we can show a similar difficulty of classification in terms of the models.

In Chapter 4 it was stressed that heats of formation of compounds also vary with the number of valence electrons, much as do the heats of formation of the homonuclear assemblies themselves. This relationship is most clearly observed in compounds where the atoms do not differ too greatly in electronegativity. We shall next consider therefore the heats of formation *from atoms* of series of oxides, carbides, and nitrides. We shall not ascribe any 'valence' in these compounds, but assume only that the atoms in the assembly provide a set of orbitals into which electrons may be placed in such a manner that the magnetic properties of the assembly are reproduced. The filling of bonding orbitals should then stabilize the assembly, while the filling of antibonding orbitals should destabilize it.

In an assembly which has the rock salt (NaCl) structure each metal is surrounded by six near neighbours of a different kind. While describing the crystal-field and molecular-orbital theories, we have shown that the symmetry of the d orbitals is such that only two (e_g) of the five d orbitals point directly at the ligands in an octahedral field. There are four additional orbitals capable of forming σ-bonds. They are the s orbital and the three p orbitals, as shown in Fig. 24.8. These six orbitals, one s, three p, and two d, are just those which contribute to the familiar d^2sp^3 hybrid orbitals, the octahedral disposition of which has already been described using valence-bond theory. Apart from these six orbitals there are three other d orbitals (t_{2g}) which bisect the angle between two octahedral bonds (Fig. 24.1). These orbitals are of the correct symmetry to form π-bonds with the π or π^* orbitals of the ligands. The two types of d bonds which are being described are shown in Figs. 24.8 and 24.9. The energy-level diagram is now as in Fig. 24.11, and we may proceed to consider the filling of orbitals in keeping with the observed magnetic moments as in Chapter 2.

At the beginning of a transition series, where there are few d electrons, there may be sufficient orbitals for all the electrons (paired and unpaired) of the ligand (which usually has a large number) and of the metal to go

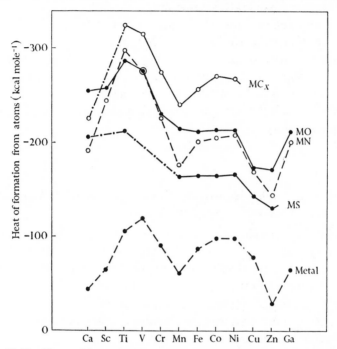

Fig. 24.23. Heats of formation from *atoms* of some series of transition-metal compounds. Compare Fig. 24.22 (*b*).

into bonding orbitals, so that the compounds have a high stability. At the end of the series the number of electrons exceeds the number of bonding orbitals, and the excess electrons must go into antibonding orbitals and hence reduce the stability of the compounds. It follows that ligands with no empty orbitals, fluoride ion for example, will be particularly suitable for binding elements early in a transition series, while ligands with empty π-acceptor orbitals will be better adapted for binding later transition metals. These generalizations can only be seen as differences in plots such as those of Fig. 24.23, and are thus more readily demonstrated in plots such as the O/S thermochemical comparison given in Chapter 16.

A consequence of the changing stability of the d, s, and p orbitals relative to a given ligand, and of the changing numbers of d electrons along any series of transition-metal compounds, is that heats of formation of compounds from free atoms fall (Fig. 24.23). We can refer this to the empirical parameter, electronegativity (Chapter 4) saying that along the transition-metal series the electronegativity of atoms increases, and the polarity of bonds tends to decrease.

Even without quantitative reasoning we can see now how a covalent model can describe in different language a set of observations which can also be discussed from the point of view of the ionic model. The two approaches have one common feature of great importance—symmetry. In particular the splitting of d orbitals in a field, ionic or covalent, follows the same pattern and is dependent on the symmetry of the ligands about the central ion. Thus the two main models should be used together in transition-metal chemistry.

Problems

1. How does a simple electrostatic field of (a) linear, and (b) tetragonal character split d orbitals? (See Fig. 28.4.)

2. (a) Show that simple electrostatic fields of (i) linear, (ii) tetragonal, symmetry split the three p orbitals, giving two low-lying orbitals and one low-lying orbital respectively, and that octahedral and tetrahedral fields do not split these orbitals.

(b) The I^+ ion in concentrated sulphuric acid is said to be paramagnetic and coloured blue due to a weak $p \leftarrow p$ absorption band. Does this accord with crystal-field arguments?

3. What is implied by assuming that the baricentre of orbitals does not change in a field? Consider first the effect of an electrostatic field and then of a small amount of covalence.

4. Show that for d^4 high-spin ions the relative energy of an octahedral over a tetrahedral field is $-\frac{3}{5}(10Dq) + \frac{2}{5}(10D'q)$.

5. Using the discussion in section 23.2 show that high-spin to low-spin changes are opposed by the greatest repulsion energies in d^5 cations (Fig. 24.6).

6. Assume that there are two ligands X and Y, which, for steric reasons, can give only octahedral, MX_6, and tetrahedral, MY_4, complexes, respectively. Considering crystal-field effects alone, show that if the tetrahedral complex is to be formed the ratio of the field strength of Y to that of X must be greater than 1·5 for high-spin d^1, d^2, d^6, and d^7 ions on the one

hand and greater than 3·375 for high-spin d^3 and d^8 ions on the other. What complications arise in the d^4 and d^9 cases?

7. Plot a diagram for tetrahedral complexes corresponding to Fig. 24.6 for octahedral complexes.

8. Show that the spin-only magnetic moment for a d^6 ion is normally 4·90 or 0·0 B.M. in an octahedral field, but 4·90 or 2·83 B.M. in a tetrahedral field.

9. What are the probable values of the spin-only magnetic moments of a d^6 ion in (a) a simple linear field, (b) a simple tetragonal field, (c) a simple octahedral field? Discuss the effect of increasing field strength.

10. Why is the colour of $[Cu(NH_3)_4]^{2+}$ different from that of $[Cu(H_2O)_6]^{2+}$?

11. Show that only six of the d^5sp^3 orbitals of a metal ion can form σ-bonds in octahedral symmetry.

12. Show that of the d^5sp^3 orbitals three can give π-bonding in an octahedral field and two in a tetrahedral field. Use Figs. 24.1 and 24.2.

13. On the basis of the crystal-field model would you expect the Mo(V) cation to occur preferentially in an octahedral or a tetrahedral field?

14. On the crystal-field model the splitting of d orbitals is shown as developing from the five d orbitals in a particular ion; see, for example, Fig. 24.3. While the same symmetry considerations are used in molecular-orbital discussion of splitting, the picture is modified in a number of ways. What are these modifications?

15. How would you expect radius-ratio considerations (Chapter 5) to affect the stereochemistry of various transition-metal cations? Consider both different valence states and different elements. Are your theoretical predictions roughly correct?

16. The magnetic moments of two Mn^{2+} compounds are

$$K_4[Mn(NCS)_6],3H_2O \quad 6·06 \text{ B.M.}$$
$$K_4[Mn(CN)_6],3H_2O \quad 2·13 \text{ B.M.}$$

Comment.

17. 'A given transition-metal ion does not always possess the same coordination number and stereochemistry. An exception is Co^{3+}, which nearly always occurs in an octahedral coordination.' Comment.

18. Account for the fact that many Co(II) complexes (e.g. $[CoCl_4]^{2-}$ and $[CoCl_3.H_2O]^-$) are tetrahedral.

19. Co_3O_4 is a normal spinel with Co(II) in tetrahedral holes of the oxygen lattice. Comment. (See section 28.11 for a discussion of the spinel structure.)

20. In the compound K_2CuF_4, each Cu atom has two F atoms at 1·95 Å, and a further four F atoms at 2·08 Å. Comment.

21. The fluoride complexes of Cu(III) and Au(III) are CuF_6^{3-} (paramagnetic) and AuF_4^- (diamagnetic). Comment.

22. Planar 4-coordination is commonly found for Rh(I), Ir(I), Ni(II), Cu(II), Pd(II), Pt(II), and Au(III). How may this be accounted for?

23. Comment on the following:
   (a) The Co^{2+} ion readily forms a tetrahedral complex chloride $[CoCl_4]^{2-}$, but the Ni^{2+} ion does so only with difficulty.
   (b) The step-wise stability constants in aqueous solution for the formation of the three complexes of Cu^{2+} with ethylenediamine are $10^{10·55}$, $10^{9·05}$, and $10^{-1·0}$.
   (c) A solution containing $[Ni(H_2O)_6]^{2+}$ is green, but on addition of cyanide the colour disappears and the complex $[Ni(CN)_4]^{2-}$ is formed.

24. Comment on the fact that the familiar hydrated sulphates of copper and nickel have the formulae $CuSO_4,5H_2O$ and $NiSO_4,7H_2O$.

25. Comment on the fact that while an aqueous solution of cobalt(III) sulphate is diamagnetic it becomes paramagnetic when a large excess of fluoride is added.

26. Can you account for the general order of ligands:

$$CN^- > en > NH_3 > pyridine > C_2O_4^{2-} > H_2O > F^- > Cl^- > Br^- > I^-$$

in the spectrochemical series? (See Chapter 28.)

27. Comment on the following series of experimental (i.e. Born–Haber) lattice energies (kcal mole^{-1}):

CaO ($-828·2$), TiO ($-927·8$), VO ($-936·1$), MnO ($-911·4$), FeO ($-937·6$), CoO ($-954·1$), NiO ($-974·2$), ZnO ($-964·4$), MnS ($-801·3$), ZnS ($-864·5$), MnSe ($-789·6$), ZnSe ($-863·1$).

28. The ionic radius of Ca^{2+} is 0·99, and that of Cd^{2+} 0·97 Å. Comment on the following lattice energies (kcal mole^{-1}) obtained from the appropriate Born–Haber cycles:

CaF$_2$ (-624), CaI$_2$ (-492), CaO (-828);
CdF$_2$ (-662), CdI$_2$ (-576), CdO (-901).

29. It will be seen from Table 24.I that the observed magnetic moments of Cr^{2+} and Mn^{3+} tend to lie below the spin-only values, while those of Fe^{2+}, Co^{2+}, and Ni^{2+} tend to lie above. Comment on these observations.

30. The word 'polarization' covers a multitude of phenomena. Can you say what they have in common? Is it possible to replace the concept by something more specific? If so what? It may be helpful to refer to Chapter 5 B.

Bibliography

C. J. BALLHAUSEN, *Introduction to Ligand Field Theory*, McGraw-Hill, New York, 1962.

F. A. COTTON, 'Ligand Field Theory', *J. Chem. Education*, 1964, **41**, 466.

F. A. COTTON, *Chemical Applications of Group Theory*, Interscience, New York, 1963.

P. GEORGE and D. S. McCLURE, The Effect of Inner Orbital Splitting on the Thermodynamic Properties of Transition Metal Compounds and Coordination Complexes, *Progress in Inorganic Chemistry*, vol. 1, ed. F. A. Cotton, Interscience, New York, 1959.

H. B. GRAY, 'Molecular Orbital Theory for Transition Metal Complexes', *J. Chem. Education*, 1964, **41**, 2.

J. S. GRIFFITH, *The Theory of Transition Metal Ions*, Cambridge University Press, 1961.

N. S. HUSH, 'Crystal Field Stabilization and Site Deformation in Crystals and Complexes containing Transition Ions', *Disc. Faraday Soc.*, 1958, **26**, 145.

C. K. JØRGENSEN, *Absorption Spectra and Chemical Bonding in Complexes*, Pergamon Press, Oxford, 1962.

J. LEWIS, 'Metal–metal Interactions in Coordination Compounds', Eighth International Conference of Coordination Chemistry, Vienna, 1964.

L. E. ORGEL, *An Introduction to Transition-Metal Chemistry, Ligand-Field Theory*, Methuen, London, 1960.

L. F. PHILLIPS, *Basic Quantum Chemistry*, Wiley, New York. 1965.

P. W. SELWOOD, *Magnetochemistry*, Interscience, New York, 1956.

The sizes of d orbitals are discussed by:

J. W. RICHARDSON, W. C. NIEUWPOORT, R. R. POWELL, and W. F. EDGELL, *J. Chem. Phys.*, 1962, **36**, 1057;

R. E. WATSON, *Phys. Rev.*, 1960, **118**, 1036, and 1960, **119**, 1934.

25 · Transition Metals: Divalent Ions

25.1. Introduction

DIVALENT IONS

Compounds in which the metal is exhibiting a formal valence of two are known for the majority of transition metals. However, for many of the elements of the second and third transition series such compounds are few, often unstable and poorly characterized, and are commonly found to have strong bonding between individual metal atoms. We shall therefore be concerned, for the most part, with the horizontal comparison provided by the divalent ions of the first transition series,

$$Ca^{2+}, \text{—}, Ti^{2+}, V^{2+}, Cr^{2+}, Mn^{2+}, Fe^{2+}, Co^{2+}, Ni^{2+}, Cu^{2+}, \text{ and } Zn^{2+},$$

and the vertical comparison provided by the divalent ions,

$$Ni^{2+}, Pd^{2+}, \text{ and } Pt^{2+}.$$

The vertical comparison, Mg^{2+}, Ca^{2+}, Sr^{2+}, and Ba^{2+}, has been discussed in Chapter 20, while the vertical comparison, Zn^{2+}, Cd^{2+}, and Hg^{2+}, will be treated in Chapters 30, 31, and 32.

The formation of the metal ions from the metals involves the metal sublimation energies and ionization potentials, which have already been discussed in Chapter 19 and Chapter 23 respectively. To make use of the ionic model it is then necessary to know the ionic radii. Here difficulties arise at once. (1) Many of the compounds of the divalent ions crystallize in non-ionic structures. Thus $TiCl_2$ and VCl_2 have the CdI_2 layer structure, while TiS, TiSe, TiTe, VS, VSe, and VTe have the NiAs alloy-like structure. Apart from PdF_2 which crystallizes in the rutile structure, there appear to be no regular ionic lattices known for Pd(II) and Pt(II) compounds; in PdO and PtO, for example, the metal atoms are surrounded by four oxygen atoms in the same plane. (2) Some even of the essentially ionic structures are distorted. This is particularly marked for the high-spin d^4 and for the d^9 ions (the Jahn–Teller effect). Thus CrF_2 and CuF_2 are isostructural with a distorted form of the rutile structure, in which there are four short M–F distances (Cr 2·00, Cu 1·93 Å) and two long M–F distances (Cr 2·43, Cu 2·27 Å). (3) Ionic radii are not constant but depend on the ligand.

Two sets of ionic radii for the divalent ions of the first transition series are plotted in Fig. 25.1. Reasonable agreement between the Pauling radii

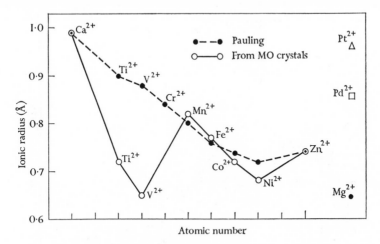

Fig. 25.1. Ionic radii of the high-spin divalent ions in the first transition series.

and the 'oxide' radii are found in the second half of the series, but the values for Ti^{2+} and V^{2+} are very different in the two sets. The Pauling radii are based on a smooth change from Ca^{2+} to Mn^{2+}, and may perhaps represent 'idealized' radii in which the effects of specific metal-ligand interactions are not present. There is thus a similarity between the general contraction in these radii and the relatively smooth contraction in the M^{3+} ions of the lanthanide series. The 'oxide' radii must to some extent reflect the M—O bond contractions which arise from π-donation to the metal ions in the first part of the series, where the d orbitals are relatively empty (see section 24.6).

The radii plotted for Pd^{2+} and Pt^{2+} are only rough estimates, although such values do appear to have been generally accepted. It will be seen that the radius of Pt^{2+} is approximately equal to that of Ca^{2+}, so that a comparison between the properties of Pt^{2+} and Ca^{2+} is likely to be particularly instructive in bringing out the effects of non-ionic bonding. In a similar manner either Mn^{2+} or Pd^{2+} may be compared with a mean of Ca^{2+} and Mg^{2+}, and Ni^{2+} with Mg^{2+}.

One general distinction between the transition-metal ions from Mn^{2+} to

Zn^{2+} and the Group IIA ions is brought out by the plot of the ionization-potential sum against the ionic radius in Fig. 25.2. It will be seen that for a given radius these transition-metal ions have considerably higher electron affinities. This distinction is even more marked when Pd^{2+} and Pt^{2+} are compared with the Group IIA ions. These higher electron affinities

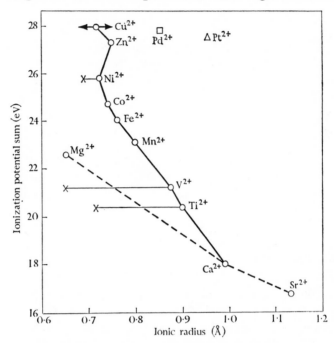

FIG. 25.2. A comparison of pre-transition and transition metals. The relation between the ionization-potential sum and the radius of the divalent ions formed. Points marked X correspond to radii derived from oxide lattices (see Fig. 25.1).

are reflected in a greater tendency for covalent bonding which increases very generally across the transition series from the pre-transition ions to the B-metal ions, and from Ni^{2+} to Pd^{2+} and Pt^{2+}. The early ions of the transition series are seen to be anomalous if radii from oxides are used and not Pauling radii; cf. Fig. 24.19. The pattern of change is clearly complicated considerably by the occupation and the symmetry properties of the d orbitals, and by the extent to which the d orbitals in particular are exposed to the ligand field. The latter will vary with the atomic number and charge of the metal atom and with the character of the ligand. We are thus led back directly to the considerations of the previous chapter.

ENERGIES AND EQUILIBRIA

In this chapter we shall be generally concerned with the way in which chemical equilibria change from one divalent ion to another. Some of the problems which we shall meet may be illustrated by considering the

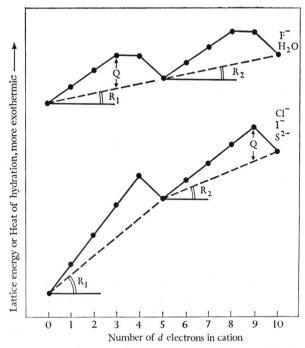

FIG. 25.3. Schematic representation of the relation between lattice (or hydration) energy and the number of d electrons for high-spin divalent ions. Upper plot (type A) corresponds to a non-polarizable ligand, lower plot (type B) to a polarizable ligand, see section 25.3.

energies of high-spin divalent ions of the first transition series in octahedral ligand fields. An example of these energies is provided by Fig. 24.12, where the lattice energies of the divalent halides of the first transition series are plotted as a function of atomic number. Similar plots are obtained for other lattice energies and for hydration energies. The main features of these plots may be represented as in Fig. 25.3, where (1) R_1 and R_2 are the slopes of the lines joining Ca^{2+} to Mn^{2+} and Mn^{2+} to Zn^{2+} respectively, and (2) Q is the extra stabilization energy above these lines. The R values are in part associated with the contraction in ion size between Ca^{2+} and Zn^{2+}, but mostly they reflect the general increase in covalence between the pre-transition and B-metal ions. The Q values are more largely associated with the symmetry effects discussed in Part A of the previous chapter.

As we have seen, these are best interpreted in terms of molecular-orbital theory, but they can often be discussed using the simpler formalism of the crystal-field approach.

The following generalizations may be made.

(1) The values of R_1 and R_2 are greater the larger and more polarizable the anion. For systems obeying an ionic model the general contraction of ions from Ca^{2+} to Mn^{2+} and from Mn^{2+} to Zn^{2+} would have led to greater values for R_1 and R_2 with *smaller* anions (cf. the change Ca^{2+} to Mg^{2+}).

(2) R_1 varies from being the same as R_2 (fluoride) to being greater than R_2 (sulphide). This may be because F^- is a small anion of low polarizability while S^{2-} is a large anion of high polarizability.

(3) The values of Q can be greater (oxide) or smaller (sulphide) in the first half of the transition series as compared with the second. O^{2-} behaves as a strong π-donor, S^{2-} is a strong σ-donor.

(4) The size of Q is usually $Fe^{2+} < Co^{2+} < Ni^{2+}$ and $Ti^{2+} < V^{2+}$ but it behaves somewhat irregularly for Cu^{2+} and Cr^{2+}, in part because of the Jahn–Teller energy, which is larger for polarizable ligands.

In considering chemical equilibria, we are most commonly concerned with the problem of a *change of ligands* by one particular metal ion, rather than with the absolute value of the ion-ligand interaction. We are thus looking at relatively small energy differences between such curves as are given in Fig. 25.3, and depending on the R and Q values almost any sequence may be expected along the divalent ions of the first transition series. In practice, however, many of these equilibria can be represented as essentially a change from a less to a more polarizable ligand (or vice versa). Some correlation might therefore be expected with the changes in the ionization-potential sums, these representing a crude measure of the tendency of the metal ion to draw electrons to itself by the formation of covalent bonds. We demonstrate this relation first of all in Fig. 25.4, where the experimental differences between the heats of formation of divalent chlorides and fluorides are plotted. The upper line gives the differences calculated on a simple ionic model using Pauling radii. The discrepancies between the calculated and the experimental values are then compared with the trends in the ionization potentials (note that the latter have a different energy scale). The relation is also brought out in Fig. 25.5, where $\log K_1$ values for the reaction

$$M(aq.)^{2+} + \text{ethylenediamine} \rightleftharpoons [M(\text{ethylenediamine})aq.]^{2+}$$

are compared with the ionization-potential sums.

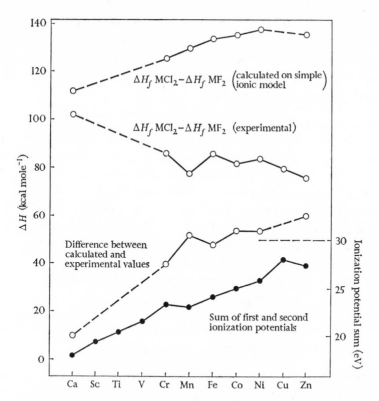

FIG. 25.4. A comparison between deviations from the ionic model in MX_2 compounds and the ionization potentials of M.

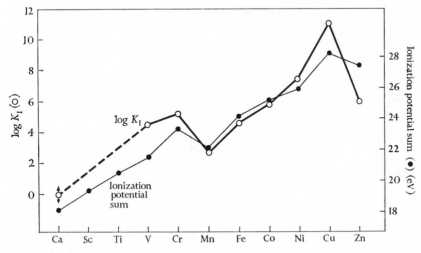

FIG. 25.5. The logarithms of first step-stability constants of ethylenediamine complexes in aqueous solution at 25 °C compared with the ionization energies of the metal atoms to give the divalent cations.

It must, however, be remembered (see Chapter 7 and section 20.6) that correlations between theoretical energy changes and observed effects may show up in free-energy (i.e. equilibria), heat, or entropy terms, but not necessarily in any or all of these.

OUTLINE OF CHAPTER

We shall follow the general pattern adopted throughout this volume, and start in section 25.2 with a discussion of structures and related properties. This will also help to illustrate a number of the more subtle effects which can become important in discussing chemical equilibria, e.g. symmetry-dependent factors and metal–metal bonding, as well as the effects of metal–ligand covalent bonding. The next four sections discuss equilibria involving the divalent ions of the first transition series.

There are three main types of equilibria to be understood.

(1) Preparation of one solid from another (section 25.3), e.g.

$$M'O + M''Cl_2 \rightleftharpoons M'Cl_2 + M''O$$

(2) Preparation of a solid from a solution or the reverse (section 25.4), e.g.

$$M(H_2O)_n^{2+} + H_2S \rightleftharpoons MS\downarrow + nH_2O + 2H^+$$

(3) The formation of complex ions, which can be written generally as an exchange reaction in solution:

$$M(H_2O)_n^{2+} + X \rightleftharpoons MX(H_2O)_{n-m}^{2+} + mH_2O$$

(3) will be treated in two sections. Section 25.5 will consider the ions from Mn^{2+} to Zn^{2+}, and section 25.6 the ions from Ca^{2+} to Mn^{2+}. All three equilibria will be controlled by the overall free energy of the reactions. As before we divide the free energy into heat, $\Delta H°$, and entropy, $T\Delta S°$, changes. For reaction (1) between two solids, the heat of reaction is likely to dominate the direction which the reaction takes, even when the metal ions differ considerably in size. In the first transition-metal series the divalent ions are rather similar in size (excluding Ca^{2+}), and it is usually found that even in complex formation all the reactions with one ligand have similar entropy changes (Table 25.I). Thus the order of free-energy changes for different transition-metal ions is largely dominated by the changes in the heat of reaction.

The vertical comparison of Ni(II), Pd(II), and Pt(II) is taken up in the final section, section 25.7. The main features of this comparison are (1) the instability of the compounds of the heavier elements, (2) the greater preference of the heavier elements to combine with polarizable ligands, (3) the greater influence of the d orbitals upon the chemistry of the heavier elements.

TABLE 25.I. *Heats (kcal mole⁻¹) and entropies (e.u.) of complex formation in aqueous solution*

(a) With one EDTA⁴⁻ at 20 °C

Ion	$\Delta H°$	$\Delta G°$	$\Delta S°$
Mg^{2+}	+3·14	−11·65	+50·5
Ca^{2+}	−6·45	−14·34	+26·9
Mn^{2+}	−5·45	−18·60	+44·5
Co^{2+}	−4·4	−21·90	+59·7
Ni^{2+}	−8·35	−24·96	+56·7
Cu^{2+}	−8·67	−25·20	+56·4
Zn^{2+}	−5·61	−22·12	+56·3

From Staveley and Randall, *Disc. Faraday Soc.*, 1958, **26**, 157.

(b) With one ethylenediamine at 25 °C

Ion	$\Delta H°$	$\Delta G°$	$\Delta S°$
Mn^{2+}	−2·80	−3·70	+3·0
Fe^{2+}	−5·05	−5·95	+3·0
Co^{2+}	−6·90	−8·10	+4·0
Ni^{2+}	−8·90	−10·55	+5·5
Cu^{2+}	−13·05	−14·70	+5·5
Zn^{2+}	−6·65	−7·70	+3·5

From Ciampolini, Paoletti, and Sacconi, *J. Chem. Soc.*, 1960, 4553.

25.2. Structures and related properties

In Chapter 5 it was shown that a consideration of cation sizes leads to a definite expectation for their coordination numbers in complexes and in crystals. This expectation is modified in two ways by the effects treated in Chapter 24. (1) Crystal-field theory predicts changes in coordination number along the series of either divalent or trivalent cations. On the whole such predictions agree with experiment for the later elements in transition series, especially when the ligand is of low polarizability. (2) Both the molecular-orbital and the valence-bond theories predict that coordination numbers with good donor ligands would fall regularly from the beginning of the transition-metal series, where they are at a maximum of 9, to the end of the series where they are as low as 4 or even 2. The conflicting demands of ion size and the various ligand-field effects imply that the actual coordination number depends on a subtle balance of different energy contributions. Here the results of the overall influence of these energies will be described, so bringing together the previous discussions of stereochemistry.

It should be noted that equilibria frequently involve a change of stereo-chemistry, e.g.

$$M(H_2O)_6^{2+} + 4HCl \rightarrow [MCl_4]^{2-} + 4H^+ + 6H_2O$$

octahedral   tetrahedral

so that the stereochemical preferences of the central ions must also have considerable effects on the positions of equilibria along a cation series.

SOLID STRUCTURES

The structures of fluorides MF_2 are largely in accord with the expectations of crystal-field theory, taking into account deviations which are interpretable in terms of the Jahn–Teller theorem. Thus while the fluorides of Mn^{2+}, Fe^{2+}, Co^{2+}, Ni^{2+}, and Pd^{2+} have nearly regular octahedral coordination of the cation, CuF_2 has a tetragonally-distorted rutile structure. The discussion of the fluoride structures is made somewhat more complicated in that the Cr^{2+} salt shows a distortion to a still lower symmetry than that of CuF_2, while the Cu^{2+} complex fluoride, $KCuF_3$, has the opposite type of tetragonal distortion, 2 nearest neighbours instead of 4, to that found in the simple fluoride. In close-packed oxide structures the divalent transition-metal ions occupy octahedral or tetrahedral sites in a manner close to that predicted by crystal-field theory. The exceptions, Cr^{2+}, Cu^{2+}, Pd^{2+}, and Pt^{2+} which are found in 4-coordinate sites, can again be explained by the gain in energy on removal of the degeneracy of the ground state. This remains true in double oxides such as spinels, and in silicates in general.

Neither complex fluorides nor complex oxides give rise to isolated complex anions in the solid state. The absence of a complex fluoride must be due to the electrostatic instability of $[MF_6]^{4-}$ relative to $[MF_4]^{2-}$, and the instability of the latter relative to a 6-coordinate polymerized lattice of formula $[(MF_3)^-]_n$. Possible complex anions containing O^{2-} would have to be $[MO_3]^{4-}$ or $[MO_4]^{6-}$, which are similarly unstable with respect to polymerized $[MO_2]^{2-}$ lattices containing $[MO_6]$ octahedra. However, unsaturated anions based on first-row non-metal elements, e.g. NO_2^- and CN^-, do give rise to octahedral $[MX_6]^{4-}$ anions. The d^8 cations are low-spin with many ligands and then give square coplanar complexes, e.g. $[M(CN)_4]^{2-}$.

In the compounds of the heavier halogens, MX_2, 6-coordination is maintained in layer lattices for all but the Cu(II), Pd(II), and Pt(II) halides and probably $CrCl_2$, $CrBr_2$, and CrI_2, as expected from crystal-field theory. In fact strong deviations from the predictions of the ionic model combined with this theory are apparent only when lattices contain extremely polarizable anions, e.g. sulphide. Moreover, as has already been pointed out, such predictions cannot be expected to be useful when metal–metal bonding is important, as for example in the NiAs structure.

The heavier halide ions and SCN^- give rise to isolated complex anions in the solid state. Complexes $[MX_4]^{2-}$ but not $[MX_6]^{4-}$ are known for most cations from V^{2+} to Zn^{2+} and for Cl^-, Br^-, and I^-. By way of contrast, many of the trivalent cations have octahedral $[MCl_6]^{3-}$ complexes. The shapes of the $[MX_4]^{2-}$ groups are very difficult to explain. $[NiCl_4]^{2-}$ is apparently a good tetrahedron, but $[CoCl_4]^{2-}$ and $[CuCl_4]^{2-}$ are both somewhat flattened (Table 25.II (a)). A trigonal bipyramidal structure is known for $[CuCl_5]^{3-}$.

TABLE 25.II. (a) Bond distances in $[MCl_4]^{2-}$ 'tetrahedra' (Å)
(after Lingafelter)

Metal	M—X¹	M—X²	MX³	MX⁴	Angles
Co	2·20	2·25		2·26	between 107° and 114°
Cu	2·25	2·22		2·23	between 99° and 127°
Zn	2·25	2·24		2·24	between 108° and 112°

(b) Bond distances in $[M(H_2O)_6]^{2+}$ 'octahedra' (after Lingafelter)

Metal	M—O¹	M—O²	M—O³	M—O in oxide (NaCl) structure
Mg	2·09	2·10	2·05	2·10
Mn	2·18	2·20	2·15	2·22
Fe	2·17	2·14	2·10	2·17
Co	2·11	2·09	2·08	2·12
Ni	2·09	2·08	2·04	2·08
Cu	2·20	2·10	1·97	1·95 (4), > 2·50 (2)
Zn	2·14	2·12	2·07	2·16
Cd	2·26	2·24	2·21	(2·35)

Note. There are three different M—O distances in all the aquo ions, which are therefore not quite octahedral.

A clearer preference by the cations for 6-coordination rather than 4-coordination is to be found in the solid hydrates and ammines. Here, with the exception of Zn^{2+}, no tetrahedral hydrate or ammine is known for the first transition series. However, in the solid state the octahedra are not perfect as is shown in Table 25.II (b). On the other hand, uncharged ligands with P and S donors are able to give tetrahedral species. Size of ligand is of very great importance in the control of geometry.

Polydentate ligands generate a geometry which is only partly controlled by the cation. In fact almost any desired geometry can be established by a suitable 'tailoring' of the ligands. An example is given in Fig. 25.6. In metallo-enzymes it appears that the polydentate binding of the protein to the metal generates unusual coordination sites, and this in turn leads to unusual kinetic properties. Examples are the zinc-containing carbonic

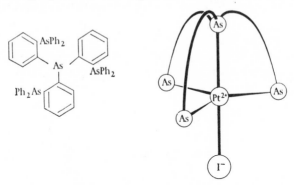

Fig. 25.6. An example of a ligand, QAS, which controls the geometry of a complex, e.g. [Pt(II)(QAS)I]+.

anhydrase and the deep blue copper-containing oxidases such as caerulo-plasmin.

COMPLEXES IN SOLUTION

The important terms controlling most solid-state equilibria are energy terms. Knowledge of the very wide range of structures actually observed shows that these terms are in very fine balance. In solution, however, where entropy effects become significant, it is often found that molecules of different stereochemistry exist in equilibrium with one another. An illustrative example is the series of chloride complexes formed at different hydrochloric acid strengths, as shown in Table 25.III.

TABLE 25.III. *Main chloride complexes of different cations in hydrochloric acid solutions*

HCl concentration	Mn^{2+}	Fe^{2+}	Co^{2+}	Ni^{2+}	Cu^{2+}	Zn^{2+}
$< N/10$	octahedral hydrated cations				tetragonal hydrate	octahedral hydrate
$\sim 1N$	some monochloride complexes, octahedral			no complex	tetragonal dichloride ?	tetrahedral dichloride ?
$10N$	higher octahedral complexes e.g. $MCl_2(H_2O)_4$		tetrahedral $CoCl_4^{2-}$	?$NiCl^+$	flattened tetrahedral $CuCl_4^{2-}$	tetrahedral $ZnCl_4^{2-}$

The least stable M^{2+} chloride complexes in this table are those of Ni^{2+}. As a result of ligand-field stabilization, nickel has a strong preference for an octahedral field as in $[Ni(H_2O_6]^{2+}$. Now the *size* of the chloride ion is such that the stable complexes of all the divalent ions, $M(H_2O)_nCl_x$ are forced toward a tetrahedral stereochemistry even when x is 1 or 2. As a consequence the Ni^{2+} ion does not give chloride complexes readily. The reverse principle, of trapping an ion in a site whose geometry is peculiarly suited to it, is used in the stabilization of Cr(II) in a tetragonal site in $Cr(N_2H_5)_2(SO_4)_2$ and of hydrated Co(III) in an octahedral site in cobalt(III) alum.

The problem of stereochemistry in solution is made more difficult because the free-energy difference between complexes of one ligand of different stereochemistries may be so small as to permit them to coexist. Thus it seems probable that cobalt(II) hydrate is 99 per cent $[Co(H_2O)_6]^{2+}$ and 1 per cent $[Co(H_2O)_4]^{2+}$. A further factor adding to the variety of species is the equilibrium between different spin states of the same cation which will be described in section 28.9. This is particularly important in the complexes of Ni^{2+} and Fe^{2+} with unsaturated nitrogen, sulphur, and phosphorus ligands. With Ni^{2+} the different spin states, furthermore, have different geometrical preferences.

In conclusion the stereochemistry of a divalent transition-metal ion (especially when it is late in a series) differs from that of a Group IIA metal ion of similar size in the variety of its compounds of *low* coordination number. The flexibility of the coordination has a major influence on the physical properties of the compounds.

METAL–METAL BONDING

Metal–metal bonding becomes more important the lower the charge on the metal and the earlier the metal is in its transition series. It is also more important in the second and third than in the first transition series, e.g. in Nb, Ta, Mo, W, and even Re halides. It has its effect upon the lattice energy of halides (Fig. 25.7) and therefore upon the values of R and Q in Fig. 25.3. Again M—M bonding increases as the ligand atoms become more polarizable, i.e. the metals have less positive charge: it is greater with heavier than with lighter halide ions and greater in sulphides than in oxides. Fig. 25.8 gives an example of the complex structures which result. M—M bonding has already been described in oxides (Chapter 13), sulphides (Chapter 16), and nitrides, etc. (Chapter 17). A generalized scheme of where this bonding occurs is shown in Fig. 25.9. It is also found in some compounds of cations which favour a tetragonal structure, e.g. Cr^{2+}, Cu^{2+}, Pd^{2+}, and Pt^{2+}, but the origin of the binding is somewhat obscure in these cases.

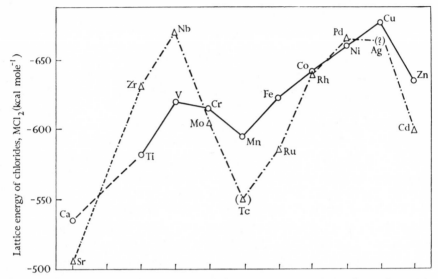

FIG. 25.7. Lattice energies of MCl_2 compounds for metals (M) in the first and second transition series. The large values for $ZrCl_2$ and $NbCl_2$ are indicative of M–M bonds.

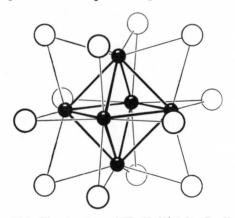

FIG. 25.8. The structure of $[Ta_6Cl_{12}]^{2+}$ (after Pauling).

STOICHEIOMETRY

The discussion of non-stoicheiometric phases has undergone radical revision in recent years. Possible approaches involve either

(1) random defects which lend themselves to a statistical treatment, or
(2) micro-domains which coexist in one crystal.

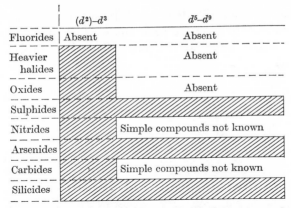

FIG. 25.9. Metal–metal bonding in the divalent compounds of metals in the first transition series (schematic). d^4 systems have been excluded because of the distortions arising from the Jahn–Teller effect.

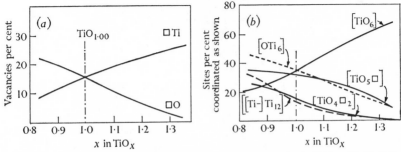

FIG. 25.10. (a) Concentrations of titanium and oxygen vacancies in TiO_x. (b) Statistics of coordination environments, $\square$ = vacancy (after Anderson).

The statistical description may be illustrated by the TiO_x phases between strongly defect $TiO_{0.8}$ and $TiO_{1.4}$. Fig. 25.10 (a) gives the oxygen, $\square O$, and the titanium, $\square Ti$, sites vacant at different compositions. The basic lattice is of NaCl structure. TiO itself has 15 per cent Ti and 15 per cent O vacancies. Fig. 25.10 (b) shows the distribution of coordination sites. The total picture is one of an occupation of sites gradually modified with composition. Apparently there are no phase changes in the whole range. Recently this notion of random distribution of defects has been modified by the concept of micro-domains. The idea is illustrated in Fig. 25.11 which shows (a) FeO (NaCl structure), randomly defective in Fe, (b) Fe_3O_4 (spinel), and (c) micro-domains of Fe_3O_4 in FeO giving the same composition as (a). The regions of micro-homogeneity are equivalent to localized regions of ordered vacancies. Ordered vacancies lead to a ready explanation of series of homologous phases such as have been frequently observed in higher oxides

(Chapter 8 and section 26.3). It is now supposed that compounds such as Cr_nS_{n+1} and $Fe_{1-x}S$ do not have wide phase regions where n or x can be varied continuously, but that the phase diagram is broken into many narrow regions.

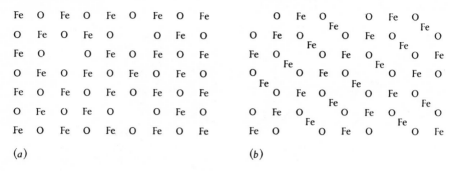

(a)   (b)

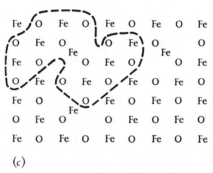

(c)

FIG. 25.11. $Fe_{1-x}O$. (a) Early proposal for structure (random hole defects). (b) Structure of Fe_3O_4 spinel; compared with (a) some atoms occupy new sites. (c) Micro-domains of Fe_3O_4 in FeO producing ordered defects (after Anderson).

The non-stoicheiometry and the presence of defects even in stoicheiometric phases of simple MX_2, MO, and MS compounds are in part the cause of the increased electronic conduction of these transition-metal compounds over those of the Group IIA metals. The greatest deviations from stoicheiometry are found in Ti^{2+} and V^{2+} compounds and these are more deeply coloured (usually black) and better electronic conductors than the compounds of the later transition-metal ions, e.g. Co^{2+} and Ni^{2+}. Some of these oxides and sulphides find use as catalysts in industrial processes.

MELTING-POINTS

In Chapter 13 and again in Chapter 20 it has been shown that increasing covalence generally lowers melting-points, for the lower coordination number of the melt or vapour allows shorter bond distances. It is against this background and the changing ionic lattice energy that the transition-metal compounds must be examined.

The melting-points of the divalent oxides in the first transition series are

$$\left(\begin{matrix} MgO \\ 2770° \end{matrix}\right) \quad \begin{matrix} CaO \\ 2600° \end{matrix} . \begin{matrix} TiO \\ 2020° \end{matrix} .. \begin{matrix} MnO \\ 1785° \end{matrix} \quad \begin{matrix} FeO \\ 1371° \end{matrix} \quad \begin{matrix} CoO \\ 1805° \end{matrix} \quad \begin{matrix} NiO \\ 1960° \end{matrix} \quad \begin{matrix} CuO \\ decomposes \end{matrix} \quad \begin{matrix} ZnO \\ 1975\,°C \end{matrix}$$
sublimes

All the compounds except ZnO (zinc blende) have the NaCl structure. The MgO value is included to show the effect of changing cation size. The melting-points of the trivalent oxides are

$$\left(\begin{matrix} Al_2O_3 \\ 2030° \end{matrix}\right) \quad \begin{matrix} Sc_2O_3 \\ 2000° \end{matrix} \quad \begin{matrix} Ti_2O_3 \\ 2130° \end{matrix} \quad \begin{matrix} V_2O_3 \\ >2000° \end{matrix} \quad \begin{matrix} Cr_2O_3 \\ 2400° \end{matrix} \quad \begin{matrix} Mn_2O_3 \\ decomposes \end{matrix} \quad \begin{matrix} Fe_2O_3 \\ 1457° \end{matrix} \quad .... \quad \begin{matrix} Ga_2O_3 \\ 1725\,°C \end{matrix}$$

Again the Al_2O_3 value is included so as to show the effect of changing cation size. All these oxides have the corundum, Al_2O_3, structure. There is a minimum in the melting-point about half-way along each of the two series. The melting-points of the halides of the same divalent metals, with Mg included as before, are

	Mg	Ca	....	Mn	Fe	Co	Ni	Cu	Zn
MF_2	1263°	1418°		930°	1100°	1200°	1450°	950°	872 °C
MCl_2	(714°)	782°		650°	677°	740°	sublimes	498°	326 °C
MI_2	(650°)	740°		638°	(587°)?	520°	797°	not stable	446 °C

In these compounds the central cation is surrounded by six halide ions with the one exception of CaF_2. Compounds of the earlier transition-metal cations have been omitted as there is considerable metal–metal bonding in them, leading to high melting-points (see Chapter 12). Copper(II) compounds have very low melting-points: the lattices of the compounds are highly distorted, and there is reason to suppose that the M—X bonds are more covalent than in the other compounds listed.

In the halide series there is the same fall in melting-point across the transition series as in the oxides, the B-metal compounds have lower melting-points than those of the pre-transition metals, and there is again a drop to a minimum value in the middle of the series. The low values of the melting-points in the middle of these series cannot arise from the changes in experimental lattice energy, e.g. MgF_2 −695, CaF_2 −624, MnF_2 −662, FeF_2 −696, CoF_2 −708; and MgI_2 −548, CaI_2 −492, FeI_2 −589, CoI_2 −605 kcal mole^{-1}. Furthermore, if the effect of ion size alone is considered, it can be seen (Fig. 25.12) that all the transition-metal compounds have lower melting-points than their size would have led us to expect. The values cannot be due merely to the change to a more covalent binding along the series, for there is good reason to suppose that the covalent binding energy in Mn^{2+} and Fe^{2+} compounds is less than that in Ni^{2+} compounds.

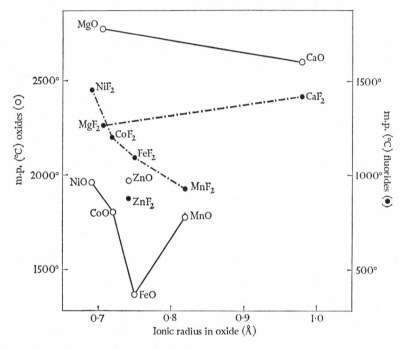

FIG. 25.12. A comparison between divalent cations in the pre-transition and the first transition series. The relationship between the melting-points of oxides and fluorides and the ionic radii of the cations as observed in oxides.

Similar remarks apply to the series of trivalent transition-metal compounds. Now a feature of transition-metal cations is that with few exceptions they readily change coordination number. The exceptions are those where the crystal-field stabilization of octahedra is greatest. Certainly in all the series of melting-points the cations which most strongly retain 6-coordination, Ni^{2+} and Cr^{3+}, have high melting-points.

The boiling-points of simple salts MX and MX_2 have not been studied. Some differences between transition-metal compounds and pre-transition metal compounds are expected from the fact that all the gaseous halides, MnF_2, CoF_2, NiF_2, CuF_2, ZnF_2, $MnCl_2$, and $ZnCl_2$ are linear whereas the halides CaF_2, SrF_2, BaF_2, $SrCl_2$, and $BaCl_2$ are bent.

25.3. Solid equilibria

COMPARISONS OF HEATS OF FORMATION

The different polarizing powers of a pre-transition and a transition-metal cation can be seen most clearly by making comparisons of heats of compound formation for cations of closely comparable radii. For example, Mg^{2+} may be compared with Ni^{2+}, the mean of Ca^{2+} and Mg^{2+} may be compared with both Mn^{2+} and Pd^{2+}, and Ca^{2+} may be compared with Pt^{2+}.

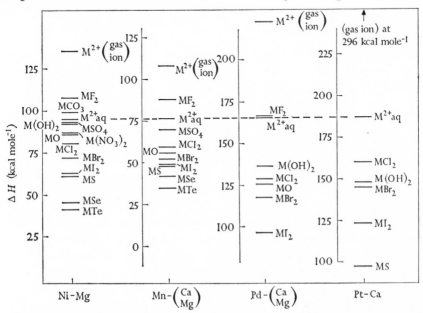

FIG. 25.13. Differences in heats of formation between pairs of compounds containing divalent metal ions of very similar ionic radii (see text).

On a purely ionic model the differences between the members of such pairs should be independent of ligand and exactly equal to the gas-ion values (i.e. differences in the sums of the sublimation energies and the first two ionization potentials) in the ideal case of equal radii. The deviations from this model are shown by the vertical spread of the values in Fig. 25.13.

Covalence increases in the expected sequence

$$\begin{matrix} Ca^{2+} \\ Mg^{2+} \end{matrix} < Mn^{2+} < Ni^{2+} < Pd^{2+} < Pt^{2+}.$$

The relative positions of two anions are roughly constant and also much as expected, but the absolute differences change considerably from cation to cation. This is important in double-decomposition reactions.

DECOMPOSITION REACTIONS

One of the simplest solid-decomposition reactions is that of an oxide by heating. The readiness with which this process takes place is measured directly by the heats of formation of oxides discussed in Chapter 13, where it was seen that $-\Delta H_f$ (oxide) goes to a minimum with the closing of the

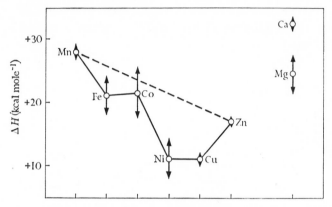

FIG. 25.14. The heats of decomposition of carbonates, $MCO_3 \to MO + CO_2$.

transition series, i.e. at Cu, Ag, and Au. Other decompositions which are readily brought about, particularly at the end of the transition series, are those of the carbonate, nitrate, nitrite, and even sulphate to form the smaller and more polarizable (see Fig. 25.13) oxide. These oxyacid salts are less stable relative to the oxides than the corresponding salts of the pre-transition elements. Elsewhere we have already noted the instability of other compounds such as peroxides and azides. The way in which the heat of reaction changes for

$$MCO_3 \to MO + CO_2$$

is shown in Fig. 25.14. There is a minimum in the stability of the carbonate at Ni^{2+} or Cu^{2+}, and the compounds are less stable than would have been expected on the grounds of ionic size alone: compare $MgCO_3$ or $CaCO_3$ shown on the right-hand side of the figure. The sulphates illustrate the same point: at red heat $FeSO_4$, $CoSO_4$, and $NiSO_4$ decompose, but $MnSO_4$ is stable. This permits a purification of $MnSO_4$.

PREPARATION OF SOLIDS BY DOUBLE DECOMPOSITION

In an exchange reaction of the type

$$M'F + M''I \to M'I + M''F$$
$$M'F_2 + M''I_2 \to M'I_2 + M''F_2$$

involving Group IA and IIA elements, the smaller cation tends to combine with the smaller anion, as is predicted by the ionic model. Thus magnesium iodide reacts with calcium fluoride to give calcium iodide and magnesium fluoride. Despite the fact that the transition-metal cations are smaller

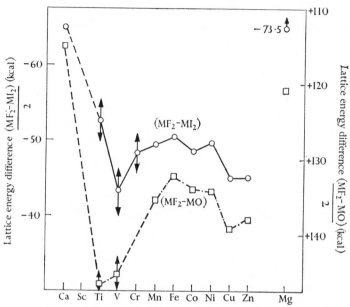

FIG. 25.15. Differences between the lattice energies of pairs of compounds in the first transition series.

than Ca^{2+}, all the transition-metal fluorides will react with calcium iodide to give their iodides and calcium fluoride (see Fig. 25.15). Fig. 24.12, the plot of the lattice energies against atomic number for fluorides and iodides, shows that the fluorides give a plot of type (A) (Fig. 25.3), weakly-polarizable anion, while the iodides give a plot of type (B), strongly-polarizable anion.

It would appear that increasing covalence is altering the order of the relative lattice energies. This view is supported by the increasing volatility of the anhydrous metal halides toward the end of the transition series.

If for the reaction

$$MX + CaY \rightarrow MY + CaX$$

the lattice-energy plots for X and Y are of type (A) in Fig. 25.3 and both $R(Y) > R(X)$ and $Q(Y) > Q(X)$ then the order of exothermicity in the reaction is:

$$(0 =) Ca^{2+} < Ti^{2+} < V^{2+} \simeq Cr^{2+} > Mn^{2+} < Fe^{2+} < Co^{2+} < Ni^{2+}$$
$$\simeq Cu^{2+} > Zn^{2+}.$$

The signs, $\simeq$, are placed where changes of R do not necessarily operate in the same direction as changes of Q. On the other hand if the lattice-energy plot for anion Y is of type (B) and that of anion X is of type (A) then the reaction may either be endothermic or exothermic, depending on the magnitude of $R(Y)$ and $R(X)$ and of $Q(Y)$ and $Q(X)$, and the heat term may favour substitution of X by Y in almost any sequence. A limited, but frequently observed order of exothermicity from Mn to Zn is

$$Mn^{2+} < Fe^{2+} < Co^{2+} < Ni^{2+} < Cu^{2+} > Zn^{2+}.$$

Variations on this order are shown in Figs. 25.14 and 25.15; in the latter case Mn^{2+} is out of sequence. Fig. 25.15 also shows the relatively high affinity for oxide of the early elements in a transition series. This arises from the strong π-donor character of oxide and the high π-acceptor character of early transition-metal ions. Surprisingly V(II) shows a relative preference for I^-. Here the data may be in error, but the effect of metal–metal bonding could also be significant. TiI_2 and VI_2 are 'semi-metals', i.e. they have *low* electronic conductivities *decreasing* with rise of temperature.

UNSATURATED LIGANDS

The exchange reaction

$$MCl_2(solid) + 2HCN(gas) \rightarrow M(CN)_2(solid) + 2HCl(gas)$$

illustrates the effects of unsaturation in the anion. The heats of the reaction are (kcal mole^{-1})

Ca^{2+}	Ni^{2+}	Zn^{2+}	Sr^{2+}	Pd^{2+}	Cd^{2+}
39·5	−3·9	11·3	45·5	−9·0	25·5

Whereas the reaction is exothermic for nickel and even more so for palladium, it is endothermic for calcium and strontium and more weakly endothermic for zinc and cadmium. These observations are completely in agreement with the theoretical discussion in section 24.6. π-bonding, with the metal as donor, becomes of great importance in the transition series, especially at the end of a series, and when the ligand has empty π^* orbitals.

ISOMERISM OF M—(XY)

An interesting type of reaction occurs when a cation can choose to bind either of two atoms of a given anion, e.g. in SCN^- or NO_2^-. The elements early in all the transition series bind to the nitrogen of thiocyanate ($\leftarrow NCS$)$^-$ and to oxygen of nitrite ($\leftarrow ONO$)$^-$, rather than to sulphur of thiocyanate

($\leftarrow$ SCN)$^-$ and nitrogen of nitrite ($\leftarrow$ NO$_2$)$^-$. The later elements, especially in the second and third transition series, bind the anions in the alternative fashion. Here the increased polarizing power of the cation results in an increased binding of the more polarizable relative to the more polar part of a ligand.

25.4. Solid-solution equilibria

HYDRATION

The heats of hydration of the divalent cations of the first transition series show the same variation with atomic number as has become familiar in lattice-energy plots (Fig. 25.16). Variations in Q with cation are much as expected on a crystal-field model, and R is rather small; compare fluoride lattice energies in Fig. 24.12. In Fig. 25.17 these heats of hydration are compared with the values of the pre-transition metal cations by plotting hydration energies as a function of the interatomic distance in the oxide. The plot is very similar to that for the oxide lattice energies (Fig. 24.19). There is no metal–metal bonding in the hydrates. The relatively high hydration energies of the later transition-metal cations are presumably associated with their high electron affinities; compare the B-metal cations also plotted in Fig. 25.17. As is the case with bond distances (section 24.12) and lattice energies (Fig. 24.12), the cations late in transition series appear to be different from those early in the series. The general chemistry of the earlier elements also is different from that of the later elements, so that it is often convenient to divide the transition-metal series into two parts, the cations before and the cations after the half-filled d sub-shell. Also included in Fig. 25.17 are points for cations outside the first transition series. The point for Pd^{2+} indicates the very considerable stabilization of the second-row transition-metal cations relative to the pre-transition ions, and the point for Hg^{2+} indicates that the stabilization from covalence is likely to be great at the end of the third series. The entropies of hydration (Table 25.IV) indicate that the hydrated Cu^{2+} ion has a different structure from the other cations, as is predicted by ligand-field theory. The values for Ca^{2+} and Mg^{2+} show the effects of changes in ion size.

TABLE 25.IV. ΔS° hydration (cal mole^{-1} deg^{-1}) of cations (relative to H$^+$) at 25 °C

Mg^{2+}	Ca^{2+}	Mn^{2+}	Fe^{2+}	Co^{2+}	Ni^{2+}	Cu^{2+}	Zn^{2+}
$-13\cdot4$	$-9\cdot2$	$-11\cdot8$	$-14\cdot6$	$-14\cdot5$	$-16\cdot2$	$-12\cdot7$	$-13\cdot4$

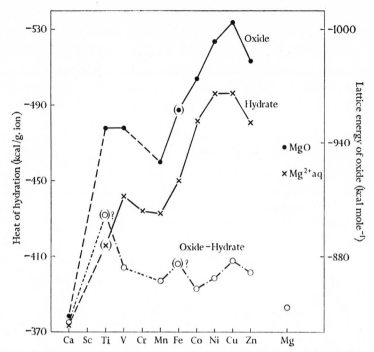

Fig. 25.16. Comparison between the heats of hydration of divalent cations and the lattice energies of oxides. The lowest curve is the difference, $[MO - M(H_2O)_n^{2+}]$, with an arbitrary zero.

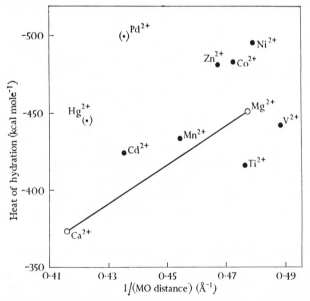

Fig. 25.17. Relationship between hydration energies and reciprocals of the M—O distances observed in oxides.

An indication of the ease of replacement of water by anions is the degree of hydration of the cations in the solid state. It is relatively easy to prepare anhydrous calcium salts of strong-acid anions, but it is very much more difficult to prepare anhydrous salts of the smaller magnesium cation with these same anions. On the other hand magnesium salts with weak-acid anions are often anhydrous or little hydrated. The salts of cations from the first transition-metal series behave rather like those of magnesium. The sulphates are hydrated and the fluorides are anhydrous. However, towards the end of the transition-metal series, e.g. at Cu^{2+}, and especially in later rows, a change in character of the cation occurs. Some typical hydrated salts are $CuCl_2,2H_2O$; $CuF_2,2H_2O$; $CuBr_2,4H_2O$; $Cu(NO_3)_2,3H_2O$; $PdCl_2,2H_2O$; and $PdSO_4,2H_2O$. In the salts of Pt^{2+} the cation is rarely if ever hydrated. As the polarizing power of the cation increases, it increasingly demands a polarizable ligand instead of the water molecule even when this ligand is a strong-acid anion, e.g. chloride.

HYDROLYSIS

Another indication of the effect of the high ionization potential of the metal atom is to be seen in the acid dissociation constants of the different hydrates (Chapter 14). Since these equilibrium constants can be considered as referring to the ligand replacement of water by hydroxide, they are also the formation constants of complex ions. The hydrolysis ultimately leads to the precipitation of hydroxides. The most acidic cation in the first transition series is Cu^{2+}, and the next most acidic cations are those of the very early transition-metals such as V^{2+} and Cr^{2+}. The latter are much harder to study because of the ease of oxidation to the higher-valence states. The hydrates of the heavier cations at the end of the other transition-metal series are also very readily hydrolysed. The general direction of these trends can be seen in Fig. 25.16, where the differences between the heats of hydrate and oxide formation are plotted. Elements showing a high preference for oxide also have a high preference for hydroxide. Many of these metals form oxides readily from hydroxides, e.g. Cu and Pt. Reactions in which water is exchanged for ligands other than hydroxide may be considered in relation to the precipitation of salts.

SOLUBILITY

For those salts in which the cation is not hydrated in the lattice, precipitation can be written as a simple exchange of ligands. Thus the heat terms will be expected to follow similar sequences to those found in solid-exchange reactions. An example is given in Fig. 25.18. In the transition series the cations of a given valence, here two, are very similar in size, Ca^{2+} alone being exceptional, so that the entropy terms should be of similar magnitude along a series of elements (Table 25.IV). As a result the heat terms dominate the *relative* free energies of reactions. The pH required to precipitate hydroxides or oxides follows the sequence

$$Ca^{2+} > Mg^{2+} > Mn^{2+} > Fe^{2+} > Cr^{2+}, Co^{2+}, Ni^{2+}, Zn^{2+} > Cu^{2+},$$

which is approximately the sequence of the heat terms in Fig. 25.16. For

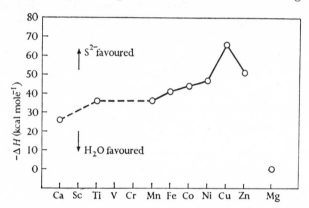

FIG. 25.18. Differences between lattice energies of sulphides and heats of hydration relative to the difference for magnesium.

the sulphides a similar order prevails (see Fig. 25.18), but the variation in the heat difference between one element and the next is much greater, and consequently there is a much greater spread of pH values for the precipitation of sulphides than for hydroxides (Figs. 25.19 and 25.20). The pH of precipitation is, of course, directly related to the solubility product. The greater selectivity of precipitation by sulphide as compared with hydroxide has led to the use of sulphide precipitation as one of the main procedures in qualitative analysis (see Chapter 34 A). This selectivity is related to a greater slope, R, in Fig. 25.3 for the polarizable sulphide than for either water or hydroxide. The similar increase in selectivity introduced by incorporating polarizable ligand atoms into *organic* reagents for precipitating metals is illustrated by the type of metal ions which react with picolinic acid, 8-hydroxyquinoline, dithiocarbamic acid, and cupferron; see section 34.5. In the solid complexes the bulky organic groups prevent metal–metal interaction, but this type of interaction may play a considerable part in reducing the solubility of some metal hydroxides and sulphides. Solubility products of hydroxides are plotted in Fig. 25.21: the values are low for the early transition metals which readily give M—M bonds. The insolubility of some sulphides early in transition-metal series, e.g. MoS_2, may

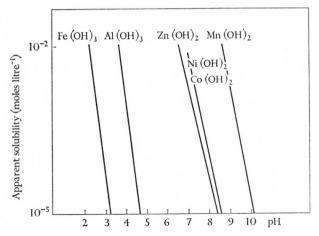

Fig. 25.19. Apparent solubility of some metal hydroxides as a function of pH.

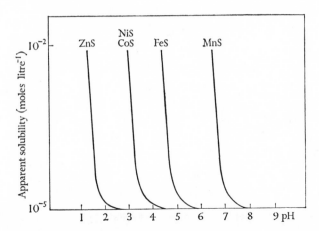

Fig. 25.20. Apparent solubility of some metal sulphides as a function of pH.
(Figs. 25.19 and 25.20 after Charlot, *Théorie et Méthode Nouvelles d'Analyse Qualitative*, Masson et Cie, Paris, 1954.)

arise in a similar way. Metal–metal bonding also has its effect upon preparative methods. Thus a common way of obtaining a chromium(II) salt reasonably stable to air oxidation is to precipitate the cation with acetate. The structure of the acetate, which is diamagnetic, is shown in Fig. 25.22. Copper(II) acetate has a similar structure, but is much more soluble perhaps because the metal–metal bonding is weaker.

The cations of the second and third transition series have relatively greater affinities for the larger anions, iodide and sulphide, than for the smaller anions, fluoride and oxide. This is partly a consequence of the increase of size, already brought out in the discussion of the pre-transition

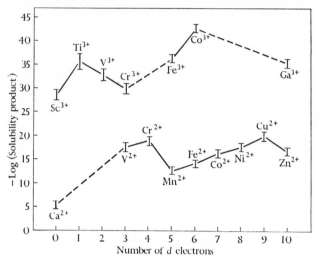

FIG. 25.21. Solubility products of metal hydroxides at 25 °C.

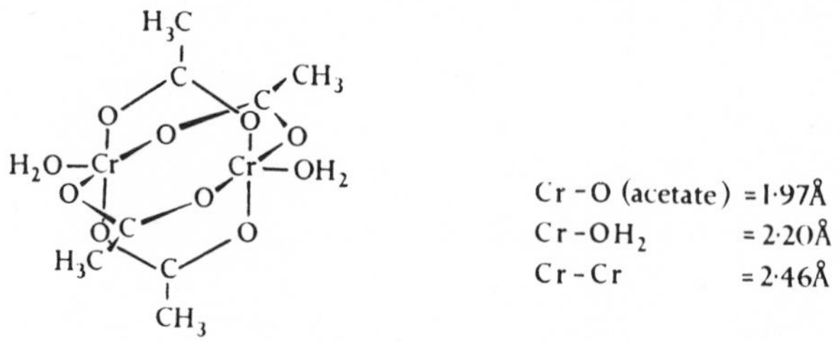

FIG. 25.22. The structure of chromium(II) acetate hydrate.

$$Cr-O \text{ (acetate)} = 1.97\text{Å}$$
$$Cr-OH_2 = 2.20\text{Å}$$
$$Cr-Cr = 2.46\text{Å}$$

metals, but it is enhanced by the increased polarizing power of these cations. Most elements of the second and third transition-metal series occur naturally as sulphides which are extremely insoluble in water. The salts of heavier halides are also more insoluble than in the first transition series, e.g. $PdCl_2$, as indeed are the oxides and hydroxides. In fact there is little simple hydrated-ion chemistry of any of these heavy cations, e.g. Pd^{2+}, Pt^{2+}, and Os^{2+}. The salts of the highly polarizable cyanide and thiocyanate anions are also insoluble and little hydrated. Their lattices may be further stabilized by $d_\pi \to \pi^*$ bonding, i.e. the anions acting as acceptor ligands. In all these cases R is large no matter what the value of Q in Fig. 25.3.

25.5. Complex ions, Mn^{2+} to Zn^{2+}

STEP-WISE STABILITY CONSTANTS OF COMPLEXES

A simple example of complex formation is the reaction between the hydrated cations and either ammonia or ethylenediamine, en,

$$M(H_2O)_n^{2+} + 6NH_3 \rightarrow M(NH_3)_6^{2+} + nH_2O$$

$$M(H_2O)_n^{2+} + 3en \rightarrow M(en)_3^{2+} + nH_2O.$$

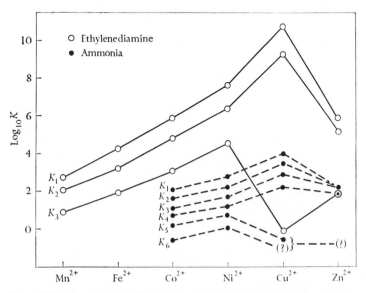

FIG. 25.23. Step-wise stability constants of ammonia and ethylenediamine complexes in aqueous solution at 25 °C.

The reaction occurs in steps (Fig. 25.23). The steps are approximately equivalent only for an ion which has essentially equivalent coordination positions. Thus Cu^{2+}, with three electrons in the two 'e_g' orbitals (section 24.3), differs from Ni^{2+}, as is shown by a comparison between the two series of step-stability constants for ethylenediamine at 25 °C and in $1\cdot0M$ KNO_3:

	$\log K_1$	$\log K_2$	$\log K_3$
Ni^{2+}	7·5	6·4	4·4
Cu^{2+}	10·8	9·3	−0·9

Statistical considerations account in part for the smaller differences between successive step-wise constants in Fig. 25.23 (see Chapter 7). In what follows we shall be concerned with the ways in which the equilibrium constants for overall reactions, such as those given above, vary with properties of the metals and ligands and not with the differences between successive step-wise constants.

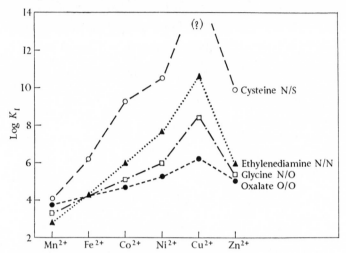

FIG. 25.24. First stability constants for a variety of ligands in aqueous solution at 25 °C. The donor atoms of the ligands are shown.

SELECTIVITY OF COMPLEX FORMATION

We shall consider first the series Mn^{2+} to Zn^{2+}. The general stability sequence for the replacement of water by more polarizable ligands is, see for example Fig. 25.24,

$$Mn^{2+} < Fe^{2+} < Co^{2+} < Ni^{2+} < Cu^{2+} > Zn^{2+}.$$

It largely reflects the changes in heats of complex formation along the series (Table 25.I). The sequence is the same for ligands in which the donor atom is oxygen, nitrogen, or sulphur, or for any combination of these donor atoms. Exceptions to this order are occasionally found with ligands which may be classified as follows. (1) Ligands which bring about a change from a high to a low spin state of certain of the cations, but not necessarily of others, e.g. cyanide and dipyridyl, see below. (2) Ligands which are particularly well suited to form complexes of one geometry rather than another or which occupy space in such a way as to introduce steric hindrance in complexes of one geometry but not of another. (3) Ligands, e.g. Cl^- and Br^-, for which, relative to water, Q is small but R is large in Fig. 25.3. Fig. 25.24 shows that the stability increments along the sequence of cations increase in the ligand atom series $O < N < S$. This is the sequence of increasing polarizability. The most important analytical reagents for the selective formation of transition-metal complexes from Mn^{2+} to Zn^{2+} bind through nitrogen or sulphur, e.g. dipyridyl, cupferron, dimethylglyoxime, dithizone, and rubeanic acid. Fig. 25.25 shows that the incre-

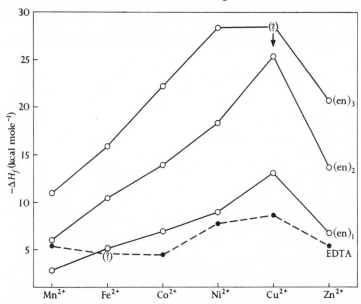

FIG. 25.25. Heats of formation of a number of complex ions from aquo ions at 25 °C.

ments in the heats of formation ($-\Delta H_f^\circ$ values) along the transition-metal series are much smaller for $ETDA^{4-}$ than for en. The peculiarly high value of $-\Delta H^\circ$ for $[Mn(EDTA)]^{2-}$ could arise from the curious hydration of this complex which in the solid state is 7-coordinate, i.e. $[Mn(EDTA)H_2O]^{2-}$. In such a case, the ΔG° values for the series of complexes may well be a more realistic basis of comparison of bond energies than the ΔH° values (Chapter 7). Any attempt to relate the ΔH° or ΔG° values to bonding parameters must also take account of the observed changes in the bond distances of different ligand atoms with a series of cations (Table 24.xxi).

The selectivity of reaction which is illustrated in Fig. 25.24 is of the greatest importance in biological systems, where zinc and copper(II) are often found bound directly to nitrogen or sulphur, while manganese(II) is more generally bound to oxygen.

THE EFFECT OF CHANGE OF SPIN STATE

A clear example of the effect of spin state upon stability constants is provided by the complexes with di-imines ($-N=C-C=N-$) such as *ortho*-phenanthroline and 2,2'-dipyridyl, as is shown in Fig. 25.26. The usual stability sequence, $Mn^{2+} < Fe^{2+} < Co^{2+} < Ni^{2+} < Cu^{2+} > Zn^{2+}$, is deranged by the different spin state of the Fe(II) complexes in which the Fe^{2+} ion is diamagnetic, with all six electrons paired, t_{2g}^6. The promotion

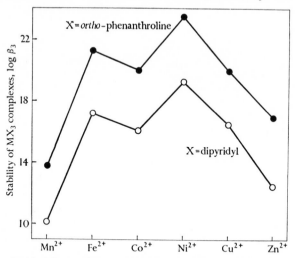

FIG. 25.26. The overall stability constants ($\beta_3 = K_1 K_2 K_3$) of the complexes of *ortho*-phenanthroline and dipyridyl in aqueous solution at 25 °C.

energy due to spin-pairing (see section 24.4) has been overcome by a greatly increased bond strength. The bond strength increase arises partly from σ-bonding, which is stronger as the internuclear distances are shorter in the low-spin compounds (this is a 'covalent' d^2sp^3 complex in valence-bond language), and partly because the overlap between empty ligand π^* orbitals and the expanded t_{2g} orbitals of the cation has increased. The sequence of stabilities is anomalous too in that the nickel complexes are more stable than those of copper. There are two contributing factors here: the stability of the copper(II) complex is lowered by steric hindrance to the formation of a *planar* structure and the stability of the *octahedral* nickel complex is increased by π-bonding.

SECOND AND THIRD TRANSITION SERIES

Low-spin complexes are less common than high-spin complexes in the first transition series, but in the second and third transition series the low-spin complexes are the more common. Low-spin complexes are generally more covalent than high-spin complexes and this will result in an increase in R and Q (Fig. 25.3) in the plot of $-\Delta H^\circ$ against atomic number. However, in the low-spin series, Q probably goes through a maximum around d^6 and d^8 rather than at the d^3 and d^8 cations. This, at least, is the prediction of crystal-field theory. Unfortunately no conclusive experimental evidence

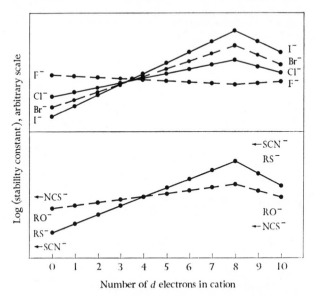

Fig. 25.27. Schematic representation of changes in the stability constants of complexes of low-spin cations of the second and third transition series.

is available on this point. Just as in the high-spin series where Q for d^4 or d^9 often exceeds that for d^3 or d^8, it is quite possible that Q for the low-spin ions will follow the sequence $d^8 > d^7 > d^6$. This will tend to occur when covalence effects become dominant. In the second and third transition series covalence is of generally greater significance than in the first series. This can be seen from the wealth of complexes of the platinum metals, Ru, Os, Rh, Ir, Pd, and Pt, with the heavier halide ions, and ligands with sulphur, phosphorus, and nitrogen atoms as donors. By way of contrast there are relatively few complexes with fluoride ion and oxygen ligands. Thermodynamic data for the compounds and complexes of these cations are not yet available. Much of the qualitative evidence from the general chemistry of the elements, such as the extreme stability of the ammine complexes in acid solutions, suggests that stability increases steadily along the transition series until Pd(II) and Pt(II). Some probable stability sequences are indicated in Fig. 25.27. Part of the contrast with the lattice-energy plots of Fig. 25.7 will be due to the absence of M—M bonds in the simple complexes.

25.6. Complex ions, Ca^{2+} to Mn^{2+}

Within this series, reliable data are almost entirely restricted to the divalent ions of Ca, V, Cr, and Mn. The general changes along the series,

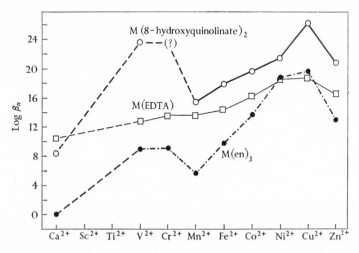

FIG. 25.28. Stability constants for complexes of ethylenediaminetetraacetate (EDTA), β_1, ethylenediamine (en), β_3, and 8-hydroxyquinolinate, β_2. $\beta_n = (K_1 K_2 \dots K_n)$.

and the relation of these changes to those in the second half of the transition series, have already been illustrated in earlier figures in this chapter. Fig. 25.28 presents some further data; the relation to the electron affinities of the cations can be seen by reference to Fig. 25.5. Some stability constants of V(II) and Cr(II) complexes are collected together in Table 25.v.

The main features of the complex-ion chemistry may be summarized as follows.

(1) The stability sequence *for the high-spin states* of divalent ions of the first part of the transition series, i.e. from Ca^{2+} to Mn^{2+}, is ligand dependent. Some sequences are given in Table 25.vi. The stability sequence in the second part of the transition series from Mn^{2+} to Zn^{2+} does not show a similar ligand dependence; see Figs. 25.24 and 25.28.

(2) Ligands RO^-, e.g. hydroxide, enolates, and phenolates, form particularly stable complexes with the cations V^{2+} and Cr^{2+} as compared with Ca^{2+} and Mn^{2+}. Fig. 25.16 showed a similar effect in the oxides of Ti^{2+}

TABLE 25.V. *Logarithms of step-wise stability constants of vanadium*(II) *and chromium*(II) *complexes at* 25 °C

Ligand	Step constant	V^{2+}	Cr^{2+}	Solvent
Ethylenediamine tetraacetate	K_1	12·7	13·6	Water
Oxalate	K_1	2·5–3·0		Water
Salicylate	K_1	6·3	8·4	Water
	K_2	4·7	6·9	
Acetyl acetonate	K_1	5·4	5·9	Water
	K_2	4·8	5·8	
	K_3	4·5		
8-Hydroxy-quinolinate	K_1	12·8		50% v/v Dioxan-water
	K_2	10·8		
Ethylenediamine	K_1	4·6	5·1	Water
	K_2	2·9	4·0	
	K_3	1·3	v. small	
2,2′-Dipyridyl	K_1	4·9	$\sim$ 4·5	Water
	K_2	4·7	$\sim$ 6·0	
	K_3	3·8	$\sim$ 3·5	

Note. The constants will vary with ionic strength.

TABLE 25.VI. *Stability sequences* Ca^{2+} *to* Mn^{2+}

Ligand	Stability constant	Sequence
Oxalate	$\log \beta_1$	$Ca^{2+} < V^{2+} < Mn^{2+}$
Ethylenediamine tetraacetate	$\log \beta_1$	$Ca^{2+} < V^{2+} < Cr^{2+} \leqslant Mn^{2+}$
Ethylenediamine and similar aliphatic N-bases	$\log \beta_1, \log \beta_2$	$Ca^{2+} < V^{2+} < Cr^{2+} > Mn^{2+}$
Salicylate	$\log \beta_1, \log \beta_2$	$Ca^{2+} < V^{2+} < Cr^{2+} > Mn^{2+}$
2,2′-Dipyridyl	$\log \beta_1$	$Ca^{2+} < V^{2+} \geqslant Cr^{2+} > Mn^{2+}$
	$\log \beta_3$	$Ca^{2+} < V^{2+} > Mn^{2+}$
Cyanide	$\log \beta_6$	$Ca^{2+} < V^{2+} < Cr^{2+} > Mn^{2+}$

β_n is the overall stability constant for n steps.

and V^{2+}. We take this to be due to the strong π-acceptor properties of the cations of metals early in a transition series. This group of ligands binds cations of metals later in the transition series, e.g. Ni^{2+}, with approximately the same strength as it binds V^{2+}.

(3) Unsaturated imines, e.g. dipyridyl, form relatively stronger complexes than saturated amines, e.g. ethylenediamine. A comparison between Ni^{2+}, $\log \beta_3$ (en) 18·5, $\log \beta_3$ (dipy) 20·0, and V^{2+} (data in Table 25.v) shows

that π-*donor* properties of the cation are *seemingly* more important in the first part of the transition series, V^{2+}, than in the second part, Ni^{2+}, although all nitrogen donors are more strongly bound in the second part of the series. This anomaly probably arises from the increased binding of aliphatic nitrogen with increase in ionization potential, $Ni > V$.

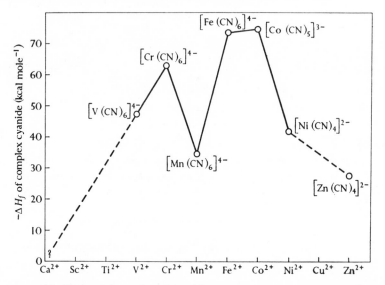

Fig. 25.29. Heats of formation of cyanide complexes from aquo-ions at 25 °C.

(4) A change of spin state probably occurs on the addition of the second dipyridyl molecule to the Cr^{2+} aquo-ion. The change of spin state of the d^4 ion is more easily achieved than that of the d^6 ion, Fe^{2+}, which changes spin state on addition of the third dipyridyl. After the change of spin state the chromium(II) dipyridyl complexes are more stable than those of vanadium(II).

In Fig. 25.29 are plotted the heats of formation of complex cyanides in water. In these complexes the cations Cr^{2+}, Mn^{2+}, Fe^{2+}, (Fe^{3+}), Co^{2+}, and Ni^{2+} are in low-spin states. Thus although the plot shows a minimum at Mn^{2+} and a maximum at Cr^{2+}, as in the previous figure, there is now a maximum at Fe^{2+} and Co^{2+} and not at Ni^{2+} (contrast dipyridyl Fig. 25.26). It is probable that π-donation by the cation is of maximum significance at about the d^6 cation; see Chapter 27 for related problems in carbonyls and aryls. The extremely low stability constant for Mn^{2+} could well be due to the high promotional energy from high-spin to low-spin state associated with d^5 systems.

THE INFLUENCE OF π-BONDING

From a consideration of the above points we conclude that the π-acceptor properties of the cations have a very considerable influence upon the stability of complex ions in the first part of the transition series. This influence is comparable in importance with the π-donor properties of the cations in the second part of the series. The cations in the early part of the series are small and their $3d$ orbitals are diffuse, making for good overlap. The low stability of oxalate and EDTA complexes (ligand is a poor π-donor) and the particularly high stability of RO^- (ligand is a good π-donor) complexes are explicable on this basis. The absence of a maximum in the plot of $\log K_1$ against atomic number in the EDTA complexes of the cations Ca^{2+} to Mn^{2+} suggests that the N-binding through σ-bonds is very weak as compared with the second part of the transition series, and this impression is strongly supported by the available evidence on bond distances in complexes (section 24.12). Thus the relatively high stability of imine and cyanide complexes remains as an anomaly.

In the second and third transition series differences between elements at the beginning and at the end are even more pronounced. The greater exposure of the d electrons even leads to polymerization in many compounds, e.g. the chlorides of Mo(II). As yet rather little is known about the complexes of these valence states as divalent compounds are of very low stability in the second and third transition series.

ANALYTICAL REAGENTS

The most common analytical reagents for the cations of the early elements in all the transition series are enolates and phenolates. These reagents will also interact with the later elements of the series where, however, reagents binding through sulphur and nitrogen are preferred. The enolates and phenolates are especially valuable for higher-valence cations. Typical reagents derived from RO^-, the essential unit, are

HO_2^-,

| peroxide | Tiron | thenoyltrifluoroacetone |

These qualitative observations are common to the three transition series and to all the valence states, e.g. V(II), Ti(III), Zr(IV), and MoO_2(VI); contrast Cu(II), Co(III), and Pt(IV).

METAL-ION AND PROTON STABILITY CONSTANTS

A plot of $\log \beta_n$, where β_n is the overall stability constant of a complex, ML_n, against pK_a, where K_a is the acid dissociation constant of HL, has often been found to yield a rough straight line, $\log \beta_n = a + bpK_a$, for a series of related ligands (see discussion of proton in Chapter 11). The slope of the line increases from cations such as Mg^{2+} and Ca^{2+} to cations such as Cu^{2+}. This suggests that b is related to the σ-polarizing power of the cation. a is usually larger for later transition metals than for pre-transition metals and may be related to π-bonding with unsaturated ligands. Unfortunately the equation is empirical in nature so that interpretation of a and b must always be suspect in the absence of a reason for linearity at all. The situation is very like that of many other linear free-energy relationships in aqueous solution, e.g. the Brønsted relationships between the logarithms of rate constants for acid-catalysed hydrolysis and the logarithms of the acid dissociation constants. There is already some evidence that over a wide range of values the free-energy relationships are curved.

25.7. The chemistry of Ni(II), Pd(II), and Pt(II)

In order to show the main changes down later Groups of the transition series, we shall now consider the chemistry of Ni, Pd, and Pt in valence state (II). The higher (IV) and lower (I, O, −I) valence states will be discussed in Chapters 26 and 27 respectively. The ease of reduction to the metal of both Pd(II) and Pt(II) has made it difficult to study some of their simple chemistry.

ELECTRON STRUCTURE

Table 25.VII gives some ionization-potential data. The ionization of d electrons is about equally difficult at Pd and Pt at low charge, but more difficult at Pd at higher charge. At low charges the ionization energy for d electrons is smallest at Ni. The ionization of s electrons is most difficult at Pt. As a consequence, the electron affinity of the nickel cation in low-valence states is smaller than that of either Pt or Pd. The d^8 configuration is, of course, of high-spin in all the gas ions. The ease with which the ions

TABLE 25.VII. *Ionization energies in the* Ni, Pd, Pt *triad* (eV)

	$d^{10} \to d^9$	$d^9s \to d^8s$	$d^9s \to d^9$		$d^9 \to d^8$
Ni	5·73	8·8	7·63	Ni$^+$	18·15
Pd	8·33	10·7	7·33	Pd$^+$	19·42
Pt	8·2	10·0	9·0	Pt$^+$	18·56

go over from high-spin to low-spin on chemical combination is Pt > Pd $\gg$ Ni. The divalent chemistry of Pd and Pt is almost restricted to the low-spin compounds, while that of Ni is divided between the high-spin and low-spin compounds, the former being predominant. Apart from the internal electron–electron repulsions, Pt < Pd < Ni, the factors determining the spin state are the effective strength and the symmetry of the field applied. A d^8 high-spin state is strongly stabilized by an octahedral field $(t_{2g}^6 e_g^2)$, while the d^8 low-spin configuration is stabilized in a tetragonal or square coplanar field. In the solid state the structures of platinum and palladium compounds are very alike, commonly 4-coordinate and planar, while those of nickel are often different, commonly octahedral. Typical examples are the halides and oxides. However, in the presence of a very strong field, the Ni^{2+} ion goes over to the low-spin state and usually takes on but four groups in a plane, e.g. in Ni(dimethylglyoximate)$_2$. It may, however, also form 5-coordinate complexes as discussed in section 24.6. Before commenting on the chemistry it is as well to realize how far Pd—X and Pt—X bonds deviate from the ionic model (Table 25.VIII). High-spin nickel complexes, even $KNiF_3$, are at least 10–20 per cent covalent but it is difficult to be more precise than this at present.

TABLE 25.VIII. *Partial ionic character from nuclear quadrupole coupling of halogens*

Halide complex	MBr_4^{2-}	MCl_6^{2-}	MBr_6^{2-}	MI_6^{2-}
Pd	60%	43%	37%	..
Pt	57%	44%	38%	30%

(After Ito, Nakamura, Kurita, Ito, and Kubo, *J. Am. Chem. Soc.*, 1961, **83**, 4256.)

STEREOCHEMICAL EQUILIBRIA OF NICKEL COMPOUNDS

While Ni^{2+} normally occupies octahedral (high-spin) or tetragonal (low-spin) sites it can be forced into a tetrahedral site. Thus in the $NiCr_2O_4$ spinel all the octahedral sites are preferentially taken by Cr^{3+} and the Ni^{2+} is left with the tetrahedral sites. In some other spinels the Ni^{2+} is distributed between both types of site. An alternative way of forcing tetrahedral geometry upon the Ni^{2+} ion is to surround it with large ligands as in $[NEt_4]_2^+[NiCl_4]^{2-}$ and in $[Ni(PPh_3)_2Cl_2]$.

In solution the balance between low-spin and high-spin configurations is very dependent upon the strength of the solvent or additional ligand interaction perpendicular to the plane of the tetragonal unit, e.g. in Ni(salicylaldiminate)$_2$. The low-spin state is the more stable the greater the splitting of the 'e_g' orbitals in the tetragonally-distorted octahedron. The equilibrium between the spin states is temperature-dependent.

Palladium and platinum compounds show neither low-spin/high-spin equilibria, nor any examples of tetrahedral symmetry. In fact the introduction of steric hindrance between the ligand molecules leads to distortions in the ligands before the immediate environment of Pd^{2+} or Pt^{2+} deviates from planarity. Again although there are some reported diamagnetic octahedral Ni^{2+} complexes, e.g. $[Ni(DAS)_3]^{2+}$ where DAS is

no such complexes are known for Pd^{2+} or Pt^{2+}.

M—M BONDS

The ability of the metals early in transition-series to form metal–metal bonds in octahedral compounds is due to the unpaired electrons in t_{2g} orbitals. In a tetragonal field the low-spin d^8 ions have all d orbitals full, except the antibonding $d_{x^2-y^2}$. Metal–metal bonding now arises in a very different way which is best seen from the structures. A typical example is Magnus's green salt, $[Pt(NH_3)_4]^{2+}[PtCl_4]^{2-}$. Here the planar units alternate along a chain of platinum atoms and the Pt—Pt bonds are in a straight line perpendicular to the planes. Similar compounds are formed from the bromide, oxalate, and probably the thiocyanate complex anions: the ammonia in the cation can be changed for a variety of amines so long as they are not too bulky. Although Pd^{2+} does, Ni^{2+} does not give this type of compound. However, all three dimethylglyoximates (DMG) form structures in which the $M(DMG)_2$ units stack with short M—M distances. These bonds may be described in terms of an interaction between the d_{z^2} lone pair on one metal atom and the empty p_z orbital of the next. The reason for the reappearance of M—M bonds at the end of the transition series is then that the geometry and the promoted low-spin electron configuration permit the metals to act as weak donors as well as strong acceptors.

THERMODYNAMICS, SOLID STATE

The heats of sublimation per atom are not very different for the three metals, Ni 101, Pd 93, and Pt 122·0 kcal mole^{-1}. However, nickel has much the lowest ionization potential so that the production of the divalent compounds of nickel is favoured relative to the corresponding reactions of Pd and Pt. A further factor stabilizing a nickel lattice is the small size of the ion as may be seen from consideration of the usual Born–Haber cycle.

$$M(gas) + X_2 \xrightarrow{\text{ionization}} M^{2+}(\text{gas ions}) + 2X^-(\text{gas ions})$$

sublimation $\uparrow$ ΔH_f $\downarrow$ lattice energy

$$M(\text{solid}) + X_2 \xrightarrow{\hspace{2cm}} MX_2$$

In fact both Pd and Pt compounds have such low heats of formation that they readily revert to the metallic state. One of the practical difficulties in preparing palladium and platinum compounds is to prevent this reaction. In this respect the platinum metals, including Ru, Os, Rh, and Ir, resemble very closely Hg and Au. If divalent compounds are wanted, the disproportionation reaction

$$2M(II) \rightarrow M + M(IV)$$

must also be avoided. The relatively high resistance to corrosion (low $-\Delta H_f$ of compounds) makes many of the *noble* metals of use in jewellery and ornaments as well as in electrical equipment.

The resemblance to B metals rather than to pre-transition metals, brought out in section 25.1, is also strongly marked in the relative stability of different compounds on descending the Group (Fig. 25.13). The chemistry of nickel reflects a high affinity for oxygen anions, but palladium and platinum have only slightly lower affinity for sulphur than for oxygen. Similarly, in passing from nickel to platinum the difference in affinity for the different halogens becomes smaller. The general feature shown here is a relative increase in the affinity for a polarizable ligand as opposed to a smaller highly polar one. In Fig. 25.13 this appears as a greater vertical spread in the differences in heats of formation.

SOLUTION CHEMISTRY

In solution and complex-ion chemistry the same trends are shown. The stability order of the halide complexes is $F^- > Cl^- > Br^- > I^-$ for Ni^{2+} (as for cations of the pre-transition and early transition metals), but it is $I^- > Br^- > Cl^- > F^-$ for Pd^{2+} and Pt^{2+}. The last two cations form many very stable complexes with ligands containing polarizable atoms such as C, P, As, and S. Pt^{2+} can also form a compound $[Pt(SnCl_3)_5]^{3-}$, a type at present unknown in Pd or Ni chemistry. Thus both Pd^{2+} and Pt^{2+} form SO_2 complexes, and Pd^{2+} can act as a catalyst for the reactions of olefins, presumably through the formation of a Pd^{2+}-olefin complex. Of particular interest as possible reaction intermediates are the allyl complexes in such bridged dimers as

$$\left[\text{allyl Pd} \begin{array}{c} Cl \\ \diagdown \diagup \\ \diagup \diagdown \\ Cl \end{array} \text{Pd allyl} \right]^{2+}.$$

They will be described in Chapter 27, together with other complexes in which the metals are bound directly to carbon.

Problems

SECTION A

1. In Chapter 20 various energies were plotted as a function of ionic radius. In this chapter energies have been plotted as a function of atomic number. Suggest good reasons for this distinction in approach.

2. Discuss the various theoretical effects which may influence Q and R in Fig. 25.3. Give examples which appear to illustrate these effects, see e.g. Figs. 25.14. to 25.29.

3. Comment on the following series of MF distances (Å) for the compounds KMF_3: Cr (four at 2·14, two at 2·01), Mn (six at 2·10), Fe (six at 2·06), Co (six at 2·04), Ni (six at 2·01), Cu (four at 2·07, two at 1·96), Zn (six at 2·03).

4. Cr(II)acetate,H_2O is dimeric and diamagnetic. Suggest a possible structure for this compound. Check with Fig. 25.22.

5. Account for the fact that, with the exception of CrO and CuO, all the oxides, MO, of the first transition series have regular NaCl structures.

6. The following structures are normally adopted:

VO, FeO, CoO, NiO (all NaCl); VS, FeS, CoS, NiS (all NiAs); TiO_2 (rutile), ZrO_2 (fluorite); TiS_2, ZrS_2 (CdI_2). Comment.

7. Describe and discuss the structures of the metal thiocyanates (see Table 31.III).

8. Discuss the occurrence of 4-, 5-, and 6-coordination.

9. The following are the infra-red stretching frequencies (cm^{-1}) of M—N bonds in $[M(NH_3)_6]Cl_2$:

Mn	Fe	Co	Ni	Cu	Zn	Cd
307	321	327	334	406	300	298

What can be deduced about the M—N bond energies, and how may these energies be interpreted?

10. The infra-red stretching frequency for CO in urea is increased in $[Pd(urea)_2Cl_2]$ and $[Pt(urea)_2Cl_2]$, but is decreased in $[Fe(urea)_6]^{3+}$, $[Cr(urea)_6]^{3+}$, and $[Zn(urea)_2Cl_2]$. Discuss the mode of binding of urea to metal cations, and compare your conclusions with the mode of binding of SCN^- to the same cations (see Table 31.III).

11. For Fe(II) complexes with 2,2'-dipyridyl (or 1,10-phenanthroline) $K_3 > K_2$. Only the tris-complex is diamagnetic. Comment.

12. The magnetic moment of Fe(II) in haemoglobin is 5·4 Bohr magnetons, but the molecule becomes diamagnetic on 'oxygenation'. CN^-, CO, and PF_3 are all haemoglobin poisons and also induce diamagnetism. Oxidation to Fe(III) results in a loss of 'oxygenation' properties. Comment on these related observations.

13. Comment on the following experimental values for the formation constants of ethylenediamine complexes (all for $1N$ KCl at 30°):

	Mn^{2+}	Fe^{2+}	Co^{2+}	Ni^{2+}	Cu^{2+}	Zn^{2+}
$\log K_1$	2·73	4·28	5·89	7·52	10·55	5·71
$\log K_2$	2·06	3·25	4·83	6·28	9·05	4·66
$\log K_3$	0·88	1·99	3·10	4·26	−1·0	1·72

14. Comment on the observation that while CO and PF_3 form a complex with haemoglobin, NF_3 does not.

15. Discuss the chemistry of the elements Ca to Zn as illustrated by their behaviour in the normal procedures of simple qualitative analysis (see Chapter 34).

16. $Zn(OH)_2$ dissolves in excess alkali, but $Ca(OH)_2$ does not. CaS is hydrolysed by water but ZnS is not. Comment.

17. The order of complex stability for divalent ions is found to follow very approximately the following sequence:

Pt > Pd > Hg > UO_2 > Be > Cu > Ni > Co > Pb > Zn > Cd > Fe > Mn > Ca > Sr > Ba.

In what ways may we seek to understand this particular series?

18. Use Fig. 25.13 to predict differences in the solubilities of anhydrous salts of Mg(II) and Ni(II).

19. Apparently divalent compounds of early transition metals are usually polymerized and deeply coloured: polymerization is not common later in the series. How may this be explained?

20. Compare the relative ease of hydrolysis of the cations Pd^{2+}, Ni^{2+}, V^{2+}, and Mn^{2+}.

21. Comment on the following heats of formation ($-\Delta H_f$, kcal mole^{-1})

$NiCl_2$ (73±2), $PdCl_2$ (43±4), $PtCl_2$ (29±3)
NiI_2 (23±2), PdI_2 (10±7), PtI_2 (4±3).

22. Au(III), Pt(II), and Pd(II) often form $[MX_4]^{n-}$ complexes. What explanation can you give?

23. Why are divalent ions so uncommon in the second and third transition series?

24. The hydrated Pd^{2+} and Pt^{2+} ions are very little known as compared with Ni^{2+}, yet the halide complexes of the former are more common than those of the latter. Comment.

SECTION B. (*Experimental*)

The following experiments demonstrate the change in character, from pre-transition- to B-metal behaviour, in the first transition-metal series. They can be carried out on a class basis. Either universal pH indicator papers or (better) pH meters are required. In all cases addition of one solution to another must be carried out gradually and observations made after each incremental addition.

Prepare $M/100$ solutions of the following salts in M HCl: $CaCl_2$, $MnCl_2$, $CoCl_2$, $NiCl_2$, $CuCl_2$, $ZnCl_2$.

(1) To a suitable volume of each of the salt solutions add M NaOH slowly, e.g. from a burette. Observe the pH of precipitation.

(2) To a suitable volume of each of the salt solutions add M NH_3 slowly, e.g. from a burette. Observe the pH of colour changes as accurately as possible and also record the pH of precipitation.

(3) Into a suitable volume of each of the salt solutions pass H_2S (or add sulphide in any other manner). Increase the pH as in (1) (and if necessary pass H_2S into the solutions at suitable pH intervals). Note the pH of precipitation. Filter the precipitates and observe which will dissolve in (*a*) acetic acid and (*b*) hydrochloric acid.

(4) To a suitable volume of each of the salt solutions add an equal volume of ethanol. To this solution add enough of a solution of 8-hydroxyquinoline in ethanol to give a 2:1 molar excess of this reagent over the metal ion. Add NaOH as in (1) observing colour changes or the formation of precipitates.

(5) Make up $M/100$ salt solutions in $M/10$ HCl. Add an equal volume of $M/100$ sodium ethylenediaminetetraacetate (EDTA). Titrate with $M/10$ NaOH. This experiment *must* be done with a pH meter.

From the above experiments you should be able to find the orders of stability of certain complexes and precipitates of the cations being considered. Furthermore, you should observe the changing selectivity of action as reagents involving oxygen-, nitrogen-, and sulphur-atom donors are studied.

Bibliography

J. S. ANDERSON, *Current Problems in Non-Stoicheiometry*, Advances in Chemistry Publication No. 39, American Chemical Society, 1963.

J. BÉNARD, 'Composés ioniques non stoechiométriques', *Tenth Solvay Conference*, ed. R. Stoops, Brussels, 1956.

R. L. CARLIN, ed., *Transition Metal Chemistry*, Arnold, London, 1965.

C. K. JØRGENSEN, *Inorganic Complexes*, Academic Press, New York, 1963.

S. E. LIVINGSTONE, 'Metal Complexes of Ligands containing Sulphur, Selenium, or Tellurium as Donor Atoms', *Quart. Rev. Chem. Soc.*, 1965, **14**, 386.

A. E. MARTELL and M. CALVIN, *Chemistry of the Metal Chelate Compounds*, Prentice-Hall, New York, 1952.

J. R. MILLER, Recent Advances in the Stereochemistry of Nickel, Palladium, and Platinum, *Advances in Inorganic Chemistry and Radiochemistry*, vol. 4, ed. H. J. Emeléus and A. G. Sharpe, Academic Press, New York, 1962.

F. J. C. ROSSOTTI, The Thermodynamics of Metal Ion Complex Formation in Solution, *Modern Coordination Chemistry*, ed. J. Lewis and R. G. Wilkins, Interscience, New York, 1960.

26 · Transition Metals: High-Valence States and Redox Equilibria

26.1. General introduction

In this chapter we wish to consider first of all (Part A) the chemistry of the transition metals in valence states greater than 2, that is in those compounds where they can be regarded, at least to some extent, as existing as ions carrying a formal charge greater than 2. It will be clear that in many cases little will be gained by starting with an ionic picture, but it is nevertheless useful to make a distinction between the class of compound treated in this chapter, and that treated in the next which is concerned essentially with low-oxidation state chemistry. Redox problems will be excluded from Part A so that attention can be directed to the general changes along transition series and down Groups at constant valence. The treatment is therefore similar to that used for the divalent ions in the previous chapter.

This similarity will be most marked in section 26.2, where the trivalent ions are considered, but even here it will be noted that the chemistry is restricted by redox considerations. Thus the increasing preference along the series for heavy halides, cyanide, sulphide, etc., which was a feature of the divalent ions is less readily demonstrated in the trivalent series, for these ligands may be oxidized by the metal ions. The study of the trivalent series is also limited by the fact that in the second and third transition series the ions are commonly in the low-spin state and do not exchange ligands rapidly. Thermodynamic data are scarce for these ions.

The limitations set by redox-potential considerations become even more significant in the higher-valence states. In addition, the small and highly-charged ions have an even greater preference for fluoride and oxide, so that the chemistry is often limited largely to fluorine and particularly to oxygen chemistry. After a general consideration of simple high-valence cations (section 26.3), the following sections are therefore devoted to oxocations (section 26.4), and to oxyanions (section 26.5). These last two sections return us to a good deal of chemistry which has already been discussed in Chapter 14.

In the higher-valence states there is considerable covalent bonding, involving especially metal ns and np orbitals. The $(n-1)d$ orbitals tend to disappear into the atomic core, especially in the first transition series. The departure from the simple ionic model should be most marked in compounds with the less electronegative elements. Section 26.6 brings out some of the general features of such compounds as carbides and nitrides, which have already been treated in Part II under the chemistry of the non-metals.

The general effects of change of valence already discussed in Part II are again apparent. Thus with increasing valence, oxides become more acidic and halides become more volatile and more readily hydrolysed.

The discussion of the individual valence states, and of the effects of ligands upon them, leads on naturally to the re-examination of redox equilibria which is the subject-matter of Part B. This completes the discussion already introduced in Chapter 23. Part B has its own introduction at the beginning of section 26.7.

PART A

HIGH-VALENCE STATES

26.2. Trivalent ions

Table 26.I lists the well-authenticated trivalent ions of the transition metals. Whereas it has been possible to make an extensive study of the divalent compounds of the last six elements of the first transition series, i.e. from Mn(II) to Zn(II), the relative instability of the trivalent state of those same elements forces us to look at this valence state in the early part, Sc(III) to Fe(III), of the same series. Unfortunately there are insufficient data to permit a detailed comparison with the divalent state in this part of the series as the lower state here is rather unstable. The trivalent state is much less stable in the early part of the second and third transition series, but becomes one of the more common states after the middle part of these series, for example Ru(III), Rh(III), Ir(III), Au(III), although it is unusual in Ni, Pd, and Pt, and absent in Zn, Cd, and Hg.

TABLE 26.I. *Well-authenticated trivalent ions*

Sc^{3+}	Ti^{3+}	V^{3+}	Cr^{3+}	Mn^{3+}	Fe^{3+}	Co^{3+}	(Ni^{3+})	(Cu^{3+})	..	Ga^{3+}
Y^{3+}	..	Nb^{3+}	Mo^{3+}	Tc^{3+}	Ru^{3+}	Rh^{3+}	(Pd^{3+})	$((Ag^{3+}))$	..	In^{3+}
La^{3+}	..	Ta^{3+}	W^{3+}	Re^{3+}	Os^{3+}	Ir^{3+}	(Pt^{3+})	Au^{3+}	..	Tl^{3+}

Parentheses enclose unusual ions.

ION SIZE

In the series of divalent ions there is a very considerable change in chemistry between the first member of the series, Ca^{2+}, and the early transition-metal ions such as Ti^{2+}. A part of this change must be related to the very rapid contraction of the divalent ions in the transition series;

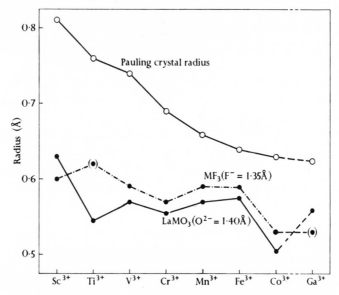

Fig. 26.1. Radii of the trivalent ions of the first transition series.

see Fig. 25.1. The contraction of the ions in the trivalent state is certainly not so great, but the situation is confused by the gross differences between Pauling radii and radii derived from the observed interatomic distances in either fluorides, MF_3, or perovskites, $LaMO_3$, the two latter agreeing very well (Fig. 26.1). The differences are especially large at Sc^{3+}. The Pauling values are based on two suppositions. (1) There is a regular sequence from K^+ to Ti^{4+}. While this leads to agreement with the observed distances for K^+ and Ca^{2+} it is in considerable error for Sc^{3+} and Ti^{4+}. (2) There is a smooth lanthanide-like contraction across the transition series. Again this is not observed, but it could be that Pauling radii represent basic theoretical radii in the absence of specific bonding. The short M—O and M—F distances could result from double bonding. ESR measurements show that Ti^{3+}—O^{2-} π-bonds ($p_\pi \rightarrow t_{2g}$) are about 60–70 per cent covalent. This means that it is impossible to have a set of trivalent ionic radii in which confidence can be placed. In order to be consistent we shall use Pauling radii, but the interested reader may like to see the effect of using observed 'radii' upon the Oxidation State Diagrams in Chapter 23. Although the latter give better quantitative agreement with experiment the whole ionic-model discussion is, of course, only of general qualitative interest.

Probably as a consequence of the small changes in real radii, the trivalent chemistries of the first element Sc and of the immediately following elements are somewhat similar. Other trivalent ions in the second and third transition series are also not very different in size. Thus the interatomic distances $M-F$ in MF_3 are Nb (1·95), Ta (1·95), Mo (1·95), Ru (1·98), Rh (1·98), Ir (2·01), Pd (2·04 Å). In the second and third transition series, where the trivalent state has been studied largely towards the end of the series, the chemistry resembles that of the B metals. Thus only a combination of studies in the first part of the first transition series with those in the later part of the other series shows how changes in the energy of d and s orbitals and in the occupancy of d orbitals affect the trivalent state. The overall changes are then seen to be not very different in kind from those observed in the divalent state.

STRUCTURES

In the first transition series the d^6, Co^{3+}, compounds cannot be compared directly with those of the other cations, for Co^{3+} goes over into a low-spin state in all compounds except the complex fluoride, CoF_6^{3-}, and some heteropolyacid anions where the cation is in a non-octahedral lattice site. The effect of the field geometry on the spin state is just that predicted by ligand-field theory. The preferred geometry is octahedral for Cr^{3+}, d^3, with tetragonal distortion for Mn^{3+}, d^4 (cf. Cr^{2+} and Cu^{2+}). While octahedral coordination appears to be generally preferred by Sc^{3+} and V^{3+}, Ti^{3+}, d^1, is found in 4-, 5-, 6-, and 8-coordination, and Fe^{3+}, d^5, which should show little preference for one symmetry over another, is known in 4-, 5-, 6-, and 7-coordinate compounds. In the compounds of the trivalent ions then coordination numbers may exceed as well as fall below six.

The compounds of the trivalent ions later in the second and third transition series are all of low spin, and generally have octahedral symmetry. Au^{3+}, d^8 (compare diamagnetic Ni^{2+}), is an exception and usually occurs in square-planar coordination. In^{3+} and Tl^{3+} often form tetrahedral complex anions $[MX_4]^-$; compare Zn^{2+}, Cd^{2+}, and Hg^{2+}.

As in the divalent compounds of the early transition metals, there is considerable metal–metal bonding in higher-valence compounds of metals early in the transition series. For example, one form of $TiCl_3$ (there are some four different forms) has an anomalously low magnetic moment, is darkly coloured, and the metal–metal distance is about 2·7 Å (compare 2·9 Å in Ti metal). It is believed that metal–metal bonding also occurs in TiI_3, $ZrCl_3$, $ZrBr_3$, ZrI_3, Ta_6Cl_{14}, Nb_6Cl_{14}, and in $K_5W_3Cl_{14}$. Again it is not only the divalent oxides such as TiO, a semi-metal, which contain metal–metal bonds. The dark colour of Ti_2O_3 and the structures of even higher oxides and halides, e.g. MoO_2 and NbI_4 (see Chapter 13), indicate considerable interaction between cations which further increases in the sulphides and nitrides. Of course all the 'interstitial' nitrides of formula MN can be formally considered as trivalent $M^{3+}N^{3-}$ compounds containing M—M bonds. However, the ionic formulation of these metal conductors is probably quite misleading.

A number of trivalent ions give compounds of formula $M_3'[M_2Cl_9]$ where M′ is an alkali metal. These compounds contain discrete $[M_2Cl_9]^{3-}$ anions with M = V, Mo, W, or Cr, but the iron compound is to be formulated as $(FeCl_4^-)_2Cl^-$ and the Ru(III) compound is of unknown structure. There is an M—M bond in the Mo, W, and V (probably) compounds, but not in the Cr compound. This is an example of the general point made in Chapter 13 that the exposure of the d orbitals in later transition series makes for stronger M—M bonding. More highly polymerized halide complex anions are also known. In $[Re_3Cl_{12}]^{3-}$ anion the Re—Re distance is 2·48 Å, while that in the metal is 2·78 Å.

PHYSICAL PROPERTIES

The halides of formula MCl_3 and MCl_4 are relatively involatile in Groups IIIA and IVA, but relatively volatile in Groups IIIB and IVB. We may attribute this change in volatility to the variation of the binding in the two parts of the Periodic Table. In Groups IIIA and IVA the binding is predominantly ionic, while in Groups IIIB and IVB it is more covalent. The Group IVB halides volatilize as the MCl_4 unit, while the IIIB halides are dimeric in the vapour, M_2X_6. The geometry around both the cations is tetrahedral in the vapour, but may be octahedral in the solid. Now for a d^3 cation especially, tetrahedral is not favoured relative to octahedral geometry by ligand-field stabilizations. Thus involatile halides might well be expected for such a cation. The data for the chlorides show that this is so.

	$ScCl_3$	$TiCl_3$	VCl_3	$CrCl_3$	$MnCl_3$	$FeCl_3$	$GaCl_3$
b.p.	967°	430° sublimes	high	> 1000 sublimes	decomp (?)	319°	200 °C

The high value for VCl_3 is probably due to metal–metal bonding. Values for $CoCl_3$, $NiCl_3$, and $ZnCl_3$ are not available as these chlorides cannot be prepared. Many of these halides are soluble in organic solvents and there they form adducts with, for example, ethers, ketones, and amines. Like $AlCl_3$ they can be used in the Friedel–Crafts' reactions. Trivalent titanium is also used in mixed titanium/aluminium alkyl halides as a catalyst in the Ziegler polymerization of ethylene (Chapter 10).

SOLID-STATE CHEMISTRY

The lattice energies of compounds of the divalent cations from Ca^{2+} to Zn^{2+} (Fig. 24.12) rise to a maximum either at d^3, V^{2+}, and d^8, Ni^{2+}, or more generally at d^4, Cr^{2+}, and d^9, Cu^{2+}. Maximum *lattice energy* of the trivalent compounds is therefore expected at d^3, Cr^{3+}, or d^4, Mn^{3+}, in the first part of the series. Although some quantitative data (Table 26.II) suggest that this may be so, these changes are not sufficiently large to be seen in *heats of formation* which fall to the d^5 cation (Fig. 26.2). The heats of formation for the divalent-ion compounds (same figure) show an increase at d^5, similar to the increase at d^{10}. The solution chemistry of the trivalent cations— see, for example, the standard electrode potentials, Chapter 9—confirms this impression. The experimental radii of the trivalent ions do not increase sharply at the half-filled sub-shell, Fig. 26.1, in direct contrast to the radii of the divalent ions, Fig. 25.1.

TABLE 26.II. *Heats of formation, ΔH_f, and lattice energies (kcal mole^{-1})*

	Sc	Ti	V	Cr	Mn	Fe	Co
ΔH_f oxide, M_2O_3 .	−410	−363	−299	−269·7	−229·4	−197·0	..
Lattice energy per metal atom . .	−1643	−1725	−1761	−1804	−1815	−1779	..
ΔH_f chloride, MCl_3 .	(−180)	−170	−137	−132·0	(−110·5)	−95·7	..
Lattice energy per metal atom . .	(−1110)	−1206	−1253	−1304	(−1305)	−1278	..
(eV) Sum of first three ionization potentials of metal	44·09	47·86	50·70	54·20	56·76	54·72	58·40

The high affinity for oxygen of elements early in the transition series, already noted in the discussion of the divalent ions, has increased further in the trivalent ions of the first transition series. Many oxyanion salts, e.g. those of iron(III), decompose to give the oxide. A simple illustration of this is the corrosion of iron which yields Fe(III)–Fe(II) oxide, while the corrosion of copper finally yields a basic carbonate of the divalent state.

Chromium also corrodes to give the trivalent oxide. Interestingly most of the elements also give mixed divalent-trivalent oxides, e.g. Cr_3O_4 and Fe_3O_4, as well as the simple oxides. These mixed oxides are usually relatively deeply coloured and good semiconductors.

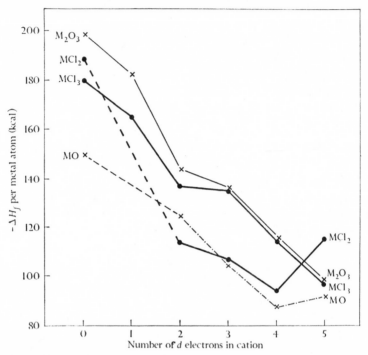

FIG. 26.2. Heats of formation of some trivalent and some divalent compounds in the first transition series.

The high affinity for oxygen donors is brought out again in the variety of complex salts which can be prepared containing these metals and oxy-anions. Tris-oxalates $[M(C_2O_4)_3]^{3-}$, and complexes of other organic acids are readily obtained but sulphato, nitrato, carbonato, and phosphato complex anions may also be prepared. The formation of these complexes, especially of the very acidic anions, is surprising. It may result from geometry of the complexes or the ability of the anions to act as π-donors despite their weak σ-donor power. Certainly this type of complex is more common in high-valence than in low-valence states, and it disappears for the trivalent cations of the later metals in each of the second and third transition series. These cations are of course π-donors rather than π-acceptors.

The trivalent ions of the second and third series have a much greater affinity for the more polarizable ligands. In part this is due to the larger size of the cations, in part to the high electron affinity of these ions especially toward the end of the series, and in part to the low-spin state of the compounds.

SOLUTION CHEMISTRY

The solution chemistry of the trivalent ions is difficult to study as they hydrolyse and polymerize readily. For example, the stable complexes of Cr^{3+}, Fe^{3+}, and Ti^{3+} with *ortho*-phenanthroline and 2,2'-dipyridyl are hydroxy-complexes which readily give either oxy- or hydroxy-bridged structures, e.g.

$$\left[(dipy)_2Fe\begin{array}{c}OH\\OH\end{array}Fe(dipy)_2\right]^{4+}.$$

One outstanding difference between Cr(III) and Co(III) complex-ion chemistry is the more frequent formation of such polymers by the Cr(III) ion. Other valence states early in transition series also give polymeric compounds in solution, e.g. many lower halides, $W_3Cl_9^{3-}$, thiocyanates, $[MoO(CNS)_3]_2$, and organic derivatives, $[MoCl_2(phenolate)_3]_2$, $[Ti(acetyl-acetonate)_2Cl]_2$.

All these polymers are of low magnetic moment. Metals early in their transition series have unpaired electrons in orbitals (t_{2g} in an octahedral field) which can form metal–metal bonds and thus help polymerization. In general the polymerization is greater in the second and third than in the first series. The kinetic stability of some of these polymers makes it difficult to study their equilibria.

Despite the hydrolysis and polymerization problem, there appears to be a very rough general order of stability constants for the trivalent cations:

$Co^{3+} > Fe^{3+} > Ga^{3+} > Cr^{3+} > Ti^{3+}$ and $Sc^{3+} >$ lanthanide cations.

The position of Mn^{3+} is unknown. This order is exemplified by the hydroxide, and 8-hydroxyquinolate complexes, but must not be considered as strictly applicable to all the complexes of these ions. Thus the logarithms of the stability constants for the EDTA complexes are Co^{3+} 36·0, Fe^{3+} 25·5, $Cr^{3+} \sim 23·0$, Sc^{3+} 23·1, and Ga^{3+} 20·3. Another exception is provided by the stability of the fluorides, $Sc^{3+} > Ga^{3+}$. The structure of the Fe^{3+} EDTA complex shows that the binding to the nitrogen is weak (a long bond), but that of the Co^{3+} complex shows that Co^{3+}—N binding is strong (a short bond, Table 24.XXI). These bond distances and the general order of the stability constants suggest that the increase in covalence with atomic number is at least as important as the crystal-field energy. In aqueous solution the earliest trivalent ions, e.g. Ti^{3+}, do not form stable complexes with amines, but these complexes are quite stable with Cr^{3+} and especially Co^{3+} ions. All the cations in the above series except Co^{3+} are precipitated as hydroxides on adding ammonia to their aqueous solutions, and their high affinity for hydroxide rather than sulphide is shown by their position in the group analysis tables, group III, relative to the position of the divalent ions of the later metals, groups II and IV. The earlier cations form halide complexes in the stability order $F^- > Cl^- > Br^- > I^-$. The reverse order holds for the low-spin ions of the second and third transition series, for the Co^{3+} ion in $[Co(CN)_5X]^{3-}$, and for the heavy B-metal cations, e.g. Tl^{3+}. This is parallel with the changes in the stability sequences of divalent ions.

The formation of halide and thiocyanate complexes of trivalent ions is put to practical use in extraction procedures. For example, Ti(III), Fe(III), Au(III), Ga(III), In(III), and Tl(III) can all be extracted into ether from acidic solutions as the complexes $(H_9O_4)^+ . MX_4^-$, where X is a halide or thiocyanate. The inability of Cr(III) and Co(III) to give these tetrahedral complexes is a further example of the relative stability of octahedral symmetry in d^3 and low-spin d^6 systems. It is sometimes observed that anionic halide complexes, $[MX_6]^{3-}$, can be extracted into non-polar solvents in the presence of alkyl amines. It is likely that hydrogen-bonding between the $[MX_6]^{3-}$ and the R_3NH^+ plays an important part in this extraction.

COMPLEX CYANIDES

A particularly interesting series of complexes of the trivalent cations are the hexacyanides, which appear to follow the stability pattern

$$Co^{3+} > Fe^{3+} > Cr^{3+} > V^{3+} > Ti^{3+} > (Ga^{3+}).$$

Both the Fe^{3+} and Co^{3+} complexes are of low spin, both are photosensitive, as is the Cr^{3+} complex, and both readily give the mono-hydroxy-penta-cyanide or the mono-aquopentacyanide instead of the hexacyanide. The $[Fe(CN)_5H_2O]^{2-}$ complex is very reactive. The water molecule may be replaced by many ligands, one of which is the NO group. The product is then diamagnetic showing that iron has become divalent and the nitroso group NO^+. The complex is known as nitroprusside. It can be titrated with two moles of base to give $[Fe(CN)_5NO_2]^{4-}$, or it may react with a sulphur-containing compound to give a sulphur adduct of the NO group. The resulting complex is deeply coloured and is the basis of the test for sulphur in organic analysis. The reactivity of the NO^+ in the complex is such that it will add many other strong nucleophiles, and it can also attack reactive methylene groups to give condensation products. There is a marked parallel between this activation of the simple NO molecule and the activation that the Fe^{3+} cation produces in organic molecules. It could be that such activation is the basis of the function of iron in many iron(III)-containing enzymes. The Fe^{3+} ion, in the high-spin state, is also used as a test reagent for phenols and hydroxamic acids, with which it gives characteristic colours. Both the activation and the colours are due to charge transfer.

Some of the complex cyanides and also mixed halide alkyl-phosphine (PR_3) complexes are able to bind H^-. The strength of this binding appears to increase at the end of transition series and in the second and third series.

KINETIC PROPERTIES

The stabilities of complexes of the trivalent ions in solution are often difficult to study because of their slow reactions. For the same reason the ions are ideal for the study of the kinetics of both substitution and oxidation-reduction reactions. The way in which the rates of these reactions vary with the number of d electrons of the central cation has already been described in Chapter 10. The observations are shown graphically in Figs. 29.3 and 29.4. It is a general observation that replacement of oxygen anions bound to cations is slower the higher the valence state, but this charge effect is not of over-riding importance until valence states around 5.

26.3. Simple high-valence cations

HIGH-VALENCE STATES

In the introduction to the transition elements it was pointed out that the higher valences, valences of 4 and greater, are to be found in the early part of the first transition series and throughout almost the whole length of the second and third series. The stability of these valences clearly increases from the first to the third series. This is explicable in terms of the greater penetration of the d electrons of higher principal quantum number ($5d > 4d > 3d$). Superimposed upon the effect of the atomic energy levels is the effect of the field of the ligands upon them. In an octahedral field, which is the one most commonly observed, the five d orbitals are split into 3 and 2 orbitals of different symmetry type. This division of the d orbitals is energetically more important in the second and third (low-spin) than in the first series (high-spin). As a result of these changes of spin state the most stable d sub-shell configurations are (1) in the first series d^3, d^5, and d^8, and (2) in the second and third series d^3, d^6, and d^8. In other field symmetries other electron configurations can become stabilized. The result of these stabilization energies is to make certain valences more noticeably stable for certain elements (Table 26.III) and these need not be the same for different elements in a given Group. In the heavier elements in the second and third transition series even-electron configurations become more stable relative to odd-electron configurations. This distinction is not unlike that between the non-metals of the first short period and other non-metals. Thus there are very few odd-electron compounds analogous to NO, NO_2, and O_2^- with the heavier non-metals such as phosphorus and sulphur. Electron pairing is more common when orbitals are highly exposed.

TABLE 26.III. *Particularly stable electron configurations*

Transition series	d^1	d^2	d^3	d^4	d^5	d^6	d^7	d^8	d^9	d^{10}
First series			Cr^{3+}		Mn^{2+}	$[Co^{3+}]$	Co^{2+}	Ni^{2+}	Cu^{2+}	Cu^+
			Mn^{4+}		Fe^{3+}					
Second series		$[Mo^{4+}]$			$[Ru^{3+}]$	$[Ru^{2+}]$		$[Pd^{2+}]$		Ag^+
						$[Rh^{3+}]$				
						$[Pd^{4+}]$				
Third series		$[W^{4+}]$	Re^{4+}	$[Os^{4+}]$		$[Ir^{3+}]$		$[Pt^{2+}]$		Au^+
						$[Pt^{4+}]$		$[Au^{3+}]$		

□ = low spin.

The high-valence compounds will now be considered in some detail. It is convenient to divide them into three classes:

(1) Compounds in which the metal ion can be formally considered to have a positive charge corresponding to its valence state, e.g. MnO_2 is an Mn^{4+}, K_2PdCl_6 is a Pd^{4+} compound (this section).

(2) Compounds in which the metal is part of an oxocation, e.g. $UO_2 . Cl_2$ and $MoO . Cl_3$ are a UO_2^{2+} and an MoO^{3+} compound respectively (section 26.4).

(3) Compounds in which the metal is part of an oxyanion, e.g. $KMnO_4$ is an MnO_4^- compound (section 26.5).

The division is somewhat arbitrary but has considerable practical value.

SIMPLE CATIONS

A number of compounds and complexes derived from M^{n+} ions are listed in Table 26.IV. Oxocations and oxyanions are excluded. The most readily studied are the 4-valent ions, the stabilities of which vary irregularly in the first series, e.g. the chemistry of Mn^{4+} is more extensive than that of either Cr^{4+} or Fe^{4+}. The irregularity reflects the stability of certain electron configurations. Particularly stable are the d^3 and d^6 ions with half-filled and completely filled t_{2g} orbitals. The same tendency appears in the second and third series where Re^{4+}, d^3, and Pd^{4+} and Pt^{4+}, d^6, are obvious examples. These two electron configurations are only strongly favoured in octahedral coordination, the latter in low-spin compounds. Eightfold (or fourfold) coordination can lead to a stabilization of other electron structures. Thus Mo and W octacyanides, d^2, are stable compounds of 4-valent cations, but no similar chromium complexes are known.

The stable valence states of all the ions are obtained by direct reaction of the elements under oxidizing conditions, e.g. with fluorine, chlorine, or oxygen present. The unstable higher valences are made by utilizing electron-transfer reagents in the step-wise oxidation from one state to the next, e.g.

$$Mo(CN)_8^{4-} + Ce^{4+} \rightarrow Mo(CN)_8^{3-} + Ce^{3+},$$

or by using oxygen-transfer reagents such as SO_5^{2-} or even O_2 which can also bring about oxidations in 2-electron steps, e.g.

$$2Mn(II)phthalocyanine + O_2 \rightarrow 2Mn(IV)O(phthalocyanine).$$

Kinetic stability of the high-valence compounds often permits detailed examination of their properties.

PROPERTIES

Much as in the lower valences the trend in properties of the 4-valent ions from the left- to the right-hand side of the Periodic Table is to more B-metal character. The stability of the fluoride and oxide diminishes relative to that of the heavier halides and sulphide. In complex ions, non-metal oxyanions, such as phenolates, carboxylates, sulphate, nitrate, and carbonate give way to ammonia, nitrite, thiocyanate, cyanide, and derivatives of phosphine and arsine, as the preferred ligands. Surprisingly, nuclear quadrupole coupling measurements suggest that all the $[MCl_6]^{2-}$ complexes from W^{4+} to Pt^{4+} are equally about 45 per cent ionic.

A second feature which changes across the series is the coordination number. In Groups IVA, VA, and VIA there are many examples of coordination numbers as high as 8, e.g. $Mo(CN)_8^{4-}$, ZrF_8^{4-}, $[V(O_2)_4]^{3-}$, $Zr(AcAc)_4^{4-}$,

TABLE 26.IV. *Examples of high-valence 'ions'*

Transition series	Formal charge on ion	IVA	VA	VIA	VIIA	VIIIa	VIIIb	VIIIc
First series	4+	Ti^{4+} hydrolysed [TiF$_6$]$^{2-}$	[VF$_6$]$^{2-}$	CrO$_2$	MnO$_2$, [MnF$_6$]$^{2-}$	Ba$_2$FeO$_4$ [Fe(DAS)$_2$Cl$_2$]$^{2+}$	[CoF$_6$]$^{2-}$ Co peroxy-complexes	[NiF$_6$]$^{2-}$ [Ni(DAS)$_2$Cl$_2$]$^{2+}$
	5+	..	[VF$_6$]$^{-}$	Cr(O$_2$)$_2$(NH$_3$)$_3$ [Cr(O$_2$)$_4$]$^{3-}$	..	..	..	..
	6+			..	..	..	..	..
Second series	4+	Zr(AcAc)$_4$	..	[Mo(CN)$_8$]$^{4-}$ [MoF$_6$]$^{2-}$	TcO$_2$ [TcCl$_6$]$^{2-}$	[RuCl$_6$]$^{2-}$	[RhCl$_6$]$^{2-}$	[PdCl$_6$]$^{2-}$ Pd(NH$_3$)$_2$ Cl$_4$
	5+	..	[NbF$_7$]$^{2-}$	[Mo(CN)$_8$]$^{3-}$	[TcCl$_4$(DAS)$_2$]$^{+}$	[RuF$_6$]$^{-}$	..	..
	6+	..	..	MoF$_6$	TcF$_6$	RuF$_6$	..	..
Third series	4+	Hf(AcAc)$_4$	..	[W(CN)$_8$]$^{4-}$ [WF$_6$]$^{2-}$	ReO$_2$ [ReCl$_6$]$^{2-}$	[OsCl$_6$]$^{2-}$ [Os(DAS)$_2$Cl$_2$]$^{2+}$	[IrCl$_6$]$^{2-}$, also ammines	[PtCl$_6$]$^{2-}$, [Pt(NH$_3$)$_6$]$^{4+}$
	5+	..	[TaF$_8$]$^{3-}$	[W(CN)$_8$]$^{3-}$	[ReCl$_4$(DAS)$_2$]$^{+}$ ReF$_6$[Re(CN)$_8$]$^{2-}$	[OsF$_6$]$^{-}$ [OsNCl$_5$]$^{2-}$ OsF$_6$	[IrF$_6$]$^{-}$ (IrO$_3$), IrF$_6$	PtF$_5$ PtF$_6$
	6+	..	..	WF$_6$				
'Fourth' series	4+	Th(AcAc)$_4$	PaF$_4$	U^{4+}(acid) not hydrolysed				
	5+	..	PaF$_5$	..				
	6+	..	..	UF$_6$				

Actinides

AcAc is acetylacetonate and DAS is bis-dimethylarsine phenylene, o-C$_6$H$_4$(As(CH$_3$)$_2$)$_2$.

$Th[N(CH_2CO_2)_3]_2$, and $ReCl_4(DAS)_2$. Some structures are shown in Fig. 26.3. Beyond Group VIIA there are very few examples of such coordination compounds, and the general maximum coordination would

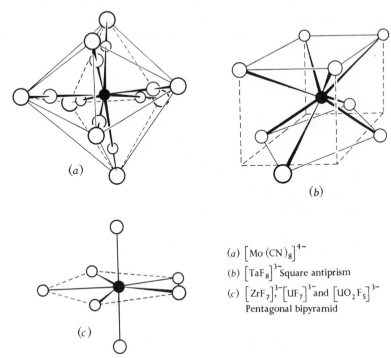

(a)

(b)

(c)

(a) $\left[Mo(CN)_8 \right]^{4-}$

(b) $\left[TaF_8 \right]^{3-}$ Square antiprism

(c) $\left[ZrF_7 \right]^{3-}$, $\left[UF_7 \right]^{3-}$ and $\left[UO_2F_5 \right]^{3-}$
Pentagonal bipyramid

FIG. 26.3. Structures of some complexes of high coordination number.

appear to be 6. Part of this change is possibly due to contraction of the core, but part must also be a reflection of the fall in the number of available empty orbitals, a change in the ligand-field splitting energies, and a change in the character of the bonds. It is remarkable that the known 8-coordinate complexes are with cations of high valence which must therefore be the smallest. Presumably the high central charge has so contracted the d orbitals as to make them valuable in bonding, d^4sp^3 in valence-bond language. It is also notable that high coordination numbers are found with large ligand atoms such as As. It could be that there is significant van der Waals' interaction between the ligand atoms themselves.

SEPARATION METHODS

The elements hafnium and tantalum occur immediately following the lanthanide series and have ionic radii very similar to those of zirconium and niobium, respectively, in the previous transition series. Thus in both Groups IVA and VA the chemistries of the two heavier elements are very similar. The elements can only be separated efficiently from one another by using ion-exchange chromatography or counter-current liquid/liquid extraction, much as described in section 21.7 on lanthanide separations.

A different fractionation procedure is involved in the separation of the noble metals of Group VIII, Ru, Rh, Pd, Os, Ir, and Pt. In this Group there are sufficient chemical differences, either in the same valence state or in the stabilities of the different valence states, for separation to be made through preferential reaction or oxidation-reduction. For example, both Os and Ru can be volatilized as the tetroxides, but osmium tetroxide has a sufficiently lower volatility to allow a separation of the two oxides. The other elements also show differences in the stability of their lower valence states. Thus Pd(IV) is readily reduced to Pd(II) while Pt is kept in the IV state. A series of separations commonly adopted is shown schematically in Table 26.v. This should be particularly noted as a series

TABLE 26.v. *Extraction of platinum metals*

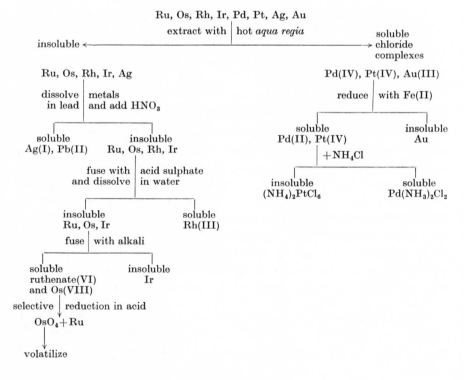

of separations using changes in oxidation state in marked contrast with the separations of the lanthanides and of Zr(IV) and Hf(IV).

STOICHEIOMETRY

At normal temperatures, the compounds of metals with only one stable high-valence state are probably quite close to stoicheiometric. However, at high temperatures, around 2500 °C, even thoria in equilibrium with an

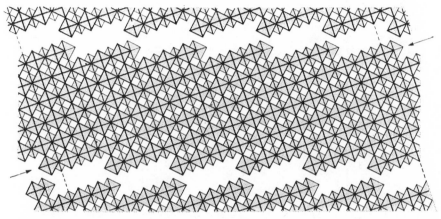

FIG. 26.4. The structure of $Mo_{18}O_{52}$; each diamond with a cross on it represents an MoO_6 octahedron and a complete layer of the octahedra would be the ReO_3 structure. The strips of the MoO_3 layers shown here are bound together by displacement along the dotted line. Arrows represent shear zigzags. (From Kihlborg, 'Non-stoicheiometry', *Adv. Chem. Ser.*, 1963, No. 39, 37.)

atmosphere of oxygen has the formula $ThO_{1.96}$. The compounds of metals with two or more highly stable valence states are generally non-stoicheiometric at much lower temperatures, and high-temperature preparations often give compounds of indefinite composition. Investigation of the equilibrium phases at high temperatures show that Ti and V oxides, for example, exist in a series of formulae M_nO_{2n-1}, while Mo and W oxides exist as a series M_nO_{3n-m}. The structure of these oxides are slabs of perfect MO_2 (rutile) or MO_3 (ReO_3 structure) (Fig. 26.4) connected by joining octahedral edges. The structures have been called shear structures as the oxygen vacancies which accumulate between the slabs of perfect structure occur along shear lines. Similar structures are known for lanthanide oxides approaching the formula MO_2, e.g. CeO_2, and for actinide oxides such as those approaching the formula M_3O_8, e.g. U_3O_8. In compounds other than oxides little is known about the details of phase-composition/structure relationships. The halides of the early transition metals of the second and

TABLE 26.VI. *Some oxocations*

Transition series	Valence	IVA	VA	VIA	VIIA	VIIIa	VIIIb	VIIIc
First series	3	TiO^+ ?	(VO^+)	..	←——— not known ———→			NiO^{2+}(?)
	4	TiO^{2+} ?	VO^{2+}	..	MnO^{2+}(rare)	FeO^{2+}(rare)	..	..
	5	..	VO^{3+}, VO_2^+	CrO^{3+}	..	..	..	..
	6	..	..	CrO_2^{2+} ?	..	..	..	..
	7	..	..	..	MnO_3^+	..	..	..
	8	..	..	..	..	..	..	..
Second series	3	none ?	?	(MoO^+) ?	← not known →	not known	..	..
	4	$(ZrO^{2+}?)$	..	..	..	RuO^{2+} ?	..	.. (not known)
	5	..	$NbO^{3+}, (NbO_2^+)$	MoO^{2+}, MoO^{3+}	TcO^{3+} ?, TcO_2^+	?	..	
	6	..	..	MoO_2^{2+}, MoO^{4+}	TcO_2^{2+} ?	RuO_2^{2+}, RuO_4^{4+}	..	
	7	..	..	..	..	RuO_2^{3+}(?)	..	
	8	..	..	..	..	..	..	..
Third series	3	none ?	?	..	ReO^+	← not known →	..	..
	4	$(HfO^{2+}?)$	..	..	ReO^{2+}	OsO^{2+} ?	..	.. (not known)
	5	..	$TaO^{3+}(TaO_2^+)$	WO^{2+}, WO^{3+}	ReO^{3+}, ReO_2^+	?	..	
	6	..	..	WO_2^{2+}, WO^{4+}	ReO^{4+}, ReO_2^{2+}	$OsO_2^{2+}, (OsO_4^{4+})$	IrO^{4+}	
	7	..	..	..	ReO_3^+, ReO_2^{3+}	OsO_2^{3+}	..	
	8	..	..	..	..	OsO_3^{2+}	..	..
'Fourth' series	3	unknown	PaO^{3+} ?	very rare or not known	..	..	..	..
	4	$(ThO^{2+}?)$	PaO_2^+ ?		..	..	..	..
	5	..	..	UO_2^+	NpO_2^+	..	..	..
	6	..	..	UO_2^{2+}	NpO_2^{2+}	..	..	..

third series are often non-stoicheiometric and are known to contain considerable M—M bonding, e.g. $NbCl_4$, NbI_4, Nb_3Cl_8, and $MoCl_3$. The M—M bonds are sometimes found in discrete clusters as in the units $[Ta_6Cl_{12}]^{2+}$, $[Re_3Cl_{12}]^{3-}$, and $[Re_2Cl_8]^{2-}$.

26.4. Oxocations

Table 26.VI collects together many of the known oxocations of the transition elements. They are of the following kinds

$$MO^+, MO^{2+}, MO^{3+},..., MO_2^+, MO_2^{2+}, MO_2^{3+}..., MO_3^+, \text{ and } MO_3^{2+},$$

and the sequence is naturally concluded with the oxides and oxyanions, e.g. MO_4, MO_4^-, and MO_4^{2-}. This type of cation is found for the most part with those elements which are amphoteric in the given valence state. Thus in Group IVA, oxocations are found at titanium, but are either less strongly marked or absent in hafnium, and probably disappear in thorium chemistry. A similar transition is observed in Group VA where, for example, the fluorides of niobium exist as a vast range of oxocation compounds and complexes, e.g. $NbOF_5^{2-}$, while tantalum fluoride chemistry is dominated by the simple fluorides, e.g. TaF_7^{2-}. This difference is used in the separation of the elements. In Group VIA the higher-valence states of chromium are strongly acidic and little is yet known of the *unstable* intermediate valence states, so that oxocations are only common in the heavier elements and particularly at uranium. In Group VIIA there are a few oxocation compounds of Mn(IV). A particularly interesting example is the compound formed in the direct and reversible reaction of manganese(II) phthalocyanine with molecular oxygen. However, in the third series, rhenium is commonly found in an oxocation throughout its high-valence states. Of the nine elements in Group VIII, osmium is the only one with a strong tendency to form oxocations although less stable MO^{2+} complexes are known, e.g. in Fe(IV), where they are important in porphyrin compounds, and in Ni(IV). Thus there is in the Periodic Table, from titanium and vanadium to rhenium and osmium, a diagonal section of elements which form stable oxocations. This section divides the elements giving stable simple cations, M^{n+}, from those which give neither simple hydrated cations nor oxocations, e.g. Pt, but usually occur in valence states of 4 and greater with polarizable ligands. The disappearance of oxocations from the chemistry of high-valence states late in each transition series is probably a consequence of the filling of the d orbitals of the cations. Oxide anions are π-donors and therefore require empty d orbitals for high stability. This is consistent with the structures of MoO_2^+ in dithiol complexes and of ReO_2^{3+} in $[ReO_2(CN)_4]^-$, where the O^{2-} groups are *cis* and not *trans* as in UO_2^{2+}.

PREPARATION

The oxocations are usually the unavoidable products of the reactions between water and the halides of the ele-

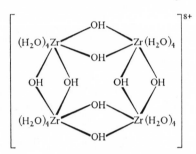

FIG. 26.5. One of the polymerized hydroxy species produced on hydrolysis of Zr^{4+} (from Wells).

ments. Examples are $UF_6 \rightarrow UO_2F_2$ and $MoCl_5 \rightarrow MoOCl_3$. Thus the ions are the partial hydrolysis products of high-valence states. This naturally raises the question why the hydrolysis of high-valence states proceeds in this manner. Hydrolysis of the chlorides of Group IIIA and frequently of Group IVA metals yields basic polymerized hydroxides, e.g. Fig. 26.5: the same type of hydrolysis is even found in beryllium. Elsewhere in the Periodic Table the hydrolysis pattern

$$MCl_n + H_2O \xrightarrow{(-HCl)} M(OH)_n \longrightarrow MO_{n/2} \text{ or } MO(OH)_{n-2}$$

occurs in the elements of the first row, and in the elements of the later non-metal Groups, e.g. $BrF_5 \rightarrow BrO_2(OH)$. Oxo-compounds are also occasionally found as the products of oxygenation.

The formation of an oxo-compound instead of a dihydroxy-compound results in an effective reduction in coordination number, in a first row atom from 4 to 3, in a second row atom from 4 to 3 or from 6 to 4, and in an atom of the transition series from 8 or 6 to a distorted arrangement which may have 1, 2, or 3 very close oxygen neighbours and a larger number of more distant ones. In these transition-metal compounds, however, the situation is anomalous in that a very small number of closest neighbours, very low coordination, is preferred in oxide complexes of elements which obtain a very high coordination number with fluoride, cyanide, and perhaps hydride, e.g. $[ReH_9]^{2-}$, even in the same valence state. The fact that fluoride gives complexes of very high coordination *with the same cations* would seem to exclude the possibility that purely electrostatic factors produce the low coordination with oxide—i.e. because the highly-charged cations are so small. An alternative explanation is that the formation of oxocations is due to double-bond formation—the d orbitals acting as acceptors for the p_π electrons of the oxide anions. This explanation is the more attractive as it is then virtually the same as that offered for low coordination in the first row of the Periodic Table (Chapter 3). The very short bond distances in the oxocation and oxyanion units (Table 26.VII) are in agreement with this explanation. The overall impression is then that there are two possible structures for the coordination of high-valence cations. In the first, electrostatic binding is decisive and the cation seeks a very high coordination number, sacrificing the larger covalent energy which would result from shorter bond distances. (At very high charge the d orbitals are considerably contracted and there can be little overlap with distant ligands.) In the second, covalent binding is decisive and the cation seeks a very low coordination number with strong overlap between its d orbitals and the orbitals of the ligand. The resulting oxo-unit acts as a cation with a lower effective positive charge and this 'cation' now has a high coordination number. The alternative which is chosen depends upon the ligand. Fluoride tends to produce the first structure, oxide and nitride the second.

TABLE 26.VII. M—O *bond distances in oxo-compounds* (Å)

Group VA		Group VIA		Group VIIA	
VO^{3+}	1·54	CrO_2Cl_2	1·57	MnO_3F	1·58
VO_4^{3-}	1·75				
		MoO_2Cl_2	1·75		
				ReO^{3+}	1·60
		UO_2^{2+}	1·67		
		UO_3	2·07		

There are several parallel situations in the Periodic Table where the optimum combination of electrostatic and covalent binding gives the central ion a choice between extreme coordination numbers, depending upon the character of the near neighbours. For example, the hydrogen bond in HF_2^- is symmetrical, but almost invariably the hydrogen-bond between oxygen or nitrogen is not symmetrical (note particularly that the difference is between fluoride and oxide ligands). Again arsenic(III) forms an oxyanion AsO_2^-, not $[HAsO_3]^{2-}$ as with phosphorus, but a fluoride AsF_3, while bromine forms a fluoride BrF_5 but an oxyacid BrO_3H. Oxygen lowers the coordination number in both examples. In certain cases equilibria are established between two differently-hydrated compounds. Thus CO_2 and H_2CO_3 coexist in solution in the ratio $10^3:1$. In the transition-metal oxides the equilibria in solution between the different forms, hydroxy-compounds and oxo-compounds, are in fine balance so that several species of different coordination coexist, for example with vanadium(V), molybdenum(V), etc.

TABLE 26.VIII. *Principal compounds of oxocations*

Ligand	TiO^{2+}	VO^{2+}	MoO_2^{2+} or WO_2^{2+}	MoO^{2+} or MoO_2^+ WO^{3+} or WO_2^+	ReO^{4+} or ReO_2^{2+}	ReO^{3+} or ReO_2^+	RuO_2^{2+}	OsO_2^{2+}
F^-		✓	✓	✓	✓			
Sulphate and acetate		✓	✓	✓				
Acetyl-acetonate and oxalate	✓	✓	✓					
OH^-		✓	✓	✓	✓		✓	
NH_3 and similar ligands				dipyridyl complexes ✓		phosphine and amine complexes {	✓	
Cl^-		weak	✓	✓	✓	✓	✓	✓
NO_2^-								✓
Br^-						✓		✓
CN^-								✓
I^-								✓

It is usually observed that the rate of exchange of hydroxide groups is very fast but that of oxo-groups is slow. Those anions which contain many OH groups act as oxidative hydroxylating agents through ˙OH radical transfer, but the oxo-compounds do not transfer O (2-electron oxidation) at all readily.

PROPERTIES

A glance at the compounds formed by the different oxocations (see examples in Table 26.viii) shows the change in character of valences across Periods and down Groups. In the table the ligands are arranged in order of their polarizability and the metals in the order of their Groups. The later transition metals are always the less electropositive. Thus OsO_2^{2+} forms complexes with cyanide, ammonia, nitrite, iodide, and bromide. In the earlier Groups there are very few complexes with any of these ligands, all the oxocation compounds being hydroxides, fluorides, and simple salts of oxyanions, e.g. NbO^{3+}, VO_2^+, TiO^{2+}. This change in character is reminiscent of the change from pre-transition to B-metal character in the lower valences of the transition-metal elements across the transition series or down one of the later A Groups. Again a preference is established for polarizable ligands rather than for small polar ligands. Carried to an extreme, this process leads to the preference for halide and nitrogen ligands over oxygen, and eventually oxocations are not observed. This is brought out most strongly in the higher-valence-state chemistry of platinum and palladium, where instead of oxocations there are complexes of the kind

$$[Pt(CN)_6]^{2-}, [PdI_6]^{2-}, [Pt(NO_2)_6]^{2-}, \text{ and } [Pd(NH_3)_6]^{4+}.$$

Change of the oxocations to lower valence also introduces more B-metal as opposed to pre-transition-metal character.

The formation of oxocations may be regarded as the ultimate extension of the increasing affinity of early transition-metal cations for RO^- anions as charge is increased. In this respect the stability of O^{2-} complexes, e.g. 'oxo' ions, is to be compared with the high relative stability of the RO^- complexes of V(II) compare Ni(II), of Cr(III) compare Co(III), and of Hf(IV) compare Pt(IV).

26.5. Oxyanions

The main oxyanions (sometimes called oxo-anions) of the transition metals are listed in Table 26.ix. In them the metals show some Group relationships with the typical elements. Thus for vanadium and phosphorus, or for chromium and sulphur, or for manganese and chlorine there

TABLE 26.IX. *Oxyanions*

Transition series	IVA	VA	VIA	VIIA	VIIIa	VIIIb	VIIIc
First series	TiO_4^{4-} ?	VO_4^{3-} (some resemblance to PO_4^{3-})	CrO_4^{2-} (cf. SO_4^{2-}) $Cr_2O_7^{2-}$	MnO_4^{2-} MnO_4^{-} (cf. ClO_4^{-})	FeO_4^{2-} (cf. SO_4^{2-})	Co(none)	Ni(none)
Second series	Zr, no evidence for simple oxyanions, only condensates	NbO_4^{3-} ? many polymeric compounds	$Mo(OH)_5$ polymers MoO_4^{2-} $Mo(OH)_6$ polymers	TcO_4^{2-} ? TcO_4^{-}	$Ru(OH)_4$ (largely basic) RuO_4^{2-} $[RuO_2(OH)_4]^{2-}$ RuO_4 $[RuO_4(OH)_2]^{2-}$	Rh, little evidence for any acidic oxide	Pd (none)
Third series	Hf, no evidence for simple oxyanions, only condensates	TaO_4^{3-} ? mainly polymeric	$W(OH)_5$ polymers WO_4^{2-} $W(OH)_6$ polymers	ReO_4^{2-} (polymeric) ? ReO_3^{-} ? ReO_4^{2-} ? ReO^{-}	Os, weak acidic properties only in lower oxidation states $[OsO_2(OH)_4]^{2-}$ $[OsO_4(OH)_2]^{2-}$ OsO_3N^{-}	I, little evidence for oxyanions	$Pt(OH)_6^{2-}$
'Fourth' series	Th(none) basic condensates	Pa(none)	U(none)	Np(none)			

←——— basic condensates ———→

is at least a superficial resemblance in the volatility of the oxides, the formation of acids (weaker in the case of the transition-metal oxides), and in the oxidizing power (stronger in the transition-metal oxides). The formulae of the anions for the metals throughout the first transition series are indicative of an oxygen coordination number of 4, as in the compounds of the typical elements.

The oxyanions of the second and third transition series are rather different from those of the first. They are much weaker acids and in acidic solution undergo condensation to polyacids. These polyacids are usually formed by the linking of octahedra, indicating that molybdates, etc., are based on 6-coordination and not 4-coordination. Six-fold coordination would appear to be common up to Group VIA and possibly in the lower valences of Group VIIA, but it is no longer favoured (radius-ratio and valence effects) in the higher valences of Groups VIIA and VIII. This is particularly noticeable in perrhenates(VII), which do not polymerize, and in the osmate(VIII) and ruthenate(VIII) anions which readily dehydrate in acid solution to give the volatile tetroxides (compare carbon in the first period). This behaviour is in contrast with that of the non-metals of the fourth period, Sb, Te, and I, which remain of high coordination in high-valence states, even in acid solution. The tetroxide of osmium is a tetramer in benzene and in this respect it may resemble the tetrameric oxide of phosphorus, cf. Os_4O_{16} and P_4O_{10}.

The acid chlorides of the second and third transition series, e.g. MoO_2Cl_2 and WO_2Cl_2, are different from those of the first series (except those of Ti and V) in that they appear to resemble more closely oxocation compounds, for example UO_2Cl_2. There is also an increased tendency for hydroxide in the acids such as $W(OH)_6$ to be replaced by heavy halides, rather than by fluoride as at the beginning of all the series, and at osmium for oxygen to be displaced even by nitrogen, e.g. in OsO_3N^-. This is another example of the usual increasing preference for less electronegative ligands on going from left to right across a transition series.

The oxyanions of the second and third transition series are much weaker oxidizing agents than those in the first series and they are much less coloured. These are both properties which may be related to the electron-acceptor properties of the central cations, first series > second series > third series.

The simple O^{2-} anion can also be replaced in these compounds by the peroxide anion, O_2^{2-}. It appears that peroxy-anions are generally stable only with central atoms which are exceptionally powerful π-electron acceptors, e.g. B (3-coordinate), S and Cr (4-coordinate). Transition-metal per-acid anions may have analytical use, as they are often highly coloured, and in certain cases can be extracted into non-aqueous solvents, e.g. V and Cr.

The hydrolysis of the anions sometimes follows a very complicated path in part controlled by thermodynamic and in part by kinetic considerations. Two examples are:

$$VO_4^{3-} \xrightarrow{\text{fast}} V_3O_9^{3-} \xrightarrow{\text{slow}} V_{10}O_?$$

$$\begin{array}{c} WO_4^{2-} \\ \text{fast} \updownarrow \\ H_2WO_4 \end{array} \xrightarrow[\text{fast}]{\text{rather}} HW_4O_{14}^{3-} \xrightarrow{\text{slow}} HW_6O_{21}^{5-} \xrightarrow[\text{slow}]{\text{very}} W_{12}O_{41}^{10-}$$

Systems of polynuclear complexes are frequently not in equilibrium with one another and studies of their *thermodynamic* properties must be proved to be time independent.

Considerable structural changes are undergone as the polymerization proceeds. In several of these structures a change of coordination number takes place and many of the salts which are written as though they contained simple oxyanions are better treated as giant-lattice mixed oxides, e.g. titanates, zirconates, etc.; see Chapter 13.

26.6. Oxidation states in carbides, nitrides, etc.

Many solid transition-metal compounds do not have a strict stoicheiometry, e.g. Mo/O systems, and even in some compounds in which the stoicheiometry is apparently clear-cut the oxidation state is unknown without a knowledge of the structure. Thus Pt in PtS_2 could be either in oxidation state IV or II according to whether or not there are simple sulphide anions in the lattice. Compounds in which there is extensive non-metal to non-metal bonding have not so far been described in this chapter, although both peroxide and persulphide systems have been mentioned. The persulphide anion can be considered to be in equilibrium with the sulphide anion, $\quad S_2^{2-} + 2e^- \rightleftharpoons 2S^{2-}.$

Clearly this couple can be balanced by a second redox couple involving a metal in two valence states,

$$2M^{n+} \rightleftharpoons 2M^{(n+1)+} + 2e^-.$$

The overall system is then

$$2M^{n+} + S_2^{2-} \rightleftharpoons 2M^{(n+1)+} + 2S^{2-}.$$

A particular example is CuS which should really be written $Cu_4(I)$

$Cu_2(II)(S_2)_2S_2$. Similar equations can be written for other anion systems capable of polymerization. Oxygen like sulphur mainly gives the dimer, O_2^{2-}, but carbon, silicon, boron, and phosphorus may be much more highly polymerized. The O_2^{2-}/O^{2-} couple is so powerful an oxidizing agent that most metals form higher-valence oxides rather than peroxides. Thus it is mainly the high-valence states which give stable peroxides, e.g. $[M(O_2)_4]^{3-}$ where M is V, Nb, Ta, or Cr, and the cation is effectively 8-coordinate. The S_2^{2-}/S^{2-} couple is a much weaker oxidizing agent and very many metals, e.g. Fe, form the persulphide as easily as the simple sulphide. Polyborides, polycarbides, polynitrides, and polyphosphides are even more weakly oxidizing and remain as polymeric anions.

Disproportionation reactions may also take place between the polymerized anion and the element, e.g.

$$M(S_2)_2^{2-} \rightarrow MS_2^{2-} + 2S.$$

The valence state of the metal is not altered in this reaction, but the stoicheiometry of the compound is changed. If, as will commonly be the case, the disproportionation equilibrium and the redox-polymerization equilibrium are simultaneously achieved then, in the *molten* state particularly, the non-metal will exist in several forms, i.e. the element and several polymerized anions. On cooling such a melt a great variety of phases may separate (Chapter 8) and these may be of almost any composition. In all but a few systems their properties and compositions are highly specific to given metals. The few exceptions are such series of compounds as the transition-metal nitrides of formula MN, and the carbides, MC. These compounds are formed at the beginning of each of the transition series and, since they assume the NaCl lattice, they may be regarded as examples of 3-valent, MN, or 4-valent, MC, compounds. Most of these compounds have been treated in Part II where a classification according to the valence state of the metal was not important. The compounds are usually metallic, but those which contain dimerized anions of the more electropositive non-metals are more frequently good semiconductors. Some examples of MX_2 compounds with the marcasite structure are given in Table 26.x. The changes in band gap are in the expected directions. The ionic model is not really applicable to these compounds but they could be formulated as $M^{4+}(X_2^{4-})$ or $M^{2+}(X_2^{2-})$.

TABLE 26.x. *Band gaps in* Ru *and* Os *compounds of* P, As, *and* Sb (eV)

M	MP_2	MPAs	MAs_2	MSb_2
Ru	1·0	0·8	0·8	0·3
Os	1·2	..	0·9	0·3

REDOX EQUILIBRIA
26.7. The first transition series
INTRODUCTION

A preliminary treatment of redox equilibria was given in Chapter 23. Aqueous-solution equilibria were summarized in the form of Oxidation State Diagrams, and solid-state equilibria by plotting heats of formation. It was further shown that the relation between these experimental data and atomic structures could be understood in very qualitative terms using an ionic model. In the next three sections, some of these equilibria will be re-examined in order to see how they will be affected by change of ligand. The discussion is necessarily restricted to certain couples because of the general lack of quantitative data about others. Nevertheless it should be possible to suggest some generalizations about these latter couples, although these generalizations will need to be more properly tested by new experimental observations. This section will concentrate on the M(III)/M(II) couple for the elements of the first transition series. The following section, section 26.8, will examine one of these, the Fe(III)/Fe(II) couple, in some detail, while the last section, section 26.9, will consider the evidence available for other redox couples.

THE M(III)/M(II) COUPLE IN THE FIRST TRANSITION SERIES

Let us begin by examining the consequences of two unjustified assumptions, namely (1) that all the species with which we shall be concerned are satisfactorily described by the simple ionic model, and (2) that all trivalent ions have the same constant radius, and all divalent ions have the same constant radius. An equivalent alternative to (2) is that the changes in radii are compensating, i.e. metals with unusually large trivalent ions have unusually large divalent ions. We should then expect that the ease of oxidation would change along the transition series in a manner given *exactly* by the changes in the third ionization potentials. The experimental observations are plotted in Fig. 26.6, where the chemical data on electrode potentials and heats of formation are plotted with a different origin from the ionization-potential data, but where the same energy scale is used throughout.

The quantitative chemical data may be extended by the following qualitative observations. VI_3 is known and decomposes above about 280 °C to give the dihalide. CrI_3 is said to be almost impossible to make and is known only as a nonahydrate.

MnBr$_3$ and MnI$_3$ are not known even as complexes. FeI$_3$ may exist in small quantities in equilibrium with FeI$_2$ and iodine. The only uncomplexed Co(III) salts appear to be CoF$_3$; CoF$_3$,3·5H$_2$O; and Co$_2$(SO$_4$)$_3$,18H$_2$O. The NiO$_2$/Ni^{2+} couple has been estimated as $+1·68$ volts in acid solution. Since the Ni^{3+} aqueous ion is not known, we must presume that the couple Ni^{3+}/Ni^{2+} is even more positive. Similarly the $E°$(OH) value would be greater than $+1·0$ volt.

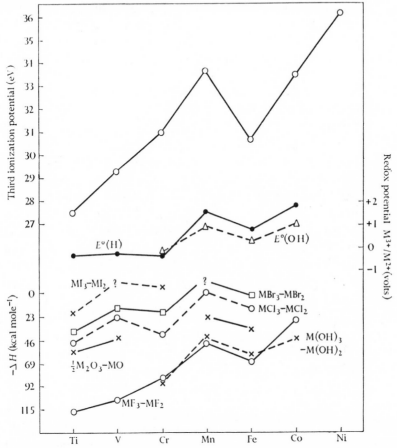

FIG. 26.6. Differences between the heats of formation of trivalent and divalent compounds, redox potentials of the M^{3+}/M^{2+} couples, and ionization potentials for M$^{2+} \rightarrow$ M^{3+} (gas ions).

Fig. 26.6 shows that while the observed redox patterns along the series reflect the general changes in the third ionization potential, the changes in the latter are much more marked. At first sight, it would seem that this might be explained in terms of the inadequacy of either or both our initial assumptions. However, a relatively simple calculation shows that changes in radii alone would be a good deal too small to account for the discrepancy, and that therefore the most significant effect must be departure from the ionic model. We have here again another example of cations of higher electron affinity (i.e. corresponding to metals of higher ionization potentials) pulling back electrons more effectively by covalent bonding.

The effectiveness with which the higher ionization potentials are neutralized by covalent bonding will clearly depend upon a number of other factors besides the ionization potentials themselves. Thus in the second transition series the third ionization potentials are uniformly lower than they are in the first, and—although adequate quantitative data are not available—we have every reason to expect that the ionization potentials will be even lower in the third transition series. In the second and third transition series, however, the d orbitals are more exposed and thus better suited in general for overlap with ligand orbitals. In the third transition series s and p orbitals will also have higher electron affinities than in the first and second series. There are no quantitative data to test the result of these differences in redox equilibria properly, but the general chemistry of the higher-valence states, where fluoride and oxide ligands do not hold the same dominance as in the first transition series, suggests that covalent bonding plays a much more significant role in stabilizing high-valence states against low. The relatively low electron affinity (see Chapter 23) *and* the more exposed nature of the $4d$ and $5d$ orbitals probably both contribute therefore to the more even balance of valence states in the second and third transition series as opposed to the first.

Further factors to be considered are orbital occupancy, ligand polarizability, symmetry effects, and especially the relative importance of σ-bonding and π-bonding. These can be most readily demonstrated by focusing attention on the Fe(III)/Fe(II) couple.

26.8. The effect of ligands on the Fe(III)/Fe(II) couple

Some potentials for the Fe(III)/Fe(II) couple in aqueous solution are listed in Table 26.XI. Anions stabilize the Fe(III) rather than the Fe(II) state: this stabilization is an entropy rather than an enthalpy effect. The neutralization of charge on a cation by combination with an anion in a complex has been shown in Chapter 7 to increase the entropy of the whole system. This change is due to a loss of hydration which is greater the higher the charge on the cation. Of the potentials of complexes with *anions* the cyanide is highest (see below). The potentials of the unsaturated phenanthroline and dipyridyl couples lie highest of all, i.e. Fe(II) is stabilized in these complexes with respect to Fe(III), if the hydrated ions are used as the reference potential. The magnetic data for the complexes, also given in Table 26.XI, show whether the cations are in low-spin or high-spin states. The phenanthroline, cyanide, and dipyridyl complexes differ from the others in this respect. Unsaturated ligands stabilize the lower-valence state, for the d^6 ion goes readily to a low-spin configuration, with such ligands and in the resulting complexes interaction with the ligands is stronger.

TABLE 26.XI. *Redox potentials for the* Fe(III)/Fe(II) *couple (volts)*

Ligand	Potential	Magnetic states
(o-phenanthroline)$_3$	+1·10	both low-spin
(Dipyridyl)$_3$	+0·96	both low-spin
(H$_2$O)$_6$ ($a_H = 1·0$)	+0·77	both high-spin
(CN$^-$)$_6$	+0·36	both low-spin
(Oxalate^{2-})$_n$ $\begin{cases} n = 3 \text{ Fe(III)} \\ n = 2 \text{ Fe(II)} \end{cases}$	+0·02	both high-spin
EDTA^{4-}	−0·12	both high-spin
(8-hydroxyquinolinate$^-$)$_3$	−0·20	Fe(III) 100% high-spin, but Fe(II) ∼70% high-spin

Fig. 26.7 shows how the redox potentials of the Fe(III)/Fe(II) 8-hydroxy-quinolinates (oxinates) vary as the pK_a values of the ligand are changed. The potentials are plotted against the basicity of the ligands. This form of plot is chosen as it is expected that the change in pK_a will give an impression of the change in σ-donor power of the ligands. In Fig. 26.7 there is a general set of ligands related by the curved line with which the Fe^{3+} ion, stronger σ-bonding, is increasingly favoured with increase in pK_a. The formyl- and cyano-substituted ligands, on the other hand, give higher potentials than expected. Both these groups are strong π-electron-attracting groups. Thus increasing unsaturation again increases the stability of the lower-valence state. Now it is important to notice that both the Fe^{2+} and Fe^{3+} ions are of high-spin in the oxinates, whereas both the ions are in low-spin states in the dipyridyl and phenanthroline complexes. The potentials of the oxinates are much lower than those of the phenanthroline complexes because of the large entropy term operative in the case of anionic ligands.

The high potentials of the couples with unsaturated, π-electron acceptor, ligands require explanation. Fe^{2+} is one of the best π-donor cations amongst high-spin divalent cations of the first transition series. On the other hand, high-spin Fe^{3+} would be expected to be a poor π-donor for it not only has a higher charge than Fe^{2+} but it has a very high ionization potential to Fe^{4+}. Thus Fe^{2+}, high-spin, will be preferentially stabilized by unsaturated ligands. A similar argument applies to the low-spin Fe^{2+}

as opposed to the low-spin Fe^{3+} state. In the low-spin Fe^{2+} cation the t_{2g} orbitals are full and there are no e_g electrons. The energy required to make this electron rearrangement is relatively small. For the Fe^{3+} ion the energy of the change of configuration is considerably greater, especially as the Racah parameters increase with charge which will make the low-spin complexes relatively less stable, and π-donor bonding is weaker anyway due to the higher charge of the cation.

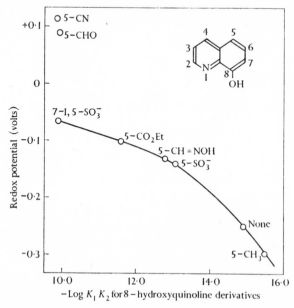

FIG. 26.7. The effect of substituents on the redox potential of the Fe^{3+}/Fe^{2+} 8-hydroxyquinolinate couple ($Fe^{3+}L_3/Fe^{2+}L_2$) and on the product of the two acid dissociation constants of the ligand, L.

Once both the cations are in low-spin states then the stability of the Fe(III) complex will increase more rapidly with ligand basicity than the Fe(II) complex, as σ-bonding is stronger in both spin states for the 3-valent ion. Thus the dependence on basicity in the series of phenanthrolines (both low-spin complexes) is the same as that in the series of oxinates (both high-spin complexes).

However, if the variation in basicity brings about a change from the high-spin to the low-spin state this change will occur first for the Fe^{2+} ion. In the region of basicity where the Fe^{2+} cation has changed to a low-spin state but the Fe^{3+} ion remains in a high-spin state the stability of the Fe(II) complex may be more sensitive to changes in basicity. This is shown in

Fig. 26.8. In a series of complexes with ligands of increasing pK_a and in which both ions change from high-spin to low-spin there may be a rise in redox potential at first (Fe^{2+} only changes to low-spin), followed later by a fall (Fe^{2+} and Fe^{3+} low-spin). Such a series of potentials is observed in biologically-important iron porphyrin complexes, and is utilized in the system of iron enzymes of higher organisms, the cytochromes.

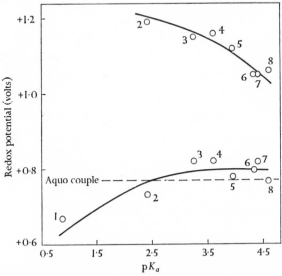

Fig. 26.8. The redox potentials of some Fe(III)/Fe(II) couples with substituted dipyridyls, L, as ligands. The top series are for low-spin complexes ML_3 in both valence states. The lower series are for low-spin $Fe(II)L_3$ and high-spin Fe(III) complexes, probably $Fe(III)L(H_2O)_4$, except for point (1) for which $Fe(II)L_3$ is high-spin also. The numbering is: (1) 4,4'-dicarboethoxy dipyridyl; (2) 5,5'-dicarboethoxy dipyridyl; (3) 4,4'-diphenyl dipyridyl; (4) dipyridyl; (5) 5,5'-dimethyl dipyridyl; (6) 4,4'-diethyl dipyridyl; (7) 4,4'-dimethyl dipyridyl; (8) 4,4'-diethyl, 5,5'-dimethyl dipyridyl. ML_3 is a thermodynamically-unstable form for Fe(III).

26.9. The effect of ligands on other redox couples

THE Cu(II)/Cu(I) COUPLE

The discussion may now be extended to other elements and different valence states. The potentials of the Cu(II)/Cu(I) couples are given in Table 26.XII. The addition of chelating anions of low polarizability (e.g. oxalate) to the system of the hydrated cations lowers the potential (i.e. favours Cu(II)). The addition of large polarizable anions, such as iodide, favours Cu(I). The addition of ammonia lowers the potential, but although the potential is also lowered by the addition of many phenanthrolines or dipyridyls, the lowering is not so marked. The Cu(I) complexes of these unsaturated ligands are relatively more stable than the complexes of saturated ligands. Steric hindrance in general will affect the complexes of the smaller Cu^{2+} more than the Cu^{+}, and there will be a greater importance of π-bonding in the lower-valence state. The last effect probably explains the stability of Cu(I) cyanides in air, and the ability of Cu(I) salt solutions to absorb and be stabilized by carbon monoxide and acetylenes. With the Cu(II)/Cu(I) couples there is, of course, no possibility of a high-spin to low-spin electron rearrangement as with the Fe(III)/Fe(II) couples. This difference explains the very high stabilization of Fe(II) relative to Fe(III) but not of Cu(I) relative to Cu(II) in phenanthroline complexes.

TABLE 26.XII. *Redox potentials of some* Cu(II)/Cu(I)
and Co(III)/Co(II) *couples (volts)*

Cu(II)/Cu(I)

		Coordination numbers	
Ligand	Potential	Cu(II)	Cu(I)
pyridine	$+0.30$	2	2
o-phenanthroline	$+0.17$	4	4
water ($a_H = 1.0$)	$+0.17$	4 (6)	?
dipyridyl	$+0.12$	4	4
ammonia	0.00	4	2
glycinate	-0.16	4	2
ethylenediamine	-0.35	4	2
oxalate	< -0.2	4	?

Co(III)/Co(II)

		Spin states	
Ligand	Potential	Co(III)	Co(II)
$(H_2O)_6$ ($a_H = 1.0$)	$+1.84$	low	high
$(NH_3)_6$	-0.10	low	high
$(CN^-)_n \begin{cases} n = 6\ \text{Co(III)} \\ n = 5\ \text{Co(II)} \end{cases}$	-0.80	low	low

THE Co(III)/Co(II) COUPLE

For the Co(III)/Co(II) couple the addition of cyanide (Table 26.XII), o-phenanthroline, or ammonia *lowers* the redox potential as much as the addition of anions. This is strikingly brought out by the reaction of H_2 with cobalt(II) cyanide to produce a complex usually regarded as one of Co(III)

$$2[Co(CN)_5]^{3-} + H_2 \rightarrow 2[Co(CN)_5H]^{3-}.$$

There is an analogous reaction of the formal Co(I) state of vitamin B_{12} (B_{12s}) with methyl iodide, which again gives the Co(III) complex.

$$Co(I) + MeI \rightarrow Co(III)Me + I^-.$$

In this couple it is the higher formal oxidation state (d^6 as opposed to d^5 in the Fe(III) case) which undergoes spin pairing more readily, and which can therefore form more effective donor $t_{2g}^* \to \pi^*$ bonds. The higher state is now stabilized by (1) greater readiness to go to low spin, (2) increase in π-acceptor, and (3) increase in σ-donor power of ligands. This is also true of the Mn(III)/Mn(II) couple (Table 26.XIII). Thus it is not possible to say generally that a given ligand will invariably stabilize a given valence state relative to another which is higher or lower. On the whole the low-valence states will be stabilized by electron-acceptor ligands, and on the whole higher-valence states will be stabilized by electron-donor ligands, but specific electron configurations will not necessarily behave in this way; compare, for example, the different elements in Table 26.XIII.

TABLE 26.XIII. *A comparison between the redox potentials of* M(III)/M(II) *couples (volts)*

Ligand	Mn(III)/Mn(II)	Fe(III)/Fe(II)	Co(III)/Co(II)
$(H_2O)_6$ ($a_H = 1.0$)	$+1.50$	$+0.71$	$+1.84$
$(CN^-)_6$	$+0.22$	$+0.36$	-0.80†
Mesoporphyrin (pyridine)$_2$	-0.39	-0.06	-0.26

† $(CN)_5$ for Co(II).

THE SECOND AND THIRD TRANSITION SERIES

The oxidation-reduction potentials so far considered refer to the elements of the first transition series. It is not anticipated that any new factors will have to be considered in the valence states of the second and third series. However, the relative importance of the different factors changes greatly. For example, the very high valence states of the second and third transition series are of greater stability due to the relative ease of ionization of the central cation. This is illustrated in Table 26.XIV where the oxidizing power of the 6-valent or 4-valent state increases along a transition series

$$Cr < Mn < Fe < Co \simeq Ni,$$

but decreases down a Group,

$$Co > Rh > Ir \quad \text{and} \quad Ni > Pd > Pt.$$

TABLE 26.XIV. *Redox couples for high valence in aqueous solution (volts)*

	$E°$ acid ($a_H = 1.0$)		$E°$ acid ($a_H = 1.0$)
Cr(VI)/Cr(III)	$+1.33$	Mn(IV)/Mn(II)	$+1.23$
Mn(VI)/Mn(III)	$+1.82$	Fe(IV)/Fe(II)	?
Fe(VI)/Fe(III)	$> +1.90$	Co(IV)/Co(II)	$\sim +1.80$
Co(VI)/Co(III)	very large $+$ve	Ni(IV)/Ni(II)	$+1.68$
Rh(VI)/Rh(III)	$(+1.4)$	Pd(IV)/Pd(II)	$+1.6$
Ir(VI)/Ir(III)	$(+1.1)$	Pt(IV)/Pt(II)	$+1.1$

Again in the majority of compounds of the second and third series, no matter what the valence state, the central-atom electron configuration is of low spin. The ions are also larger, which together with this prevalence of low-spin systems, makes ionic contributions less important relative to those of covalence. This will be particularly true toward the end of the transition series. These points can be made by reference to Oxidation State Diagrams.

The Oxidation State Diagrams considered in Chapter 23 give an impression of the stability of the oxidation states in the presence of water. (The qualitative success of the ionic model probably depended on this choice of solvent.) A change in ligand brings about some changes in the diagrams. Perhaps the simplest potentials to consider are either those in a series of halide solids—fluorides, chlorides, and bromides (see section 26.7)—or those in the series—oxides, sulphides, and selenides. In each series the heavier ligands bring about an increased relative stability of the lower-valence states, but the effect is much more marked in the first transition series than in the second series. We must suppose then that Fig. 23.11 (or Fig. 23.12) would be even more markedly curved for the sulphides and heavier halides. The highest sulphides known in the first transition series are TiS_2, VS_2, (V_2S_5?), Cr_2S_3, MnS, FeS, CoS, NiS, CuS, and ZnS: the sulphides of apparently higher-valence should be formulated as lower sulphides with S—S bonds. In the third series, however, the highest sulphide parallels the highest oxide remarkably closely—Ta_2S_5, WS_3, Re_2S_7, Os (uncertain), IrS_3, PtS_2, and Au_2S_3. All of these compounds are simple sulphides without S—S bonds. The difference between the stabilities of sulphides and oxides is extremely small toward the end of these series (Chapter 16). A similar situation is found in the iodides as compared with the fluorides, for although only low-valence iodides occur in the first transition series the following are known in the third series: WI_4, ReI_4 (K_2ReI_6), OsI_4 (K_2OsI_6), IrI_3, and PtI_4. The two sets of compounds emphasize again the considerable affinity of large cations for large anions.

Apart from indications about the relative stability of oxidation states which can be obtained from the free energy of formation of solids, data are available on oxidation-reduction potentials for some complex halides, thiocyanates, cyanides, etc., in aqueous solution. All the halide and pseudo-halide anions give quite stable high-valence complexes in the second and third transition series, e.g. with Mo, W, Re, and Pt complexes are known up to a valence of at least 4. Table 26.xv shows that the potentials of the halide couples are usually more negative, high-valence stabilized, than the

TABLE 26.XV. *Redox potentials of some halide couples (volts)*

	Standard aqueous (acid, $a_H = 1.0$)	$(Cl^-)_n$	$(Br^-)_n$	$(I^-)_n$
Ru(III)/(II)	−0·10	+0·08	..	..
Ru(IV)/(II)	+0·56	+0·50	..	..
Ru(IV)/(III)	..	+0·90	..	..
Os(IV)/(III)	+1·40	+0·45	+0·45	..
Rh(IV)/(III)	+1·40	+1·20	..	..
Ir(IV)/(III)	+0·70	+1·02	+0·99	..
Pd(IV)/(II)	+1·60	+1·29	+0·99	+0·48
Pt(IV)/(II)	+1·10	+0·74	+0·64	+0·39
Au(III)/(I)	+1·40	+0·94	+0·82	..

standard values for the aqueous redox couples. With platinum and palladium the *higher* valence state is clearly favoured by the heavier halides. The palladium and platinum potentials are for the reactions

$$[MX_6]^{2-}+2e^- \rightarrow [MX_4]^{2-}+2X^-$$

rather than for simple reduction at constant coordination number, but allowance for the hydration energy of X^- does not alter the order of the potentials. This is quite contrary to the situation in the first series. The ruthenium potentials show that the higher-valence state is hardly favoured by chloride, suggesting that it is only at the end of the transition series that the stability of the high-valence halide is greater than that of the lower-valence halide.

The effect of unsaturation in the ligand can be seen by comparing the two potentials

$$[PtCl_2(CN)_4]^{2-}+2e^- \rightleftharpoons 2Cl^-+[Pt(CN)_4]^{2-}, \quad E^\circ = +0.89,$$
$$[PtCl_6]^{2-}+2e^- \rightleftharpoons 2Cl^-+[PtCl_4]^{2-}, \quad E^\circ = +0.72 \text{ volts.}$$

The lower-valence state is stabilized relatively more by cyanide than by the halides in general, but both stabilize the high-valence state relative to water.

Clearly the ligands which most effectively stabilize low-valence states, e.g. M^{2+} (often high-spin), in the first transition series are not those which are most effective in later series. For example, the higher-valence state is stabilized increasingly in the following orders of ligands:

Cu(II)/Cu(I): $Cl^- <$ pyridine $< H_2O < NH_3 <$ en

Co(III)/Co(II): $Cl^- \leqslant H_2O <$ pyridine $< NH_3 <$ en

Table 26.XVI shows that the order for the Ru(III)/Ru(II) (low-spin) couple is

pyridine $< NH_3 < H_2O <$ en $< Cl^-$.

TABLE 26.XVI. Ru(III)/Ru(II) *couples* (*volts*)

Formula of complex	Potential
[Ru(dipy)₃]	+1·26
[Ru(dipy)₂py₂]	+1·25
[Ru(dipy)₂(NH₃)₂]	+0·87
[Ru(dipy)₂en]	+0·74
[Ru(dipy)₁py₄]	+1·25
[Ru(dipy)₁py₃(H₂O)]	+1·04
[Ru(dipy)₁py₂(H₂O)₂]	+0·78
[Ru(dipy)₁py₃Cl]	+0·89
[Ru(dipy)₁Cl₄]	+0·35

dipy is 2,2′-dipyridyl.

Chloride is here very effective in stabilizing the higher-valence state and has become extremely different from the unsaturated ligand pyridine. No doubt the factors affecting these very different orders will be clarified as more evidence accumulates. Two factors which must be considered are (1) that as both the ions become larger, entropy terms become less important and steric hindrance around the higher-valence ion is also less important, and (2) that covalence is sufficient to remove the dominance of fluorine and oxygen in high-valence states of the later and heavier transition metals. These factors will have a general effect on Oxidation State Diagrams.

UNUSUAL VALENCE STATES

Intermediate valence states are common in transition-metal compounds. However, it is particularly difficult to obtain +1 states generally and +3 states in the Ni, Pd, and Pt Group. The problem of the +1 state is largely that of the high stability of the metal. The kinetic stabilization of very low valence states will be described in Chapter 27. The +3 state of Ni, Pd, and Pt has been prepared in combination with the ligands

maleonitriledithiolate   toluene-3,4-dithiolate

The stabilization of these and similar unusual valence states may be brought about by the extensive delocalization of the electrons over the ligands, and this may explain the apparent stability of the high-valence complexes of DAS listed in Table 26.IV.

USE OF LIGANDS IN THE CONTROL OF REDOX POTENTIALS

Examination of the series of couples we have discussed so far indicates that the relative stabilization of one valence state compared with another is an extremely subtle process. Some generalizations are worth making, but they are only guides to thinking and not exact rules.

(1) Small or highly-charged saturated ligands, particularly fluoride, oxide, and oxyanions, stabilize high-valence states.

(2) Large charged saturated ligands favour lower-valence states. Good examples are methide, iodide, and sulphide. There are two reasons for this. (i) The electrostatic energy difference between high-valence and low-valence states is reduced. (ii) The anions in this class are good reducing agents, whereas the anions in the first class are poor reducing agents. The stabilization of high-valence rather than low-valence states is not just a problem of the relative binding strength of the anion to the two valence states, but in practice is also dependent upon the potential established by the ligand in contact with its own oxidized state.

(3) Unsaturated neutral molecules of low dipole moment stabilize low-valence states, e.g. carbon monoxide, ethylene, acetylene, and benzene. $d_\pi \to \pi^*$ bonding is important here. We describe their complexes in Chapter 27.

(4) The effect of saturated ligands such as ammonia which have dipole moments comparable with water but which are more polarizable is very difficult to predict. These ligands would appear to stabilize most effectively a range of intermediate valence states from $+2$ to $+4$.

(5) It is equally difficult to predict the effect of polar 'unsaturated' ligands such as dipyridyl, pyridine, cyanide, phosphines, and arsines, for these ligands are usually very polarizable and therefore adapt themselves to the demands of the cation to which they are bound. Once again compounds of a whole range of intermediate valence states from $+1$ to $+4$ can readily be formed by these ligands. Which particular state is the most stable turns on small factors, such as the relative stability of the different spin states of a given valence state of a particular element, and on the stereochemistry demanded by the ligand and the central ion in this spin state.

Problems

1. In both their atomic diameters (for $CN = 12$, Zr 3·19, Hf 3·17 Å) and their ionic radii (Zr^{4+} 0·80, Hf^{4+} 0·81 Å) Zr and Hf are very similar. This is also true of their general chemistry. How may this be accounted for?

2. (a) Write down structures for the following five compounds:

$PtCl_4,6NH_3$ (5 ions); $PtCl_4,5NH_3$ (4 ions); $PtCl_4,4NH_3$ (3 ions); $PtCl_4$, $3NH_3$ (2 ions); $PtCl_4,2NH_3$ (no ions).

(b) Pt(IV) compounds are generally octahedral, while the Pt(II) compounds are square-planar coordinated. Give reasons to explain why this is so.

3. The anion of Reinecke's salt $NH_4[Cr(NCS)_4(NH_3)_2]$ and that of K_2PtCl_6 are used to precipitate large organic cations. What are the advantages of using these anions? Consider their sizes, charges, kinetic stabilities, oxidation-reduction potentials, and colours.

4. In the spinel Mn_3O_4, $Mn^{2+}(Mn^{3+})_2O_4$, which cation will choose which type of hole? (See Table 24.III.)

5. Comment on the acid dissociation constants, K, of $[Co(NH_3)_5H_2O]^{3+}$, $\log K = -5·7$, and $[Pt(NH_3)_4(H_2O)_2]^{4+}$, $\log K = -2·0$. What is known about the acidity of $[Co(H_2O)_6]^{3+}$ and $[Pt(H_2O)_6]^{4+}$?

6. For the following ions the order of stability of halogeno-complexes is $F^- \gg Cl^- > Br^- > I^-$ (class 'a' metals):

$$Fe^{3+}, Ce^{3+}, U^{4+}, Zr^{4+},$$

but for the ions:

$$Cu^+, Ag^+, Cd^{2+}, Hg^{2+}, Pt^{2+}$$

the order is $I^- > Br^- > Cl^- > F^-$ (class 'b' metals). Comment.

7. Comment on the following approximate stability constants

	$\log K_1$			
	F^-	Cl^-	Br^-	I^-
Fe^{3+}	5·2	1·5	0·6	?
Sc^{3+}	6·2	0·0	< 0·0	≪ 0·0
$[Co(CN)_5H_2O]^{2-}$	≪ 0·0	≪ 0·0	< 0·0	1·6

What do you deduce from these figures about the classification of all the cations of the first transition series as class 'a'?

8. For the formation of complexes between acetylacetonate ion and trivalent cations the following stability sequence has been observed experimentally:

$$Fe > Ga > Al > Sc > In > Y > Pr > Ce > La.$$

Comment. Where would you expect Cr^{3+} to appear in the series?

9. What are the possible isomeric forms of $K_3[Cr(C_2O_4)_3]$ and $K[Cr(C_2O_4)_2 (H_2O)_2]$? How would you separate the isomers? Would the spectra or the thermodynamic stabilities of the isomeric forms differ?

10. PtF_4, and $[PdF_6]^{2-}$ are immediately hydrolysed by water but the $[HfF_8]^{4-}$ complex is stable to hydrolysis. Comment.

11. Pt(IV) forms stable compounds and complexes with I^- but Au(III) and Tl(III) do not. Why is this?

12. Pt(IV) forms compounds with the acetylacetonate ion in which the Pt is bound to the central carbon atom of the ligand, e.g. in $[Pt(acetylacetonate)(dipyridyl)(CH_3)_2]$ and in $[Pt(CH_3)_3(acetylacetonate)]_2$. The only other common cation to do this is H^+. What does this tell us about the character of Pt(IV)?

13. The heats of formation ($-\Delta H_f$, kcal mole^{-1}) of the following compounds are $K_4[Mo(CN)_8],2H_2O$ 246·6, $K_4[W(CN)_8],2H_2O$ 272·8, $K_4[Mo(OH)_4 (CN)_4],6H_2O$ 803·6, $K_4[W(OH)_4(CN)_4],4H_2O$ 707·2, H_2O(liquid) 68·2. What can be deduced about the relative affinities of W^{4+} and Mo^{4+} for CN^- as compared with OH^-?

14. The infra-red frequencies of the M—C bonds in $[M(CN)_6]^{3-}$ in the stretching frequency region are (cm^{-1}):

M =	Cr	Mn	Fe	Co
ν_1	458	483	506	564
ν_2	339	361	389	416

Comment upon the changes in bond strength along the series. Do these changes agree with expectations based on crystal-field or molecular-orbital theory?

15. A common reagent for ruthenium(III) is a substituted thioxamide, but the best reagents for detecting lanthanides(III) are phenolates or enolates. Why?

16. The melting-points and boiling-points (°C) of some fluorides are:

			m.p.			
	Mo	W	Ru	Os	Ir	Pt
MF_5	77	(110)	107	70	(80)	155(s)
MF_6	17	(2·3)	54	32	44	57

			b.p.			
	Mo	W	Ru	Os	Ir	Pt
MF_5	213	(240)	270	225	(230)	155
MF_6	35	17	(decomp.)	47	53	..

How may these figures be interpreted?

17. The structure of NbI_4 consists of infinite chains of iodine octahedra. The Nb atoms are in off-centre positions in the octahedra, so that each Nb atom has one near Nb neighbour as well as six near I neighbours. The compound is diamagnetic. Comment.

18. How can M—OH be distinguished from M=O?

19. Deviation from a regular octahedral symmetry of oxygen atoms around the central ion tends to increase along the following series:

$$Hf^{4+} < Zr^{4+} < Ti^{4+} < Ta^{5+} < Nb^{5+} < W^{6+} < Mo^{6+} < V^{5+} < Cr^{6+} < Mn^{7+}.$$

Can you suggest any explanations for this?

20. The structure of baddeleyite, ZrO_2, is roughly 7-coordinate with the shortest Zr—O distance 2·04 Å. The Re—O distance in $ReOCl_3(PR_3)_2$ is 1·58 while the Re—Cl distance is 2·45 Å. Account for these observations.

21. Comment on the bond distances and angle in $Cr_2O_7^{2-}$, Cr—O (bridge) = 1·9 Å, Cr—O (terminal) = 1·6 Å, $\angle$ Cr—O—Cr = 115°. Refer to Chapter 14 for corresponding data on condensed non-metal acid anions.

22. The bond distances in $[(RuCl_5)_2O]^{4-}$ are Ru—Cl 2·34 and Ru—O 1·80 Å: the Ru—O—Ru angle is 180°. Is it necessary to postulate double-bonding from Ru to O in order to explain these results?

23. What factors might lead $[ReO_2(CN)_4]^{3-}$ to have a cis or a trans structure? Why do the oxocations of rhenium form complexes such as this and $ReOCl_3(PR_3)_3$ with highly polarizable ligands?

24. How may we account for the general observation that the highest oxidation states of the transition metals are found in their compounds with fluorine, and especially with oxygen? (E.g. the following highest oxidation states, fluoride first then oxide: Ti (4, 4), V (5, 5), Cr (5, 6), Mn (4, 7), Fe (3, 6), Co (4, 4), Ni (4, 4).)

25. The addition of fluoride ion to a weakly acidic solution of iron(III) chloride removes the colour, and makes it harder to reduce the Fe^{3+} ion to Fe^{2+}. In the titration of Fe^{2+} ion with dichromate using sodium diphenylamine sulphonate as indicator, phosphoric acid is added to give a quantitative endpoint. Standard potentials in acid solution are $Cr_2O_7^{2-},H^+/$ Cr^{3+} 1·33, Fe^{3+}/Fe^{2+} 0·77 and Indicator (oxidized)/Indicator (reduced) 0·83 volts. Comment on these related observations.

26. 'All the complexes of Mo(VI) and W(VI) are anionic and restricted to fluorine and/or oxygen ligands.' Comment.

27. According to Sidgwick the stable valence states in Group VIA may be represented by

Cr	6	(5)	((4))	<u>3</u>	2
Mo	<u>6</u>	5	4	3	(2)
W	<u>6</u>	5	4	(3)	(2)
U	<u>6</u>	5	<u>4</u>	3	(2)

where the most stable states are doubly-underlined and the next most stable singly-underlined. Single brackets means that the state rarely occurs, and double brackets that the state is doubtful. Amplify, illustrate, and comment.

28. Pentafluorides are known for the following transition metals: V, Cr, Nb, Mo, Ru, Ta, Re, Os, and Pt. Hexafluorides are known for Mo, W, Re, Os, Ir, and Pt. Comment on these observations.

29. Calculate VE values for the aquo-ions of Ti^{3+}, V^{3+}, Cr^{3+}, and Co^{3+} using ionic radii derived from the MO or MF distances plotted in Fig. 26.1. Compare your results with the experimental values of Fig. 23.11.

30. Cr_2S_3 appears to be the highest known sulphide of chromium yet molybdenum and tungsten give series of sulphides up to MoS_2, MoS_3, WS_2, and WS_3. Comment.

31. In the presence of CN^-, Co(II) salts are oxidized to the Co(III) state while Cu(II) salts are reduced to the Cu(I) state. Contrast also the effect of adding NH_3, Cl^-, SCN^- to the divalent state of these two elements.

32. How would you account for the fact that while the Co^{3+}/Co^{2+} couple normally liberates oxygen from water, it liberates hydrogen in the presence of cyanide ion?

33. Comment on the following colours:

$ReCl_3$ red, $ReBr_3$ red-brown, ReI_3 black, ReF_4 pale blue, $ReCl_4$ red, ReI_4 black, ReF_5 yellow, ReF_6 yellow, and ReF_7 very pale yellow if coloured.

34. The product of the reaction $MnSO_4 + KMnO_4 \xrightarrow[H_2SO_4]{conc.} Mn(SO_4)_2$ has the stoicheiometry shown, but it is black. Discuss the possible formulations of the sulphate. What experiments could be used to check your hypotheses?

35. How may the following be explained? Irradiation of aqueous Fe^{3+} solutions containing methylmethacrylate monomer with ultraviolet radiation from a mercury lamp gives rise to the formation of methylmethacrylate polymer. Iron(III) oxalate is used in one form of actinometer: the light absorbed is measured by the CO_2 produced, or the Fe^{2+} formed.

36. The Fe(III)/Fe(II) *ortho*-phenanthroline couple is used as an indicator in some oxidation-reduction titrations. Its potential is $+1\cdot10$ volts. Would it be of value in the titration of (1) Fe(II) by dichromate, (2) $[IrCl_6]^{3-}$ by dichromate, (3) of any of the complexes in Table 26.xvi by dichromate?

Bibliography

J. S. ANDERSON, 'Some Basic Problems of Solid-State Chemistry', *Proc. Chem. Soc.*, 1964, 166.

D. C. BRADLEY, Metal Alkoxides, *Progress in Inorganic Chemistry*, vol. 2, ed. F. A. Cotton, Interscience, New York, 1960.

D. A. BUCKINGHAM and A. M. SARGESON, Oxidation-Reduction Potentials as Functions of Donor Atom and Ligand, *Chelating Agents and Metal Chelates*, ed. F. P. Dwyer and D. P. Mellor, Academic Press, New York, 1964.

A. CARRINGTON and M. C. R. SYMONS, 'Structure and Reactivity of the Oxyanions of Transition Metals', *Chem. Rev.*, 1963, **63**, 443.

J. D. DUNITZ and L. E. ORGEL, Stereochemistry of Ionic Solids, *Advances in Inorganic Chemistry and Radiochemistry*, vol. 2, ed. H. J. Emeléus and A. G. Sharpe, Academic Press, New York, 1960.

R. S. NYHOLM and M. C. TOBE, The Stabilization of Oxidation States of the Transition Metals, *Advances in Inorganic Chemistry and Radiochemistry*, vol. 5, ed. H. J. Emeléus and A. G. Sharpe, Academic Press, New York, 1963.

R. D. PEACOCK, Some Fluorine Compounds of Transition Metals, *Progress in Inorganic Chemistr*, vol. 2, ed. F. A. Cotton, Interscience, New York, 1960.

J. SELBIN, 'Metal Oxocations', *J. Chem. Educ.*, 1964, **41**, 86.

A. G. SHARPE, Transition Metal Fluorides and their Complexes, *Advances in Fluorine Chemistry*, vol. 1, ed. M. Stacey, J. C. Tatlow, and A. G. Sharpe, Butterworths, London, 1960.

L. G. SILLÉN, 'Quantitative Studies of Hydrolytic Equilibria', *Quart. Rev. Chem. Soc.*, 1959, **13**, 146.

Non-Stoicheiometry, Advances in Chemistry Publication No. 39, American Chemical Society, 1963.

27 · Transition Metals: Organometallic and Related Compounds

27.1. Introduction

TYPES OF COMPOUND

The compounds to be discussed in this chapter are formed from transition-metal *atoms* or ions of low charge and ligands of the types shown in Table

TABLE 27.I. *Ligands of complexes to be described in this chapter*

Unsaturated			Saturated
monodentate	bidentate	tridentate	monodentate
CO, RNC, N_2, RCN, RC≡CR.	C_4H_4, 2,2'-dipyridyl, orthophenanthroline.	C_6H_6.	
NO^+, CN^-, $RC≡C^-$.	$C_3H_5^-$, $(C_2R_2)^{2-}$.	$C_5H_5^-$, $C_7H_7^+$.	H^-, R^-.
$R_2C=CR_2$, O_2.			
NO^-, $R_2C=CR^-$.			
PR_3, AsR_3, SR_2, SeR_2.			(I^-), (Br^-), (RS^-).

The ligands are arranged in a given column in groups of 'effectively' isoelectronic ligands, but charged species are separated from those that do not carry a charge. Ligands containing atoms not in the first row of the Periodic Table come last. $C_5H_5^-$ is the cyclopentadienide ion. R is an alkyl or aryl group, e.g. —CH_3, —C_6H_5, or even a substituted alkyl or aryl such as —CF_3 or —C_6F_5.

27.I. Many of the ligands bind through carbon and the title of the chapter has been chosen so as to stress this point. The dominant interest will not lie in metal to carbon σ-bonded systems such as the alkyls, as it will in the compounds of the B metals, Chapter 33, for the majority of the organometallic compounds of the transition metals are considerably stabilized by π-bonding. Undoubtedly there is also much σ-bonding and the cooperative acceptor (σ) and donor (π) bonding of transition metals to these ligands has been called a *synergic* effect. The ligands themselves are divided in the table and in the chapter on the bases of (1) the number of coordination positions they *normally* fill, i.e. when not acting as bridging groups; (2) their electronic structure, i.e. ligands which have equivalent numbers of acceptor and donor orbitals are grouped together (such ligands are isoelectronic in some cases, e.g. CO, CN^-, and *effectively isoelectronic* in others, e.g. CO and R—NC, or benzene and the cyclopentadienide ion); (3) the *formal* charge which they carry. Thus CO and $RC{\equiv}C^-$, and O_2 and $R_2C{=}CR^-$ are all normally monodentate and can be considered as two pairs of effectively isoelectronic ligands, but CO and O_2 are uncharged while $RC{\equiv}C^-$ and $R_2C{=}CR^-$ carry a formal charge of one. The complexes of unsaturated ligands will be described in section 27.2 and those of saturated ligands in section 27.4.

OXIDATION STATE OF METAL

In some of these complexes the oxidation state of the metal is obviously low, e.g. Cr is in the zero oxidation state in $Cr(CO)_6$ or $Cr(benzene)_2$. In other compounds the oxidation state is not so obvious. For example, $Cr(\pi$-cyclopentadienyl$)_2$ can be treated as a compound of chromium in oxidation state zero, or as an ionic compound $Cr^{2+}(Cp^-)_2$ of oxidation state two. Partly because we consider that in this compound the real charge on the chromium is far lower than $+2$, and partly because of the resemblance between this compound and $Cr(benzene)_2$, where the oxidation state is obviously zero, compounds of such ligands as *cyclopentadienyl* will often be regarded as containing atoms rather than ions. In other circumstances, however, such as the discussion of the relative stability of cyclopentadienyl and chlorine compounds, it will be convenient to treat the metals as cations and the ligand as *cyclopentadienide* (Cp^-). Mo in $[MoCp_2Cl_2]^+$ may then be said to be in an oxidation state of $+5$, and the stabilization of higher oxidation states of Mo by cyclopentadienide, for example, can be compared with that in cyanides, e.g. $[Mo(CN)_8]^{3-}$.

ORBITALS AVAILABLE FOR BONDING

Although it may be sometimes convenient to describe these complexes in terms of ions, their stability cannot possibly be explained on the basis of the simple ionic model. Thus Fig. 24.16 shows that simple ionic species of oxidation state around 0 and $+1$ are likely to be unstable either to disproportionation or to simple decomposition. The reason for stability must be sought therefore in the covalent model.

At the beginning of Chapter 23, it was shown that s, p, and d orbitals are increasingly stabilized along a transition series. At the very beginning of the series the order is $ns > np$ and $(n-1)d$, and at the end it is $(n-1)d \gg ns \gg np$. Thus in the centre of the series the d and s orbitals are of very comparable energy and the p orbitals are not remotely different. For orbitals of approximately equal energy, we have shown that stability may well rest on a full utilization of all orbitals. One consequence of this is the 8-electron valence shell of the 'typical' elements of the two short periods (Chapter 3). In the long periods we might perhaps expect a corresponding 18-electron or noble-gas rule. The principal factor stabilizing both organometallic and simple organic compounds will then be very similar. The incomplete $(n-1)d$ sub-shells play thus an entirely different type of role in these compounds from that played by the $4f$ sub-shell of the lanthanides or, for that matter, by the $3d$ sub-shell in the *ionic* compounds of the elements of the first transition series. The exact roles played by the various orbitals depend, of course, upon the metal considered. At the beginning of a transition series, ionic considerations may well be important even in compounds with organic ligands. In the middle of the series the contributions from the ns, np, and $(n-1)d$ orbitals are possibly about equal, but as the B metals are approached the d orbitals become part of the core and the separation between s and p orbitals becomes large. From the chemistry of elements in Group IB it appears that the s orbitals have become of dominant significance. The 18-electron rule should thus be most applicable in the Groups of the transition series around VI and be less important both earlier and later.

PARALLELS WITH ORGANIC CHEMISTRY

The most notable feature of organic chemistry is that reactions are controlled by *kinetic* factors. This arises from the low stability of the two possible kinds of transition state—those formed by unimolecular dissociation $(S_N 1)$ and by bimolecular addition $(S_N 2)$. The kinetic stability is associated with the stability of particular groups of molecular orbitals. For example, in saturated compounds it is linked with the filling of the sp^3 orbitals of the valence shell. Many organometallic compounds of the transition metals also have kinetic stability. This has frequently been associated with the 18-electron rule—the filling of all the stable bonding orbitals so that bond-breaking $(S_N 1)$ or addition $(S_N 2)$ are difficult. (In Chapter 29 it will be shown that kinetic stability arises in certain complex ions, e.g. $[Co(NH_3)_6]^{3+}$ and $[Fe(CN)_6]^{4-}$, which for a similar reason have no low-energy transition states.)

Much as with organic compounds then, organometallic compounds are often kinetically stable to attack by oxygen, although such reactions will be highly favoured thermodynamically. Thus the methods of experimental study used in organic chemistry and in the chemistry of the low oxidation states of transition metals are often somewhat similar.

There is, however, an important novel feature in the reactions of the organometallic compounds. The binding together of a transition metal and the less electronegative non-metals, e.g. carbon, leads to a high polarization of both. The polarization provides new ways of adjusting the stereochemistry and particularly the reactivity of the metals and the non-metals. For example, new reaction paths for carbon compounds, such as that in which a CO is inserted between two atoms, become possible in systems with metal-carbon bonds. We shall consider this reactivity after we have examined the methods of preparation, and the properties and types of compound which have been prepared. Fortunately the preparation methods can be treated in a quite general way.

PREPARATION

Direct reactions between some ligands, e.g. CO, and metals are possible—as in the Mond reaction giving $Ni(CO)_4$—but the most general methods for preparing these compounds involve the use of reducing agents. These methods may be classified as follows.

(1) A strong reducing agent is added, e.g. N_2H_4, $S_2O_4^{2-}$, BH_4^-, sodium or potassium amalgam:

$$RNC + N_2H_4 + Ni(acetate)_2 \xrightarrow{KOH} Ni(RNC)_4 + N_2 + K(acetate).$$

The reduction may be effected in liquid ammonia, usually with metallic potassium:

$$[Pt(NH_3)_4]Cl_2 + 2K \rightarrow Pt(NH_3)_4 + 2KCl.$$

(2) Electrolytic reduction:

$$[Ni(CN)_4]^{2-} \xrightarrow[\text{liquid NH}_3]{+2e^-} [Ni(CN)_4]^{4-}.$$

(3) The ligand acts as reducing agent, e.g. CO:

$$OsO_4 + 9CO \rightarrow Os(CO)_5 + 4CO_2.$$

(4) The metal salt acts as a reducing agent. For example, chromium(II) salts disproportionate as follows:

$$PhNC + Cr(acetate)_2 \rightarrow Cr(PhNC)_6 + Cr(acetate)_3.$$

In some cases the main substitution reaction is a separate step from the reduction as in the following use of a Grignard reagent:

$$\text{Ph.MgBr} + \text{CrCl}_3 \rightarrow [\text{CrPh}_2]^+ \xrightarrow{\text{reduce}} \text{Cr}(\text{C}_6\text{H}_6)_2.$$

Grignard reagents are also of quite general applicability in substitution reactions of metal halides. There is a close resemblance with organic syntheses in this and many other procedures. For example, the conventional Friedel Crafts' reaction,

$$\text{CH}_3\text{Cl} + \text{C}_6\text{H}_6 \xrightarrow{\text{AlCl}_3} \text{PhCH}_3,$$

is catalysed by aluminium chloride, as is the reaction

$$6\text{C}_6\text{H}_6 + 3\text{CrCl}_3 + 2\text{Al} + \text{AlCl}_3 \rightarrow 3[(\text{C}_6\text{H}_6)_2\text{Cr}]^+[\text{AlCl}_4]^-,$$

which is one route to the preparation of dibenzenechromium.

In organic chemistry borohydrides are used as selective hydrogenating agents. Borohydrides also react with derivatives of metals in low oxidation states, either giving a metal-hydrogen or a hydrogen-ligand bond. Methylating agents such as CH_3I can be used to methylate reactive organic groups, and they can also be used in the direct methylation of low-oxidation states or of metal hydrides. An example of this reaction is the synthesis of vitamin B_{12} coenzyme analogues which have Co(III)-carbon bonds. The compound vitamin B_{12a} (see Fig. 27.12) is reduced by CrCl_2 or electrolytically to a green compound of formal oxidation state Co(I). Reaction with CH_3I gives $\text{Co(III)CH}_3^- + \text{HI}$. Finally a general extension of these parallels is possible to the attack by such nucleophilic reagents as sulphite and cyanide at positive carbon or at the positive metal atom of a low-oxidation-state compound. Both positive carbon, e.g. in a carbonyl group $\text{R}_2\text{C}=\text{O}$, and low-valence metals appear to demand the more highly polarizable atoms of the ligand as neighbours, i.e. S rather than O of SO_3^{2-} and C rather than N of CN^-.

27.2. Compounds with unsaturated ligands

CARBONYL COMPLEXES

Pure carbonyls are formed by the elements from Group VA to Group VIII in the Periodic Table, but are not as yet known for the pre-transition metals, B metals, palladium, and platinum (see Table 27.II). Pure carbonyls of metals with an even atomic number may contain one or more metal atoms. In general, however, only carbonyls containing more than one metal atom are formed by metals with an odd number of electrons, although V(CO)_6 is an exception. All the carbonyls can be prepared in a similar manner by

TABLE 27.II. *Formulae, melting-points* (°C) *and colours of some carbonyls*

Group	VA	VIA	VIIA	VIIIa	VIIIb	VIIIc
	$V(CO)_6$	$Cr(CO)_6$	$Mn_2(CO)_{10}$	$Fe(CO)_5$	$Co_2(CO)_8$	$Ni(CO)_4$
	decomp.	sublimes	155°	−20°	51°	−25°
	70°	*in vacuo*				
	sublimes					
	in vacuo					
	black-purple	colourless	yellow	yellow	dark orange	colourless
	paramagnetic					
				$Fe_2(CO)_9$	$[Co(CO)_3]_4$	
				decomp.	decomp. 60°	
				100°		
				bronze	black	
				$Fe_3(CO)_{12}$		
				decomp. 140°		
				dark green		
		$Mo(CO)_6$		$Ru(CO)_5$	$Rh_2(CO)_8$	
		sublimes		−22°	76°	
		in vacuo				
		colourless		colourless	orange	
				$Ru_3(CO)_{12}$	$[Rh(CO)_3]_n$	
				orange	red	
					$[Rh_4(CO)_{11}]_n$	
					black	
		$W(CO)_6$	$Re_2(CO)_{10}$	$Os(CO)_5$	$Ir_2(CO)_8$	
		sublimes	177°	−15°	sublimes	
		in vacuo				
		colourless	colourless	colourless	yellow green	
				$Os_3(CO)_{12}$	$[Ir(CO)_3]_n$	
				224°		
				bright	yellow	
				yellow		

Note deepening of colour with polymerization.

the action of CO and, where necessary, reducing agents (e.g. metallic sodium) on the metals or metal salts at high temperature and pressure, sometimes in the presence of catalysts (e.g. ethers). They are volatile molecular compounds. Their structures may be complex, for the CO group can either act as a simple monodentate ligand or as a bridge between two metal atoms. Some carbonyl structures are shown in Fig. 27.1. The different arrangements of the CO groups can be distinguished by the infra-red spectra of the compounds.

The *iso*-nitrile, RNC, complexes are very closely related to the carbonyls for the CO and the RNC groups are effectively isoelectronic. The comparison of such ligands is generally helpful in the systematization of organometallic chemistry.

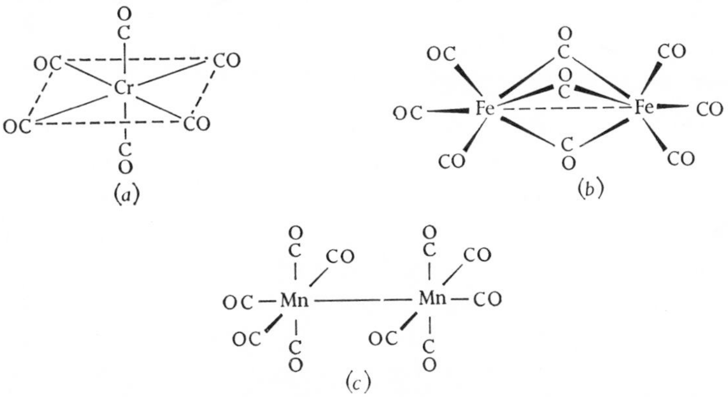

FIG. 27.1. Structures of carbonyls showing (a) a simple monomeric compound, (b) a bridged carbonyl with M—M bonding, and (c) a carbonyl with an M—M bond but no bridging groups. In the solid state $Mn_2(CO)_{10}$ has a staggered configuration.

CARBONYL HALIDES

Carbonyl halides are known from Group VIIA to Group IB. With the exception of $Ni(CO)_4$, carbonyl halides are the only stable carbonyls of both Groups VIIIc and IB (Table 27.III). Inspection of the table shows that the majority of the formulae of carbonyl halides cannot easily be explained by reference to an 18-electron configuration. A similar difficulty

TABLE 27.III. *Some carbonyl halides*

VIIA	VIIIA	VIIIb	VIIIc	IB
$Mn(CO)_5X$ $[Mn(CO_4)X]_2$	$Fe(CO)_5X_2$? $Fe(CO)_4X_2$ $Fe(CO)_2X_2$ $Fe(CO)_2X$ $[Fe(CO)_3X_2]_2$	$Co(CO)X_2$		$Cu(CO)X$
	$Ru(CO)_2X_2$ $Ru(CO)X$	$[Rh(CO)_2X]_2$	$[Pd(CO)X_2]_n$	
$Re(CO)_5X$	$Os(CO)_4X_2$ $Os(CO)_3X_2$ $Os(CO)_2X_2$ $[Os(CO)_4X]_2$	$Ir(CO)_3X$ $Ir(CO)_3X_2$	$Pt(CO)_2X_2$ $[Pt(CO)X_2]_2$ $H[Pt(CO)X_3]$	$Au(CO)X$
18-electron rule obeyed	sometimes obeyed	fails	fails	fails

X may be Cl, Br, or I. Some of these compounds are polymers.

is experienced in explaining the formulae of mixed carbonyl hydrides, nitrosyl chlorides (Table 27.v), cyanides, and isocyanides. It is particularly noticeable that heavier metals prefer to form carbonyl halides rather than pure carbonyls, and that of these halides the iodides are the most stable.

CYANIDE AND ACETYLIDE COMPLEXES

Low-oxidation-state compounds can be prepared by coordination of the CN group in one of three forms, the cyanide ion, the *iso*-nitrile group, or the nitrile group. Low-valence cyanides are known from about Group VA onwards. They are extremely unstable in air or often even in water, and are usually prepared by electrolytic reduction or by reduction in liquid ammonia with potassium metal. More general examples of cyanides are quoted in Table 27.iv. While ionic and simple σ-bonded cyanides are found elsewhere, nitrile compounds are only known in transition-metal chemistry.

$RC{\equiv}C^-$, where R is an organic group, is very similar to cyanide and forms a range of compounds including simple ionic salts, e.g. $K^+C_2R^-$, σ-bonded complexes such as CuC_2R, and complexes in which π-bonding is possibly more dominant, e.g. $K_3[Co(C_2R)_6]$. In crystals of acetylides the anion binds to further metal atoms, acting as a π-donor like ethylene

$$RC{\equiv}C\text{---}Cu$$
$$\uparrow$$
$$Cu\text{---}C{\equiv}CR.$$

The differences between the complexes of cyanides (Table 27.iv) and acetylides on the one hand and of carbonyls (Table 27.ii) and *iso*-nitriles on the other may be associated with the charge carried by the former ligands. All the ligands are similar in that they are effectively isoelectronic, usually monodentate although they can also act as bridging ligands, and form isostructural compounds. The major differences between the groups of compounds are the greater range of the combining metals and the greater stability of higher oxidation states with the charged ligands. The stability constants of some cyanides have been discussed in Chapters 25 and 26. We shall discuss their stability further below.

ACETYLENE COMPLEXES

Several types of complex, σ-bonded or π-bonded, can be obtained from acetylene and its derivatives. C_2H_2 is more acidic than ethylene and readily gives acetylides, C_2H^- derivatives. Thus its π-complexes are most easily studied if the hydrogen atoms are replaced by methyl or phenyl

TABLE 27.IV. *Some complex cyanides*

Valence state	VA	VIA	VIIA	VIIIa	VIIIb	VIIIc	IB	IIB
3	$V(CN)_6^{3-}$	$Cr(CN)_6^{3-}$		$Fe(CN)_6^{3-}$	$Co(CN)_6^{3-}$			
2	$V(CN)_6^{4-}$	$Cr(CN)_6^{4-}$	$Mn(CN)_6^{4-}$	$Fe(CN)_6^{4-}$	$Co(CN)_6^{4-}$	$Ni(CN)_4^{2-}$	$Cu(CN)_4^{2-}$	$Zn(CN)_4^{2-}$
1			$Mn(CN)_6^{5-}$				$Cu(CN)_2^{-}$	
0						$Ni(CN)_4^{4-}$		

Valence state	VA	VIA	VIIA	VIIIa	VIIIb	VIIIc	IB	IIB
5		$Mo(CN)_8^{3-}$						
4		$Mo(CN)_8^{4-}$						
3		$Mo(CN)_8^{5-}$		$Ru(CN)_6^{3-}$	$Rh(CN)_6^{3-}$			
2				$Ru(CN)_6^{4-}$		$Pd(CN)_4^{2-}$		$Cd(CN)_4^{2-}$
1								
0						$Pd(CN)_4^{4-}$		

Valence state	VA	VIA	VIIA	VIIIa	VIIIb	VIIIc	IB	IIB
5		$W(CN)_8^{3-}$						
4		$W(CN)_8^{4-}$	$Re(CN)_8^{4-}$					
3				$Os(CN)_6^{3-}$	$Ir(CN)_6^{3-}$			
2				$Os(CN)_6^{4-}$		$Pt(CN)_4^{2-}$		$Hg(CN)_4^{2-}$

groups. Acetylene derivatives can form simple π-complexes (cf. Fig. 27.5), but it is also able to form two π-bonds as in the molecule shown in Fig. 27.2. The geometry around the Pt atom and around the carbon atoms is unknown, but clearly very great strain is involved in this molecule.

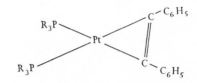

FIG. 27.2. A platinum-acetylene complex.

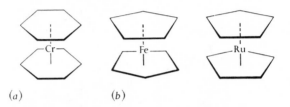

(a)   (b)

FIG. 27.3. (a) A typical bis-arene complex. (b) Two different structures of bis-π-cyclopentadienyl complexes in the *solid* state.

NITROSYL COMPLEXES

Nitrosyl complexes will not be described in any detail as they bear a formal resemblance to the carbonyls. There are very few pure nitrosyls (Table 27.v). The NO group usually becomes NO^+ on combination and is thus isoelectronic with CO. The two extreme forms NO and NO^+ can be characterized by differences in infra-red absorption.

ARENE COMPLEXES

The arene (e.g. benzene) sandwich compounds (Fig. 27.3 (a)) are restricted to a part of the Periodic Table (Table 27.vi) similar to that for the carbonyls. Like the carbonyls they are formed only with metals in very low-oxidation states. The benzene ring can be thought of as a tridentate ligand. It appears that the regular hexagonal structure of the ring is not broken by combination with the metal. Its reactivity is low, like that of free benzene, and it can undergo substitution without dissociation. It does not appear that the benzene ring can act as a bridging sandwich-ligand, but two metal atoms can be 'sandwiched' between two benzenes.

TABLE 27.v. *Some nitrosyls*

	VIA	VIIA	VIIIa	VIIIb	VIIIc	IB
Nitrosyls with only neutral ligands		$Mn(CO)_4NO$ $Mn(NO)_3CO$	$Fe(NO)_2(CO)_2$ $Fe(NO)_4(?)$ $Fe(NO)_2(phenan)$ $Ru(NO)_5(?)$	$Co(NO)(CO)_3$ $Co(CO)(NO)(phenan)$		$Cu(NO)_{3-4}^{2+}(?)$
Nitrosyl halides and related compounds	$Cr(Cp)(NO)_2Cl$ $Cr(NO)_2(R_2NCS_2)_2$		$Fe(NO)_2I$ $Fe(NO)_3Cl$ $Fe(NO)Cl$ $Fe(NO)(R_2NCS_2)_2$ $Ru(NO)X_2$ $Ru(NO)X_3$ $Ru(NO)(R_2NCS_2)_2$ $Os(NO)X_2$	$Co(NO)_2Cl$ $Co(NO)_2Br$ $Co(NO)_2I$ $Co(NO)I(phenan)$	$Ni(NO)X$ $Ni(NO)OH$ $Pd(NO)_2Cl_2$ $Pt(NO)_2Cl_2$	
Other nitrosyl complexes	$[Cr(NO)(H_2O)_5]^{3+}$	$K_3[Mn(CN)_5NO]$	$K_2[Fe(CN)_5NO]$ $M[Fe_4(NO)_7S_3]$ $M_2[Fe(NO)_4S_2]$ $K_2[RuCl_5(NO)]$ $K_2[Ru(CN)_5(NO)]$	$[Co(NH_3)_5NO]X_2$	$K_2[Ni(CN)_3NO]$ $M[PtCl_3NO]$	

N.B. Many nitrosyl-thio compounds of various kinds are known. Phenan is orthophenanthroline. X is Cl, Br, or I. Some of the above compounds are not fully characterized: the degree of polymerization is often unknown and additional donors, e.g. solvent molecules, may complete the coordination sphere.

TABLE 27.VI. *Some bis-arene (Ar) and bis-π-cyclopentadienyl (Cp) complexes*

IA	IIA	IIIA	IVA	VA	VIA	VIIA	VIIIa	VIIIb	VIIIc	IB	IIB	IIIB
KCp ionic	$CaCp_2$ ionic	$ScCp_3$ ionic	$TiCp_2$ $TiCp_2Cl_2$	VCp_2 $[VCp_2]^+$ VCp_2Cl_2	$CrCp_2$ $[CrCp_2]^+$	$MnCp_2$	$FeCp_2$ $[FeCp_2]^+$	$CoCp_2$ $[CoCp_2]^+$	$NiCp_2$ $[NiCp_2]^+$		$ZnCp_2$	$GaCp_3$
				VAr_2	$CrAr_2$		$[FeAr_2]^{2+}$	$[CoAr_2]^{3+}$				
$RbCp$ ionic	$SrCp_2$ ionic	YCp_3 ionic	$ZrCp_2Cl_2$	$NbCp_2Cl_3$	$MoCp_2Cl_2$ $[MoCp_2Cl_2]^+$ $[MoCp_2H_2]^+$		$RuCp_2$	$[RhCp_2]^+$			$CdCp_2$?	$InCp_3$
					$MoAr_2$		$[RuAr_2]^{2+}$	$[RhAr_2]^{3+}$				
$CsCp$ ionic	$BaCp_2$ ionic	$LaCp_3$ ionic	$HfCp_2Cl_2$	$TaCp_2Cl_3$	WCp_2Cl_2 $[WCp_2Cl_2]^+$ $[WCp_2H_3]^+$	$ReCp_2H$ $[ReCp_2H_2]^+$	$OsCp_2$	$[IrCp_2]^+$			$HgCp_2$ (σ)	$TlCp$ ionic ?
					WAr_2	$[ReAr_2]^+$	$[OsAr_2]^{2+}$	$[IrAr_2]^{3+}$				

Notes. (1) IA, IIA, and IIIA ionic cyclopentadienides, and IIB and IIIB cyclopentadienyls are included for completeness. (2) In Group VIIIc there are mono-π-cyclopentadienyls such as $PtCp(\pi\text{-allyl})$ and there are compounds which may be π- or σ-bonded in Group IB, e.g. $[CuCpPEt_3]$. (3) There are also a great variety of mono-arenes and mono-π-cyclopentadienyls and some tris-arenes and tris-π-cyclopentadienyls in Groups IVA to VIIIc. (4) In general in the compounds MCp_2X_n, X may be halide, pseudo-halide, hydride, or a σ-bonded organic residue. (5) Ar is most frequently benzene or mesitylene.

CYCLOPENTADIENYL COMPOUNDS

Another very extensive series of organometallic compounds of the transition metals are those containing the C_5H_5, Cp, group (Table 27.VI). Three types of compound may be distinguished. (1) Ionic compounds containing simple Cp^- anions, formed with the metals of Groups IA, IIA, IIIA, and part at least of Group IVA. They are often called cyclopentadienides. (2) Compounds which are more nearly in the same class as the carbonyls, formed extensively with atoms throughout the transition-metal series, e.g. from vanadium to nickel. The general structure of these compounds is given in Fig. 27.3 (b). They are π-cyclopentadienyls but have also been called sandwich compounds for very obvious reasons. However, the sandwich structure is common to both cyclopentadienyls of metals which readily form carbonyls, Groups VA to VIII, and to many ionic cyclopentadienides, e.g. $MgCp_2$ and $ThCp_4$, and it is only the lower chemical reactivity of the former which distinguishes them from the latter. (3) Compounds containing simple σ-bonds, e.g. with hydrogen and mercury. They are sometimes called σ-cyclopentadienyls: σ-bonded cyclopentadienyls may also be formed by metals such as Fe when all but one coordination position is blocked, e.g.

$$Fe(\pi\text{-}Cp)(CO)_2(\sigma\text{-}Cp).$$

The π-cyclopentadienyls can be formally considered as existing over a wide range of oxidation states of a given metal (Table 27.VI) and in this they again resemble cyanides.†

SOME GENERAL COMMENTS

Each of the monodentate ligands, CO, NO^+, CN^-, RNC, and RCN, has all its π-bonding orbitals full and all its π*-antibonding orbitals empty. Benzene and the cyclopentadienide ion have their orbitals occupied in the same way. However, the differences in the charges carried make benzene complexes similar to carbonyls and nitriles, and cyclopentadienide complexes like cyanides. Both the range of elements and the range of oxidation states of any one element in cyanides and cyclopentadienides greatly exceeds those of carbonyls and arenes. On the same basis NO^+ may be compared with the tropylium cation $C_7H_7^+$.

All the ligands are similar in that they generate very high effective ligand fields. This is shown by the magnetic moments of the carbonyl, cyanide, benzene, and bis-π-cyclopentadienyl compounds. Even in the first transition-metal series the d electrons of the metals are largely forced into low-

† Carborane compounds analogous to the π-cyclopentadienyls have been prepared by Hawthorne et al., J. Am. Chem. Soc. 1965, **87**, 1818.

spin configurations, e.g. Fig. 27.4. In this figure, manganese (d^5) is a marked exception but its spin-pairing energy is very high. $MnCp_2$ is rather like an ionic cyclopentadienide in reactivity.

Since N_2 is isoelectronic with CO, methods of activation of N_2 are being sought from a consideration of the ways in which CO is activated in metal complexes.

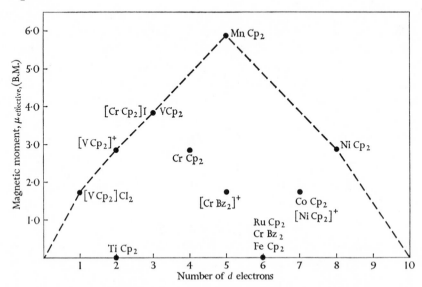

FIG. 27.4. The magnetic moments of bis-arene and bis-π-cyclopentadienyl complexes. The broken line joins the magnetic moments of high-spin complexes. Bz = benzene.

NON-CONJUGATED OLEFINIC COMPLEXES

Although it is relatively easy for non-conjugated olefins such as ethylene to occupy one or two coordination positions, it has proved experimentally more difficult to obtain *pure* ethylene complexes corresponding to the pure carbonyls, arenes, and cyclopentadienyls. A typical mixed complex is $C_2H_4Pt(PPh_3)Br_2$ (Fig. 27.5) in which the ethylene π orbital is thought to act as a σ-donor to platinum, and the antibonding (otherwise unoccupied) π^* orbitals as 'π'-acceptors to the orbitals of the metal atom. Table 27.VII indicates some of the metals which bind ethylene in this way. The metals inside the triangle readily form ethylenic complexes in aqueous solution, and their compounds are often used therefore as catalysts for the reactions of substituted ethylenes. The elements enclosed in the rectangle of Table 27.VII are for the most part known to give ethylene complexes in mixed carbonyls. It could well be that the difference between the two groups of metals is an historical accident rather than of fundamental significance. Carbonyls are convenient starting-points for the preparations of the low-oxidation-state compounds of the metals in the centre of the transition series, but carbonyls are not available for Pd, Pt, Cu, Ag, Au, and Hg. Co, Ni, Rh, and Ir give mixed complexes containing ethylene and phosphines.

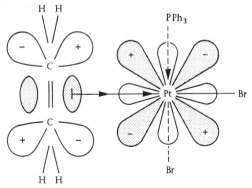

FIG. 27.5. *d*-Orbitals of platinum(II) and π-orbitals of ethylene; donor orbitals are shaded. The bonds shown broken are perpendicular to the plane of the paper.

TABLE 27.VII. *Metals known to give complexes with non-conjugated olefins*

Ti	V	Cr	Mn	Fe	Co	Ni	Cu	
	Nb	Mo	(Tc)	Ru	Rh	Pd	Ag	Cd
	Ta	W	Re	Os	Ir	Pt	Au	Hg

A chelating non-conjugated olefin such as 1:5 cyclooctadiene, can occupy two coordination positions of a metal. Pure olefinic compounds have been prepared using this and similar ligands, e.g.

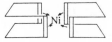

in which the geometry around the nickel has not yet been determined.

π-ALLYL† COMPLEXES

The ethylene molecule can only act as a donor through its π electrons; the vinyl anion, $C_2H_3^-$, binds directly to cobalt(III) of vitamin B_{12} as a simple σ-bonded ligand; the allyl radical $CH_2\!=\!CH\!-\!CH_2^\cdot$, can form a

† There is some discussion as to the proper nomenclature for these compounds. π-allenyl would be consistent with π-cyclopentadienyl.

simple σ-bond as in allyl chloride, $CH_2{=}CHCH_2Cl$ or a 3-electron π complex (compare the cyclopentadienyl 5-electron π complexes). In the π-allyl compounds the metal atom is associated with three carbon atoms, and the ligand could be equally well thought of as the allenyl anion. The anion is similar to that derived from cyclopentadienyl, and pure sandwich compounds of the kind shown in Fig. 27.6 have also been prepared. Examples

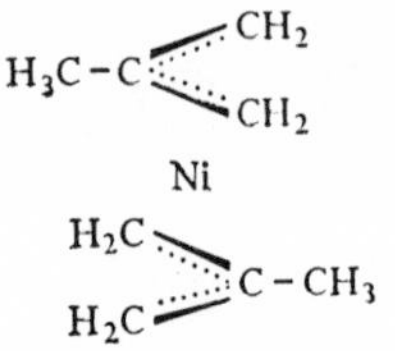

FIG. 27.6. The proposed structure of nickel
bis-π-2-methylallyl (after Wilke).

are included in Table 27.VIII. Such π-allyl complexes are frequently formed by the reaction of a Grignard reagent

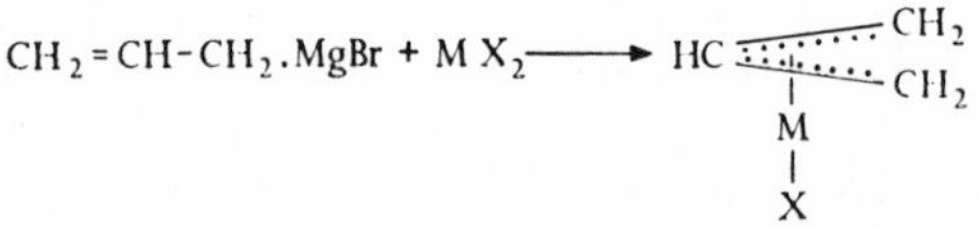

$$CH_2{=}CH{-}CH_2.MgBr + MX_2 \longrightarrow HC \cdots \begin{array}{c} CH_2 \\ | \\ M \\ | \\ X \end{array} CH_2$$

The group X can be of almost any kind shown in Table 27.I.

TABLE 27.VIII. *Some π-allyl complexes* $(R = C_3H_5)$

	VR$_3$†	CrR$_3$†	FeR$_3$†	CoR$_3$†	NiR$_2$
ZrR$_4$†		MoR$_4$			PdR$_2$
		WR$_4$			PtR$_2$

† Not fully characterized as π-allyl complexes: they could contain some σ-allyl linkages.

Some of these mixed compounds were amongst the first π-allyl complexes known. An alternative preparative route, which has general importance in the synthesis of organometallic compounds, starts from a preformed σ-bonded compound according to the scheme

$$mM'X_n{+}nM''R_m \longrightarrow mM'R_n{+}nM''X_m$$
$$(\sigma\text{-bonded})$$

donor, e.g. butadiene or a phosphine

novel unsaturated $\xleftarrow[\text{light}]{\text{heat}}$ (π-allyl complex, isolated where M' is Ni)
organic compounds

where M' is a transition metal, M'' a pre-transition metal usually aluminium or magnesium, X is a halogen, and R a saturated group such as ethyl.

A typical overall reaction taking place via a π-allyl complex is:

$$CrO_2Cl_2 + AlEt_3 + C_4H_6 \longrightarrow$$

The intermediates in such reactions as the last have been isolated and shown to be π-allyl complexes; see section 27.5.

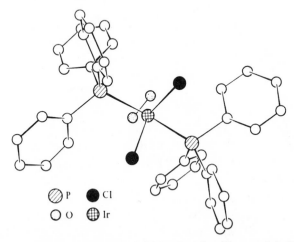

FIG. 27.7. The structure of $IrCl_2(PPh_3)_2O_2$ (after Ibers and LaPlaca, *Eighth International Conference on Coordination Chemistry* (ed. Gutmann), Springer-Verlag, Vienna, 1964).

It appears therefore that non-conjugated ligands are more stable in these complexes than the conjugated ligands which might have been formed. In the absence of complexing, conjugation would have increased stability. The formation of the non-conjugated ligand could arise from the repulsion between the negative charges carried in the π-allyl groups, or through the steric requirements of chelation.

OXYGEN COMPLEXES

The reactivity of oxygen prevents the study of most of its complexes. However, it is now known to form at least two series of compounds. In the first series it is bidentate, and binds to two metal atoms, e.g. as in $\{[Co(NH_3)_5]_2O_2\}^{6+}$. In the second series it is monodentate, and binds very like C_2H_4, as in Fig. 27.7. There may also be complexes of the type

$$M{\leftarrow}O{\diagdown}_O.$$

The class to which oxyhaemoglobin belongs is not yet known.

Oxygen in its diamagnetic low-lying excited state is effectively iso-electronic with ethylene. Other comparable ligands are ketones, aldehydes, NO^-, R_2C=NH, and nitroso compounds RNO. Nitroso aromatic compounds, especially nitrosophenols, are of great importance in analytical chemistry and are known to occur with iron in biological systems. Their complexes are readily formed directly by the oxidation of metal–oxime complexes.

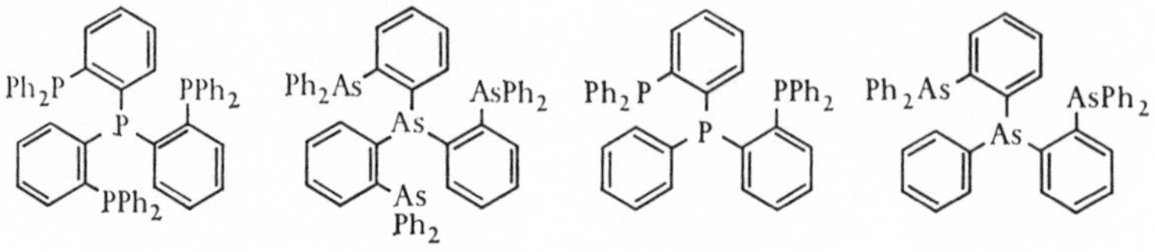

FIG. 27.8. Arsenic and phosphorus ligands giving rise to particular stereochemistries, see Fig. 25.6.

HEAVIER NON-METAL ATOMS AS LIGANDS

A further series of ligands which help to stabilize compounds of very low oxidation states have atoms of Group V and VI, i.e. (N), P, As, Sb, S, and Se as the donor centres. Iodide should perhaps be included in the series. Some compounds formed by these ligands have been described in Chapter 17. The main ligands are imines, PF_3, PR_3, AsR_3, SbR_3, SR_2, and SeR_2, where R can be either aliphatic or aromatic. Complexes of many metals from oxidation state -1 to $+4$ can be prepared, e.g. $Pt(PEt_3)_4$. With chosen polydentate ligands, almost any geometry can be stabilized around the central metal. Fig. 27.8 gives some examples of ligands which force certain types of stereochemistry. Only in the first row is it essential that the coordinating atom, C or N, should be *in an unsaturated molecule* if it is to stabilize low-oxidation states effectively, for the elements of later rows in the Periodic Table, P and S, etc., can form π-acceptor bonds utilizing their nd orbitals. Such bonding is not possible in the first row where the acceptor states must be *empty* antibonding π^* orbitals of the ligand.

Ligands which have been found to stabilize the zero or other low-oxidation states all have in common low electronegativity, easy polarizability, and strong π-acceptor properties. The properties of the metals which form these complexes and compounds are complementary. The metals are of relatively high electronegativity (for metals), of high polarizing power and are strong π-electron donors. Moreover, they are themselves polarizable so that the mutual interaction of the metal and ligands is co-operative or synergic. The compounds are generally of low-spin, since in the low-spin state metals are both better σ-electron acceptors and π-electron donors than in high-spin states. It is also easier to form these compounds with the transition metals of the second and third series, as these metals are more readily excited to spin-paired states and their $(n-1)d$ electrons are more exposed to ligands. In these two transition series much more is known of the chemistry of the compounds of very low oxidation states than is known of simple divalent and trivalent compounds.

METAL–METAL BONDS

Metal–metal bonding is often observed in low-oxidation-state compounds. Fig. 27.1 (c) gives one example and several others are to be found in section 27.5. In some cases ligands such as CO, R_2Se, R_2S, RNC, or even an organic ring act as bridges, Fig. 27.1 (b).

27.3. Electron configuration and the stability of compounds with unsaturated ligands

The relative stabilities of coordination compounds are often rationalized in terms of the tendency of the central atom to acquire electrons up to the nearest noble-gas structure. For example, boron trihalides act as acceptors to amines and boron trimethyl will form a carbonyl. For the transition-metal series the next noble gas is rather far away in the Periodic Table, and it is therefore somewhat surprising that in many of the compounds we have just described the metal appears to attain a noble-gas configuration by the coordination of ligands. This will be further illustrated in two series of compounds.

CARBONYLS

Some heats of formation for carbonyls are given in Table 27.IX. The very stable simple carbonyls are formed with the metals in the middle of the transition series and nearly all the stable ones conform to the noble-gas

TABLE 27.IX. ΔH_f° of metal carbonyls (kcal mole^{-1}) at 25 °C

$V(CO)_6$ value unknown	$Cr(CO)_6$	$Fe(CO)_5$	$Ni(CO)_4$
	$-257 \cdot 6$	$-187 \cdot 8$	$-151 \cdot 6$
	$Mo(CO)_6$ $-234 \cdot 8$		$Pd(CO)_4$ not known
	$W(CO)_6$ $-227 \cdot 3$		$Pt(CO)_4$ not known or very unstable

ΔH_f° for CO is $-26 \cdot 4$ kcal mole^{-1}.

or 18-electron rule. A more generalized and schematic picture of the relation between stability and atomic number is given in Fig. 27.9. The stability falls abruptly at the end of the transition series, suggesting that back donation of *exposed d* electrons to CO is very important. However,

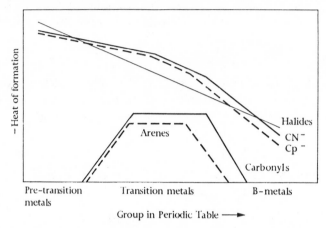

FIG. 27.9. A schematic representation of the heats of formation of low-oxidation-state compounds.

the dominant feature is the formation of that number of σ-bonds which gives the 18-electron structure, see the molecular-orbital diagram, Fig. 24.11. Stability (relative to the metal) decreases down Group VIA, and must fall down Group VIII.

AROMATIC LIGANDS

The most stable bis-π-arene compound is either dibenzenechromium or dibenzenevanadium. The stability falls at nickel, in contrast with the carbonyls.

In order to explain the stability of these aromatic complexes we cannot use the molecular-orbital energy-level diagram, Fig. 24.11, which was used for the simple octahedral complexes and which is therefore applicable to chromium hexacarbonyl. In the sandwich complexes the symmetry is lower. The appropriate energy-level diagram for dibenzenechromium is given in Fig. 27.10, and it can be used to show in a rough-and-ready way why the stability of sandwich complexes falls more rapidly after the d^6 atom than does the stability of the carbonyls, cyanides, and nitrosyls. It is important to note that all the latter group of ligands are monodentate, so that the geometry of the complex can be readily adjusted to match the available empty orbitals of the metal. Symmetry is continuously modified

in the series of carbonyls in order to maintain stability. The cyclopentadienyl and benzene ligands are best regarded as tridentate and their
transition-metal complexes are strongly stabilized in the sandwich symmetry only (Fig. 27.3). Stability is now rigidly associated with the pattern

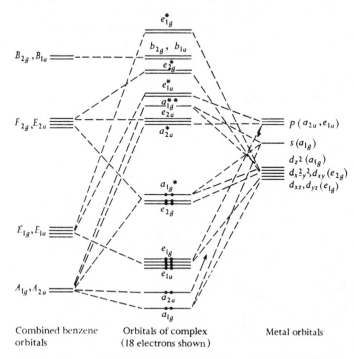

Combined benzene   Orbitals of complex   Metal orbitals
orbitals   (18 electrons shown)

Fig. 27.10. A molecular-orbital diagram for Cr(benzene)$_2$. (Symmetry
labels refer to the D_{6h} point group.) Filled orbitals are indicated.

of energy levels set up in this symmetry. The situation is like that which
gives rise to the $(4n+2)$ rule of aromatic stability where $(2n+1)$ is the
number of bonding π-orbitals.

Some of the orbitals are shown in Fig. 27.11. The labels should be compared with those for an octahedral field (Fig. 24.11). The metal orbitals on
the right of Fig. 27.10 are the five d orbitals labelled with the z-axis perpendicular to the sandwich, one s orbital, and three p orbitals. Their symmetry
labels are s, d_{z^2} (a_{1g}); p_z (a_{2u}); p_x, p_y (e_{1u}); d_{zx}, d_{zy} (e_{1g}); and d_{xy}, $d_{x^2-y^2}$ (e_{2g}).
The splitting between the orbitals of different symmetry type due to elec-
trostatic factors will be quite small and they have only been separated in
the figure in order to follow their later combination. Now the metal orbitals will combine with ligand orbitals of the same symmetry class. In rela-

tion to the symmetry of the complex, each benzene orbital can be combined with the identical orbital of the other benzene ring in two ways. The lowest benzene π (aromatic) orbitals of the 'streamer' kind, one from each benzene, have nodes only in the planes of the benzene rings, and taken in combination are therefore either of the A_{1g} or A_{2u} type symmetry. The next highest, the least stable π-bonding orbitals of each of the ring systems, also have one nodal plane perpendicular to the ring. The combined symmetry is then E_{1g} or E_{1u}. The first antibonding π^* orbitals, which are empty in benzene or in the cyclopentadienide anion, have two perpendicular nodal planes and are then of E_{2u} or E_{2g} symmetry when combined. It is now a simple matter to match symmetries of the metal and of the ligand orbitals, but it is very difficult to predict the relative energies of the resulting molecular orbitals.

The matching of orbitals is shown in Fig. 27.10. The lowest π orbitals (A_{2u} and A_{1g}) are stabilized by mixing with $4s$, $4p_z$, and $3d_{z^2}$. This combination leads to two very stable orbitals, and three orbitals of decreasing stability due to the energy separation of d, s, and p metal atomic orbitals. The four E_{1u} plus E_{1g} ligand orbitals may also combine with two d and two p metal orbitals to give rise to four stable and four unstable molecular orbitals. Finally, there are the combinations of ligand orbitals of E_{2g} symmetry with the metal d_{xy} and $d_{x^2-y^2}$ (e_{2g}) orbitals. These give two orbitals which are only somewhat stabilized, because the high energy of E_{2g} of the ligand does not add much to the stabilization of the d orbitals of the metal. The other ligand orbitals do not interact with metal orbitals. Pictorial representations of some of these combinations are shown in Fig. 27.11. The energy-level diagram gives certainly *eight* orbitals separated from the next four orbitals. The separation amongst these four is uncertain, but it is possible that the a_{1g}^* molecular orbital lies lower than the others and the diagram accentuates this. There are now *nine* stable orbitals which will take the eighteen electrons of the noble-gas configuration and no more. It is not possible to predict convincingly that the 18-electron configuration will be the most stable, but it cannot be far from the most stable. The diagram for cyclopentadienyl complexes is very similar indeed despite the different symmetry, D_{5d} and D_{5h} point groups (Fig. 27.3 (*b*)).

The stability of the complexes can now be discussed. As there are eight or nine stable orbitals, only six of which can be filled by ligand electrons, the greatest stability will be expected with around four or six electrons per metal atom or ion. Otherwise either electrons must be added to unstable orbitals or stable orbitals are unfilled. A plot of stability against atomic number should rise to a maximum and then fall. The filling first of bonding and then of antibonding orbitals has a similar consequence to that observed in the diatomic molecules (Chapter 3) and in simpler complexes (Chapter 24). Thus in particular scandium, yttrium, and the lanthanides, and

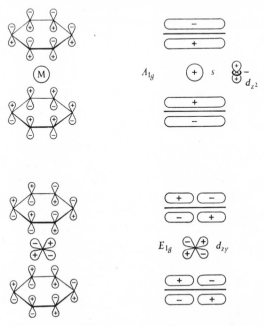

FIG. 27.11. Some of the orbitals of Fig. 27.10.

copper, silver, and gold are not expected to and do not give benzene complexes of the same kind as the usual transition-metal arenes. Copper and silver give 'ethylene'-type complexes with benzene in which the metal lies directly under one bond of the ring.

The interest in the theory of bis-arene and bis-π-cyclopentadienyl compounds must not be allowed to hide the more general theoretical problems of complexes of low symmetry in which there may be a mixture of ligands. For these systems it is usual to simplify theoretical considerations by treating each ligand and its interaction with the metal separately. Such a procedure permits a counting of electrons associated with the metal and a general check of the 18-electron rule. Thus CO is a 2-electron donor, cyclopentadienide is a 6-electron donor, and the π-allyl group is a 3-electron donor. It is observed that the 18-electron rule is generally valid, and especially for Group VI and VII metals.

THE 18-ELECTRON RULE

The 18-electron rule which is described in the introduction to this chapter has a rough empirical value, but it is not derivable from any well-defined theoretical treatment which has universal applicability. Each complex involving a new stereochemistry has to be treated separately, and the combined ligand and metal orbitals may lead to the prediction of a specific thermodynamic stability of the metal complexes with 18 electrons. For example, the nickel cyclobutadiene complexes were predicted in this way before they were prepared. However, in some symmetries 18 electrons will not be associated with high stability. Even where symmetry considerations predict stability, the separation in energy of the ns, np, and $(n-1)d$ atomic orbitals may reduce the degree to which the group of 18 electrons is favoured. Thus platinum and palladium have relatively slight ability to form carbonyls, cyclopentadienyls, and benzene complexes. These metals have the greatest stabilization of $(n-1)d$ as opposed to np orbitals. There is some evidence that 16 electrons is the most stable grouping in the complexes of these metals. A similar problem arises in the compounds of the Group IB and IIB metals, where cations such as Hg^{2+} give linear complexes, e.g. $[Hg(NH_3)_2]^{2+}$, which do not obey the 18-electron rule. Here the evidence is in favour of a stable group of 14 electrons. Naturally the 18-electron rule is more likely to fail if a major contribution to binding comes from electrostatic interactions, as in $[Cd(NH_3)_6]^{2+}$.

CHARGED LIGANDS

Unlike the benzene-sandwich compounds and the carbonyls, the cyclopentadienide-sandwich compounds and cyanide complexes are stable with transition metals over a wide range of the Periodic Table (Fig. 27.9). The arene and carbonyl complexes owe their stability to a large degree to π-bonding. Cyclopentadienide and cyanide can be compared with simple anions, e.g. chloride, and they are also considerably stabilized by electrostatic binding. Furthermore, they are strong bases: this proton affinity presumably implies that they are strong σ-donors. Now whereas the structure of cyanide as a ligand permits it to be a strong σ-donor and π-acceptor at the same time, cyclopentadienide exercises these two functions best in different geometries. The stability of the sandwich structure is then an indication of the relative strength of σ- and π-bonding. At the end of the transition series the σ-bonding dominates. Earlier in the series the situation is confused by the electrostatic term which favours the same sandwich structure as π-bonding. For example, this structure occurs in the magnesium and uranium compounds. As the electrostatic model favours the sandwich structure, great caution is necessary in the discussion of the relative stabilities of the orbitals shown in Fig. 27.10.

Perhaps the simplest way of discussing the stability of cyclopentadienyl compounds is to treat them from the ionic point of view as $M^{2+}Cp_2^-$, i.e. as cyclopentadienides. As M changes from a pre-transition to a B metal, a steady fall in heat of formation is expected as for a halide (Chapter 12). Superimposed on this fall is the effect of π-bonding. The data on the carbonyls and on the cyanides (Fig. 25.29) show that this produces strong increments in stability from the d^3 to the d^8 cations. Thus the heats of formation of cyclopentadienide compounds conform to the pattern given in Fig. 27.9. Comparison with the halide data (Chapter 12) explains why a usual preparative method for bis-π-cyclopentadienyl compounds is the reaction of a metal halide with sodium cyclopentadienide,

$$2Na^+Cp^- + MCl_2 \rightarrow MCp_2 + 2Na^+Cl^-.$$

It also explains why when iron(II) chloride is added to any *ionic* cyclopentadienide it gives ferrocene. This reaction has been used diagnostically. Thus iron(II) chloride reacts rapidly with manganese *bis*-cyclopentadienyl giving ferrocene and $MnCl_2$. It may be that because of the high spin-pairing energy in Mn(II), d^5, manganese *bis*-cyclopentadienyl should be termed 'ionic'. It is quite probable too that there should be a dip in the plot of stability against atomic number (Fig. 27.9) at $MnCp_2$, just as a dip is observed in the stability of the cyanides (Fig. 25.29).

27.4. Compounds with saturated ligands

For metals in the middle and towards the end of the transition series, low oxidation states are stabilized mainly by unsaturated ligands such as benzene, carbon monoxide, and cyanide. At the beginning of the transition series, low oxidation states are stabilized not so much by these ligands as by easily polarizable groups such as iodide, sulphide, and phosphorus- and arsenic-containing ligands. Even at the end of the transition series these ligands are moderately effective in the stabilization of low oxidation states. Presumably the difference between the ligands lies in their different σ-bonding capabilities.

Hydride and carbanions such as CH_3^- also form important compounds with low oxidation states, but are only able to form σ-bonds. With metals at the beginning of a transition series, their compounds are like pre-transition 'ionic' hydrides, while later in the series they become more closely related to the σ-bonded hydrides of B-subgroup elements. Most frequently their compounds also contain unsaturated ligands which are good π-acceptors, such as carbon monoxide, cyclopentadienyl, and phosphine derivatives. Typical series of such mixed compounds are the carbonyl hydrides and alkyls. It is not unlikely that a major stabilization in these compounds is due to the *cis*-effect, the strong donor character of the one ligand being transmitted to the π-acceptor orbitals of the other through a perpendicular interaction (Fig. 29.9).

σ-BONDED ALKYL ORGANOMETALLIC COMPOUNDS

The reaction of transition-metal halides, particularly the iodide, with methyllithium or a Grignard compound such as phenyl magnesium iodide yields a σ-bonded alkyl or aryl. Compounds which have been prepared in this way are tetramethyltitanium and diphenylmanganese. Many organometallic compounds are known in which the metal is σ-bonded to carbon and also bound to π-bonding ligands, for example carbonyls and complexes of phosphine and cyclopentadienyl. Provided that the metal complexes are handled in organic solvents, normally in the absence of oxygen as well as water, it would appear that σ-bonded transition-metal carbon compounds can be readily prepared. A few organometallic compounds can also be prepared in aqueous media. Thus a dichloromethyl compound is formed by the direct reaction of chromium(II) chloride with chloroform,

$$CHCl_3 + 2Cr^{2+} + 10H_2O \rightarrow [Cr(H_2O)_5CHCl_2]^{2+} + [Cr(H_2O)_5Cl]^{2+},$$

and $[Co(CN)_5(C_6H_5CH_2)]^{3-}$ from $[Co(CN)_5H]^{3-}$ and $C_6H_5CH_2Br$. Direct reaction in water of alkyl iodide with the Co(I) oxidation state of vitamin B_{12} yields a metal-alkyl bond as in the B_{12} coenzyme analogues (Fig. 27.12). The use of heavily substituted phenyl compounds has produced novel stereochemistries and spin states for a number of metals with σ-bonded carbon ligands. The iron compound, $Fe(C_6Cl_5)_2(PR_3)_2$, has two unpaired electrons and is thought to be square coplanar.

HYDRIDES OF TRANSITION-METAL COMPLEXES

Although few pure hydrides or alkyls of transition metals are known, hydride and alkyl groups are common in mixed complexes. The formulae of some typical hydrides are:

Fe	Ru	Os	$X_nMY_4H_{(2-n)}$	'octahedral'
Co	Rh	Ir	$X_nMY_3H_{(3-n)}$	'octahedral'
(Ni) ?	Pd	Pt	XMY_2H	square planar

where X is a halide ion and Y is an unsaturated ligand such as PEt_3, CO, or CN^-. It is most convenient to regard hydrogen as H^- in all these mixed complexes. There are now more than 100 such compounds known,

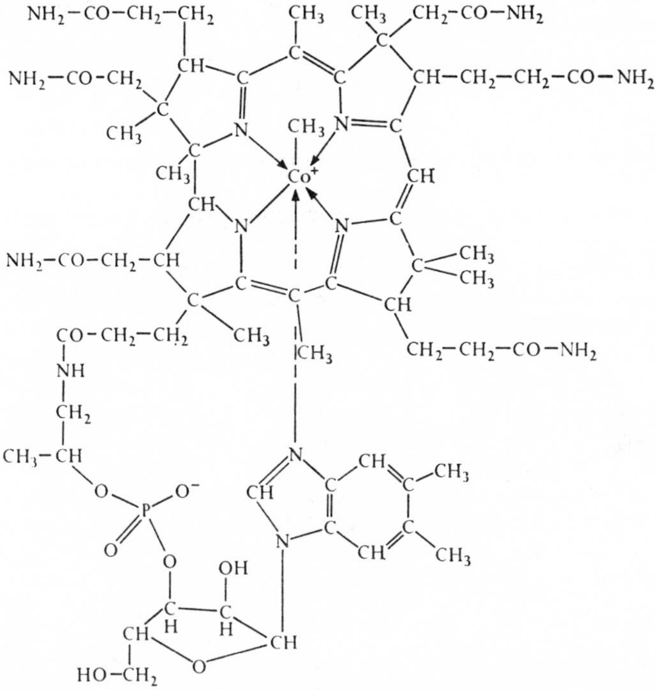

FIG. 27.12. The methyl analogue of coenzyme B_{12} (after Hodgkin and co-workers).

see, for example, Table 27.x. As usual the compounds of Ni, Pd, and Pt do not obey the 18-electron rule. The stability of the M—H bond, as judged by its thermal stability, is Pt > Pd > Ni, which is the same as the order of strengths of the M-alkyl bond in complexes such as $RM(PR_3)_2X$, where X is a halogen and R an alkyl or aryl. (Note that the M-alkyl bond can be thought of as M^+—Alk^-.)

TABLE 27.x. *Some metal hydride derivatives*

Group VIA	VIIA	VIIIa	VIIIb	VIIIc
	$HMn(CO)_5$	$H_2Fe(CO)_4$	$HCo(CO)_4$	
			$[HCo(CN)_5]^{3-}$	
		$HRuCl(CO)(PPh_3)_3$	$HRhCl_2(AsMePh_2)_2$	$HPdCl(PPh_3)_2$
H_2WCp_2	$HReCp_2$	$HOsCl(CO)(PPh_3)_3$	$HIrCl(SbPh_3)_3$	$HPtBr[P(C_2H_5)_3]_2$
	$[H_9Re]^{2-}$			
	$H_3Re(PPh_3)_2$			

The definitive electronic distribution of the M—H bond is unknown and discussion has been confused by the following apparently contradictory facts.

(1) The hydride derivatives are coplanar but not quite square, for the groups adjacent to the hydrogen are bent towards it

$$X—Pt\underset{Y}{\overset{Y}{\diagdown}}H.$$

Thus the Pt—H bond has the opposite stereochemical effect from a lone pair of electrons.

(2) The dipole moment apparently indicates a strong shift of negative charge towards the platinum, i.e. $H^+—Pt^-$ *not* $H^-—Pt^+$.

(3) The proton nuclear magnetic resonance spectra indicate a very high diamagnetic screening of the hydrogen, which can mean that the proton is either in a region of high electron density or of a paramagnetic centre. High diamagnetic screening suggests the formulation $H^-—Pt^+$. However, more sophisticated theory, which takes into account the temperature-independent paramagnetism of the Pt, suggests that the NMR result may indicate very little about the electron density near the hydrogen. The method is incidentally the most powerful known for the detection of metal-hydrogen bonds.

(4) The spectroscopic d–d transitions of some central cations, e.g. Pt, bound to H show that H as a ligand produces as strong a splitting, Δ, as any other ligand. The next greatest fields are provided by CH_3^-, CO, and CN^-. However, in some other hydrides hydrogen appears to be as weak a ligand as water.

It could well be that the Pt—H (and Pt—C(alkyl)) bonds are best regarded just as very strong σ-bonds. (This view would cover points (1), (2), and (4).) It is likely that the negative charge carried by the hydrogen is greater in compounds with elements at the beginning of transition series than at the end, and perhaps the case of hydrogen as a ligand is one where the electron distribution is very dependent upon the atom to which it is bound. Recently a neutron diffraction study of $[ReH_9]^{2-}$ has shown the Re—H bond length to be that expected for a normal covalent bond.

27.5. Reactivity and Structures

FACTORS CONTROLLING REACTIVITY

The reaction mechanisms of simple non-metal compounds of carbon, boron, and nitrogen have been discussed in Chapter 10. Chapter 29 will describe and analyse the reaction mechanisms of the transition-metal compounds containing simple ligands such as H_2O, NH_3, and Cl^- and metals in formal valence states of 2 or 3. In this section the reactions of the organometallic compounds of the transition metals are described, for it would appear that special mechanisms must be proposed in order to account for their peculiarities. As stressed in Chapter 10, the mechanism of a reaction is often controlled by the ease with which a compound can go into a new stereochemical configuration. For tetrahedral carbon compounds reactions occur via a 3- or 5-coordinate transition state while for the octahedral transition-metal compounds the change is to either a 5- or 7-coordinate transition state. Slowness of reaction is then related to the relatively high stability of the ground-state stereochemistry. In organometallic compounds of transition metals some of the structures generate low-lying excited states just as in the case of the metal arenes; see Fig. 27.10. Thus although both $[Co(NH_3)_6]^{3+}$ and $[Cr(benzene)_2]$ obey the 18-electron rule they do not have equal kinetic stability. Similarly the CH_3 in M—CH_3 need not be very like that in CH_3Cl, for in M—CH_3 the carbon carries negative charge which may well make a 5-coordinate carbon system relatively stable. Thus inspection of the structures of some organometallic compounds shows that both metal and carbon readily accept unorthodox stereochemistries.

UNORTHODOX STRUCTURES†

The stereochemistry of the carbon atoms will be considered first. High coordination is *usual* for carbon in the carbides of transition metals, or, for that matter, for nitrogen in nitrides and for boron in some borides (Chapter 17). Most organic compounds are written with carbon atoms forming four bonds, but in combination with metals and especially transition metals carbon can form five or six 'bonds'. Fig. 27.13 shows the structure of $Fe_5C(CO)_{15}$. The carbon atom is here surrounded by five iron atoms, of which four (B) in a plane are equivalent. In some metal methyls, such as those of beryllium, indium, and aluminium (section 33.6), carbon also appears to form five 'bonds' to its neighbours.

The structure of the ethylene compounds of platinum has been given in Fig. 27.5. The structure is regarded as being formed from an orthodox ethylene molecule acting as σ-donor to the platinum. However, platinum orbitals can also overlap the antibonding orbitals of the carbon so that it is legitimate to look upon the structure as containing a 5-bonded carbon of unorthodox stereochemistry (Fig. 27.14). The PtC_2 system may be regarded as a 3-membered ring. All the unsaturated molecules which form complexes with the transition metals can be considered in this unorthodox manner by giving greater weight to what are normally called the σ-bonds

† The formula of $(CO)_5WC(Ph)OMe$ suggests that there is a double bond between a carbon atom and a metal.

than to the π-bonds. For example, the bonding in dibenzenechromium or ferrocene is usually written so as to maintain the orthodox orbitals of the ring systems. The advantage in adopting a different set of equivalent

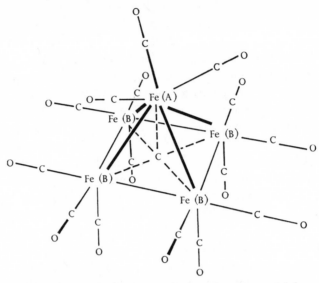

FIG. 27.13. The structure of Fe$_5$C(CO)$_{15}$ (after Braye, Dahl, Hübel, and Wampler, *J. Am. Chem. Soc.*, 1962, **84**, 4633).

FIG. 27.14. The PtC$_2$ 3-membered ring.

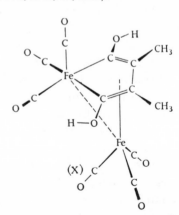

FIG. 27.15. The structure of Fe$_2$(CO)$_6$C$_6$H$_8$O$_2$ (after Hock and Mills, *Proc. Chem. Soc.*, 1958, 233).

orbitals is that they give a different impression of the stable geometric requirements around the carbon.

For still more complicated structures in which more than one metal atom is involved, a complete failure of bond prediction is apparent. Fig. 27.15 gives the structure of $Fe_2(CO)_6C_6H_8O_2$, written so as to maintain the conventional bonds of carbon. However, the CO group labelled X does not form a linear M—C—O set of atoms, and it is not altogether clear how the bonding between the lower iron atom and the ring is to be described.

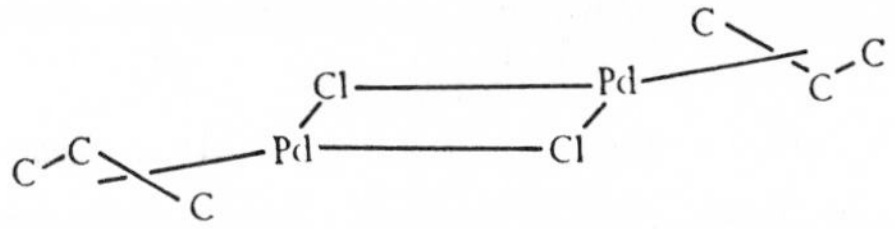

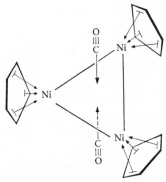

FIG. 27.16. The structure of $[PdCl(C_3H_5)]_2$ (after Rowe, *Proc. Chem. Soc.*, 1962, 66).

FIG. 27.17. The structure of $Ni_3(\pi\text{-}Cp)_3(CO)_2$ (after Hock and Mills, *Advances in the Chemistry of Coordination Compounds*, ed. Kirschner, p. 640, Macmillan, New York, 1961).

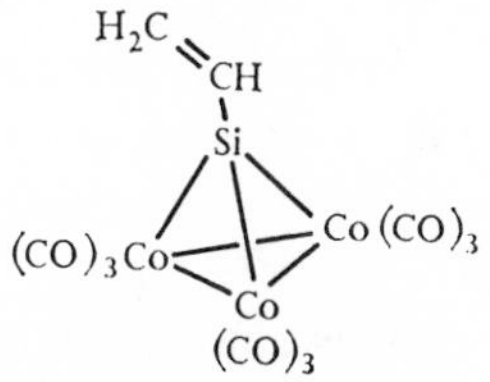

FIG. 27.18. The proposed structure of $Co_3(CO)_9(SiC_2H_3)$ (after Kettle and Khan, *Proc. Chem. Soc.*, 1962, 82).

Another example of this kind is the structure of the π-allyl complex, $[PdCl(C_3H_5)]_2$. In this molecule (Fig. 27.16) the double bond is delocalized in the π-allyl residue. Although the allyl group could be regarded as bound in much the same way as cyclopentadienyl, the structure may also be written with simple σ-bonds from the metal to the terminal carbon atoms, so losing the orthodox impression of the carbon atom bound only by four bonds. In some structures a choice can be made between maintaining 8 electrons around carbon or 18 electrons around the metal. One of the two rules associated with these numbers must then be broken. A further example is the nickel carbonyl derivative illustrated in Fig. 27.17, which is in no sense a case of an orthodox carbon compound. It is certain that many more compounds of this kind will be synthesized in the near future. It would appear that the conventional idea of the behaviour of a 'tetrahedral' carbon atom has restricted utility when carbon is bound to metallic elements. Other non-metallic elements, particularly H, B, N, Si, (Al), P, and S can also be expected to behave anomalously when bound to metals. An example of a proposed structure is given in Fig. 27.18: other compounds such as $K[OsO_3N]$ have been very little studied as yet.

While the above discussion has stressed the peculiarities of the carbon atom bound to a metal, the geometry around the metal itself must not be overlooked. In, for example, the palladium-π-allyl (Fig. 27.16) in which the double bond is delocalized, the idea of four coplanar bonds from the metal could be abandoned in favour of 5-coordination to three carbon atoms and two chlorides. Inspection of Figs. 27.12 to 27.17 shows that the binding of the metal in these complexes cannot be interpreted with the same simple picture of the coordinate bond as works quite well in other complexes.

In most of these compounds the positions of the hydrogen atoms have not been determined. In metal hydrides such as ZrH_2, the hydrogen sits in a tetrahedral hole (Chapter 11). In electron-deficient hydrides, hydrogen atoms sit between two atoms of intermediate electronegativity, e.g. B, Be, or Al. Transition metals are of comparable electronegativity with these elements, and evidence is accumulating which shows that hydrogen may be shared between a transition metal and a non-metal such as carbon or boron. Thus $(\pi\text{-Cp})Co(C_5H_6)$ probably has the structure (A), where a hydrogen is somewhat bonded to the cobalt, and $Ti(\pi\text{-Cp})_2BH_4$ has the structure (B). $[Cr_2(CO)_{10}H]^-$ and $[Fe(CO)_{11}H]^-$ both have bridging H atoms. As unusual stereochemistries are often being found in the same compound for hydrogen, metal, and carbon it is not surprising that the reactions of these compounds are forming a new branch of chemistry.

(A)   (B)

NOVEL REACTIONS OF ORGANOMETALLIC COMPOUNDS

The reactions at a carbon atom will be considered first. Perhaps the simplest reaction is the rearrangement from a σ-bonded carbon to a π-bonded carbon and its reverse. Ethyl manganese pentacarbonyl undergoes the reversible reaction

$$(CO)_5Mn\text{---}CH_2CH_3 \underset{+H^-}{\overset{-H^-}{\rightleftarrows}} \left[(CO)_5Mn \leftarrow \overset{CH_2}{\underset{CH_2}{\|}}\right]^+$$

Hydride removal is brought about by triphenylcarbonium borontetra-fluoride, $Ph_3C^+BF_4^-$, and hydride addition by borohydride. On the other hand, the reaction of ethylene with Hg^{2+} in alkali yields $Hg^{2+}.\overline{C}H_2CH_2OH$. The relative stability of the σ-bonded and π-bonded systems derived from ethylene is controlled by the two very different metals. Generally the metal atoms later in a transition series increasingly favour σ-bonding.

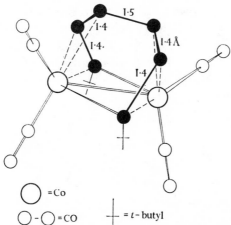

○ = Co 　 ○-○ = CO 　 ╀ = t-butyl

FIG. 27.19. The structure of $Co_2(CO)_4(C_2HBu^t)_2(C_2H_2)$ (after Mills and Robinson, *Proc. Chem. Soc.*, 1964, 187).

An example of a catalysed polymerization is the effect of Ph_3Cr(tetra-hydrofuran)$_3$ on substituted acetylenes yielding hexa-substituted benzenes. If the phenyl groups are replaced by alkyls, the alkyl may be incorporated in the polymerizing acetylene so that 5- or 6-membered rings are produced.

$$Cr\,(Me\,)_3 + C_2\,R_2 \longrightarrow$$

$$Cr\,(Et\,)_3 + C_2\,R_2 \longrightarrow$$

The preparation of 1,2-di-t-butyl benzene, which is difficult by conventional methods because of steric hindrance, can be achieved by Br_2 oxidation of $Co_2(CO)_4(C_2HBu^t)_2(C_2H_2)$. The structure of this complex (Fig. 27.19) shows that the required six carbon chain is already present but not as a ring. The chain intermediate is of the π-allyl type at each end.

The frequent rearrangement of compounds formed from combinations of saturated alkyl and unsaturated conjugated compounds to give π-allyl complexes such as that mentioned above suggests that these complexes are particularly stable. One reason for the high stability of the complexes could be their polarity, the π-allyl group taking on negative charge. The charge itself will also make the groups reactive, so that on leaving the metal atom they readily undergo polymerization, ring closure, or hydride abstraction (see above). The particular course of the reaction is controlled by the nature of the central metal atom and of the other groups attached to it. Thus the two compounds NiR_2 and PdR_2, $R = \pi$-allyl, react differently with butadiene:

$$NiR_2 + C_4H_6 \longrightarrow$$

$$PdR_2 + C_4H_6 \longrightarrow$$

and whereas $[(C_6H_{11})_3P]_2Ni(\text{propylene})$ can be prepared, $[(C_6H_5)_3P]_2$ $Ni(\text{propylene})$ cannot. An example showing that the nature of the ring or chain compound finally produced is under the control of the ligands is provided by the observations that (1) one gram of $Ni(1:5:9$ cyclododeca-triene) catalyses the reaction of butadiene to $1:5:9$ cyclododecatriene (at the rate of a kilogram/hour), but (2) the addition of substituted phosphine to the reaction mixture diverts the butadiene to $1:5$ cyclooctadiene. The nature of the intermediate in these reactions is very likely to be a π-allyl complex, for $RuCl_2(C_{12}H_{18})$ has been isolated and its crystal structure shows a C_{12} chain with a central double bond and two terminal allyl residues (Fig. 27.20). This is very like the C_6 intermediate of Fig. 27.19.

The novel reactions of these organometallic compounds must be seen, of course, against the background of their more conventional chemistry such as is illustrated in Fig. 27.21.

For comparison with Fig. 27.21, Fig. 27.22 illustrates some of the relatively simple substitution reactions of $Fe(CO)_5$. Many of the reactions are general to other carbonyls. Interest here will centre on the novel incorporations of CO rather than on these substitutions. For example, the compound of stoicheiometry $Co(CO)_4(CH_3)$ is found to be an equilibrium mixture of $CH_3Co(CO)_4$ and $CH_3COCo(CO)_3$. Here a CO group is readily inserted between a σ-bonded methyl and a metal atom. The

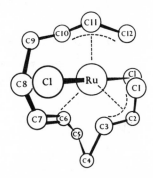

FIG. 27.20. The structure of $RuCl_2(C_{12}H_{18})$ (after Lydon, Nicholson, Shaw, and Truter, *Proc. Chem. Soc.*, 1964, 421).

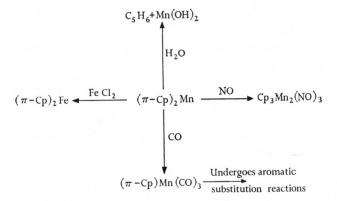

FIG. 27.21. Substitution reactions of $Mn(\pi\text{-}Cp)_2$.

equilibration provides some evidence that the insertion is an internal rearrangement, and this is confirmed by the following reaction

$$Fe(Cp)(CO)_2(CH_3) + PPh_3 \rightarrow Fe(Cp)(CO)(COCH_3)(PPh_3),$$

and by the fact that labelled (^{14}C) CO of $CH_3Mn(CO)_5$ has been shown to be incorporated in an acetyl group in the reaction with unlabelled CO,

$$CH_3Mn(\overset{*}{C}O)_5 + CO \rightarrow CH_3\overset{*}{C}OMn(\overset{*}{C}O)_4CO.$$

A comparable reaction is the exchange of CO between CO(gas) and acetic anhydride in the presence of $Co_2(CO)_8$. The incorporation can involve

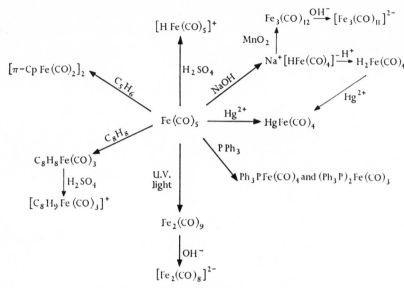

FIG. 27.22. Substitution reactions of $Fe(CO)_5$.

atoms other than carbon and lead to cyclic compounds as follows

The reaction of carbonyls with unsaturated aliphatic compounds, especially acetylenes, leads to more complex reactions. A typical example is the reaction of iron carbonyls with $RC{\equiv}CR$. Some of the products of this reaction appear to be:

The compound $Fe_5C(CO)_{15}$ (Fig. 27.13) is also formed in this reaction. The products include molecules formed by the reaction of C_2R_2 with itself, Fe, and CO.

The products of the reaction of the hydride $[HFe(CO)_4]^-$ with $RC\equiv CR$ are rather different. Amongst them is $Fe_2(CO)_6C_6H_8O_2$ shown in Fig. 27.15.

REACTIONS OF HYDRIDES

It is possible to hydrogenate, mainly with reagents such as borohydrides, a large number of carbonyls, cyclopentadienyls, etc. The attack of H^- may be on the metal or the ligand as in such reactions as

$$[(Cp)Fe(CO)_3]^+ + BH_4^- \rightarrow (Cp)FeH(CO)_2$$

and

$$[(Cp)Fe(CO)_2PPh_3]^+ + BH_4^- \rightarrow (CpH)Fe(CO)_2PPh_3.$$

Direct attack of hydrogen itself is unusual but occurs in, for example,

$$Co_2(CO)_8 + H_2 \rightarrow 2Co(CO)_4H.$$

The attack on the metal or on the ligand is under the control of the further ligands as above or of the metal, e.g.

$$[M(C_5H_5)_2]^+ + H^- \rightarrow M(C_5H_5)(C_5H_6) \quad M = Co \text{ or } Rh,$$

$$[M(C_5H_5)_2]^{2+} + 2H^- \rightarrow MH_2(C_5H_5)_2 \quad M = Mo \text{ or } W.$$

The catalytic action of cobalt carbonyl in the reaction of olefins, hydrogen, and carbon monoxide to give largely RCHO, ROH, and RCOR is an outstanding example of the numerous reactions which one molecule can bring about. The reaction has been called the Fischer–Tropsch or 'oxo'-synthesis, but is now more generally called hydroformylation. The first step of the reaction path is the formation of $HCo(CO)_4$ which then reacts as follows

$$HCo(CO)_4 + R_2C{=}CH_2 \rightleftharpoons R_2CHCH_2.Co(CO)_4$$

$$Co_2(CO)_8 + R_2CHCH_2CHO \xleftarrow[CO]{H_2} R_2CHCH_2CO.Co(CO)_3$$

The aldehyde can also be reduced in the reaction by the path

$$RCH{=}O$$
$$\downarrow$$
$$RCHO + HCo(CO)_4 \longrightarrow HCo(CO)_3 + CO$$
$$\downarrow +HCo(CO)_4$$
$$RCH_2OH + Co_2(CO)_8$$

The postulated intermediate is effectively isoelectronic with ethylene or O_2 complexes.

Many of the above examples have been taken from the carbonyls of metals of the first transition series. Mixed complexes of the kind described

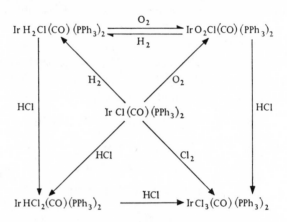

FIG. 27.23. Substitution reactions of IrClCO(PPh₃)₂ (after Vaska).

in the early sections of this chapter in which there are several ligands, and complexes of metals of the second transition series also give rise to novel reactive species. Thus Fig. 27.23 shows how chlorine, hydrogen, and oxygen (Fig. 27.7) can exchange places around iridium.

The examples given in this section have shown that the products of reactions of organometallic complexes can depend on very minor adjustments in the electronegativity of and steric hindrance around the atoms. The electronegativity of the metal is easily controlled by change of oxidation state or change of coordination partners. Very sensitive control of the reactions is thus theoretically possible. It could well be that biological systems have already developed such modified organometallic catalysts for there is a vast realm of iron-porphyrin and cobalt-corrin complexes, in which a great variety of additional ligands are bound to the metal. It is not yet clear how these catalysts work, although for both the porphyrins and corrins it has been postulated that the methene carbon bridges are activated by the metal ions and that groups are transferred from the metal to the non-metal quite readily. In one molecule (B_{12}) there is a 2-electron redox system and a readily produced carbanion (corrin complexes), while in Fe(III) complexes 1-electron shifts between the organic ring and the inorganic central atom are extremely plausible.

Problems

1. 'Although CO forms many complexes with low-valence transition metals, it does not do so with the halides of Al and B which are strong Lewis acids.' Comment.

2. How may the diamagnetism of $Fe_2(CO)_9$ be accounted for?

3. The 'normal' CO stretching frequency in a carbonyl such as $Ni(CO)_4$ is at $\sim$ 2050 cm^{-1}, while that of an organic CO as in acetone is at a considerably lower frequency, $\sim$ 1700 cm^{-1}. How does this information help in the prediction of structural features of the following carbonyls from their C—O stretching frequencies (cm^{-1})?

$Fe_2(CO)_9$	2082, 2019, 1829
$Co_2(CO)_8$	2070, 2043, 2025, 1858
$[Co(CO)_3]_x$	2067, 2087, 1866
$Fe_2(\pi\text{-}Cp)_2(CO)_4$	2054, 2005, 1958, 1786
$Mn_2(CO)_{10}$	2068, 2039, 2006
$[Ru(CO)_2I_2]_n$	2050, 1995

4. Show that the following compounds all conform to the 18-electron rule:
$Fe(CO)_5$, $Cr(CO)_6$, $(C_5H_5)Mn(CO)_3$, $(C_5H_5)V(CO)_4$, $Fe(CO)_2(NO)_2$, $Cr(R_3P)_3(CO)_3$, $Co(CO)_3NO$, $Cr(C_6H_6)_2$.

5. Suggest why it is that low oxidation states of the transition metals tend to be produced in combination with the following ligands:
CO (especially), CN^-, RNC, aromatic nitrogen heterocycles (e.g. dipyridyl), PR_3 and AsR_3, 'aromatic' hydrocarbons (e.g. benzene, cyclopentadienide), acetylenes, olefins, acetylides.

6. Explain why it is that arsines are more effective than amines in stabilizing the lower oxidation states of the transition metals.

7. Acetylene has a stretching frequency around 2000 cm^{-1} while that of ethylene is at 1650 cm^{-1}. What can be deduced about the structure of the complex $Pt(PPh_3)_2(RC\equiv CR')$ for which the C—C stretching frequency is at 1700 cm^{-1}?

8. For the reaction $Ni(s) + 4CO(g) \rightarrow Ni(CO)_4(g)$ at 25 °C, $\Delta G° = -5.8$ kcal mole^{-1}, and $\Delta S° = -99.3$ cal deg^{-1} mole^{-1}. Calculate the equilibrium constant K_p at 25°, and estimate what it would be at 140°. Comment on your results.

9. The mean dissociation energies for the process $M(CO)_6(g) \rightarrow M(g) +$ $6CO(g)$ have been computed as 30 kcal mole^{-1} for $Cr(CO)_6$, 36 kcal mole^{-1} for $Mo(CO)_6$, and 42 kcal mole^{-1} for $W(CO)_6$. Comment.

10. Replacement of CO in $Ni(CO)_4$ to give $Ni(PCl_3)_4$ or $Ni(CO)_3SbCl_3$ takes place with the trihalides of P and Sb, but not with those of N or with the pentahalides of P and Sb. Comment.

11. PF_3 forms more stable complexes with Ni in the zero oxidation state than does $P(CH_3)_3$. Comment.

12. Metal–metal bonds in carbonyls are often shorter than metal-atom diameters in pure metals. How can you explain this?

13. The monocyclopentadienyl carbonyls of the transition metals are usually dimeric for even atomic number elements and monomeric for odd atomic number elements. Why?

14. It has been suggested that in organometallic compounds the ligands should be classified according to the number of 'bonds' they are thought to form and thence the number of electrons they donate to the central cation: CH_3 is a 1-electron ligand, ethylene a 2-electron ligand, benzene is a 6-electron ligand. Classify the compounds in the different sections of this chapter using the above scheme.

15. In general what are the differences between charged ligands such as CN^- and Cp^- and the uncharged ligands such as CO, RNC, and C_6H_6?

16. The Pt—H stretching frequencies in *trans*-$(PEt_3)_2PtHX$ are

X =	NO^-	Cl^-	Br^-	I^-	NO_2^-	SCN^-	CN^-	
	2242	2183	2178	2156	2150	2112	2041	cm^{-1}

Comment upon the relationship of the *trans*-effect to the spectrochemical series (section 24.5).

17. The NMR hyperfine structure of the proton resonance absorption shows that coupling between the nuclear spin of the proton and that of a *trans* ^{31}P in $HM(PEt_3)X_2$ is three to four times greater than in the *cis* compound. Comment upon this fact.

18. Discuss the acid dissociation constants (moles litre^{-1}) in water of the following hydrides

$$HCo(CO)_4 \sim 1; \quad HMn(CO)_5 \sim 10^{-7}; \quad HCo(CO)_3PR_3 \sim 10^{-7}.$$

19. $Ni(CO)_4$ is tetrahedral, while $Ni(CN)_4^{2-}$ is planar, yet both are diamagnetic. Comment.

20. Suggest in molecular-orbital terms the possible electronic structures of:

$(Cp_2Co)^+$, $(Benzene_2.Fe)^{2+}$, $Ni(PCl_3)_4$, $Cr(CO)_4(PPh_3)_2$.

21. $MnCp_2$ is paramagnetic with five unpaired spins. Deduce a possible energy-level diagram for this compound corresponding to Fig. 27.10.

22. How would you expect the energy-level diagram for ferrocene to differ from that for $Cr(benzene)_2$?

23. Oxygen is known to be bound as $\overset{O}{\underset{O}{\|}} \to Ir$ in $Ir(CO)(PR_3)_2(Cl)O_2$. Discuss the bonding orbitals. Why are oxygen complexes generally less stable than those of ethylene?

24. Perfluoro compounds, e.g. CF_3I and C_6F_5I, are much used in the preparation of organometallic compounds of transition metals. What advantages have they over simple hydrocarbon derivatives?

25. The order of thermal stability is apparently $M-CF_3 > M-COCH_3 > M-C_6H_5 > M-CH_3$. What explanations can you offer for this order?

26. Discuss possible mechanisms for the following reaction sequence:

$NaMn(CO)_5 + ClCH_2CH=CH_2 \to \sigma\text{-allyl-}Mn(CO)_5$

$$\xrightarrow[\text{ultra-violet radiation}]{\text{heat or}} \pi\text{-allyl-}Mn(CO)_4.$$

27. What explanation can you offer for the observation that the $C=C$ stretching frequency is at 1650 cm^{-1} in free ethylene and at $\sim 1500 \text{ cm}^{-1}$ in the ethylene complexes of transition metals? A similar reduction in the $C=O$ stretching frequency is observed between $(CH_3)_2CO$ and $M-CO-CH_3$ compounds. Does the same explanation apply?

28. How could you demonstrate whether or not cyclopentadienyl, ethylene, and benzene groups can rotate in organometallic compounds?

29. What can you deduce from the fact that the NMR spectrum of some metal allyls, i.e. $(CH_2CHCH_2)MR_n$, shows that four H-atoms are equivalent, with the fifth H atom different from the others?

30. Discuss the nature of the bonding in such structures as those given in Figs. 27.13 and 27.15.

Bibliography

M. A. BENNETT, 'Olefin and Acetylene Complexes of Transition Metals', *Chem. Rev.*, 1962, **62**, 611.

J. CHATT, P. L. PAUSON, and L. M. VENANZI, Metal Carbonyls and Related Compounds, *Organometallic Chemistry*, Am. Chem. Soc. Monograph No. 147, p. 468, 1960.

F. A. COTTON, *Chemical Applications of Group Theory*, Interscience, New York, 1963, pp. 117–82.

D. P. CRAIG and R. S. NYHOLM, The Nature of the Metal-Ligand Bond, *Chelating Agents and Metal Chelates*, ed. F. P. Dwyer and D. P. Mellor, Academic Press, 1964.

E. O. FISCHER and H. P. FRITZ, Compounds of Aromatic Ring Systems and Metals, *Advances in Inorganic Chemistry and Radiochemistry*, vol. 1, ed. H. J. Eméleus and A. G. Sharpe, Academic Press, New York, 1959.

M. L. H. GREEN and D. J. JONES, Hydride-Complexes of Transition Metals, *Advances in Inorganic Chemistry and Radiochemistry*, vol. 7, ed. H. J. Eméleus and A. G. Sharpe, Academic Press, New York, 1965.

W. P. GRIFFITH, 'Cyanide Complexes of the Transition Metals', *Quart. Rev. Chem. Soc.*, 1962, **16**, 188.

R. G. GUY and B. L. SHAW, Olefin, Acetylene, and π-Allylic Complexes of Transition Metals, *Advances in Inorganic Chemistry and Radiochemistry*, vol. 4, ed. H. J. Eméleus and A. G. Sharpe, Academic Press, New York, 1962.

R. B. KING *Transition-Metal Compounds*, vol. 1 of *Organometallic Syntheses*, ed. J. J. Eisch, Academic Press, New York, 1965.

J. LEWIS, 'Transition-Metal–Nitric Oxide Complexes', *Sci. Prog.*, 1959, **47**, 506.

L. MALATESTA, Isocyanide Complexes of Metals, *Progress in Inorganic Chemistry*, vol. 1, ed. F. A. Cotton, Interscience, New York, 1959.

R. NAST, *Complex Acetylides of Transition Metals*, Special Publication No. 13, Chemical Society, London, 1959.

D. SEYFORTH, Vinyl Compounds of Metals, *Progress in Inorganic Chemistry*, vol. 3, ed. F. A. Cotton, Interscience, New York, 1962.

H. W. STERNBERG and I. WENDER, *Metal Carbonyls and Related Compounds as Catalytic Intermediates in Organic Syntheses*, Special Publication No. 13, Chemical Society, London, 1959.

L. M. VENANZI, 'Complexes of Tetradentate Ligands containing Phosphorus and Arsenic', *Angew. Chem.* Int. Ed. 1964, **3**, 453.

G. WILKINSON and F. A. COTTON, Cyclopentadienyl and Arene Metal Compounds, *Progress in Inorganic Chemistry*, vol. 1, ed. F. A. Cotton, Interscience, New York 1959.

28 · Transition Metals: Electronic Spectra and Magnetism

28.1. Introduction

This chapter is in some measure a continuation of Chapter 24 A, for the theoretical treatment is centred on the effects of the ligand field on atomic energy levels. Much of the theory is difficult. It is also highly specialized, and the reader who is little interested in spectroscopic and magnetic properties can pass directly on to Chapter 29. However, these properties not only have intrinsic interest but their interpretation also helps to increase our understanding of the thermodynamic and kinetic properties of transition-metal compounds. Magnetic properties are closely dependent on the nature of states very close in energy to the ground state but spectroscopic properties depend upon differences between the ground and excited states. Thermodynamic properties belong to the ground states. Kinetic properties are controlled by differences between the ground states and the transition states of the reactions. These transition states can sometimes be related to the excited states observed in spectroscopy, and in this way spectroscopic observations may provide a greater insight into kinetics than thermodynamics.

MAJOR INTERACTION ENERGIES

The main concern of this chapter is the description of the energy states of atoms or ions with incomplete d sub-shells. Knowledge about the ground states of the sub-shells can be obtained from the study of magnetic properties, and knowledge about the differences between the ground and the excited states from spectroscopic transitions involving internal rearrangements of the d^n electrons within the incomplete d sub-shell. Such rearrangements are associated with changes in the energy of the atom or ion. The major energies to be considered are: (1) The interaction of the electrons with the nucleus from which they are incompletely screened by the inner shells. This energy and its dependence on penetration have been discussed in Chapter 23. (2) The electron–electron repulsions. (3) The energy of the coupling of the magnetic moments due to the spin and the orbital angular momenta of the electrons. For rearrangement of the d^n electrons within the d sub-shell, it is often assumed as a first approximation that energy (1) is unchanged so that the study of d–d spectroscopic transitions gives evidence about electron–electron repulsion and spin-orbit coupling. The differences in the repulsion for different states of one d^n configuration may be expressed in terms of two Racah parameters, B and C. The spin-orbit coupling energy is given by a third one-electron parameter, ζ. Information about these parameters may also be obtained from magnetic measurements. The properties of gaseous ions will be examined first: their energy levels show clearly how the two energies, (2) and (3), depend on the specific atom considered (nuclear charge) and on the ionization state of that atom.

In any d^n *configuration* all the electrons have $l = 2$. Each electron is distinguished by (a) its spin, s, which can have the values $\frac{1}{2}$ or $-\frac{1}{2}$, and (b) the orientation of l in space, i.e. m_l (see Chapter 1) which can have values $+2, +1, 0, -1$, and -2. In nearly all the atoms and ions which we shall consider electron–electron repulsions are more important than spin-orbit interactions. In such cases it is convenient to consider first the splitting of the configuration into *terms*† characterized by (a) the sum, S, of individual s values, and (b) the vector sum, L, of the l values. These terms are labelled

$$^{(2S+1)}L,$$

where $2S+1$ is called the *multiplicity*. As a result of spin-orbit coupling, each term is split further; the resulting states may be labelled by use of J values. Each J value corresponds to a possible vector addition of S and L, so that the total number of J values for one term is the same as the multiplicity, or $2L+1$ if $S > L$. This method of deriving labels for the possible energy states is known as Russell–Saunders or LS coupling. When spin-orbit interactions are more important than electron–electron repulsions, it is more appropriate to consider first the coupling of s and l for individual electrons to give j vectors, and *then* the resultant jj coupling between the individual electrons.

† There is some confusion in the literature over the use of the words term, state, and level, which are often treated as though they were completely interchangeable. We shall use the word *term* to distinguish in atoms between the different ways of combining s and l separately in Russell–Saunders coupling. In transition-metal compounds it will be necessary to introduce the word *component* to identify the effects of the ligand field on the terms. An actual atom or compound will exist in one of many *states*. Transitions between these states give rise to absorption or emission spectra, the frequencies of which will depend upon the energy *levels* of the states. Analysis of spectra makes possible the labelling of states with term or component symbols, but the experimental resolution is often not sufficient to distinguish the states of different J values: these can be distinguished, however, by a full analysis of various magnetic measurements.

The theoretical treatment of the spectra and the magnetic properties of the transition-metal *compounds* starts from the gaseous ions and introduces the ligands as a field. This may be considered as producing a fourth energy (4) which modifies the gas-ion electron energies. Whereas in the study of a

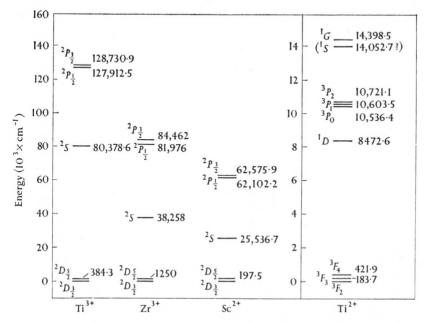

FIG. 28.1. The energy levels of the gaseous ions Ti^{3+}, Zr^{3+}, Sc^{2+} (d^1), and Ti^{2+} (d^2).

gaseous ion the parameters B, C, and ζ tell us something about the effective nuclear charge felt by the electrons, the changes in these parameters in *compounds* reveal the extent to which the electrons are no longer solely under the influence of the metal nucleus. It is thus the changes in the energy terms (2) and (3) as a consequence of the relative significance of (1) and (4) which are examined.

ILLUSTRATIVE EXAMPLES, GASEOUS IONS WITH ONE d ELECTRON

The energy levels of the Ti^{3+}, Zr^{3+}, and Sc^{2+} gaseous ions are given in Fig. 28.1. In each case the lowest configuration is $3d^1$ which gives rise to just one ^2D term. The multiplicity is 2 and the orbital momentum is 2 ($L = D$). The lowest J state of this term is obtained by opposing L and S, $J = 2 - \frac{1}{2} = \frac{3}{2}$, to give $^2D_{\frac{3}{2}}$. The next state is $^2D_{\frac{5}{2}}$ which is 384·3, 1250, and 197·5 cm^{-1} higher respectively for the three cations. The next low-lying states of the gaseous ions are ^2S ($4s^1$), $^2P_{\frac{1}{2}}$, and $^2P_{\frac{3}{2}}$ (both $4p^1$). There is here a simple relationship between the one-electron configuration labels, d^1, s^1, p^1, and the spectroscopic term labels, ^2D, ^2S, ^2P.

The separations between individual J states of a particular term and between the terms themselves are atom dependent as is shown in Fig. 28.1, but changes of atomic number and charge do not alter the two separations in the same way. The separations between the terms depend on the formal charge on the atoms, e.g. $Ti^{3+} > Sc^{2+}$, but decrease on changing from a $3d$ to a $4d$ electron, e.g. $Ti^{3+} > Zr^{3+}$, since the average distance of the $4d$ electron from the nucleus is greater. The separations between J states of the same term are greater the less the electron cloud is spread out from the nucleus, e.g. $Sc^{2+} < Ti^{3+}$, and increase rapidly with atomic number, roughly as Z^4. They are also greater for penetrating orbitals than for non-penetrating orbitals, e.g. $4d(Zr^{3+}) > 3d(Ti^{3+})$, and $4p(Ti^{3+}) > 3d(Ti^{3+})$. The last case is seen in the greater separations in the ^2P as opposed to those in the ^2D terms (Fig. 28.1).

Except at very high temperatures, the magnetic moment of an atom or ion depends only on the occupancy of the J states belonging to the ground-state term. For light atoms spin-orbit coupling energies, which determine the J-state separations, are so small that all the J states of this term are well populated at room temperature. When $kT \ll \zeta$, as it is in heavier atoms especially with penetrating electrons (compare Zr^{3+} and Ti^{3+}), only the lowest J states are appreciably populated.

ELECTRON–ELECTRON INTERACTIONS AND RACAH PARAMETERS

In order to illustrate electron–electron repulsion energies, we shall now consider the case of Ti^{2+} (Fig. 28.1). The ground-state configuration is $3d^2$ and gives rise to five terms: ^3F, ^3P, ^1D, ^1G, and ^1S. The origin of the different terms is as follows. The spins of the two d electrons may be opposed, $S = 0$, so that the multiplicity $= 1$ (singlets), or they may combine, $S = 1$, so that the multiplicity $= 3$ (triplets). The two electrons both have $l = 2$. Allowing for the limitations imposed by the Pauli exclusion principle, F and P terms, $L = 3$ and 1, then arise for the triplets, while S, D, and G terms, $L = 0$, 2, and 4 arise for the singlets. A method for deriving these terms is outlined in problem 21.19, and in Chapter 1 for the analogous p^2 case. (See also White, *Introduction to Atomic Spectra*, McGraw-Hill, New York, 1934, sections 12.1 and 13.11, or Ballhausen.)

It is usual to express the differences in electron–electron repulsion energies which arise between the different terms of one d^n electron configuration, here d^2, in the form $mB+nC$, where B and C are the Racah parameters. Values of mB relative to the ground state of a d^n atom or ion are derived from considering how changes of L alter electron–electron repulsion, and, knowing mB, nC values are obtained from how changes in S alter this repulsion. There is a rough relationship between B and C, $C \simeq 4B$. The B and C parameters themselves are determined experimentally from the spectra. Thus for a d^2 ion the separation between ^3F and ^3P is $15B$, and the separations between ^3F and ^1D, ^1G, and ^1S are respectively $5B+2C$, $12B+2C$, and $22B+7C$. The empirical values of B and C which can be obtained for different atoms and ions from an analysis of spectra permit a comparison of the strength of electron–electron repulsions independent of the spectroscopic term analysis from which they are derived. B and C are then found to be inversely related to the spatial extension of the orbitals in different atoms and ions. Naturally for a given principal quantum number they increase with the degree of ionization and the atomic number of the element.

The electron–electron repulsion may be expressed more generally in terms of Slater–Condon–Shortley parameters which are related to Racah parameters for d electrons by the equations

$$B = F_2 - 5F_4, \qquad C = 35F_4.$$

The F_k parameters can be calculated from radial wave functions for the electrons involved in mutual repulsion, but the best calculations are usually in error by at least 10 per cent.

THE INFLUENCE OF THE LIGAND FIELD

In Chapter 21 it was shown that in the lanthanide compounds the energy levels of the f^n configurations of the central cations are not markedly different from those in the gaseous ions. Furthermore, the third energy (3) is subsidiary to (2) so that LS coupling is a good approximation in the treatment of their spectroscopic and magnetic properties. In the actinide compounds the magnetic interactions (3) are as big as the electron–electron repulsions and actinide properties cannot be understood without immediate reference to spin-orbit coupling between individual electrons. The ligand field around an actinide ion also has a definite though small effect on all energies, but it can be largely ignored as the order of the energies is $(1) > (3), (2) \gg$ ligand field.

In transition-metal compounds the three energy terms controlling the d^n sub-shell properties can no longer be considered in isolation from the field of the ligands. In the simplest theory this field is regarded as exerting an effect only on the angular distribution of electrons around the central nucleus, and internal parameters of the atom are not altered by the field. However, B, C, and ζ are found experimentally to be smaller, sometimes considerably smaller, than in gaseous ions. The properties of transition-metal compounds are thus dependent in a complicated way upon the internal energies of gaseous ions, the character of the ligand field, and upon the effect of these two upon one another. Because of the approximations involved in rigorous treatments of such problems the analysis will be made empirically.

From spectroscopic and magnetic measurements, B, C, and ζ, and the way in which these quantities are affected by changing charge and ligand field may be determined. In the first transition series and in the presence of most ligands the most important of the three energies (2), (3), and (4) is (2), the internal electron–electron repulsion. High-spin states are preferred in most compounds: the ligand-field effect is a relatively minor energy. The spectroscopic and magnetic properties show ζ to be small for these elements too. In the second, and especially in the third, transition-metal series the order of importance of the energies can become: external field $\geqslant$ spin-orbit coupling $\geqslant$ electron–electron repulsion. The reasons for the changes in order of importance are (a) the greater penetration by the d electrons which increases the magnitude of ζ particularly since the nucleus carries a higher charge, and (b) the greater spread of the d orbitals on the outside of the atoms, leading to decreased B and C, and a greater effect of the external field. As a consequence most of the compounds of the second and third transition series are of low spin and, as ζ is relatively large, a complicated theory of magnetic moments is required. As stressed above the splitting between J states here is also large compared with kT, and this introduces further complications: see Part B of this chapter.

INTRODUCTION TO SPECTROSCOPY SECTIONS

In the discussion of the spectra of complexes in Part A of this chapter, transitions between different energy states will be expressed in terms of B, C, and the ligand-field splitting energy, Δ.† In order to illustrate

† In this chapter $10Dq$ is used as a measure of the theoretical field strength in the ground state, as in Chapter 24. Naïve assumptions then lead to a correspondence between $10Dq$ and spectroscopic splitting energies (Fig. 24.3). More sophisticated analysis does not generate this equivalence and thus a second *empirical* splitting energy is obtained from experimental spectroscopy which we shall call Δ. We should point out that this distinction between the theoretical $10Dq$ and the experimental Δ is not commonly made. The relationship between $10Dq$ and Δ will be discussed later.

the analysis, the d^1 case will be considered first (section 28.3), for it shows clearly the effect of the ligand-field strength on the extent of the splitting of a term. The d^2 case which is treated next (section 28.4) is more complicated, for, as seen above, many terms arise in the gaseous ions and their splitting patterns are more complex; furthermore, the components of different terms can interact. The d^3 case which follows permits a clearer discussion of the Racah parameter B, while the d^5 case illustrates spin-forbidden transitions. Low-spin systems are discussed briefly following the high-spin systems. The d^9, d^6, and d^4 high-spin systems are described simply by analogy with the d^1 case, while the d^7 and d^8 cases are described by reference to the d^3 and d^2 cases. This is permissible because there are formal similarities between one hole and one electron. The account of d–d transitions is concluded with sections which examine the chemical significance of the spectrochemical series, i.e. changes of Δ with ligand (section 28.5) and the nephelauxetic series, i.e. changes of B and C with ligand (section 28.6). The final section of Part A is an examination of chemical aspects of charge-transfer spectra (section 28.7).

INTRODUCTION TO MAGNETISM SECTIONS

The second part of the chapter is restricted to a discussion of magnetism. Section 28.8 analyses the reasons for the observed magnetic moments of high-spin transition-metal complexes. The main consideration in section 28.9 is that of high-spin/low-spin equilibria, which involves a discussion of the effect of ligands on B, C and the splitting between states. The variation of the spin-orbit coupling parameter with metal and ligand is described in section 28.10. The theoretical situations which are readily handled are those in which the energy of this coupling is either much smaller or much greater than kT, and where it is much smaller or much larger than the splitting between states. In the final section (28.11) the effect of interaction between magnetic centres is discussed.

PART A

SPECTRA

28.2. Spectra of inorganic compounds—intensity

DESCRIPTION OF SPECTRA

The different ways of plotting a spectrum may be clarified by considering the axes of Fig. 28.2. The abscissa is labelled with three different scales: cm^{-1} (the wave-number which is directly related to energy and frequency), Å (10^{-8} cm), and mμ (10^{-7} cm) (both wavelengths). The ordinate is labelled optical density, which is related to the ratio of the intensity of the incident radiation, I_0, and that of the emergent radiation, I. For a solution of concentration c, and for a path length through the sample, l, the equation connecting these quantities is

$$\text{optical density} = \log_{10}(I_0/I) = cl\epsilon,$$

where the molar extinction coefficient, ϵ, is the optical density under standard reference conditions, $c = 1\cdot0$ mole litre^{-1} and $l = 1\cdot0$ cm. ϵ is

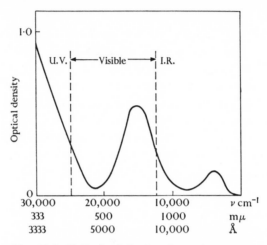

Fig. 28.2. Methods of plotting absorption spectra.

specifically defined only at a given frequency. The integrated band intensity, the area under the curve in Fig. 28.2 using cm^{-1} on the abscissa, is a measure of the probability of a transition from one energy level to another on absorption of light. This probability is theoretically proportional to the square of a quantity known as the transition dipole moment.

CHARACTER OF SPECTRA—ENERGY REGIONS

The absorption spectrum may be divided into three regions of energy. The visible region extends from 4000 to 8000 Å (25,000 cm^{-1} to 12,500 cm^{-1}) and separates the ultra-violet (higher energy than 25,000 cm^{-1}) from the infra-red (lower energy than 12,500 cm^{-1}). Apart from making a distinction which is obvious to the eye, the division is convenient because the absorption of visible and ultra-violet radiation is largely associated with electron excitations (albeit coupled with vibrational and rotational changes), while the infra-red absorption is associated with vibrational (and rotational) excitation of the nuclei with respect to one another.

Some examples of coloured complexes are listed in Fig. 28.3 opposite a colour chart. The colour of a compound is determined by the light which it does not absorb. A compound which is blue to the eye absorbs radiation in the red and vice versa. Cu(II) sulphate solutions are blue and the hydrated Cu(II) ion absorbs in the region from about 15,000 cm^{-1}–10,000 cm^{-1}, i.e. in the red.

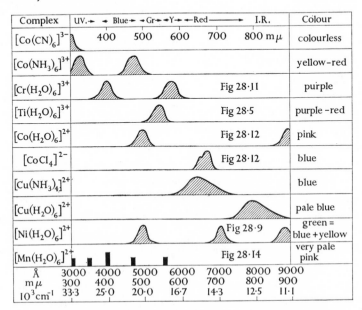

FIG. 28.3. The relationship between the colours and the d-d absorption spectra of some inorganic complexes. The long-wavelength bands of Co^{2+}(aq.) and Ni^{2+}(aq,) lie further in the infra-red than depicted.

INTENSITY OF ABSORPTION

Wave-mechanical considerations show that the absorption of energy by atoms or molecules is only highly probable when certain symmetry relationships hold between the wave functions of the ground and excited states. These symmetry restrictions can be expressed as selection rules. In the hydrogen atom the rules are (1) that the spin must not change on excitation and (2) that on excitation the orbital-angular-momentum quantum number, l, must change by ± 1, i.e. transitions such as $2s \leftrightarrow 2p$, $2s \leftrightarrow 3p$ are allowed but transitions such as $1s \leftrightarrow 2s$ and $3s \leftrightarrow 3d$ are not. (Inspection of these latter transitions shows that they are closely related to the rule that a change $u \leftrightarrow g$ is permitted and a change of either $u \leftrightarrow u$ or $g \leftrightarrow g$ is not; see section 28.3.) In atoms containing more than one electron the selection rules become $\Delta L = \pm 1$ and $\Delta S = 0$. In molecules a similar set of selection rules can be derived, but now consideration must be given to both the symmetries of the electronic and the vibrational states. As the vibrational transitions are of much lower energy than the electronic transitions, there are many vibrational transitions which can be coupled with each electronic transition. In molecules the line spectra of atoms and ions are therefore broadened into bands of closely spaced lines which are not usually resolved, e.g. Fig. 28.2.

Even in those molecules which we may treat to a first approximation as containing discrete central atoms or ions, e.g. a complex ion of a transition metal, the vibrations of the ligands are somewhat coupled with the electronic transitions. This vibronic coupling interferes with the simplicity of the atomic selection rules by destroying the symmetry relationships between atomic states. Its practical result is that transitions forbidden in atoms, $\Delta L = 0$, become partially permitted in a complex ion. However, this group of formally-forbidden transitions cannot be as probable as those which are directly allowed by the selection rules for purely electronic transitions. The degree to which a transition is permitted depends upon the selection rule which it breaks and the strength of the vibronic coupling. Table 28.1 indicates the different types of absorption intensity that are observed for some complex ions when different selection rules are broken. In inorganic chemistry the most interesting 'forbidden' transitions are the excitations of electrons within higher angular momentum configurations, i.e. f–f and d–d transitions. The colours of the lanthanide and the transition-metal ions (respectively) are largely due to these $\Delta L = 0$ transitions. The energies of the d–d or f–f transitions are usually not as large as those associated with allowed molecular or atomic excitations, and the transitions therefore lie in or near to the visible region of the spectrum. Hence colour is a usual property of lanthanide, actinide, and transition-metal compounds. It is thus possible to build up a *qualitative* picture of both the intensity and position of the absorption bands of inorganic ions and complexes from an extension of the discussion of the hydrogen-atom spectrum.

MOLECULAR TRANSITIONS

Molecules have absorption bands which cannot be interpreted in terms of transitions centred on individual atoms. The absorption may be of two main types. The first can be interpreted in terms of electronic transitions between molecular orbitals essentially without charge redistribution in the

TABLE 28.I. *Intensities of absorption*

Class of transition	Probability	Maximum intensity $\log_{10} \epsilon$	Typical transition†	Example
$\Delta L = \pm 1$	fully allowed	$+3$ to $+5$	$s^1 p^1 \leftarrow s^2$ singlet	calcium atom
$\Delta L = \pm 2$ or 0	orbitally forbidden	0 to $+2$	$d \leftarrow d$	copper(II) sulphate
$\Delta S = \pm 1$	spin forbidden	-2 to 0	$s^1 p^1 \leftarrow s^2$ triplet	mercury atom
$\Delta S = \pm 1$ and $\Delta L = 0$	spin and orbitally forbidden	< -1	$d \leftarrow d$ with change of multiplicity	manganese(II) sulphate

molecules, the second in terms of charge-transfer. Just as in atoms, a set of one-electron orbitals of differing symmetry can be ascribed to molecules, e.g. σ, π, etc., orbitals which correspond to the set of atomic orbitals, s, p, etc. The transitions between these molecular orbitals obey selection rules and hence are related to intense bands, or break them to different degrees and are related to weaker bands. The one-electron transitions,† $\pi^* \leftarrow \pi$, $\pi^* \leftarrow$ lone pair, $\sigma^* \leftarrow \sigma$, are particularly familiar in organic molecules, but they have an important place in the spectra of inorganic compounds too. However, the energy separation between these molecular orbitals is usually only small enough to give colour if (1) the molecules are very large and unsaturated, e.g. dye-stuffs, or (2) if the molecules contain heavy atoms. Thus low-energy absorption due to molecular electronic transitions is to be expected in large unsaturated assemblies of small atoms, e.g. long-chain carbon compounds and $(PNCl_2)_n$ polymers, and in both the small and larger molecules of heavier atoms, e.g. iodine and bromine. (There are a number of molecules, e.g. NO_2, which are weakly coloured where absorption is due to forbidden transitions, but these are somewhat special cases.)

CHARGE TRANSFER

There still remain coloured complex ions and molecules for which the above explanations of the intensities and the energies of the transitions are apparently unsatisfactory. It is observed that these transitions occur only when the ligand or the cation is either strongly reducing or oxidizing and

† In keeping with spectroscopic convention, the upper state is written first so that an absorption transition is represented as $B \leftarrow A$, and an emission transition as $B \rightarrow A$.

its partner has the opposite oxidation-reduction characteristic. For example, the iron(III) thiocyanate ion, $[Fe(III)(NCS)]^{2+}$, is intensely red, although $[Al(III)(NCS)]^{2+}$ is colourless; copper(II) bromide is black although $MgBr_2$ is colourless. Bromide and thiocyanate are reducing agents; iron(III) and copper(II) are oxidizing agents. This suggests that the absorption process is due essentially to electron transfer from the reducing agent to the oxidizing agent. The spectra have been termed charge-transfer spectra, i.e. they may be likened to reversible photochemical oxidation/reductions and may precede irreversible chemical oxidation-reduction, e.g. in iron(III) phenolate or thiocyanate. In the last eventuality, photochemical reactions, radicals such as $SCN^{\cdot}$ are observed, and polymerized products are frequently obtained, e.g. thiocyanogen. The simplest model for these spectra depends upon the allocation of electrons to definite atoms rather than to molecular orbitals: they are really being described then by an ionic theory. Charge-transfer bands are often extremely intense and are the basis of many colorimetric methods for the detection and analysis of metals. The intensity arises from the considerable magnitude of the

TABLE 28.II. *Some pigments*

Yellow (orange)	*Red*	*Blue (violet)*	*Green*	*White*
Yellow ochre* (hydrated Fe(III) oxide)	Red ochre* (calcined Fe(III) oxide)	Prussian blue* KFe(III) [Fe(II)(CN)$_6$]	Scheele's green (d) (CuHAsO$_3$)	Flake white (basic Pb(II) carbonate)
Patent yellow* (PbO,PbCl$_2$)	Vermilion* (HgS)	Thenard's blue (d) (CoO,Al$_2$O$_3$)	Cobalt green (d) (CoO,ZnO)	Zinc white (ZnO)
Chrome yellow** (PbCrO$_4$)	Iodine red* (HgI$_2$)	Synthetic ultramarine (Na$_8$Al$_6$Si$_6$O$_{24}$S$_2$)	Opaque chromium oxide (d) (Cr$_2$O$_3$)	Titanium white (TiO$_2$)
Lemon yellow** (BaCrO$_4$)	Cadmium red (CdS/Se)	Cobalt violet (d) [Co$_3$(PO$_4$)$_2$]	Emerald green (d) [CuAc$_2$, 3Cu(AsO$_2$)$_2$]	
Cadmium yellow*		Cerulean blue (d) (CoO,nSnO$_2$)	Viridian (d) (Cr$_2$O$_3$,2H$_2$O)	
Aureolin (d) K$_3$[Co(NO$_2$)$_6$],6H$_2$O		Manganese violet (d) [(NH$_4$)Mn(P$_2$O$_7$)]		
		Manganese blue** (BaMnO$_4$)		
		Monastral blue (m) (Copper phthalocyanine, C$_{32}$H$_{16}$N$_8$Cu)		

For those marked with a single asterisk, colour can be regarded as charge transfer from an ionic ground state. For those marked (m) colour is due to allowed molecular transitions in an organic molecule. In those marked (d) colour is due to d–d transitions. The chromates and manganates are marked with a double asterisk to show that the transitions are related to charge-transfer transitions within the anions.

transition dipole moment, but the selection rules which apply to the transitions are in all ways the same as those which are applied to molecules in general.

As an illustration of the different ways in which colour arises in familiar substances, Table 28.II gives a series of paint pigments with the origin of each colour indicated at the bottom of the table.

28.3. Spectroscopic labels and the one-electron case

In the following sections ligand-field symmetries will be considered much as in Chapter 24 A. In order to remind the reader of the approach, the subject will be reintroduced using the simple crystal-field language, but the formalism is consistent with either this or the molecular-orbital method.

We first consider a cation with one d electron in a simple octahedral field of point negative charges. Two of the d orbitals, $d_{x^2-y^2}$ and d_{z^2}, are largely concentrated along the axes of the octahedron, while the other three are largely concentrated so as to bisect the same directions (Fig. 24.1). The orbitals $d_{x^2-y^2}$ and d_{z^2} will be of higher energy than the orbitals d_{xy}, d_{yz}, and d_{xz}, as an electron in one of the latter orbitals avoids the field of negative point charges to a greater degree than it does in the former. Thus an octahedral field will split the five d orbitals into three low-lying orbitals of one symmetry type, and two of another symmetry and of higher energy. Now orbital degeneracy can be further removed by a decrease in the symmetry of the field. Consider thus a small tetragonal distortion obtained by moving two of the non-adjacent point charges to a greater distance from the central atom or ion than the other four. The splitting which results is shown in Fig. 28.4. The rhombohedral field case where all degeneracy has been removed by further lowering of symmetry is shown in the same figure. In such circumstances four transitions are possible (Fig. 28.4). The number of absorption bands will thus depend upon the symmetry of the ligand field.

LABELLING SCHEMES

In the introduction it has been shown how atomic electron configurations give rise to spectroscopic terms. The term label gives the total degeneracy. Thus ^3F has a spin degeneracy, usually referred to as the multiplicity, of 3, and an orbital degeneracy of 7 giving $7 \times 3 = 21$ possible energy states. Alternatively, the different J values of the ^3F term can be written $^3F_4$, $^3F_3$, and $^3F_2$, and the total degeneracy as $\sum (2J+1) = 9+7+5 = 21$ energy states. The ^3F term is split by any field of less than spherical symmetry.

Symbols are required for the split *components,* which are related to the possible states of the system in a particular field, and it is helpful if these express as much as possible about the degeneracy and the symmetry in this field. The labels for the three split components of the ^3F term in an *octahedral* field are $^3T_{1g}$, $^3T_{2g}$, and $^3A_{2g}$.

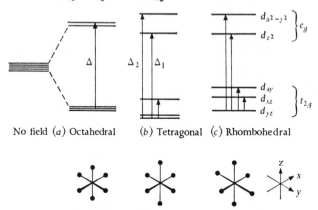

FIG. 28.4. Splitting of d orbitals in (a) octahedral, (b) tetragonal, and (c) rhombohedral fields. The e_g and t_{2g} labels strictly refer to an octahedral field only. Δ corresponds to the *observed* energy of an electronic transition.

These labels give the following information. Each component has a spin multiplicity of 3. The capital letter refers to the *dimension of an irreducible representation* in group theory (see problem 28.19), but it is equivalent in spectroscopy to the orbital degeneracy. Thus A (and B) are orbitally non-degenerate, E is 2-fold orbitally degenerate and T is 3-fold orbitally degenerate. B, antisymmetric, differs from A, symmetric, only in the effect of rotation by $2\pi/n$ degrees about the n-fold principal symmetry axis. The subscripts refer to further symmetry properties of the representation. g (gerade or even) and u (ungerade or odd) refer to the effect of inversion about a centre. Thus if the wave function changes sign on inversion through the centre it is u. They only act as relevant labels for systems with an inversion centre, e.g. for octahedra but not for tetrahedra. Used with the symbol A (or B), the subscripts 1 and 2 state that the wave function is symmetric or antisymmetric respectively either with respect to a 2-fold rotational axis perpendicular to the principal axis, or to a plane of symmetry which includes the principal axis. The subscripts 1 and 2 for E and T require a more detailed mathematical exposition and will just be used as labels. The possible components arising from the different occupations of n electrons in d orbitals are given in Table 28.III for two important field symmetries. In the third and fourth columns of the table alternative labelling schemes are given though they will not be used here. The one-electron case, now to be discussed, provides a simple illustration of the use of these symbols as it is relatively free from complications.

TABLE 28.III. *Symmetry labels in octahedral and tetrahedral fields*

Octahedral field, O_h (Mulliken)	Tetrahedral field, T_d (Mulliken)	Bethe	Van Vleck
A_{1g}	A_1	Γ_1	
A_{2g}	A_2	Γ_2	
E_g	E	Γ_3	d_γ
T_{1g}	T_1	Γ_4	
T_{2g}	T_2	Γ_5	d_ϵ

N.B. A tetrahedron has no centre of inversion.

COLOUR OF Ti³⁺ SALTS, ORGEL DIAGRAMS

Titanium(III) compounds (one d electron) are weakly coloured while Ti(IV) compounds (no d electrons) are colourless. The weakness of the colour indicates that the absorption arises from a forbidden d–d transition. The colours of the salts, TiF_3 (purple or violet), $TiCl_3$ (violet), $Ti(H_2O)_6Br_3$ (violet), are an indication that there is absorption around 5000 Å (Fig. 28.5). Analysis of the absorption spectra shows that in each case there is more than one band, but that the different bands lie close together. These observations are very readily interpreted by the theory so far outlined, and by reference to Fig. 28.4 (*a*). In the ground state, $^2T_{2g}$, of Ti³⁺ the single electron is in one of the d_{xy}, d_{xz}, or d_{zy} low-lying orbitals (t_{2g}), when the ion is surrounded by an octahedron of, for example, water molecules. However, the other possible state, ^2E_g, with the d electron in either the $d_{x^2-y^2}$ or the d_{z^2} orbital (e_g), is not much less stable than the ground state. The forbidden d–d transition is therefore of quite low energy corresponding to the visible part of the spectrum. There would be no more to be said about the colour of titanium(III) salts, but for the fact that the octahedron of ligands undergoes distortion due to the one d electron. The presence of this one electron in either the xy, xz, or yz orbitals makes the x, y, and z axes non-equivalent. The Jahn–Teller theorem states that orbitally-degenerate ground states will distort so as to remove degeneracy. Thus the presence of one d electron removes the degeneracy of the d_{xy}, d_{xz}, and d_{yz} orbitals as well as of the $d_{x^2-y^2}$ and d_{z^2}, so that several rather similar transitions occur (Figs. 28.4 and 28.5). (Note that the labels of the octahedral field are no longer strictly correct.) A set of overlapping or even separate absorption bands is frequently observed in titanium(III) spectra, whereas only one would have been expected for a simple octahedral field. (Thermal equilibria between distorted ground states and distortions in excited states are both referred to under the heading of the 'dynamic' Jahn–Teller effect.)

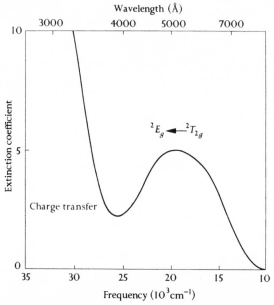

FIG. 28.5. The absorption spectrum of $[Ti(H_2O)_6]^{3+}$. Contrast the asymmetric band shape with that in Fig. 28.11.

Another way of interpreting these spectra in diagrammatic form is to plot the theoretical variation of the energy levels of the spectroscopic states of different symmetry as a function of the field strength, Dq. This is referred to as an Orgel diagram. The slopes of the plots are based on the theory described in Chapter 24 A. Fig. 28.6 shows the splitting for the d^1 system. The atomic ground term is ^2D (orbital angular momentum $= 2$, spin $= \frac{1}{2}$). The D implies that the term is 5-fold orbitally degenerate. It is split by the octahedral field into a T_{2g} symmetry component which is 3-fold orbitally degenerate, and an E_g component which is 2-fold orbitally degenerate and of higher energy. (All atomic d orbitals are g, gerade or even.) In this simple case there is a correspondence between the states (the components of the term) and the configurations (i.e. t_{2g}^1 or e_g^1), since there is but one electron. Thus either Fig. 28.4 or Fig. 28.6 can be used to illustrate the spectra. The levels in the Cu^{2+} ion are inverted relative to those of the Ti^{3+} ion for clearly the odd electron will be in an e_g orbital of Cu^{2+},

d^9, but in a t_{2g} orbital of Ti^{3+}, d^1. Fig. 28.6 includes this relationship. The diagram is inverted by a change of field symmetry from octahedral to tetrahedral (section 24.3). The figure can be made to include this feature of the splitting so long as it is remembered that the strength of the field provided by four ligands is smaller than that provided by six of the same

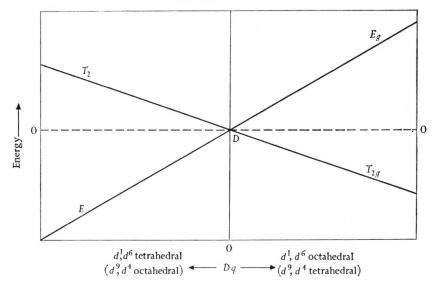

FIG. 28.6. The theoretical effect of increasing field strength on the energy levels of a d^1 ion in either an octahedral or a tetrahedral environment (an Orgel Diagram). For the d^n cases in parentheses the g labels should be transferred to the left-hand side. The slope of the E line is $+6$ and that of the T_2 line is -4.

ligands at the same distance (Chapter 24). Thus the positions of the different ligands on the abscissa in the figure will vary with the field geometry. Some tetrahedral (distorted) complexes of Ti^{3+} and Cu^{2+} are known, and they absorb in the near infra-red rather than in the visible.

28.4. Two or more electrons

For a d^1 (or d^9) cation there is a correspondence between the configurations and the states in an octahedral or a tetrahedral ligand field, e.g. between t_2^1 and e^1 and $^2T_2$ and ^2E. The situation is usually less straightforward when there are two or more d electrons, and it becomes necessary to distinguish two extreme models for the effect of the ligand field: (1) the strong-field approximation, in which it is assumed that the electrostatic splitting, $10Dq$, is very large compared with repulsive interaction between electrons in the sub-shell, and (2) the weak-field approximation, where $10Dq$ is relatively small.

The weak-field approximation gives a good account of the lanthanide compounds, but is less successful when applied to transition-metal compounds. In the first transition series the 'real' field strength is probably intermediate between the two approximations, and while the strong-field assumptions are quite good for $4d^n$ and $5d^n$ compounds, complications are introduced by the considerable magnitude of spin-orbit interactions.

TWO (OR EIGHT) d ELECTRONS—STRONG-FIELD

We shall consider the states which can arise from the possible configurations $t_{2g}^a e_g^b$ in an octahedral field. For a d^2 cation with parallel spins (multiplicity, $2S+1 = 3$) the *three* possible configurations give rise to *four* states, the energies of which

$$
\begin{array}{lll}
e_g^2 & {}^3A_{2g} & 20Dq-3B \\
e_g^1 t_{2g}^1 & \left\{ \begin{array}{l} {}^3T_{1g} \\ {}^3T_{2g} \end{array} \right. & \begin{array}{l} 10Dq+9B \\ 10Dq-3B \end{array} \\
t_{2g}^2 & {}^3T_{1g} & 0
\end{array}
$$

are expressed relative to the ground state. The orbital parts of the energies are computed relative to the baricentre for the one-electron orbitals, t_{2g} and e_g, i.e. $-8Dq$ for t_{2g}^2, $+2Dq$ for $t_{2g}^1 e_g^1$, and $+12Dq$ for e_g^2. As in the theory of free ions, the differences in electron-electron repulsion energies between the different states can be expressed as Racah energies, mB. The $t_{2g}^1 e_g^1$ configuration gives rise to two triplet states ${}^3T_{1g}$ and ${}^3T_{2g}$, differing in energy by $12B$, for essentially the same reason that the d^2 free ion has the ${}^3F$ and ${}^3P$ terms, split apart by $15B$. Both these triplets and the singlet states which can also arise, are shown on the right-hand side of Fig. 28.7.

We may make use of the 'hole formalism', according to which a configuration $t_{2g}^a e_g^b$ gives rise to the same states as the hole configuration, $t_{2g}^{6-a} e_g^{4-b}$. This means that an octahedral d^n complex has ligand-field states of the same symmetry as a d^{10-n} complex but with their energy sequence inverted. An octahedral d^8 complex for example has the following states which have the same dependence of the energies on Dq but different electron–electron repulsion energies from the d^2 cations.

$$
\begin{array}{lll}
t_{2g}^4 e_g^4 \ (\equiv t_{2g}^2) & {}^3T_{1g} & 20Dq+3B \\
t_{2g}^5 e_g^3 \ (\equiv t_{2g}^1 e_g^1) & \left\{ \begin{array}{l} {}^3T_{1g} \\ {}^3T_{2g} \end{array} \right. & \begin{array}{l} 10Dq+12B \\ 10Dq \end{array} \\
t_{2g}^6 e_g^2 \ (\equiv e_g^2) & {}^3A_{2g} & 0
\end{array}
$$

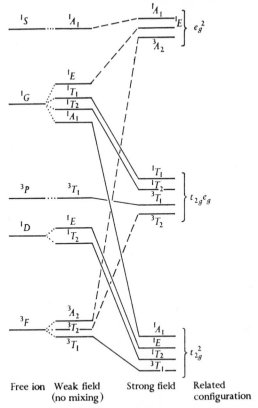

Free ion   Weak field   Strong field   Related
         (no mixing)   configuration

FIG. 28.7. Correlation diagram showing the relationship between the extreme limits of no field and that of a very strong field of octahedral symmetry.

The hole formalism implies that states arising from a tetrahedral d^n system are of the same symmetry type and of the same energy sequence as the states arising from an octahedral d^{10-n} system. An example is given in Fig. 28.6.

A major application of the above approximation is in the assignment of the 'd–d' bands in the absorption spectra of transition-metal complexes. Furthermore, we may subsequently use the approximation to obtain empirical values of the splitting energy (Δ by our definition in section 28.1 but frequently put equal to $10Dq$) and B. Thus for d^8 cations the energy of the first spin-allowed transition, $^3T_{2g} \leftarrow {}^3A_{2g}$, gives the splitting energy directly, and the $^3T_{1g} \leftarrow {}^3A_{2g}$ transition energy then provides a value for Racah's B. It is found that B in a complex is usually considerably less than in the free ion (nephelauxetic effect—see section 28.6).

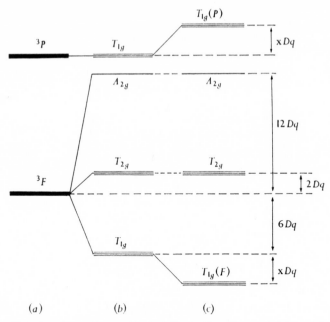

FIG. 28.8. An alternative method of illustrating the weak-field mixing of components from different terms in d^2. (a) Field-free terms. (b) Octahedral field applied with no mixing. (c) Mixing added to (b).

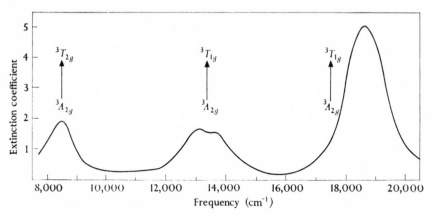

FIG. 28.9. The absorption spectrum of $[Ni(H_2O)_6]^{2+}$ showing probable assignments.

The strong-field energies given above are a good approximation only when $10Dq \gg mB$. As Dq is reduced relative to B, the two $^3T_{1g}$ states, initially arising from pure configurations, become mixed to an extent which increases with diminishing Dq. This correction to the strong-field approximation at intermediate field strengths is known as *configurational inter-action*. It means that the ground state of a d^2 system in an octahedral field is some mixture of the strong-field triplet configurations, t_{2g}^2 and $t_{2g}^1 e_g^1$.

TWO (OR EIGHT) d ELECTRONS—WEAK-FIELD

Here the electrostatic field of the ligands is regarded as a weak perturbation upon the states of the free ion. The lowest Russell–Saunders term of the d^2 ion is ^3F and in a weak octahedral field this is split into the components $^3T_{1g}$, $^3T_{2g}$, and $^3A_{2g}$ as shown in Fig. 28.8 (b). The energies of these components relative to their baricentre may be expressed as functions of the parameter Dq, which is identical with the parameter which occurs in the strong-field approximation. (Note, however, that the baricentre was there defined for the one-electron *orbitals* whereas here it is defined for the many-electron *states*.)

The free d^2 ion also has a low-lying ^3P term, differing from the ^3F ground term in its total orbital angular momentum, and hence by an amount $15B$ in inter-electron repulsion energy. This ^3P term is not split by the field and gives rise to a $^3T_{1g}$ state only. The $^3T_{1g}(F)$ and $^3T_{1g}(P)$ states, having the same spin and orbital symmetry, will be mixed by the field, Fig. 28.8 (c). The lower energy $^3T_{1g}(F)$ state is stabilized by this mixing to an extent calculable in terms of Dq and Racah's parameter, B, while the $^3T_{1g}(P)$ will be destabilized by a similar amount. In an octahedral field the degree of mixing increases with ligand-field strength.

The field dependences of the energies of the weak-field octahedral d^2 states are represented on the right-hand side of Fig. 28.10. In the construction of such diagrams it is assumed that the weak-field approximation maintains its validity over a considerable range of Dq: the energies of the $^3T_{2g}$ and $^3A_{2g}$ states then vary linearly as $2Dq$ and $12Dq$, respectively. For very small Dq the energy of the $^3T_{1g}(F)$ changes as $-6Dq$ while the $^3T_{1g}(P)$ energy is assumed independent of Dq. However, the mixing of the latter two states causes their energy plots to curve away from one another.

A d^n ion gives rise to the same Russell–Saunders terms as a d^{10-n} ion, though the splitting patterns of these terms in a given field, octahedral or tetrahedral, are inverted relative to one another. Thus the energies of the weak-field states of an octahedral d^8 system are given on the left-hand side of Fig. 28.10. In this case the $^3T_{1g}(F)$ and $^3T_{1g}(P)$ levels at first approach one another in energy but their mixing, which increases with Dq, then causes the plots to repel each other.

Diagrams such as Fig. 28.10 are also used in the assignment of the 'd–d'

spectra of transition-metal complexes. It is easy to see how the same assignment can arise from both weak-field and strong-field analyses of a spectrum, e.g. from an examination of Fig. 28.10 and the correlation diagram of Fig. 28.7. A typical assignment, of $Ni(H_2O)_6^{2+}$, is shown in Fig. 28.9.

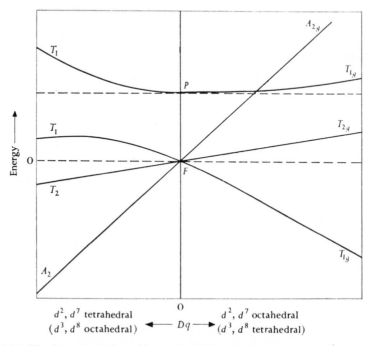

FIG. 28.10. The theoretical effect of increasing field strength on the weak-field energy levels of the F and P terms of a d^2 or d^7 ion in octahedral and tetrahedral environments. Compare Figs. 28.9, 28.11, and 28.12.

Now as Dq increases the weak-field assumptions soon lose their validity and the strong-field approximation becomes more appropriate. In the transition from the weak-field to the strong-field limit the initially pure $^3T_{1g}(F)$ and $^3T_{1g}(P)$ states are progressively contaminated with each other until in the strong-field limit ($10Dq \gg mB$) the states are generated as pure configurations, t_{2g}^2 and $t_{2g}^1 e_g^1$. Ligand fields of intermediate strength may therefore be approached from either of the two extremes, and if weak-field or strong-field approximations are applied *exactly* they yield identical results. The relationship between the two approximations for any d^n system can be shown in a correlation diagram such as Fig. 28.7, where the singlet states are included in addition to the triplets already discussed.

THE d^3 CASE AND OTHER HIGH-SPIN SYSTEMS

The *lowest* Russell–Saunders terms of a free d^3 cation are ^4F and ^4P, with the same L-values as the lowest terms of d^2 and d^8 ions. In fact the weak-field scheme for an octahedral d^3 complex may be represented by

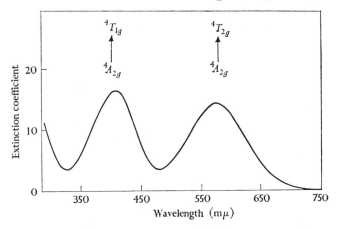

FIG. 28.11. The absorption spectrum of $[Cr(H_2O)_6]^{3+}$.

the same diagram as that for an octahedral d^8 complex, left-hand part of Fig. 28.10; similarly, the field dependence of the weak-field energies of a high-spin d^7 octahedral system is illustrated by the right-hand part of Fig. 28.10. Both the weak-field and strong-field energies for the d^3 system are given in Table 28.IV. For intermediate field strengths, allowance

TABLE 28.IV. *State energies (relative to the ground state) of a d^3 octahedral complex*

Weak-field scheme			Strong-field scheme		
^4P	$^4T_{1g}$	$12Dq+x'$	$20Dq+3B+y$	$^4T_{1g}$	$t^1_{2g}e^2_g$
	$^4T_{1g}$	$18Dq-x'$	$10Dq+12B-y'$	$^4T_{1g}$	$t^2_{2g}e^1_g$
^4F	$^4T_{2g}$	$10Dq$	$10Dq$	$^4T_{2g}$	
	$^4A_{2g}$	0	0	$^4A_{2g}$	t^3_{2g}

Notes. x and x', which change with Dq, are the energy corrections, including Racah energies, at intermediate field strengths, for the mixing of $^4T_{1g}$ weak-field states under the electrostatic perturbation. y and y', which also vary with Dq (y and y' increase with diminishing Dq) are corrections to the strong-field energies, when configurational interaction is included.

must be made for the interaction between the two $^4T_{1g}$ states. With such corrections, the weak-field and the strong-field approximations give the same energies. The assignment of 'd–d' spectra is usually a straightforward matter, Fig. 28.11 and Table 28.V.

The high-spin d^4 case is very similar to the d^1 case. The lowest term is ^5D which is split by the field into ^5E_g (lower energy) and $^5T_{2g}$ components. It is easy to see how these components correlate with the strong-field configurations, $t_{2g}^3 e_g^1$ and $t_{2g}^2 e_g^2$ respectively. In fact high-spin d^4 may be represented on the same Orgel diagram as d^1, d^6, and d^9, Fig. 28.6, omitting higher states.

TABLE 28.V. *Assignment of bands and their positions in transition-metal complexes*

Complex	Structure (symmetry)	Ground state	Position of observed bands and excited states (cm^{-1})			
$[Cu(II)(H_2O)_6]^{2+}$	Octahedral with tetragonal distortion	(^2E_g)	9400	12,600	$(^2T_{2g})$†	
$[Cu(II)(NH_3)_6]^{2+}$	,,	(^2E_g)	11,600	15,100	$(^2T_{2g})$†	
$[Ni(II)(H_2O)_6]^{2+}$	Octahedral	$^3A_{2g}$	8500	$^3T_{2g}$	13,500	$^3T_{1g}$
$[Ni(II)(NH_3)_6]^{2+}$	,,	$^3A_{2g}$	10,750	$^3T_{2g}$	17,500	$^3T_{1g}$
$[Co(III)(H_2O)_6]^{3+}$	Octahedral	$^1A_{1g}$	16,600	$^1T_{1g}$	24,900	$^1T_{2g}$
$[Co(III)(NH_3)_6]^{3+}$	,,	$^1A_{1g}$	21,000	$^1T_{1g}$	29,500	$^1T_{2g}$
$[Co(III)(CN)_6]^{3-}$	,,	$^1A_{1g}$	32,200	$^1T_{1g}$	38,600	$^1T_{2g}$
$[Co(III)(oxalate)_3]^{3-}$	~Octahedral	$^1A_{1g}$	16,500	$^1T_{1g}$	23,800	$^1T_{2g}$
$[Co(II)(H_2O)_6]^{2+}$	Octahedral	$^4T_{1g}$	8500	$^4T_{2g}$	19,500	$^4A_{2g}$
$[Co(II)Cl_4]^{2-}$	Tetrahedral	$^4A_2$	6300	$^4T_2$	15,000	$^4T_1$
$[Cr(III)(oxalate)_3]^{3-}$	~Octahedral	$^4A_{2g}$	17,400	$^4T_{2g}$	24,000	$^4T_{1g}$
$[Cr(III)(NH_3)_6]^{3+}$	Octahedral	$^4A_{2g}$	21,500	$^4T_{2g}$	28,000	$^4T_{1g}$
$[Ti(III)(H_2O)_6]^{3+}$	Octahedral with rhombic distortion	$(^2T_{2g})$	20,300	(^2E_g)‡		
$[Mn(II)(H_2O)_6]^{2+}$	Octahedral	$^6A_{1g}$	No spin-allowed transitions			

Only transitions within the splitting of the two lowest atomic terms are included. There are many transitions to higher energy states arising from other terms.

† The separation of the second band depends upon the extent of the tetragonal distortion (Jahn–Teller effect), see Fig. 28.4, but octahedral labels are kept for convenience.

‡ The band in the Ti(III) complexes is probably comprised of several overlapping bands which arise from the rhombohedral distortion (see Fig. 28.4). Octahedral labels are again kept for convenience.

AN EXAMPLE OF OCTAHEDRAL AND TETRAHEDRAL FIELDS—Co^{2+} SPECTRA

The spectra of transition-metal complexes are dependent upon field symmetry and field strength. The Co^{2+} ion illustrates the symmetry dependence. The pink hydrated ion $[Co(H_2O)_6]^{2+}$, with an octahedral arrangement of H_2O molecules about the central cation, has absorption bands at 520 mμ (19,500 cm^{-1}), $\epsilon_{max} \simeq 10$ (Fig. 28.12), and at 1200 mμ (8500 cm^{-1}), $\epsilon_{max} \simeq 3$. The transitions, right-hand side of Fig. 28.10, are derived from the ^4F atomic term and are $^4T_{2g} \leftarrow {}^4T_{1g}$ (low energy) and $^4A_{2g} \leftarrow {}^4T_{1g}$ (high energy). The energy levels have the same symmetry as those of the Cr^{3+} ion but are inverted, i.e. holes replace electrons. In a

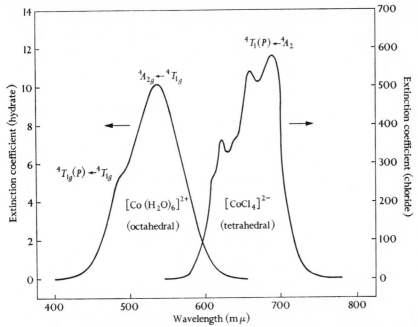

Fig. 28.12. The visible absorption spectra of $[Co(H_2O)_6]^{2+}$ and $[CoCl_4]^{2-}$. Note the intensity scale differences. The splitting of the $[CoCl_4]^{2-}$ band is due to spin-orbit coupling.

tetrahedral field the levels and the splitting diagram are inverted with respect to an octahedral field, so that the Co(II) tetrahedral is the same as the Cr(III) octahedral case (Fig. 28.10). A typical example is the spectrum of $[CoCl_4]^{2-}$ with absorption bands at 690 mμ (15,000 cm^{-1}), $\epsilon_{max} \simeq 600$ (Fig. 28.12), and 1580 mμ (6300 cm^{-1}), $\epsilon_{max} \simeq 100$. Apart from the shift to longer wavelength due to the smaller splitting in the tetrahedral field, there is also a big difference in intensity, that in the tetrahedral field spectrum being the greater. The reason for this is that, in contrast to an octahedral field, a tetrahedral field has no centre of inversion, so that d–d transitions in a tetrahedral field are orbitally allowed.

THE d^5 CASE (HIGH SPIN)

The terms of spin $\frac{5}{2}$ and spin $\frac{3}{2}$ of Mn^{2+} are ^6S, ^4G, ^4P, ^4D, and ^4F. Fig. 28.13 gives the Orgel diagram relevant to this ion. The reasons for the changes in slope of the lines is left as an exercise for the reader. All the transitions between the states are extremely weak as they are forbidden by two atomic selection rules, $\Delta L = \pm 1$ and $\Delta S = 0$. Thus Mn^{2+} salts are only faintly coloured (Fig. 28.14). The bands can be assigned from Fig. 28.13.

In all the Orgel diagrams the positions of the various terms must be

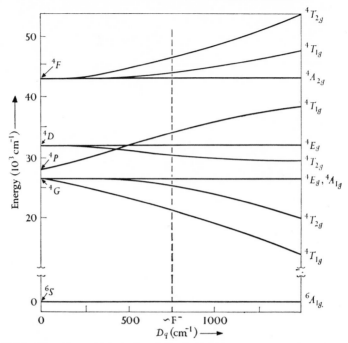

FIG. 28.13. The effect of increasing field strength on the energy levels of a d^5 ion in an octahedral field. Note the position of F^- and compare Fig. 28.14.

taken from atomic spectra. In so far as the ligand field alters the Racah parameters B and C it alters the term separations. The Orgel diagrams then suffer discontinuous modification as the field strength is changed. This change often makes assignment of transitions difficult even in high symmetry, but the situation becomes far more complicated in those cases where the symmetry is lower.

LOW-SPIN SYSTEMS

The spectra of low-spin systems can be handled in a very similar manner to those of high-spin systems of the same symmetry. In some cases, e.g. d^3 (high-spin) and d^6 (low-spin), there are very close parallels. Thus the Cr^{3+} spectra and the Co^{3+} spectra are very alike. The relationship between the lowest excited states of the ions is shown in Table 28.v. For details of these and other cases, see, for example, the books by Ballhausen, Cotton, and Jørgensen given in the bibliography at the end of this chapter. Difficulties in assignment arise through the lowering of symmetry often found in low-spin systems. Thus in $[Mo(CN)_8]^{4-}$ the d^2 (low-spin) ion is in a square antiprism, and d^8 (low-spin) ions are found in simple tetragonal

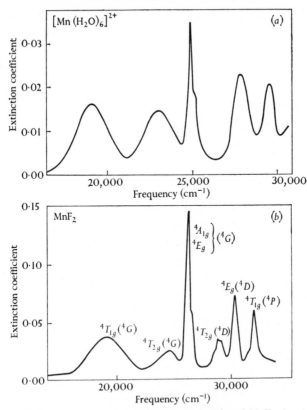

FIG. 28.14. The absorption spectra of $[Mn(H_2O)_6]^{2+}$ and MnF_2 showing the effect of changing the ligands composing the octahedral field. Probable assignments of the excited states are given for MnF_2.

structures. The assignment of the bands of square coplanar $[PtCl_4]^{2-}$ has been the subject of discussion for some ten years, although there now appears to be general agreement.

28.5. Field strength—the spectrochemical series

THE POSITIONS OF ABSORPTION BANDS

Copper(II) compounds have the following colours and band positions:

			λ_{max} $(m\mu)$
Anhydrous sulphate	almost white		$\sim$1000
Anhydrous carbonate	very pale blue		850
Hydrated salts, e.g. sulphate and nitrate .	blue		750
Tetra-ammine salts	deep violet-blue		600

The d–d transitions involved are very similar to those of Ti^{3+} (section 28.3), as the nine and one d electron cases are formally similar from the point of view of symmetry arguments (Fig. 28.6). Thus the energy separation of ground, E_g, and excited, T_{2g}, states follows the sequence

$$NH_3 > H_2O > CO_3^{2-} > SO_4^{2-}.$$

(Octahedral labels have been kept in order to relate the discussion to Fig. 28.6.)

The simplest explanation for this series, which would follow directly from the crystal-field model (Chapter 24) is that it is the series of increasing electrostatic field strengths, $10Dq$, felt by the d electrons, i.e. there is an equivalence between Δ and $10Dq$. Now when the energies, Δ, obtained from spectra using either transitions such as that of Cu^{2+} where there is no Racah energy change, or those for which appropriate corrections may be made, are compared for a large number of different cations, it is found that there is an approximately constant ligand series, the Fajans–Tsuchida *spectrochemical series*:

$$CO > CN^- > NO_2^- > \text{o-phenanthroline} > \text{ethylenediamine} > NH_3 >$$

$$(\leftarrow \overline{N}CS) > H_2O > OH^- > F^- > NO_3^- > Cl^- > (\leftarrow \overline{S}CN) > S^{2-} \geqslant Br^- > I^-.$$

This Δ order is obviously not one of decreasing electrostatic field, for then it would have been related to some simple function of the charge on the ligand and of the increase of its distance from the cation. Quite contrary to this expectation, for example, the order for oxygen ligands alone is

$$H_2O > \text{oxalate} > \begin{Bmatrix} OH^- \\ PO_4^{3-} \end{Bmatrix} > CO_3^{2-} > NO_3^- > SO_4^{2-}.$$

This order is not related to any other obvious property of these anions, either e.g. to acid dissociation constants—which have been related to charge density on the oxygen atoms—or to the order of stability constants of complex ions. Again unsaturated neutral molecules and unsaturated anions produce larger fields than do most saturated neutral molecules and anions. (Exceptions are hydride and methyl carbanion, which may give rise to large Δ values.)

The order of Δ can be arranged according to the position of ligand atoms in the Periodic Table:

$$
\begin{array}{c}
H \\
\| \\
C > N > O > F \\
\wedge \quad \vee \quad \vee \\
P > S > Cl \\
\| \quad \vee \quad \vee \\
As > Se > Br \\
\vee \\
I
\end{array}
$$

This arrangement stresses the lack of correlation with any electrostatic-field parameter. It does, however, receive an explanation on molecular-orbital theory.

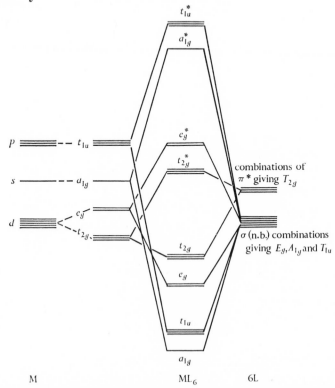

FIG. 28.15. The molecular-orbital diagram for the orbitals of a metal ion in an octahedral complex. Ligand combinations of T_{2g} symmetry arise from $\pi^*(CN^-)$, $nd(S^{2-})$, and $p_\pi(F^-)$ orbitals of the individual ligands of which only the π^* are shown.

MOLECULAR-ORBITAL APPROACH TO Δ

The simple electrostatic representation of a spectroscopic transition is modified in the molecular-orbital description. Thus, see Fig. 28.15, the e_g orbitals of the octahedral-field transition $e_g \leftrightarrow t_{2g}$ (left-hand side) are raised to e_g^* orbitals by σ-donor ligands while the t_{2g} orbitals are lowered by π-acceptor ligands. π-donor ligands put electrons into t_{2g}^* orbitals and can hence give rise to an $e_g^* \leftrightarrow t_{2g}^*$ transition. We may thus explain qualitatively the spectrochemical series

very strong σ-donors and π-acceptors		saturated neutral molecules		very weak σ-donors and π-donor anions
H^-, CH_3^-, CN^-, CO, NO_2^-	>	NH_3, H_2O	>	F^-, SO_4^{2-}, Cl^-, Br^-, I^-

Molecular-orbital theory also explains why neutral phosphorus ligands, PR_3, may give a stronger 'field' than neutral nitrogen ligands, NR_3, and why sulphide and chloride ions respectively give weaker 'fields' than oxide

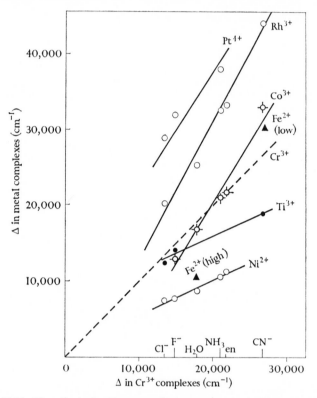

FIG. 28.16. The effect of cation upon the increments in Δ along the spectro-chemical series. All cations are compared with Cr^{3+}. Examples of both high-spin and low-spin Fe^{2+} complexes are given.

and fluoride ions. The only good π-acceptor of these ligands is PR_3 through the $3d$ orbitals of P. The other ligands act as π-donors in M—L complexes.

The splitting parameter Δ is also found to depend on the electron affinity of the metal orbitals and their occupancy. This is shown in Fig. 28.16, which plots Δ for Cr^{3+} complexes against Δ for the corresponding complexes of other cations. The plot shows that Δ varies more rapidly with ligand (along the spectrochemical series) in the order Rh^{3+}, $Co^{3+} > Cr^{3+} > Ti^{3+}$. For divalent ions the order $Pd^{2+} > Ni^{2+} > Co^{2+}$, Fe^{2+} has been found and in general Δ for $M^{4+} > M^{3+} > M^{2+}$ and for $5d > 4d > 3d$ cations. These orders are very much what might have been expected from covalent considerations and in fact many recent calculations show that Δ is strongly dependent on covalence. The history of the theoretical interpretation of Δ is outlined in Table 28.VI (a). The greatest success of the calculation of Δ is shown in Table 28.VI (b). It is still far from clear, however, that even the most sophisticated theory is satisfactory, and it may be necessary to

TABLE 28.VI (a). *The development of ligand-field calculations*

Authors	Model	Remarks
Van Vleck (1939)	Point-charge crystal-field model, crude d-wave functions	Apparently quite good agreement between $10Dq$ and Δ.
Kleiner (1952)	Van Vleck method improved by allowing for polarization of ligand	Calculated $10Dq$ of opposite sign to Δ.
Tanabe and Sugano (1956)	Better wave functions than Van Vleck, exchange included in an electrostatic model	Calculated $10Dq$ much larger than Δ.
Freeman and Watson (1960)	The most refined electrostatic treatment	Calculated $10Dq$ much too small.
Wolfsberg and Helmholz (1952)	Covalent (LCAO-MO) treatment of semi-empirical character	Of doubtful quantitative significance.
Jarrett (1959)	Formal consideration of molecular-orbital method	Different Dq should be used for each different state.
Schulman and Sugano (1963)	Sophisticated molecular-orbital method	Apparently very good agreement between theory and experiment.
Keffer *et al.* (1959)	Covalent calculations based on valence-bond method	Not quantitative(?)
Rimmer and Hubbard (1964)		
Watson and Freeman (1964)	Reconsideration of Schulman and Sugano method	Model considered to be unrealistic.

(b) *Contributions to* $10Dq$ (cm^{-1}) *in* $KNiF_3$

Van Vleck, point charge	$+1400$	
Kleiner's correction and electron exchange	-4000	$\left. \begin{array}{c} \end{array} \right\} -2600 \left. \begin{array}{c} \\ \\ \end{array} \right\} +1100$
Freeman and Watson	$+3700$	
Additional terms:		
Covalence	$+5300$	
Calculated	$+6400$	
Observed Δ	$+7250$	

The total calculation is that of Schulman and Sugano, *Technical Report of the Institute of Solid State Physics*, Ser. A, No. 66, January (1963), University of Tokyo, and *Phys. Rev.*, 1963, **130**, 506 and 517. See also Watson and Freeman, *Phys. Rev.* 1964, **134**, 1526.

consider changes in covalence and inter-electron repulsion from ground to excited states.

The effect of different metal ions on the relative values of Δ for two ligands is also firmly associated with covalence changes (Table 28.VII). The difference between Δ for H_2O and for ethylenediamine, for example, increases along the series $Mn^{2+} < Co^{2+} < Ni^{2+} < (Cu)^{2+} < (Pd^{2+})$ and $Cr^{3+} < Co^{3+} < Rh^{3+}$. These orders correlate with the changing electron affinity of d orbitals and are probably related to increasing σ-bonding.

TABLE 28.VII. *Spectroscopic splitting parameters,* Δ *(cm^{-1})*

	Mn^{2+}	Fe^{2+}	Co^{2+}	Ni^{2+}	Cu^{2+}	Pd^{2+}	Cr^{3+}	Co^{3+}	Rh^{3+}
H_2O	7800	10,400	9700	8500	(12,600)	(26,400)	17,400	19,100	27,700
En	9000	..	11,300	11,600	(16,400)	(34,900)	21,900	24,000	35,300
Difference	1200	..	1600	3100	(3800)	(8500)	4500	4900	7600

The difference increases with the electronegativity and the charge of the cation. These are both related to the polarizing power of the cation. Δ is also large for low-spin systems. Brackets enclose values observed in tetragonal fields.

Ligands binding through oxygen have a greater influence on thermo-dynamic stability earlier in transition series, whereas ligands binding through nitrogen have a greater influence later in the series. However, with both types of ligand bonding energies *rise* through the series. Table 28.VII shows that the factors which affect the thermodynamic properties are not necessarily of dominating influence in the spectra, since Δ for water falls along the series $Fe^{2+} > Co^{2+} > Ni^{2+}$, while the binding of water increases. It is probable that the particular order of Δ for water arises from the π-donor character of the oxygen. π-bonding plays an important role in controlling Δ, see above, but it is quite uncertain how large its contribution is relative to that in thermodynamic problems. Evidence such as this suggests that correlation between Δ and theoretical parameters of a ground-state field ($10Dq$) may be incorrect.

It is as well to note here the loss in precision which must be accepted on abandoning the simple electrostatic crystal-field model in favour of molecular-orbital theory.

(1) The field of a ligand becomes cation-dependent.

(2) The size of the cation orbitals becomes ligand-dependent.

(3) The electron–electron repulsion energies, Racah parameters, of the central cation become ligand-dependent.

(4) The spin-orbit coupling constants become ligand-dependent.

(5) The electron distribution of the electrons not formally involved in a spectral transition is not necessarily the same in an excited state as in the ground state of a complex.

Thus although molecular-orbital theory is immediately successful in describing semi-quantitatively the spectrochemical series, the simple definition of the splitting parameter, Δ, has been sacrificed. This follows especially from (5), for we are not in a position (e.g. in an octahedral field) to say how much the interaction between e_g and σ-ligand orbitals and between t_{2g} and π^*- and π-ligand orbitals changes with occupation of the orbitals, i.e. with excitation of the electrons. It is known from NMR, ESR, and neutron-diffraction measurements (Table 24.XIV) that the degree of covalence changes considerably with the occupation of t_{2g} orbitals in the series Mn^{2+} to Ni^{2+}. The simple correlation between thermodynamic (*ground-state*) properties, such as $10Dq$ defined in Chapter 24, and spectroscopic (difference between ground and excited state) properties, Δ, which was an integral part of crystal-field and the simplest form of molecular-orbital theory, may also be lost. It is for this reason that we have chosen to use the two symbols Δ and Dq in the discussion of splitting.

28.6. The nephelauxetic series

In section 28.1 it has been shown that inter-electron repulsion energies may be expressed in terms of the Racah parameters, which can be found from spectroscopic measurements. The values of B (cm^{-1}) for some gaseous ions are given in Table 28.VIII. Electron repulsion increases both with nuclear charge and with the total charge on a given atom, i.e. as the d-electron core contracts, in any one transition series. The electron–electron repulsion decreases from the first to the second and third transition series. The values of B are closely related to the values of C, the additional parameter which is involved on change of multiplicity from that of the ground state. As a rough guide $C \simeq 4B$. The values of B (and C) are very sensitive to changes in environment (Table 28.IX).

TABLE 28.VIII. *Electron–electron repulsion parameter B* (cm^{-1})

d^2	d^3	d^4	d^5	d^6	d^7	d^8
	V^{2+}	Cr^{2+}	Mn^{2+}	Fe^{2+}	Co^{2+}	Ni^{2+}
	760	830	960	1060	970	1080
V^{3+}	Cr^{3+}	Mn^{3+}	Fe^{3+}	Co^{3+}		
860	1020	1140	1090	$\sim$1100		
	Mn^{4+}	Fe^{4+}				
	1060	1150				

d^6		Co^{3+}	Rh^{3+}	Ir^{3+}
		$\sim$1100	720	660

The formation of a metal-ligand bond involves some transfer of electrons to the ns and np orbitals of the metal. As a result of the penetration of these orbitals inside the core of the $(n-1)d$ electrons the s–p covalence could alter the energy of the d orbitals, independently of the symmetry of the field of ligands, by decreasing the effective nuclear charge seen by the d electrons. The d electron would then spread out, and the electron-

TABLE 28.IX. *The value* (cm^{-1}) *of B in gaseous ions and in octahedral complexes* (*after Jørgensen*)

Ligands		Cr(III)	Co(III)	Ni(II)	Rh(III)	Ir(III)
Gaseous ion	(None)	1020	∼1100	1080	720	660
F⁻	(6 F)	820	..	960	..	..
H_2O	(6 O)	725	670	940	530	..
Ammonia	(6 N)	650	615	890	430	..
Ethylenediamine	(6 N)	620	590	850	420	..
Oxalate	(6 O)	620	540	..	..	..
Cl⁻	(6 Cl)	510	..	760	350	300
Cyanide	(6 C)	530	460	..	..	..
Br⁻	(6 Br)	..	..	740	290	250

repulsion energies would fall. The importance of this effect is difficult to estimate and it may well be small. Changes in B may also be brought about by covalence involving a change in the occupancy of the d orbitals themselves. Again the orbitals will effectively spread out as covalence increases, i.e. delocalization of d electrons will decrease electron–electron repulsion. This is now thought to be a major factor affecting B.

THE NEPHELAUXETIC SERIES

From the decreases in the values of B when a complex ion is compared with a gas ion, a ligand series has been built up called the nephelauxetic (cloud-expanding) series which, it is suggested, represents the spread of the electron away from its parent nucleus on increase of covalent character in the binding of a given cation. The series is

$$I^- > Br^- > \leftarrow SCN^- \geqslant CN^- \geqslant Cl^- > OH^- > \leftarrow NCS^- > NH_3 > RCO_2^-$$
$$> H_2O > F^-.$$

This is a totally different series from the spectrochemical series. It appears to reflect the polarizability of the ligand, to which covalence might well be related (Chapter 24 B) much more than does the spectrochemical series which by comparison appears over-sensitive to π-bonding. These spectroscopic series therefore assess different properties of the ligand field.

NEPHELAUXETIC SERIES FOR CATIONS

The inter-electron repulsions for cations are naturally both cation-dependent and charge-dependent. As the charge increases the ions contract and the inter-electron repulsion energies increase. The repulsions between d electrons diminish from the first to the second and third transition series: inter-electron repulsion energies in the second and third series have about two-thirds of the value of those found in the first series for ions of the same charge. The reduction of B (and C) for a given ligand is also cation-dependent in the following order:

$$Mn^{2+} < V^{2+} < Ni^{2+} < Mo^{3+} < Re^{4+} < Cr^{3+} < Fe^{3+} < Os^{4+} < Ir^{3+} < Rh^{3+}$$
$$< Co^{3+} < Mn^{4+} < Pt^{4+}.$$

This sequence reflects therefore an increasing ease of deformation of the d electron cloud. It is interesting that the Mn^{2+} ion comes lowest, for this would suggest that Mn^{2+} is less covalent than other cations. In fact the orders of sensitivity of B are in general those expected if covalence is proportional to the ionization energy required to make the cations from atoms. This estimate of covalence based on spectroscopic data may be compared with that deduced from thermodynamic effects in Chapters 25 and 26, and that found from other physical measurements in Chapter 24 B.

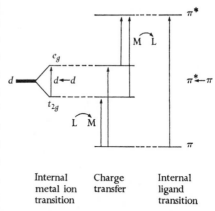

| Internal metal ion transition | Charge transfer | Internal ligand transition |

FIG. 28.17. Charge-transfer transitions involving π and π^* orbitals in an octahedral complex.

28.7. Charge-transfer spectra†

Charge-transfer transitions take place between orbitals largely localized in different parts of molecules or complexes, M—L. Fig. 28.17 shows the relationship between certain charge-transfer transitions, d–d transitions, and internal transitions of ligands in an octahedral complex. Charge-transfer transitions between σ orbitals have been omitted to avoid confusion in the figure. The direction of charge-transfer depends upon the relative energy and occupancy of the orbitals of both the ligand and the metal ion. Many ligands which are unsaturated and neutral, e.g. pyridine, have low-lying π^* orbitals available to accept electrons while ligands which have occupied high-energy orbitals of π symmetry with respect to M—L, e.g. RO^- and I^-, will donate electrons to the cation. The energies and occupancies of cation orbitals are such that most cations are better electron acceptors than donors. Naturally the higher the valence state and the more stable the empty orbitals of the cation, the easier is charge transfer to the metal. The opposite is true of charge transfer to the ligand. Cations

† Whenever a specific direction of charge-transfer is indicated in the following discussion, it will refer to the transfer of *negative* charge.

of low valence state or with electrons in unstable orbitals give rise to spectra corresponding to charge transfer from metal to ligand. The occupied orbitals of low-spin cations (excited states of the free ions) are particularly unstable due to internal electron–electron repulsion and this is a major factor facilitating the transition $M \frown L$. Examples of the different cases are given in Table 28.x. A knowledge of the relative symmetry of the ground and excited states is essential to the consideration of the intensity of the charge-transfer transitions, but this part of spectroscopic theory will not be described here and we shall concentrate upon the more chemical aspects.

TABLE 28.x. *Charge-transfer spectra*

Metal and oxidation state	Ligands and reagents	Electron transfer towards
Fe(III), Ti(IV), Mo(V), V(V), Mn(III)	phenolates, oxinates, Tiron, tannins, SCN^-, N_3^-, O_2^{2-}, I^-	cation
Fe(II)†, Cr(II)†, V(II), Cu(I), Cr(I)†, Co(I)†	di-imines, dipyridyl, o-phenanthroline	ligand
Fe(III)†, Cu(II), Mn(III)	oxime anions, e.g. of dimethylglyoximate	cation
Ni(II)†, Fe(II)†, Cu(I), Pd(II)†	oxime anions, e.g. of dimethylglyoximate	ligand

† Low-spin cations

CHARGE-TRANSFER TO THE LIGAND

For charge-transfer from metal to ligand the more reducing the metal and the more oxidizing the ligand the lower is the energy of the transition. Thus in the second half of the first transition series the complexes of copper(I) and iron(II) (low-spin) have charge-transfer bands at low energy as compared with nickel(II) (high-spin or low-spin) and cobalt(II) (high-spin or low-spin). This is put to use in analysis. Dipyridyl and *ortho*-phenanthroline give intense colours with Cu(I) and Fe(II) (low-spin), but not with Ni(II) (high-spin) or Co(II) (high-spin) or even with Co(III) (low-spin). In the first half of the transition series low-valence ions are strongly reducing and, even in high-spin states, such ions as V^{2+} are deeply coloured when in combination with electron acceptors, e.g. dipyridyl. Most of the ligands which give rise to such low-energy transitions are unsaturated organic molecules. Complexes of simple unsaturated molecules such as CO and NO have strongly-stabilized occupied orbitals of π symmetry and do not have very stable π^* orbitals. Therefore they do not give rise to low-energy charge-transfer transitions.

CHARGE TRANSFER TO THE METAL

For charge transfer from ligand to metal the frequency is smaller the more oxidizing the cation and the more reducing the ligand, and therefore in general for cations of a given charge type the later they occur in a transition-metal series. Thus charge-transfer absorption in the visible spectrum is more common in complexes of iron(III) than in those of chromium(III). This accounts for the widespread use of iron(III) in colour tests in organic chemistry, e.g. for phenols and hydroxamic acids. The copper(II) complexes show low-energy charge-transfer bands more frequently than the corresponding cobalt(II) or nickel(II) complexes. Other examples are given in Table 28.x. The ligands which act as good donors are inorganic anions such as S^{2-}, O^{2-}, OH^-, Br^-, I^-, N_3^-, and SCN^- and these anions substituted by alkyl or aryl groups, e.g. phenolates, sulphydryl compounds.

Some interesting periodic correlations are found amongst these charge-transfer spectra. In oxyanion complexes the sequences of *wavelength* of the first $\overset{\frown}{M \quad L}$ charge-transfer bands are:

Oxidation state VII	$MnO_4^- >$	$TcO_4^- >$	ReO_4^-
	V	V	V
Oxidation state VI	$CrO_4^{2-} >$	molybdates >	tungstates
	V	V	V
Oxidation state V	$VO_4^{3-} >$	niobates >	tantalates

The orders are those of the oxidizing power of the central 'cations'. The charge-transfer bands of these oxyanions have been extensively used in analytical colorimetric procedures.

METAL-METAL CHARGE TRANSFER $M^{n+} \overset{\frown}{\quad} M^{(n+1)+}$

A number of inorganic compounds contain a metal in two valence states. A typical example is Prussian blue $K[Fe(III)\{Fe(II)(CN)_6\}]$ where Fe(III) is high-spin and Fe(II) is low-spin as shown by the study of the Mössbauer effect. Here the charge transfer occurs from the t_{2g} orbitals of Fe(II) to the t_{2g} orbitals of Fe(III) via intervening CN^-.

It is a curious observation that many of the compounds which contain an atom in two valence states are blue, e.g. Fe(II)Fe(III) silicates, Ce(III) doped in CeO_2, Eu(II) in Eu_2O_3, Mo(V) in MoO_3, and W(V) in WO_3. In terms of the simplest form of the Mulliken theory of charge transfer the frequency of the absorption ν is related to the ionization potential of the donor I_D, the electron acceptor energy of the acceptor E_A, and the change of electrostatic energy, ΔE, due to the charge transfer by the equation

$$h\nu = I_D - E_A + \Delta E,$$

where h is Planck's constant. In the case of $M^{n+} \to M^{(n+1)+}$ charge transfer, $I_D = E_A$ and $h\nu = \Delta E$. On an ionic model it is then easily shown that ΔE is given by

$$\Delta E = \frac{K(r_{M^{n+}} - r_{M^{(n+1)+}})}{r_{M^{n+}} + r_{M^{(n+1)+}}},$$

where r is a metal-ligand distance and K is characteristic of a given lattice and, for example, would be constant for different pairs of metal ions in an octahedral oxide site. Thus if all such charge transfers give blue colours the contraction on change of charge (at equilibrium) should be approximately linearly dependent upon $r_{M^{n+}} r_{M^{(n+1)+}}$. In crystals this is found to be so.

CHARGE TRANSFER AND BIOLOGICAL SYSTEMS

The spectra of many metal-containing oxidases and electron-transfer enzymes show strong charge-transfer bands. Thus Fe(III) (high-spin) porphyrin complexes have absorption bands at around 1000 mμ, i.e. in the near infra-red, which may be attributed to charge transfer, $L \overset{\frown}{} M$. There are also many intensely blue copper(II) enzymes in which the coordinating groups are unknown but which are also coloured due to such charge transfer. The low-spin Co(I) complex of vitamin B_{12}, called vitamin B_{12s}, and some of the low-spin Fe(II) porphyrin complexes show charge-transfer bands of the opposite sense, i.e. $M \overset{\frown}{} L$.

PART B

MAGNETISM

28.8. Spin and orbital contributions to magnetic moments

FREE IONS

For the ions under consideration Russell–Saunders coupling is a good approximation and the lowest energy state has the maximum value of S and the highest possible L compatible with this value of S, in accordance with Hund's rules. Fig. 28.18 gives the $L:S$ scheme for a free d^2 system, including spin-orbit coupling. The number of J states is $2S+1$ or $2L+1$, whichever is the smaller. The lowest J state has $J = L-S$ if the d subshell is less than half-filled and $J = L+S$ if it is more than half-filled. Thus the $^3F_2$ state lies lowest in Fig. 28.18. A magnetic field further splits each of the J states into $2J+1$ closely-spaced M_J levels.

We must now consider the Boltzmann distribution over the energy states, i.e. it is necessary to examine the magnitudes of the different energy separations relative to kT. The terms are separated by energies much greater than kT, while the M_J separations are much less than kT. Interest centres therefore on the splittings between the J states of the lowest term. Two important cases arise: (1) $s:l$ coupling energy $\gg kT$; and (2)

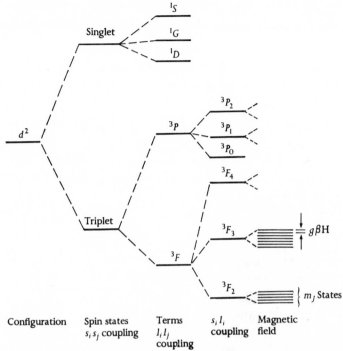

Configuration	Spin states $s_i s_j$ coupling	Terms $l_i l_j$ coupling	$s_i l_i$ coupling	Magnetic field

FIG. 28.18. The J states of a gaseous d^2 ion showing their splitting in a magnetic field.

$s:l$ coupling energy $\simeq kT$. In the first case only the lowest J state is occupied and, in a magnetic field, there is just the Boltzmann distribution over the M_J levels. The susceptibility can then be shown to obey the simple Curie law $\chi = N\mu^2/3kT$ where μ is given by

$$\mu = g\sqrt{\{J(J+1)\}} \text{ B.M.}$$

and
$$g = 1 + \frac{J(J+1)+S(S+1)-L(L+1)}{2J(J+1)}.$$

There are no data for gas ions to test this equation. However, in lanthanide *compounds* the $4f^n$ ions are hardly perturbed by their chemical environment and spin-orbit coupling energies are large. It is found that their magnetic moments agree well with the above theory, see section 21.6.

Case (1) does not apply to transition-metal ions of the first series since the J-state separations are about equal to kT, e.g. for V^{3+} the $^3F_3$ state lies

318 cm^{-1} above $^3F_2$, the ground state, and kT at room temperature is ~ 250 cm^{-1}. Thus only at very low temperatures will case (1) apply. More generally, case (2), there will be a complicated Boltzmann distribution of *free* ions over the excited J states. Fortunately in $3d^n$ *compounds* we may often neglect this distribution as the orbital contributions to magnetic moments are partially or completely 'quenched' by the ligand field.

COMPLEXES OF THE FIRST TRANSITION SERIES

In Table 28.xi the experimental magnetic moments of some hexa-aquo-cations of the first transition series are compared with the moments expected from the formula $\mu = g\sqrt{\{J(J+1)\}}$. As expected the agreement is very poor. In fact the values are closer to a 'spin-only' formula,

$$\mu = 2\sqrt{\{S(S+1)\}},$$

which is obtained from the Russell–Saunders coupling by putting $L = 0$. We shall now inquire how it is possible for the orbital contribution to be so reduced or quenched in a complex.

TABLE 28.XI. *Magnetic moments of aquo-cations in the first transition series*

Number of d electrons	Ion	Free-ion ground state	S	L	J	μ^2 (expt.)	$g^2J(J+1)$	$4S(S+1)$
0	K$^+$,Ca^{2+},Sc^{3+}	$^1S_0$	0	0	0	0	0	0
1	Ti^{3+}	$^2D_{\frac{3}{2}}$	$\frac{1}{2}$	2	$\frac{3}{2}$	2·9	2·4	3
2	V^{3+}	$^3F_2$	1	3	2	6·8	2·67	8
3	V^{2+},Cr^{3+}	$^4F_{\frac{3}{2}}$	$\frac{3}{2}$	3	$\frac{3}{2}$	14·8	0·6	15
4	Cr^{2+},Mn^{3+}	$^5D_0$	2	2	0	(23·3)	0	24
5	Mn^{2+},Fe^{3+}	$^6S_{\frac{5}{2}}$	$\frac{5}{2}$	0	$\frac{5}{2}$	34·0	35	35
6	Fe^{2+}	$^5D_4$	2	2	4	28·7	45	24
7	Co^{2+}	$^4F_{\frac{9}{2}}$	$\frac{3}{2}$	3	$\frac{9}{2}$	24·0	44	15
8	Ni^{2+}	$^3F_4$	1	3	4	9·7	31·3	8
9	Cu^{2+}	$^2D_{\frac{5}{2}}$	$\frac{1}{2}$	2	$\frac{5}{2}$	3·35	12·6	3
10	Cu$^+$,Zn^{2+}	$^1S_0$	0	0	0	0	0	0

The effect of the ligand field may be seen from the following simplified argument. An electron has orbital angular momentum about an axis only when the orbital it occupies may be transformed into an entirely *equivalent* and *degenerate* orbital by simple rotation about the axis in question. In a free atom or ion, the d_{xy} and $d_{x^2-y^2}$ orbitals are related by rotation by $45°$ about the z-axis (where z is any direction, since all directions are equivalent), and an electron in either of these orbitals possesses $\pm 2(h/2\pi)$ units of angular momentum about this axis. Similarly an electron in either of the d_{xz} and d_{yz} orbitals, related by rotation by $90°$ about the z-axis, has $\pm 1(h/2\pi)$ units of angular momentum. A d_{z^2} electron has zero angular momentum about the z-axis.

In a complex certain directions are physically defined by the ligands, and the 5-fold degeneracy of the d-orbitals is removed by the ligand field. In an octahedral field the d_{xz} and $d_{yz}(t_{2g})$ orbitals remain rotationally and *energetically* equivalent, and are therefore still associated with $\pm 1(h/2\pi)$ units of orbital angular momentum about the z-axis. However, the $d_{xy}(t_{2g})$ and $d_{x^2-y^2}(e_g)$ orbitals are no longer degenerate, so that an electron in either of these orbitals possesses no orbital momentum about the z-axis; the contribution of a d_{xy} or $d_{x^2-y^2}$ electron to the orbital magnetic moment is thus always quenched by the ligand field. As an electron in d_{z^2} also has no orbital angular momentum about the z-axis no orbital contribution can arise from e_g electrons.

It is now an easy matter to predict which d^n octahedral complexes should have the orbital magnetic moment entirely, and which partially, quenched. For example, when a complex has the ground configuration high-spin t_{2g}^3, quenching is complete because the total orbital angular momentum is zero but this is not true of t_{2g}^1 or t_{2g}^2 configurations. Thus, since octahedral-field splittings are so large that there can be no significant *thermal population* of excited states with only partly quenched orbital momentum, the following systems will be expected to have magnetic moments given by the spin-only formula:

$$\text{high-spin} \quad t_{2g}^3({}^4A_{2g}),\ t_{2g}^3 e_g^1({}^5E_g),\ t_{2g}^3 e_g^2({}^6A_{1g}),$$
$$t_{2g}^6 e_g^2({}^3A_{2g}),\ t_{2g}^6 e_g^3({}^2E_g)$$
$$\text{low-spin} \quad t_{2g}^6({}^1A_{1g}),\ t_{2g}^6 e_g^1({}^2E_g).$$

The remaining ground configurations should retain some orbital angular momentum about the z-axis:

$$\text{high-spin} \quad t_{2g}^1({}^2T_{2g}),\ t_{2g}^2({}^3T_{1g}),\ t_{2g}^4 e_g^2({}^5T_{2g}),\ t_{2g}^5 e_g^2({}^4T_{1g})$$
$$\text{low-spin} \quad t_{2g}^4({}^3T_{1g}),\ t_{2g}^5({}^2T_{2g}).$$

The orbital contribution should result in a magnetic moment less than spin-only value when there are less than five d electrons, but greater for more than five d electrons. (Note that throughout the discussion we are using strong-field language, though application of the weak-field approximation would lead to precisely the same conclusions.)

Tetrahedral complexes may be considered in an analogous fashion: thus the orbital magnetic moment should completely disappear in the configurations

$$\text{high-spin} \quad e^1({}^2E),\ e^2({}^3A_2),\ e^2t_2^3({}^6A_1),\ e^3t_2^3({}^5E),\ e^4t_3^3({}^4A_1),$$
$$\text{low-spin} \quad e^3({}^2E),\ e^4({}^1A_1),$$

but be only partly quenched in

$$\text{high-spin} \quad e^2 t_2^1 (^4T_1), \ e^2 t_2^2 (^5T_2), \ e^4 t_2^4 (^3T_1), \ e^4 t_2^5 (^2T_1),$$

$$\text{low-spin} \quad e^3 t_2^1 (^3T_1), \ e^3 t_2^2 (^4T_2), \ e^4 t_2^1 (^2T_2), \ e^4 t_2^2 (^3T_1).$$

These predictions may be compared with the data of Table 28.XI for the octahedral aquo-complexes of the first transition series. Deviations from spin-only values are expected towards higher values for $Co^{2+} (t_{2g}^5 e_g^2)$ and $Fe^{2+} (t_{2g}^4 e_g^2)$, and towards lower values for $Ti^{3+} (t_{2g}^1)$ and $V^{3+} (t_{2g}^2)$, as is in fact observed.

However, the deviations from spin-only values are frequently very small, e.g. Ti^{3+}, Cr^{2+}, Cu^{2+}. This arises because orbital degeneracy in the ligand field may be further removed by static Jahn–Teller distortions. The Jahn–Teller theorem states that a symmetrical non-linear molecule in an orbitally degenerate state will distort in such a way as to remove the degeneracy. In the case of d^4 and d^9 systems in octahedral or tetra-hedral fields there are tetragonal distortions of a sufficient magnitude to be detectable by X-ray crystallography (e.g. Cr^{2+} and Cu^{2+}), and to be seen in d–d spectra. The distortions in other cases are usually of smaller magni-tude, although they are frequently indicated by the irregular shape of 'd–d' absorption bands, e.g. $[Ti(H_2O)_6]^{3+}$. Smaller static distortions towards lower symmetry are detected by direct measurement of g, i.e. by ESR studies; for example, the presence of a trigonal component of the ligand field is indicated for hexa-coordinated V^{3+}. (Even if Jahn–Teller effects were absent, however, spin-orbit coupling would introduce small splittings in orbitally degenerate ground states, just as the Russell–Saunders terms of free ions are split into J-components. These splittings are often of the same order of magnitude as those arising from the Jahn–Teller mechanism.)

The above discussion leads us to expect that, strictly speaking, no orbital degeneracy will remain in a complex, and that therefore the orbital contri-bution should be even smaller than it is. In practice, in the first transition series, Jahn–Teller effects associated with degeneracy in t_2 orbitals and the splitting of the ground state by spin-orbit coupling are both small compared with kT at room temperature. As a consequence of vibrational motion, some orbital contribution is usually observed for cations with T ground states. In addition, orbital contributions are 'sustained' by spin-orbit coupling which mixes components of excited states into the ground state. This coupling is discussed in section 28.10, but, before proceeding to this, we shall first examine some simple cases in which it is a reason-able approximation to consider spin and orbital effects separately.

28.9. Examples of spin-pairing and orbital-quenching

Despite the complications discussed above, the magnetic moment of a complex can still be obtained provided that the general equation $\chi = N\mu^2/3k(T-K)$ holds, where K is a constant. The moment can then be used to derive the spin state of the central cation (section 24.2) or used as a guide to the stereochemistry of a complex.

THERMAL EQUILIBRIA BETWEEN SPIN STATES

Strong ligand fields can bring about spin pairing in complexes by overcoming the electron–electron repulsion energies represented for the free-gas cations by the Racah parameters (section 24.4). Here we examine two

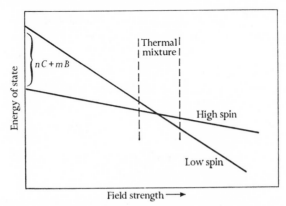

FIG. 28.19. The separation between high-spin and low-spin states of a cation as a function of field strength.

further extensions of these ideas. Let $mB+nC$ (Racah energy) be the energy separation between two spin states in the absence of a field. On application of a field of increasing strength the separation between the two spin states changes so as to favour low-spin over high-spin systems (Fig. 28.19). At certain field strengths there will be an energy separation between the two of the order of kT, when a chemical equilibrium mixture of the compounds will be observed. This situation is frequently realized and is of the greatest significance in biologically-important complexes. It will be recognized that if there is little difference in energy between two states then both will contribute to chemical and physical properties of the system. For example, even if only a small proportion of a high-spin state is present in an equilibrium, the rates of reactions (of the supposed low-spin state) may be governed by the high-spin state and by the rate at which the low-spin goes over into the high-spin state. In molecules such

as the cytochromes and the cobalt(II) forms of the corrins it is as yet unknown which of the spin states is important in controlling reactivity. It
has also been found that for many nickel complexes changes of solvent
will bring about a partial or complete change of spin state. Again it is
sometimes found that the spin state of a complex ion in a solid differs
from that in solution. Finally, even in a solid the magnetic criteria for
the geometry of a complex, although usually satisfactory, can be completely misleading. A bizarre example is the case of the nickel complex,
$Ni(PhCH_2PPh_2)_2Br_2$, where $PhCH_2$ is benzyl, which crystallizes as a mixture of stereoisomers of two different spin states.

CHANGES OF SPIN STATE WITH LIGAND

The analysis of spectra has shown that C, like B, falls in the order of the
nephelauxetic series. The ligands which bring about the greatest reduction
in these parameters are cyanide, dipyridyl, and sulphur and phosphorus
ligands, while amongst halides, chloride, bromide, and iodide are more
effective than fluoride. These ligands are not necessarily the ligands giving
the greatest value of Δ. For example, Δ for fluoride is greater than for
chloride (spectrochemical series), although fluoride is more likely to
generate a high-spin complex than any other ligand: $KPdF_3$ is the only
high-spin Pd^{2+} salt known. Fluoride is a weakly polarizable ligand. The
order of the effectiveness of ligands in inducing spin pairing (Table 28.XII)

TABLE 28.XII. *Order of strength of ligands based on spin-pairing in complexes*

$$
\begin{array}{ccc}
CN^- > & NH_3 > & OH^- > & F^- \\
\wedge & \wedge & & \wedge \\
PR_3 > & SR^- & > & Cl^- \\
\| & \| & & \vee \\
AsR_3 > & SeR^- & > & Br^- \\
& \vee & & \vee \\
& TeR^- & & I^-
\end{array}
$$

Spin-pairing increases with increase of the negative charge on the ligand atom.

is a mixture of that of the nephelauxetic series, section 28.6, and that of
the spectrochemical series, section 28.5. Here is another reason for supposing that the correlation between spectroscopic changes and thermodynamic quantities cannot be expected to be a close one. As well as
providing a splitting energy, Δ, the ligand modifies all the electron–electron
repulsion energies in the central ion. In other words, the ligand not only
splits the spectroscopic terms of the free ion, but it also changes the 'bari-
centres' (energy centres of gravity) of the components by modifying the
radial part of the wave functions. Another way of studying this effect is
to determine spin-orbit coupling parameters in complexes.

ORBITAL QUENCHING AND STEREOCHEMISTRY

For the Co^{2+} ion, for example, the quenching of the orbital magnetic moment leads to a diagnostic method for tetrahedral as opposed to octahedral complexes, which is quite successful and which can be correlated with spectroscopic data. The tetrahedral distribution of ligands, as was noted before, leads to a weaker field than the octahedral distribution. In complexes of ligands which give approximately the same field, the main d–d transition in the visible is then at shorter wavelengths (pink complexes) for the octahedral complexes and at longer wavelengths (blue complexes) for tetrahedral complexes; see Fig. 28.12. (There is also an infra-red band in both cases.) The tetrahedral complexes are expected to have a lower

TABLE 28.XIII. *Magnetic moments of* Co^{2+} *complexes*

Complex	Colour	μ (B.M.)	Probable stereochemistry
$Co(H_2O)_6^{2+}$ . . .	pink	5·1	octahedral
$CoCl_2(aniline)_2(EtOH)_2$.	pink	5·0	,,
$CoBr_2(aniline)_2(EtOH)_2$.	pink	5·0	,,
$CoCl_2(aniline)_2$ . .	blue	4·40	tetrahedral
$CoBr_2(aniline)_2$ . .	blue	4·46	,,
$CoI_2(aniline)_2$ . . .	blue	4·61	,,
$Co(SCN)_4^{2-}$ . . .	blue	4·40	,,
$CoCl_4^{2-}$	blue	4·60	,,
$CoBr_4^{2-}$	blue	4·72	,,
CoI_4^{2-}	blue	4·88	,,

magnetic moment since the ground state is orbitally non-degenerate. The change in colour of Co^{2+} complexes from pink to blue should therefore be accompanied by a fall in magnetic moment. This is illustrated in Table 28.XIII. (The colours of Co^{2+} and Ni^{2+} complexes also change radically when there is a change of spin.)

28.10. Spin-orbit coupling

Although spin-orbit coupling is not of great importance in the consideration of the spectra of complexes in the first transition series, it is of very great importance in magnetism. Its neglect so far in the discussion here has been necessary in order to give a clear account of orbital-momentum 'quenching' by the ligand field. In simple terms, spin-orbit coupling opposes this quenching as it tends to sustain orbital angular momentum by coupling it with spin angular momentum, which is not directly influenced by the ligand field. In the absence of spin-orbit coupling we should frequently (or, if the Jahn–Teller effect is strong, always) expect to observe agreement with the spin-only formula, $\mu = g\sqrt{\{S(S+1)\}}$, where

g is 2·0023 (the difference from 2·0000 being due to a relativistic correction). In practice the values of g found using the above equation deviate considerably from the free-electron value. For example the values in

TABLE 28.XIV. *Magnetic and spectroscopic parameters for* Cr^{3+} *in oxide lattices*

	g	Nuclear hyperfine splitting constant $A \times 10^{-4}(cm^{-1})$	First optical transition (cm^{-1})	Second optical transition (cm^{-1})
in MgO . . .	1·9797	16·0	16,200	22,700
in Al_2O_3 . . .	1·988	17·0	18,150	25,730
in TiO_2 . . .	1·975	17·0	17,500	24,430
in $SrTiO_3$ . .	1·976	16·2	19,300	~27,000
$Cr(AcAc)_3$ . .	1·983	. .	17,500	24,000
$[Cr(H_2O)_6]^{3+}$ in $(NH_4)Al(SO_4)_2\,12H_2O$.	1·976	. .	17,400	24,400
$[Cr(H_2O)_6]^{3+}$ in $Zn[SiF_6]\,6H_2O$.	1·970	. .	. .	. .
$[Cr(CN)_6]^{3-}$ . .	1·993	. .	26,600	32,200

Cr(III) complexes, Table 28.XIV, are all low. Now in this case spin-orbit coupling mixes one of the spin-orbit components of the excited state, $^4T_{1g}$, into the $^4A_{2g}$ ground state. The amount of mixing in this example is inversely proportional to the energy separation between these states, and g is given by

$$g = g_s\left\{1 \pm \frac{\text{constant } \zeta}{\Delta}\right\}$$

where the constant depends upon the number of d electrons and the field symmetry, ζ is the one-electron spin-orbit coupling parameter, and the sign is negative before the half-filled shell and positive after it. As Δ increases g approaches 2·0023 (g_s) as is seen for Cr(III) in the series $H_2O \leqslant O^{2-} < CN^-$, Table 28.XIV. Experimental measurement of both Δ and g, the latter from susceptibility data or directly from electron spin resonance spectra, has shown that ζ is considerably smaller in complexes than in the free-gas ion. This has been interpreted in terms of the covalence of the complex. Thus just as with spectroscopic data a full understanding of magnetic properties awaits a better understanding of covalence.

The case of the Cu(II) complexes permits a further illustration of the effects which influence g. The Cu(II) complexes show a strong distortion from octahedral to tetragonal geometry due to the Jahn–Teller effect. There is no orbital degeneracy and the value of g should therefore be given by the free-electron value, 2·0023, i.e. neglecting spin-orbit coupling. Experimentally g may vary from 1·8 to 2·5, so that in fact the effect of spin-orbit coupling is very marked. In the ground state the unpaired electron of the copper(II) ion occupies the $d_{x^2-y^2}$ orbital. Spin-orbit coupling mixes the ground state with components of excited states in which the odd electron is in either the d_{xy} or the d_{xz} (or d_{yz}) orbitals. As the energies of these orbitals are different the magnetic properties are anisotropic and the measurement of g in different directions in crystals can give information about stereochemistry. In the copper(II) complexes the two different values of g are

$$g_{\parallel} = g_s + \frac{8\zeta\alpha^2}{\Delta_1},$$

perpendicular to the plane of the complex (parallel to the symmetry axis),

$$g_{\perp} = g_s + \frac{2\zeta\beta^2}{\Delta_2},$$

parallel to the plane of the complex, where Δ_1 is the energy for the transition $d_{x^2-y^2} \leftarrow d_{xy}$ and Δ_2 that for the transition $d_{x^2-y^2} \leftarrow d_{xz}$, and where the parameters α and β are found to be less than $1\cdot0$ so that they effectively reduce ζ. In fact it has been shown that α^2 and β^2 can be considered as

TABLE 28.XV. *Magnetic and bonding parameters of some* Cu^{2+} *complexes as obtained from ESR measurements*

Ligands	Coordinating groups	$g_{\perp}$	$g_{\parallel}$	Δ (cm^{-1})	α^2	β^2
$(H_2O)_6$	6O	2·083	2·397	13,500	0·85	$\sim1\cdot0$
$(oxalate)_2(H_2O)_2$	6O	2·078	2·316	13,500	0·80	?
$(acetylacetonate)_2$ $(H_2O)_2$	4O+2O ?	2·053	2·266	15,000	0·75	0·87
$(salicylaldiminate)_2$	2N+2O	2·045	2·200	16,300	0·76	0·78
$(imidazole)_4(H_2O)_2$	4N+2O	2·063	2·230	16,800	?	?
phthalocyanine	4N+(2N)	2·045	2·165	?	0·82	0·59
$(dithiocarbamate)_2$	4S	<2·047	<2·137	?	0·53	(0·85)

Δ is often given as an average of Δ_1 and Δ_2.

When $\alpha^2 = \beta^2 = 1\cdot0$ the complex is regarded as 100 per cent ionic.

measures of covalent bonding. Thus g, together with Δ values, gives an indication of the field character. It is found that α and β are ligand-dependent, much as would be expected from the nephelauxetic series. Table 28.xv gives some results. Much caution needs to be observed in the interpretation of such observations in cases where the symmetry is not rigidly established.

The general inference which has been drawn from a large number of such measurements is that the odd electrons have considerable probability of being on coordinated atoms even in high-spin complexes of such little polarizable ligands as fluoride. Thus in $KNiF_3$, a salt of Ni^{2+}, there appears to be some 5 per cent of an unpaired electron on each of the fluorides. The degree to which the unpaired electrons appear on neighbouring atoms seems also to increase from high-spin to low-spin cations, and from the lighter to the heavier elements. Such a result is of great importance in the understanding of the reactivity induced in organic ligands coordinated to transition metals. For example, electron spin resonance has been used in the study of copper-, iron-, and molybdenum-containing enzymes. In many of the enzymes the resonance signal shows that the unpaired electron of the cations is very delocalized. Generally delocalization increases from Mn^{2+} to Cu^{2+} (Chapter 24).

KOTANI DIAGRAMS

In many low-spin octahedral complexes, especially of the heavier transition metals of the second and third series, a complicated dependence of magnetic susceptibility on temperature is observed at low temperatures. This occurs when ζ is quite large relative to kT.

With less than six d electrons in an octahedral field the unpaired electrons are in t_{2g} rather than e_g orbitals. The t_{2g} orbitals are triply degenerate, and, since the e_g/t_{2g} splitting is large, only a small contribution would be expected from the orbital magnetic moment in the absence of strong spin-orbit coupling. Spin-only values to be expected are shown on the right-hand side of Table 28.XI. At high temperatures, since $\zeta < kT$, a similar result would be obtained even considering spin-orbit coupling, as all the J states will be considerably populated. Now on lowering the temperature (provided that the s and l vectors are strongly coupled) the electrons will begin to populate the lowest J states preferentially as ζ approaches kT. The calculated variations of magnetic moments with kT/ζ, using a Boltzmann distribution over J states, are as shown in Fig. 28.20. For example in the t_{2g}^1 case, where l and s are opposed in the lowest J state, μ approaches zero at 0 °K. For the complexes of cations such as molybdenum, ruthenium, osmium, and rhenium, ζ becomes comparable with kT at temperatures near to room temperature, and for complexes of first series transition-metal ions at temperatures around 50 °K. Much more complicated behaviour is expected and observed in fields of lower symmetry.

HYPERFINE STRUCTURE

Many atomic nuclei possess spin angular momentum and associated magnetic moments. The magnetic field of the nucleus couples with the magnetic field of the electrons. Thus the ^{55}Mn nucleus of spin $I = \frac{5}{2}$ couples with the electron spin of the ^{6}S state of the Mn^{2+} ion giving rise to an ESR spectrum of six, $(2I+1)$, lines. Fig. 28.21 gives the spectra of two other cations as illustrations of this point. This hyperfine structure can be

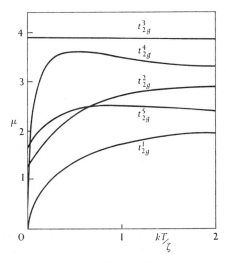

Fig. 28.20. The calculated variation of magnetic moment with temperature for octahedral cations of different configurations (a Kotani diagram).

described in terms of a splitting constant A, which simply measures the separation between the lines. It is usually quoted in oersteds, units of magnetic field, as ESR measurements are made by sweeping the magnetic field while absorbing radiation of fixed frequency. Now A will depend on the strength of the magnetic interaction between the nucleus and the electron, and will obviously be affected by covalence which spreads the electrons on to the neighbouring ligands. Table 28.XVI gives some A values for Mn^{2+} compounds. Similar series have been found for Cr^{3+}, Mo^{5+}, and V^{2+}.

Coupling may also occur with the spin of the ligand nucleus. This was first observed in the case of $[IrCl_6]^{2-}$, t_{2g}^5, the ESR spectrum of which is shown in Fig. 28.22. The coupling between each of the ^{35}Cl and ^{37}Cl nuclei (both nuclei are present and have nuclear spins of $\frac{3}{2}$) and the electron gives four lines. Coupling also takes place with the nuclear spin of the Ir so that the spectrum is complicated. From the coupling it is estimated that the unpaired electron spends only 70 per cent of the time on the Ir nucleus.

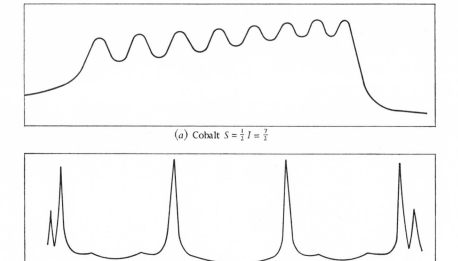

(a) Cobalt $S = \frac{1}{2}$ $I = \frac{7}{2}$

(b) Copper $S = \frac{1}{2}$ $I = \frac{3}{2}$ ^{63}Cu and ^{65}Cu

FIG. 28.21. Hyperfine structure in ESR spectra. (a) Co^{2+} (low spin) showing eight lines ($I = \frac{7}{2}$). (b) Cu^{2+} showing four main lines due to ^{63}Cu ($I = \frac{3}{2}$): the two extreme lines are two of the four lines due to ^{65}Cu ($I = \frac{3}{2}$).

TABLE 28.XVI. *Dependence of hyperfine splitting constant, A, on ligand*

Ligand	F$^-$	H$_2$O	CO$_3^{2-}$	O^{2-}	S^{2-}	Se^{2-}	Te^{2-}
A (oersteds)	98	98	94	80–90	69	65	59

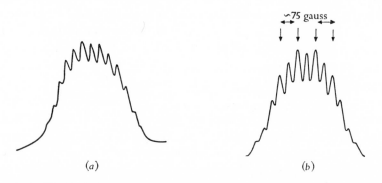

(a)   (b)

FIG. 28.22. (a) The ESR signal due to [IrCl$_6$]$^{2-}$ which has an electron spin $= \frac{1}{2}$, two types of Cl nuclei, ^{35}Cl ($I = \frac{3}{2}$), and ^{37}Cl ($I = \frac{3}{2}$), and an Ir atom of $I = \frac{3}{2}$. (b) The calculated signal showing the separation of peaks due to ^{35}Cl (after Griffiths and Owen *Proc. Roy. Soc.*, 1954, A**226**, 96). The term gauss is often used loosely instead of oersted.

CHANGE OF INTERATOMIC DISTANCE WITH CONSTANT LIGAND

The effects on bond parameters of changing the coordinating atom are now seen to be exceedingly complicated. Recently efforts have been made to study a given cation in the field of a fixed ligand atom but with varying M—L distances. This may be accomplished by the use of very high pressures or by doping the cation into various host lattices. Some data on Cr^{3+} in four different oxides have been collected in Table 28.xiv. As is well known, Cr^{3+} can give rise to green or red crystals (rubies) in different oxide lattices. Table 28.xiv shows that the changes of Δ, related to the energy of the first transition, the Racah parameter B, related to the difference in energy between the first two transitions, the nuclear hyper-fine splitting constant A, and g (which is, of course, related to ζ/Δ) do not vary in the same manner, although all the changes in these parameters have been attributed to covalence. It would appear that the contribution of covalence is still little understood.

TEMPERATURE-INDEPENDENT PARAMAGNETISM

Certain compounds are found to show a small paramagnetism despite the fact that their ground states have no unpaired electrons. The magnetic field distorts the electron distribution of a given orbital, and in so doing causes mixing of certain higher states into the ground state. The mixing decreases with increase of the energy difference between the states which are mixed. This *induced* susceptibility of the ground state is temperature-independent: it has been studied particularly in d^6 (low spin) Co^{3+} complexes and in the permanganate anion. This is a second-order Zeeman effect in which the effect of the magnetic field is proportional to H^2 rather than H. There is a related NMR line-shift of the central nucleus.

28.11. Cation-cation interaction

A set of magnetic dipoles of atoms in a lattice is frequently found to have a paramagnetic susceptibility, χ, obeying the Curie–Weiss law $\chi = C/(T - \theta_C)$. θ_C is the temperature at which the susceptibility goes to infinity, and we shall take this as implying that all the separate magnetic dipoles now act co-operatively, i.e. their interaction has overcome thermal randomization. The substances are said to be *ferromagnetic* below θ_C. The value of θ_C measures the strength of the interaction. Table 28.xvii shows that it is larger for transition metals than for lanthanide metals, as would be expected from the orbitals involved. It is also higher in compounds of more polarizable ligands, but can be quite high even in oxides.

The alignment which sets in at a given temperature may be ferromagnetic, as described, or *anti-ferromagnetic*, with magnetic dipoles aligned so as to produce no resultant magnetic field. In this case the critical temperature, T_c, below which the magnetic dipoles are no longer randomly aligned is sometimes called the Néel temperature. The susceptibility equation found

TABLE 28.XVII. *Magnetic transition temperatures*

Ferromagnetic substances	θ_C, Curie temperature (°K)	Anti-ferro- magnetic substances	T_c, Néel temperature (°K)
Fe	1043	Cr	475
Ni	631	α-Mn	∼100
Gd	289	CrSb	725
Dy	105	MnSe	∼150
Cu_2MnAl	603	MnS	165
MnBi	630	MnO	122
MnSb	587	FeO	198
MnAs	318		
Mn_4N	745		
MnB	533		
CrTe	336		
CrO_2	390		
$CoO.Fe_2O_3$	583		
UH_3	180		

experimentally is now $\chi = C/(T+\theta_N)$. Many metals, especially in the later transition series are anti-ferromagnetic. Of special interest are the series of substances in Table 28.XVII. The metals which are ferromagnetic in the transition-metal or lanthanide series are found after the half-filled sub-shell, whereas before the half-filled sub-shell they are anti-ferromagnetic. Again Group V compounds of manganese (e.g. MnAs) are ferromagnetic whereas its Group VI compounds are anti-ferromagnetic. There is, as yet, no clear reason for these differences in behaviour.

FERRITES

In compounds which contain two magnetic atoms, such as $CoO.Fe_2O_3$, there can arise combinations of ferromagnetic and anti-ferromagnetic systems. Some of these compounds crystallize in the spinel structure, in which there are two types of lattice position for the cations. For every 32 oxygen ions there are 8 tetrahedral holes and 16 octahedral holes for cations. In an inverse Fe^{3+} spinel (Table 28.XVIII), all the tetrahedral holes and half the octahedral holes are occupied by Fe^{3+}. As the interaction between the spins in the different sites is usually anti-ferromagnetic, the Fe^{3+} ions should not give rise to any bulk magnetism. If the remaining octahedral-site cations act co-operatively, ferromagnetism can result. Many of these compounds, e.g. $MgFe_2O_4$, show some magnetism despite the aligning of Fe^{3+} spins and they have been called *ferrimagnetics*.

SUPER-EXCHANGE

An interesting problem in the properties of the ferromagnetics and anti-ferromagnetics is the nature of the interaction between the magnetic transition-metal cations. The oxides are amongst the simplest compounds to examine as they can be thought of as ionic (Chapter 13). However, the

TABLE 28.XVIII. *Properties of ferrite spinels*

AB_2O_4 compound	Total spins	A spins	Observed 'spins'
$MnFe_2O_4$	15	5	4·6
$FeFe_2O_4$	14	4	4·1
$CoFe_2O_4$	13	3	3·7
$NiFe_2O_4$	12	2	2·3
$CuFe_2O_4$	11	1	1·3
$ZnFe_2O_4$	10	0	0·0
$MgFe_2O_4$	10	0	1·1

In these compounds some of the A cations may occupy tetrahedral sites.

electrical conductivity of ferrites is quite high and the magnetic inter-action between metal ions, as judged by the Curie or Néel temperatures, is strong. It has been suggested that the oxygen atoms in the lattice per-mit a special type of quantum-mechanical exchange (*super-exchange*) of electrons from one type of transition metal to another which produces both these physical properties. It depends on the occupancy of d orbitals and in spinels, for example, gives rise to ferromagnetism for two sites of the same symmetry but anti-ferromagnetism for two sites of different symmetry. Fluorides and chlorides have much lower Curie temperatures, e.g. $MnF_2 72°K$ and $CoCl_2$ 25 °K, than compounds of heavy-atom anions such as tellurium and antimony where ferromagnetic interactions are stronger. These changes parallel the changes in electrical conductivity of the solids and presumably the electron spin density on the non-metal. The magnetic interactions in solids should therefore be related to the processes of oxidation and reduc-tion, the movement of electrons through bridging atoms. An understand-ing is required not only of the activation energy for such movement but also of the mobility of electrons and holes in a lattice. Table 28.XIX shows how mobility under an applied voltage varies for some typical semiconduc-tors. The general trend for mobility to be lower the lighter the non-metal in a 'salt' and the higher the valence state of the central cation is much in keeping with our general ideas about the interaction between the wave functions on one atom and its neighbours. In dealing with the theory of such solids as are grouped in Table 28.XIX there is a need to use band theory at one extreme and ionic theory at the other. Mobility of the low order given for TiO_2 may be interpreted in terms of a 'hopping' of electrons from one centre to another, while mobility at the other end of the scale is best treated as a continuous motion, i.e. as in a band or free-electron approach.

TABLE 28.XIX. *Some properties of typical semiconductors*

Substance	Mobility (cm^2 $volt^{-1}$ sec^{-1})	Activation energy (kcal)
Graphite	10,000	~0·0
Germanium	3000	18
GaSb	5000	16
PbS	400	9·0
ZnO	200	70
Cu_2O	100	45
TiO_2	0·7	70
NaCl	very low < 1·0	very high > 120

Problems

SECTION A

1. What is meant by the symbol ^3F? Show that it represents a total degeneracy of 21.

2. What are the J states of ^4P? Show that the sum of the degeneracies of the separate J states is 12.

3. Is the separation of J states likely to be greater in the terms of the molybdenum ions than in those of the chromium ions?

4. How does the magnitude of the charge on an atom alter term separations and J-state splittings?

5. The ground states of V and Ta are spectroscopically labelled ^4F as is the first excited state of Nb. The J state splittings are (in cm^{-1}) 137, 186, 230 (V); 444, 567, 651 (Nb*); 2010, 1954, 1657 (Ta). Comment.

6. What is Russell–Saunders coupling and why does it break down in heavy atoms?

7. Using the procedure of Problem 19, Chapter 21, show that the spectroscopic terms for two d electrons are ^3F, ^3P, ^1D, ^1G, ^1S.

8. Comment on the following table which gives the energies (in cm^{-1}) for different J values of the ground (spectroscopic) states of C, O, and Pb.

In each case the energies are quoted relative to the J state with the lowest energy.

	$^3P_0$	$^3P_1$	$^3P_2$
C	0·0	16·4	43·5
O	226·5	158·5	0·0
Pb	0·0	7819·4	10,650·5

9. What factors affect the intensity of an electronic absorption spectrum?

10. Strong electronic transitions of simple systems are usually observed in the ultra-violet but weak transitions often appear in the visible. Why? Consider the cases of Cl_2, Eu^{2+}, and $[CuCl_4]^{2-}$.

11. Bees are blind to the red end of the spectrum but are able to see into the ultra-violet. Can you suggest some compounds which will appear 'coloured' to a bee but white to us?

12. In a tetrahedral environment Mn^{2+} has a green-yellow colour, much more intense than the normal pink of the octahedrally coordinated ion. Comment.

13. In an octahedral field spectroscopic terms of the free Mn^{2+} gas ion are split as follows (see Fig. 28.13):

$$^4F \rightarrow {}^4T_{2g} + {}^4T_{1g} + {}^4A_{2g}; \qquad {}^4D \rightarrow {}^4E_g + {}^4T_{2g}; \qquad {}^4P \rightarrow {}^4T_{1g};$$
$$^4G \rightarrow {}^4E_g + {}^4A_{1g} + {}^4T_{2g} + {}^4T_{1g}.$$

Show that for each term the overall number of states has been preserved. What will the ground-state label of the Mn^{2+} ion be (a) in the gas state, (b) in an octahedral field?

14. The absorption spectra of both hydrated Cu^{2+} and Ti^{3+} do not consist of one simple symmetrical band. Suggest why this may be so.

15. Comment on the following energies of absorption maxima (10^3 cm^{-1}):

$V(H_2O)_6^{2+}$ 12·3, 18·5; $V(H_2O)_6^{3+}$ 17·8, 25·7; $Cr(NH_3)_6^{3+}$ 21·5, 28·0; $[FeF_6]^{3-}$ 14·2, 19·7, 25·4, 28·8, 30·2; $[Fe(CN)_6]^{4-}$ 31·0, (39); $[PtCl_6]^{2-}$ 28·3, (> 33).

16. Iodide ion is oxidized by the Fe^{3+} ion. The complex $[Fe(NCS)]^{2+}$ is an intense purple. The following are the standard redox potentials in acid solution:

I_2/I^- +0·54, $(CNS)_2/CNS^-$ ~ +0·77, Fe^{3+}/Fe^{2+} +0·77 volts.

Comment on any relationship between these observations.

17. A *laser* is a device for obtaining *very sharp* emission lines in spectra and has special value in communications. What transitions of the ruby are particularly useful in lasers and why? (Consider excitation to $^4T_{2g}(F)$

followed by radiationless transition to ^2E_g or $^2T_{1g}$ and then return to the ground state by consulting an Orgel diagram for Cr^{3+}.)

18. How is information about Racah parameters obtained? From Figs. 28.9 and 28.11 determine Δ and B values. Compare these B values with those given for the gas ions in Table 28.VIII and comment.

19. The following is the group-theory *character table* for the *point group O*. This describes the different types of symmetry which are five in this case. (A character is the *truce of a matrix* which represents the particular operation, but this need not concern us here.)

O	E	$8C_3$	$3C_2$	$6C_2'$	$6C_4$
A_1	1	1	1	1	1
A_2	1	1	1	-1	-1
E	2	-1	2	0	0
$T_1(x, y, z)$	3	0	-1	-1	1
T_2	3	0	-1	1	-1

E is the identity *operation* and C_n is the operation of rotating by $2\pi/n$ about a specified axis. The octahedral point group (O_h) is obtained from O by adding the operation of inversion through the centre (*point*) of symmetry, in which case the *irreducible representations* $(A_1, ..., T_2)$ are further distinguished by the subscripts g (gerade) and u (ungerade). The characters listed under E correspond to the *dimensions* of the irreducible representations, i.e. to the degeneracies of the orbitals or states which form *bases* for the irreducible representations.

(a) Show that an octahedral complex MX_6 possesses the following symmetry axes: $4C_3$ (i.e. four 3-fold axes), $3C_2$ (coincident with the C_4 axes), $6C_2'$, and $3C_4$. (N.B. Only two symmetry operations correspond, for example, to each of the C_3 axes, namely C_3 and C_3^2, since $C_3^3 = E$.)

(b) The characters (χ) of the representations for which atomic wave functions of orbital quantum number l form a basis may be calculated from the equations

$$\chi(E) = 2l+1, \qquad \chi(C_n) = \frac{\sin(2l+1)\pi/n}{\sin \pi/n}.$$

Show that s and p orbitals *transform as the irreducible representations* a_{1g} and t_{1u}, respectively, and, using the fact that the characters of a *reducible representation* equal sums of the characters of the component irreducible representations, show that d, f, and g orbitals form bases for the representations e_g+t_{2g}, $a_{2u}+t_{1u}+t_{2u}$, and $a_{1g}+e_g+t_{1g}+t_{2g}$, respectively. We say that the d orbitals are 'split' by the octahedral field into (component) e_g

and t_{2g} orbitals, etc. (Exactly the same procedure may be used to determine the splitting of atomic terms characterized by a quantum number L, see Fig. 28.7.)

(c) The characters of a *direct-product* representation are obtained by multiplication of the individual characters. For example, the characters of the direct product $E \times T_2$ are 6, 0, -2, 0, 0, and the representation is reducible to the components $T_1 + T_2$. Hence find the terms arising from the strong-field configurations t_{2g}^2, $t_{2g} e_g$, and e_g^2 (see Fig. 28.7).

(d) In the theory of spectra of octahedral complexes, an electric dipole transition between states of orbital symmetries Γ_i and Γ_j is 'allowed' only if the direct-product representation $\Gamma_i \times \Gamma_j$ contains (i.e. as a component) the irreducible representation $T_{1u}(x, y, z)$. Show that (provided also that $u \leftrightarrow g$) the following transitions are orbitally allowed within an octahedral complex:

$$A_1 \leftrightarrow T_1, \quad A_2 \leftrightarrow T_2, \quad E \leftrightarrow T_1, \quad E \leftrightarrow T_2, \quad T_1 \leftrightarrow T_2.$$

(For explanation and extension see especially Cotton, *Chemical Applications of Group Theory*, Interscience, New York, 1963, chapter 8.)

20. Account for the following magnetic moments (Bohr magnetons) observed in various complexes:

V^{4+} 1·7 to 1·8, V^{3+} 2·6 to 2·8, Gd^{3+} 7·94, Ni^{2+} 2·8 to 4·0.

21. The magnetic moments in the tetrahedral Co(II) complexes ((CoX_4)$^-$) are approximately

NCS^- 4·4, Cl^- 4·6, Br^- 4·7, I^- 4·9 B.M.

Comment and relate to the position of the ligands in the spectrochemical series.

22. Explain the following observations.

When excess of ammonium thiocyanate is added to aqueous cobalt(II) nitrate the absorption maximum moves from ~ 500 mμ to ~ 700 mμ and the molar extinction coefficient increases 60-fold. On addition of mercury(II) nitrate, a precipitate forms with a spectrum very like that of the cobalt thiocyanate solution (wavelength of maximum absorption ~ 700 mμ). The precipitate contains 42·0 per cent Hg and 12·0 per cent Co. The magnetic moment of the cobalt is $\mu_{eff} = 4\cdot4$ B.M. (Atomic weights: Hg 200·6; Co 58·9.)

23. Suggest an electronic structure for the 'brown ring' complex $(FeNO)^{2+}$ (aq.) which has a magnetic moment of 3·90 B.M.

24. Potassium nickel oxalate is paramagnetic ($\mu_{\text{eff}} = 3\cdot2$ B.M.) but potassium nickel dithio-oxalate, $K_2Ni(C_2O_2S_2)_2$ is diamagnetic. Bis-α-benzoin-monoxime nickel, $(C_6H_5.CHOH.C.NO.C_6H_5)_2Ni$, is diamagnetic, but bis-α-benzil-monoxime nickel $(C_6H_5.CO.C.NO.C_6H_5)_2Ni$, is paramagnetic ($\mu_{\text{eff}} = 3\cdot6$ B.M.). How may this information be interpreted?

25. Comment on the magnetic moments of the following complexes of DAS (*o*-phenylene-bis-dimethylarsine; for formula see, for example, Table 24.vii), dipy (2,2'-dipyridyl) and of phenan (*o*-phenanthroline)

Complex	μ_{eff}
[Ni(phenan)₃](ClO₄)₂	3·10 B.M.
[Co(DAS)₃](ClO₄)₂	1·92 B.M.
[Co(dipy)₃](ClO₄)₂	4·85 B.M.
[FeBr₂(DAS)₂]	diamagnetic
[FeBr₂(phenan)₂]	4·9 B.M.
[Fe(phenan)₃]Br₂	diamagnetic

26. Comment on the magnetic susceptibility (at 300 °K) of the following compounds:

(*a*) $K_3[CoF_6]$ ($\mu_{\text{eff}} = 5\cdot5$ B.M.), K_3CuF_6 ($\mu_{\text{eff}} = 2\cdot8$ B.M.), and $K_2[NiF_6]$ (diamagnetic);

(*b*) $[Ph_3MeAs]_2[NiCl_4]$ ($\mu_{\text{eff}} = 4\cdot1$ B.M.), $K_2Ni(CN)_4$ (diamagnetic), and $[Ni(NH_3)_6]Cl_2$ ($\mu_{\text{eff}} = 3\cdot1$ B.M.);

(*c*) $V_2(SO_4)_3,3H_2O$ ($\mu_{\text{eff}} = 2\cdot6$ B.M.), $K_3W_2Cl_9$ ($\mu_{\text{eff}} = 0\cdot46$ B.M.), and $Pr_2(SO_4)_3,8H_2O$ ($\mu_{\text{eff}} = 3\cdot6$ B.M.);

(*d*) $K_2[RuCl_6]$ ($\mu_{\text{eff}} = 2\cdot9$ B.M.), $K_2[OsCl_6]$ ($\mu_{\text{eff}} = 1\cdot2$ B.M.), and $K_4[Ru_2Cl_{10}O],H_2O$ (diamagnetic);

(*e*) $KMnO_4$ ($\chi_M = +70 \times 10^{-6}$ c.g.s./mole) and $[Co(NH_3)_6]Cl_3$ ($\chi_M = +100 \times 10^{-6}$ c.g.s./mole).

27. The *g* factor for the compound $[Cu(H_2O)_6]^{2+}[SiF_6]^{2-}$ is isotropic at room temperature, but anisotropic at low temperatures. How do these facts affect the interpretation of the Jahn–Teller effect?

28. Comment on the following magnetic moments (B.M.)

Rb₂[MoOCl₅] 1·69	Rb₂[WOCl₅] 1·54
Rb₂[MoOBr₅] 1·73	Rb₂[WOBr₅] 1·37

In solution the *g* value for $[MoOCl_5]^{2-}$ is 1·947 and that for $[VO]^{2+}$ is 1·962. Why are the values less than 2·0023?

29. The bond distances in Ni(thioacetamide)$_4$Cl$_2$ (high-spin) are Ni—S 2·46 and Ni—Cl 2·40 and 2·52 Å; in diamagnetic Ni(thiosemicarbazide)$_2$SO$_4$ they are Ni—S 2·17 and Ni—N 1·90 Å; in diamagnetic Ni(thiosemi-carbazidate)$_2$ they are Ni—S 2·15 and Ni—N 1·91 Å. The Ni—N distance in the high-spin Ni(ammines) is 2·15 Å. What significance do these distances have?

SECTION B. (*Experimental*)

1. Obtain samples of CoSO$_4$,7H$_2$O; NiSO$_4$,7H$_2$O; CuSO$_4$,5H$_2$O; Cr$_2$(SO$_4$)$_3$, 15H$_2$O; Fe$_2$(SO$_4$)$_3$,12H$_2$O. Explain the colours of these salts with the help of the figures provided in this chapter.

Carry out the following series of colour reactions with each of the five salts. Record the colours observed in a chart with the same column and row headings as that shown below. Discuss in as much detail as you can the transitions likely to be involved in producing the colours. Compare your considerations with those given in the chart. The ligands are arranged in the chart in the order of the spectrochemical series.

To separate 1-ml portions of $M/10$ solutions of the sulphates in $N/10$ sulphuric acid add slowly:

(1) 10 ml concentrated hydrochloric acid,
(2) 10 ml dilute (2M) NaOH,
(3) Sodium hydroxide pellets,
(4) 5 ml M potassium thiocyanate,
(5) 5 ml strong (880) ammonia,
(6) 5 ml M potassium cyanide.

Salt	conc. HCl	Solid hydrate	dil. NaOH	conc. NaOH	KNCS	880 NH$_3$	KCN
CoSO$_4$	C	d–d	A E later	C E later	A then C	E D later	D E later
NiSO$_4$	A	d–d	A	A	A	A	D
CuSO$_4$	A, B	d–d	A	A	A, B	A	E
Cr$_2$(SO$_4$)$_3$	A	d–d	A	A	A	A	A
Fe$_2$(SO$_4$)$_3$	B	edge of charge transfer	B	B	B E partly	B	D, A

A change of d–d band position from hydrate. D change of spin state.
B appearance of charge-transfer band. E change of valence state.
C change of stereochemistry.

2. Confirm experimentally the following observations on colour reactions and comment upon the colours produced:

Addition of potassium hexacyanoferrate(II) to (1) Ag^+ (white); (2) Fe^{3+} (blue); (3) Ca^{2+} (white); and (4) Cu^{2+} (brown).

Addition of potassium hexacyanoferrate(III) to (1) Ag^+ (orange-red); (2) Cu^{2+} (green); (3) Co^{2+} (pink-red); and (4) very strong solutions Tl^+ (deep-brown).

Addition of potassium chromate to (1) Pb^{2+} (yellow); and (2) Ag^+ (red-brown).

Bibliography

C. J. BALLHAUSEN, *Introduction to Ligand Field Theory*, McGraw-Hill, New York, 1962.

A. CARRINGTON and H. C. LONGUET-HIGGINS, 'Electron Resonance in Crystalline Transition-Metal Compounds', *Quart. Rev. Chem. Soc.*, 1960, **14**, 427.

F. A. COTTON, *Chemical Applications of Group Theory*, Interscience, New York, 1963.

F. A. COTTON, 'The Infra-Red Spectra of Transition Metal Complexes', *Modern Coordination Chemistry*, eds. J. Lewis and R. G. Wilkins, Interscience, New York, 1960.

N. DAVIDSON, 'Investigations into Charge Transfer Interactions', *J. Am. Chem. Soc.*, 1949, **71**, 3809 and 3845, and 1950, **72**, 3168.

T. M. DUNN, The Visible and Ultra-Violet Spectra of Complex Compounds, *Modern Coordination Chemistry*, ed. J. Lewis and R. G. Wilkins, Interscience, New York, 1960.

B. N. FIGGIS and J. LEWIS, The Magnetic Properties of Transition Metal Complexes, *Progress in Inorganic Chemistry*, vol. 6, ed. F. A. Cotton, Interscience, New York, 1964.

J. B. GOODENOUGH, *Magnetism and the Chemical Bond*, Interscience, New York, 1963.

J. S. GRIFFITH, *The Theory of Transition-Metal Ions*, Cambridge University Press, 1961.

C. K. JØRGENSEN, *Inorganic Complexes*, Academic Press, New York, 1963.

C. K. JØRGENSEN, *Absorption Spectra and Chemical Bonding in Complexes*, Pergamon Press, Oxford, 1962.

J. N. MURRELL, 'The Theory of Charge Transfer Spectra', *Quart. Rev. Chem. Soc.*, 1961, **15**, 191.

L. E. ORGEL, *An Introduction to Transition-Metal Chemistry, Ligand-Field Theory*, Methuen, London, 1960.

P. W. SELWOOD, *Magnetochemistry*, Interscience, New York, 1956.

29 · Transition Metals: Kinetics and Mechanisms

29.1. Introduction

The subject of reaction kinetics has been introduced in Chapter 10 in terms of the transition-state theory. On this theory the rate of a reaction is related to the activation free-energy change between the reactants and a postulated transition state. The properties of such transition states are not readily open to experimental study. As an approximation, it is often presumed therefore that these transition states are similar to known or likely intermediates along the reaction path. The intermediates are either recognized through their physical properties, e.g. spectra, or are postulated on the basis of a general chemical knowledge of the reactants. Clearly the understanding of kinetics is on much less secure ground than that of thermodynamics. Nevertheless a great deal of experimental information is available about rates of reactions and especially about those of transition-metal complexes. In this chapter a selection of the data will be made in order to illustrate both the variation of rates with transition-metal ion and with ligand and the ways of thinking about reaction mechanisms. It must be understood, however, that the interpretation of the kinetics of transition-metal complexes is at a relatively early stage of development, and is open to considerable revision. The introductory sections of Chapter 10 could be read again with profit before starting this chapter.

The discussion will start with the graphical presentation of rate data for a number of reaction systems in order to bring out some common features of and some differences between the rates of substitution reactions and those of oxidation-reduction reactions. The section immediately following, 29.2, looks more closely at the mechanisms of substitution reactions and particularly at the interpretation of their activation energies. So far nearly all the interpretation has been in terms of crystal-field theory, because of its simplicity. The subsequent sections, 29.3–29.5, analyse aspects of electron-transfer and atom-transfer reactions (oxidation and reduction), concentrating mainly upon *inner-sphere* and *outer-sphere* mechanisms. Again it is the activation energy of the reactions which is most difficult to understand. In section 29.5 some assistance in this problem is sought by reference to the properties of solids.

VARIATION OF REACTION RATE WITH ATOMIC NUMBER

The essential features of the variation of reaction rate with change of central-metal cation are presented in Figs. 29.1 to 29.4. The examples in

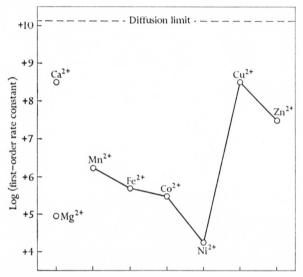

FIG. 29.1. First-order rate constants (sec^{-1}) for the dissociation of water from the aquated ions, the initial step in the reaction with SO_4^{2-}. (Data from Eigen, *Seventh International Conference on Coordination Chemistry*, Plenary Lecture No. 6, Butterworths, London, 1963.)

the figures are a few of a large number which bring out the same general points. Fig. 29.1 shows the rate of dissociation of water from the divalent cations from Mn^{2+} to Zn^{2+}. Fig. 29.2 gives schematically the range of rate constants which have been observed for hydrolysis and substitution reactions with the same cations. Fig. 29.3 (*b*) presents the corresponding data for the trivalent cations from Sc^{3+} to Co^{3+}. Fig. 29.4 gives the rate of electron exchange between the M^{2+} and M^{3+} cations from V to Co.

The figures permit a comparison of the variation of the rates of substitution reactions and redox reactions with atomic number. All the figures have a number of features in common, but also one or two striking differences.

(1) The ions which have three, six, or eight d electrons react most slowly. This is exemplified by the behaviour of Cr^{3+}—d^3, Co^{3+} and, for some reactions only, Fe^{2+}—d^6 and Ni^{2+}—d^8. The generalization is valid for substitution, hydrolysis, and redox reactions so long as the ligands are saturated.

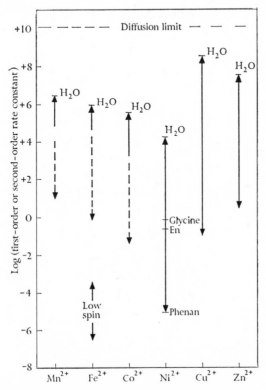

Fig. 29.2. The regions over which the rate constants for substitution of ligands (or hydrolysis) in complexes extend. Figure relates to high-spin complexes except where indicated for Fe^{2+}. The values for the replacement of water are as in Fig. 29.1. (Data from Stranks.)

(2) With unsaturated ligands, such as cyanide and o-phenanthroline, the ligand-exchange reactions are slower than with saturated ligands, but the redox reactions are now fast with the d^3, d^6 (and d^8) ions. This illustrates a special facility for electron transport amongst these ligands. The same ligands slow down rather than accelerate hydrolysis.

(3) In general the exchange of ligands in low-spin complexes is slower than in those of high-spin. Thus the diamagnetic low-spin $[Co(oxalate)_3]^{3-}$ reacts much more slowly than paramagnetic high-spin $[Fe(oxalate)_3]^{3-}$.

Although both ions are d^6, diamagnetic $[Fe(CN)_6]^{4-}$ exchanges ligands slowly, but $[Fe(H_2O)_6]^{2+}$ (high-spin) exchanges H_2O very rapidly.

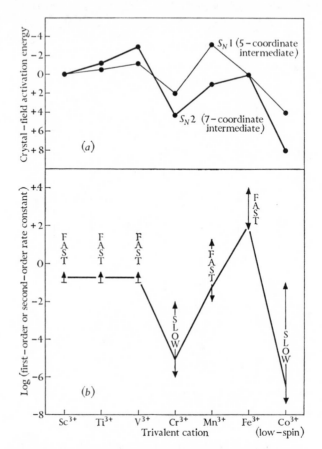

FIG. 29.3. (a) Crystal-field activation energies calculated by the method described in the text, see Table 29.II. (b) Quantitative indication of the relative rate constants for substitution reactions of trivalent ions. Figure 29.3(a) and (b) relates to high-spin ions except for Co^{3+} (data from Stranks).

Experimental studies not recorded in the figures show also that:

(4) Low-spin d^8 complexes which have four ligands in a plane exchange ligands moderately slowly, more slowly than d^8 high-spin octahedral complexes, but much faster than octahedral low-spin complexes. Thus Ni(II) (low-spin) reacts more rapidly than Co(III) and Fe(II) (low-spin).

(5) Ligand exchange in the second and third transition series is usually

slower than in the first series. Thus the rate of aquation of $[M(NH_3)_5Cl]^{2+}$ follows the metal order Co > Rh > Ir. This may be due to the increasing 'b' character of the metal ions.

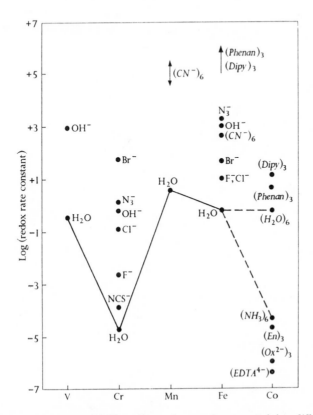

Fig. 29.4. Rate of M^{3+}/M^{2+} exchange in complexes containing different ligands. Unless indicated there is but one ligand of the kind shown, the rest of the ligands being water. Low-spin complexes are italicized. The values for aquo ions are joined together but in the case of Co^{3+} the aquo ion is atypical, and the lower broken line to the ammine is more representative of the change in rate from Fe to Co. (Data from Stranks.)

The broad similarities in the figures (see point (1) above) could mean that either (a) the different reactions, ligand-exchange, hydrolysis, and redox, go by the same mechanisms, these being especially restricted for certain electron configurations, or (b) no matter what the mechanism, similar energy restrictions apply which are peculiar to certain cations. The possible mechanisms will be examined first.

29.2. Substitution reactions

ORDER OF REACTION

The rates of substitution reactions are commonly found to be either dependent on the concentration of the metal complex and independent of that of the incoming ligand (first order), or dependent on the product of

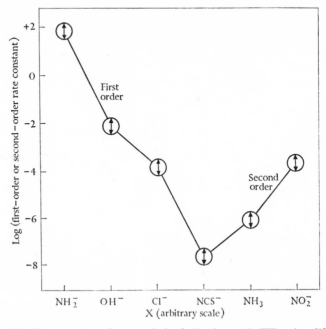

Fig. 29.5. Rate constants for a typical substitution at Co(III) using different internal groups, $[Co(en)_2ClX]^{n+}+H_2O \rightarrow [Co(en)_2(H_2O)X]^{(n+1)+}+Cl^-$.

these concentrations (second order). Fig. 29.5 shows that the change from one order to the other may depend on small changes of the ligand in a complex. The figure is deliberately arranged so as to give a sequence of rate constants, and the line drawn in the figure has no theoretical significance. From many results of the type shown in Fig. 29.5 the following generalizations appear to hold. (1) For a particular cation, reaction rates tend to be either slow or fast, i.e. the gross distinctions between cations are independent of the order of the reaction. Thus Co(III) substitution reactions are nearly always slow. The general comparisons in Figs. 29.1 to 29.4 are usually valid without consideration of kinetic order. (2) The rate of first-order reactions is increased by electron-donor substituents, X. (3) The rate of second-order reactions is also ligand-dependent but appears to increase as the electron-acceptor power of the ligand increases, e.g. $NO_2^- > NH_3$ and NCS^-. All these observations can be interpreted in terms of two simple mechanisms.

MECHANISM OF SUBSTITUTION

It has often been assumed that the first-order reactions have a unimolecular mechanism, and that the second-order reactions have a bimolecular mechanism. If this were so the transition states derived from an octahedral complex would be related to a 5-coordinate and a 7-coordinate complex, respectively. The slow reactions of d^3, d^6 (low-spin), and d^8 (high-spin) complexes would be taken then as an indication of the high stability of their octahedral ground-states. These mechanisms will be examined in detail below. It follows too that Cl^- should dissociate with difficulty from $[Co(en)_2XCl]$ if X is a good electron acceptor, so that second-order kinetics would be favoured. The second-order reaction should also be preferred if X is neutral, for there is then a higher charge on the complex, or if X occupies a small volume around Co^{3+}. These points are generally supported by the data.

Despite this simple agreement between theory and experimental observation the details of the mechanisms of substitution have proved difficult to settle. To begin with there is always the possibility of acid-base catalysis. Base catalysis could involve the removal of a proton by an entering ligand. Thus the first step of an hydroxyl attack could involve the equilibrium

$$[Co(NH_3)_4(H_2O)X^-]^{2+}+OH^- \rightleftharpoons [Co(NH_3)_4OH^-X^-]^++H_2O,$$

which is not a substitution at the cobalt, followed by

$$[Co(NH_3)_4OH^-X^-]^+ \rightarrow [Co(NH_3)_4OH^-]^{2+}+X^- \quad (S_N1, \text{ slow unimolecular})$$

and $\quad [Co(NH_3)_4OH^-]^{2+}+H_2O \rightarrow [Co(NH_3)_4(H_2O)OH^-]^{2+}$ (fast).

It is then very difficult to distinguish this S_N1 reaction from an overall S_N2 attack by hydroxide

$$[Co(NH_3)_4(H_2O)X]^{2+}+OH^- \rightarrow 7\text{-coordinate complex}$$
$$\rightarrow [Co(NH_3)_4(H_2O)OH^-]^{2+}+X^-.$$

That hydrolysis of the ligand can in fact be important is shown by the rate constants (litre mole^{-1} sec^{-1}) for mono-complex formation of various Fe^{3+} complexes from the hydrate:

$$F^- (5\times10^3), \text{ HF } (11\cdot4); N_3^- (1\cdot6\times10^5), HN_3 (4\cdot0).$$

In each case attack by the anion is much faster. Again attack on

$[Fe(H_2O)_5OH^-]^{2+}$ is faster than on $[Fe(H_2O)_6]^{3+}$ by some 10^3-fold for neutral molecules such as HF and HN_3.

It is also possible for confusion to arise in reactions involving the replacement of solvent in a complex, for this can be written as a direct attack (S_N2), or as a loss of solvent (S_N1) followed by an attack on the intermediate by the reagent. The overall rate expression may well be dependent upon the second step. However, the close parallel which is often observed between the rate of replacement of water and the rate of water exchange in a coordination sphere may indicate that in many cases the dissociation of water is the rate-controlling step. For example, the first-order rate constants for the displacement of H_2O in $[Co(en)_2NO_2H_2O]^{2+}$ are independent

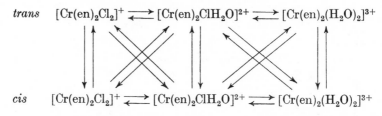

FIG. 29.6. Species present in the hydrolysis of $[CrIII(ethylenediamine)_2Cl_2]^+$, as shown by ion-exchange chromatography. There are twenty-two possible rate constants in this hydrolysis reaction.

of the anion attacking. In practice the concentration of solvent is not readily open to experimental variation, and dependence of rate upon it must be studied by using isotopes, e.g. D_2O. The study of reaction rates in aqueous solution is also made difficult by the ready formation of ion pairs. The rate of replacement of water in the second coordination sphere is very rapid, usually diffusion-controlled, and a small equilibrium ion-pair concentration may greatly affect rates.

Another difficulty with the reactions of coordination complexes is the great number of paths which may be used simultaneously. Thus although it is often found that the products are relatively simple when a reaction has gone to completion, a variety of 'products' may be present at intermediate stages. Many analytical observations during the course of apparently simple substitutions show that these reactions are often quite complicated. For example, chromatographic analysis of the Cr(III) complexes present during the hydrolysis of trans-$[Cr(III)(ethylenediamine)_2 Cl_2]^+$ has shown that the scheme given in Fig. 29.6 is necessary, although the overwhelmingly important final product is the trans-diaquo-compound. That all these complexes could be detected shows that the free-energy differences between the isomers must be small and that the reactions of all of them are slow, no matter what the mechanisms.

The mechanism of a reaction can also be examined by studying its steric course. Thus in the $S_N 1$ mechanism

Reactant   Intermediate   Product

trans $M(en)_2X_2 \longrightarrow M(en)_2X \longrightarrow M(en)_2XH_2O$

trigonal   *cis* and *trans*
bipyramid

$M(en)_2X \longrightarrow M(en)_2XH_2O$ *trans*

tetragonal
pyramid

the two possible intermediates are clearly distinguishable from the nature of the products. The $S_N 2$ mechanism will be generally expected to give a *trans* product as well since steric factors favour attack by the incoming water molecule at the same side as the leaving group. (Studies of the Walden inversion (carbon chemistry) indicate, however, that 'back' attack is also possible.) Unfortunately the experimental results have not always been as unambiguous as this simple picture suggests. In particular the lability of the *trans* $M(en)_2XH_2O$ complex may be so great that its partial conversion to the *cis* form could lead to a mistaken conclusion as to the mechanism of the reaction.

In summary, although a large number of substitution reactions have been examined, there are only a few cases where an $S_N 1$ mechanism has been firmly established, and there do not appear to be any for which an $S_N 2$ mechanism has been convincingly proven.

ACTIVATION ENERGY

The data in Table 29.1 show that the complexes which have slow substitution reactions have high activation energies rather than highly unfavourable activation entropies. A reaction with an activation energy greater than 20 kcal and little positive activation entropy will be slow at room temperature. Thus we should seek for the peculiarities of the cations having slow reactions in the energies of their compounds and transition states. This means, for example, that it is the electron configuration of Co^{3+} which gives it special kinetic stability. Now it is a well-recognized observation that the most thermodynamically-stable complexes of the transition-metal ions are not necessarily the most kinetically-stable; compare Figs. 29.1–29.4 with figures in Chapters 25 and 26. Kinetic stability involves the

TABLE 29.I. *Heats and entropies of activation for substitution reactions in aqueous solution at 25 °C*

Reaction	$\Delta G^{\ddagger}$ (kcal mole^{-1})	$\Delta H^{\ddagger}$ (kcal mole^{-1})	$\Delta S^{\ddagger}$ (cal deg^{-1} mole^{-1})	Comment
$Cr(H_2O)_6^{3+} + H_2\overset{*}{O}$	28·0 ?	28	0 ?	slow
$Cr(H_2O)_6^{3+} + SCN^-$	25·4	25·7	1	slow
$Cr(H_2O)_6^{3+} + urea$	24·3	21·0	−11	slow
$[Co(NH_3)_5H_2O]^{3+} + SO_4^{2-}$	18·6	23·7	17	intermediate to slow
$Ni(CN)_4^{2-} + \overset{*}{Ni}(glycinate)_2$	20·6	17·3	−11	strong-field tetragonal d^8: intermediate rate
$Fe(H_2O)_6^{3+} + SCN^-$	11·5	12·7	4	fast
$Co(H_2O)_6^{2+} + SCN^-$	9·6	15	18	fast

* = isotope.

difference between the stability of the transition state and the ground state. It is the latter alone which controls the thermodynamic stability.

CATION DEPENDENCE

Since the *variation* of reaction rate with change of metal cation appears to be roughly independent of reaction order and of the particular ligand being replaced or attacking, this subsection will not be concerned with further analysis of the reaction mechanisms.

It might have been expected that the rate of substitution in ML would become progressively slower on passing from cations of the pre-transition metals to the cations of the B metals since the M—L bond energy is increasing and the bond polarity decreasing along the transition series. However, it is clear from Chapter 10 and Figs. 29.1–29.3 that this is not so. The changes in ionic radii in the transition series are also irregular, and it is worth noting that, with some exceptions to be discussed below, the rate of exchange of water in transition-metal and pre-transition complexes is fairly closely related to ion-size (Fig. 29.7). The relation between rate and charge is also obvious from the figure. However, unlike the thermodynamic situation, the B-metal cations are kinetically quite different from the cations of adjacent transition-metal elements. In Chapter 10 it was deduced that an important factor determining the behaviour of different cations was the ease with which they could change coordination number. In this respect, comparison with melting-point data (Fig. 25.12) is quite revealing.

Cations with the electron configurations d^3, d^6 (low-spin), and d^8 are, however, considerably more inert than size alone would suggest. The d^3 and d^6 (low-spin) cases could perhaps be attributed to especially strong (covalent) bond formation (valence-bond theory), as these configurations

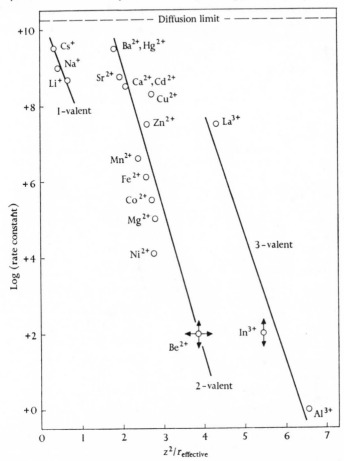

FIG. 29.7. The relation between rates of water substitution on cations and the function (cation charge)^2/(cation radius $+0.85$ Å).

permit the formation of d^2sp^3 hybrid orbitals (section 24.7). However, this explanation leaves the relatively slow reactions of d^8 (high-spin) ions without a convincing rationalization.

CRYSTAL-FIELD THEORY

A more satisfying theory of substitution reactions considers the relative ligand-field energies of the ground and transition states. For *octahedral* complexes 5-coordinate, $S_N 1$, and 7-coordinate, $S_N 2$, complexes are the most probable reaction intermediates, and it is to be expected that such intermediates will resemble the respective transition states closely. Contributions to the activation energies may be estimated simply from the differences in *crystal-field* stabilization energies between the states of different geometry. The stabilization energies (Table 29.II) are calculated using

TABLE 29.II. *Relative crystal-field energies for cations in three different field symmetries (after Basolo and Pearson, 1958)*

	High-spin							Low-spin
Number of d electrons	5	6	7	8	9	10		
	0	1	2	3	4	5	6	6
	Mn^{2+}	Fe^{2+}	Co^{2+}	Ni^{2+}	Cu^{2+}	Zn^{2+}		
	Ca^{2+}	Sc^{2+}	Ti^{2+}	V^{2+}	Cr^{2+}	Mn^{2+}	Fe^{2+}	Fe^{2+}
	Sc^{3+}	Ti^{3+}	V^{3+}	Cr^{3+}	Mn^{3+}	Fe^{3+}	Co^{3+}	Co^{3+}
Symmetry								
(a) Octahedral, 6-coordinate	0	−4	−8	−12	−6	0	−4	−24
(b) Square pyramidal, 5-coordinate	0	−4·57	−9·14	−10	−9·14	0	−4·57	−20
(c) Pentagonal bipyramidal, 7-coordinate	0	−5·28	−10·56	−7·74	−4·93	0	−5·28	−15·48
6 → 5 (b)−(a)	0	−0·57	−1·14	+2	−3·14	0	−0·57	+4·00
6 → 7 (c)−(a)	0	−1·28	−2·56	+4·26	+1·07	0	−1·28	+8·52
Sign of contribution to $\Delta H^{\ddagger}$	0	—	—	+	±	0	—	+

	Low-spin						
Number of d electrons	4	5	6	7	8	9	10
	Mn^{3+}	Fe^{3+}	Co^{3+}		Pd^{2+} Pt^{2+}		Zn^{2+}
Symmetry							
(a) Octahedral, 6-coordinate	−16	−20	−24	−18	−12	−6	0
(b) Square pyramidal, 5-coordinate	−14·57	−19·14	−20·0	−19·14	−10·0	−9·14	0
(c) Pentagonal bipyramidal, 7-coordinate	−13·02	−18·30	−15·48	−12·66	−7·74	−4·93	0
6 → 5 (b)−(a)	+1·43	+0·86	+4·00	−1·14	+2·00	−3·14	0
6 → 7 (c)−(a)	+2·98	+1·70	+8·52	+5·34	+4·26	+1·07	0
Sign of contribution to $\Delta H^{\ddagger}$	+	+	+	±	+	±	0

a *constant* value of Dq independent of the symmetry of the field. Positive *differences* between the transition state and the octahedral state (Table 29.II) should lead to slow reactions and occur for: (1) dissociation to a 5-coordinate intermediate at d^3, high-spin d^8, and low-spin d^4, d^5, d^6, and d^8 ions, and (2) association to a 7-coordinate intermediate at high-spin d^3, (d^4), d^8, and (d^9) and low-spin d^4, d^5, d^6, d^7, and d^8 ions. The prediction of the ions which react most slowly by either the $S_N 1$ or the $S_N 2$ mechanism is largely in agreement with experiment (Figs. 29.1, 29.2, and especially 29.3).

The table also predicts that for d^3, d^6 (low-spin), or d^8 cations, the $S_N 1$

mechanism is of lower activation energy than the $S_N 2$. Thus it offers an explanation for the preponderance of unimolecular reactions.

For the same cations the crystal-field approach predicts that the rates of either $S_N 2$ or $S_N 1$ substitution reactions should be smaller the greater the field, Dq, at the metal. However, if spectra are used to give the field-strength order (see section 24.5), the theory does not always agree well with experiment. Thus, for example, the rate of the reaction

$$[\text{Pt(dien)X}]^+ + \text{py} \rightarrow [\text{Pt(dien)py}]^{2+} + \text{X}^-,$$

where dien is $NH_2CH_2CH_2NHCH_2CH_2NH_2$ and py is pyridine, follows the order of X^-,

$$NO_3^- > Cl^- > Br^- > I^- > N_3^- > SCN^- > NO_2^- > CN^-,$$

while the spectrochemical series is

$$I^- < Br^- < Cl^- < NO_3^- < N_3^- < SCN^- < NO_2^- < CN^-.$$

It would appear that a molecular-orbital model for the interaction between d orbitals, or rather the split d orbitals, is required in which ligand π-bonding with t_{2g} and σ-bonding with e_g orbitals is described (section 24.6).

The calculations further predict that the reactions of high-spin d^1, d^2, (d^4), d^6, d^7, and (d^9), and perhaps of low-spin d^7 complexes should be faster than those of d^0, d^5, and d^{10} complexes. In so far as this has been tested this prediction is unsuccessful. Possibly this is due to the simplifying assumption used in obtaining Table 29.II that Dq does not change with symmetry. It appears that for ions with these configurations the presence of the $(n-1)d$ orbitals and electrons has little influence on reactivity (Fig. 29.7). This is unlike the effect of nd orbitals in the second period (Chapter 10). By way of contrast, low-spin complexes of the second and third transition series appear to be generally inert from Group IVA to Group VIII, to some extent independent of valence state and of the number of d electrons, and despite the fact that crystal-field activation energies are not always large (Table 29.II). There is a strong suggestion here that the covalent character of bonds, which is greater in low-spin systems, is at least of equal importance with the symmetry changes from the ground to the transition states and that the ionic approach, while helping with the second problem, cannot indicate the important factors in the first. The spectroscopic splitting parameter, Δ, is greater in the second and third than in the first transition series. Clearly a more satisfactory treatment could be developed from molecular-orbital theory, but this is not yet possible.

In field symmetries other than octahedral, replacement rates by either mechanism will be grossly altered, and the above order of rates for different metals (octahedral complexes) will no longer be expected. Experimental evidence is not available on this point.

THE *trans*-EFFECT

The influence of the π-bonding as well as of the σ-bonding orbitals in controlling the kinetic properties of transition-metal complexes is shown too in the effect of one coordination ligand X upon the *lability* of another Y in the same coordination complex (Fig. 29.8). The best examples are found in the complexes of platinum(II), $PtXYZ_2$, where the two ligands Z complete the planar arrangement of four ligands around divalent platinum, and in some *trans* octahedral $Co(III)Z_4XY$ complexes. We know that (1) certain ligands X tend to favour *rapid* substitution of Y, when Y is in the *trans* position relative to X, and (2) this rate increase is relatively independent of the nature of the entering ligand. The series of coordinated ligands X of decreasing *trans*-labilizing influence in Pt(II) compounds is

$$H^- > CN^- \simeq C_2H_4 \simeq CO \simeq CH_3^- \simeq NO \sim SC(NH_2)_2 \simeq PR_3 > NO_2^-$$
$$> I^- > NCS^- > Br^- > Cl^- > py > RNH_2 \sim NH_3 > OH^- > H_2O$$

but a different order has been found for substitutions at octahedral Pt(IV),

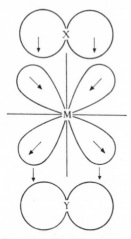

FIG. 29.8. Possible origin of *trans*-stabilization. Arrows show electron drift which would reduce nucleophilic attack on M—Y.

Co(III), and Rh(III). Crudely it would appear that a combination of the best π-electron acceptor and the best σ-donor (most polarizable) is the most strongly *trans*-labilizing ligand. There is no clear correlation between the above series and either the spectrochemical or nephelauxetic series (section 28.6). The order is not very different from that given above for the ease of replacement of X in $[Pt(dien)X]^+$ by pyridine. The relative rate of attack by an incoming ligand gives a series somewhat like that of the *trans*-series itself,. which is surprising. Anomalously the thermodynamic *trans*-effect measured by the relative stability of the binding of a ligand X in the presence of different *trans*-ligands Y is often small.

The *trans*-effect has been used in the synthesis of inorganic complexes (problem 29.14). It is of the greatest importance in the vitamin B_{12} (Co^{3+}) and porphyrin (Fe^{2+}) series of complexes. The attachment of a carbanion to the Co^{3+} of B_{12} coenzyme makes the binding at the sixth coordination position of the cobalt very weak, so that these cobalt(III) complexes are surprisingly labile. Crystal structure data show that even the bond from Co^{3+} to Cl^- is longer in these systems than in more conventional complexes.

THE *cis*-EFFECT

A d orbital is strongly influenced by all nearby ligands in its own plane. This situation arises because the d orbital has a symmetry associated with more than one single axis. Thus the d_{xy} orbital can transmit effects from the x to the y axis, through π-bonding (perpendicular conjugation, Fig. 29.9). Ligands *cis* as well as *trans* to a particular ligand come under its influence. The *cis*-effect has been little investigated though it may sometimes be more important than the *trans*-effect, e.g. especially in octahedral Co(III) complexes.

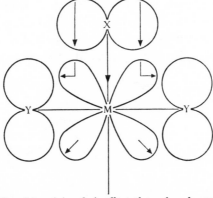

FIG. 29.9. Possible origin of *cis*-effect through σ-donor or through π-donor (perpendicular conjugation) power of X.

In the biologically-significant complexes of iron (porphyrins) and of cobalt (corrins) which form the active-centres of the important haem-carrying proteins and of the B_{12} coenzyme, respectively, the protein groups bound to the metal perpendicular to the ring affect the planar ring through a strong *cis*-effect. In these compounds it has been shown that the *cis*-effect follows an order close to that of the nephelauxetic series. At the present time the interpretation of the two effects, *cis* and *trans*, is not satisfactory. There is some suggestion that in its thermodynamic influence the *cis*-effect may be the stronger. In kinetics the *trans*-effect is usually the more marked. In both effects the relative importance of π-bonding and σ-bonding is open to debate.

29.3. Electron-transfer mechanisms

Oxidation-reduction reactions may proceed via three main mechanisms.
(1) Formation of a complex M_1XM_2 in which the two metal ions are bridged

by a ligand. This involves, therefore a *substitution* in which some other ligand is lost from M_1 or M_2 followed by an electron transfer, and is called an inner-sphere mechanism. (2) Electron transfer in a 'collision' complex without substitution occurring. This is called an outer-sphere mechanism. (3) Atom transfer. This mechanism may be likened to ion transport in solids but is not simply related to electron-transfer. It involves the movement of an atom, e.g. O, or a group, e.g. $OH^{\cdot}$, from one coordination centre to another.

ACTIVATION ENERGY

For low-spin ions the activation energies of oxidation-reduction reactions are lower than those of substitution reactions (e.g. Table 29.III). This indicates that the formation of the transition states with ions such as Co^{3+} does not proceed through the replacement of a ligand in the coordination sphere of these cations. On the other hand, the activation energies for the

TABLE 29.III. *Activation energies of substitution and redox reactions*

Reaction	Spin state	Reaction type	Activation energy (kcal)
$[Co(NH_3)_5Cl]^{2+}+H_2O$	low-spin	substitution	22·9
$[Fe(phenanthroline)_3]^{2+}+H_2O$	low-spin	substitution	32·0
$[Fe(H_2O)_6]^{3+}+SCN^-$	high-spin	substitution	12·7
$[Ni(phenanthroline)_3]^{2+}+$ phenanthroline*	high-spin	substitution	25·0
$[Co(EDTA)]^{2-}+\overset{*}{Co}{}^{2+}$	high-spin	substitution	12·4
$[\overset{*}{Fe}(CN)_6]^{4-}+[Fe(CN)_6]^{3-}$	low-spin	redox	4·7
$[\overset{*}{Co}(NH_3)_6]^{2+}+[Co(NH_3)_6]^{3+}$	low-spin	redox	13·5
$[\overset{*}{Fe}(H_2O)_6]^{2+}+[Fe(H_2O)_6]^{3+}$	high-spin	redox	9·9
$MnO_4^{2-}+MnO_4^-$		redox	10·5

* indicates isotopically labelled species.

reactions of the more labile complexes, e.g. of Co(II) and Fe(III), are of the same order as those for substitution in the complexes. The overall similarity in the rates of the redox reactions (Fig. 29.4), and of the replacement reactions (Fig. 29.2), may then be somewhat misleading. This can be seen too from the fact that it is often the large opposing entropy effects which make electron-exchange reactions slow, whereas it is the opposing heat terms which makes substitution slow. An increased understanding of these differences can be obtained by comparing the effects of different ligands upon the rates of redox reactions and upon the rates of substitution reactions. This can be done by reference to the figures generally or by a detailed examination of the bridge mechanism to which we shall now proceed.

INNER-SPHERE REACTIONS

The simplest type of bridge mechanism that can be studied is the oxidation of a cation by a higher-valence cation of the same metal. This study is particularly rewarding if one of the ions, for example the Cr^{3+} ion, does not exchange ligands rapidly. Thus in the redox reaction

$$[(NH_3)_5Cr^{3+}X] + \overset{*}{Cr}{}^{2+} \rightarrow [\overset{*}{Cr}{}^{3+}X] + Cr^{2+} + 5NH_3,$$

or generally

$$M_a^{n+}X + M_b^{(n-1)+} \rightarrow M_b^{n+}X + M_a^{(n-1)+},$$

the ligand X is never freed from association with one of the two metal ions. The analysis of the products (usually employing radioactive isotopes of X) can help to decide whether the path of the reaction is one involving a bridge, such as the species Cr(III)–X–Cr(II), or one involving an outer-sphere mechanism. The rate is dependent upon the bridging ligand as the constants in Table 29.IV show. Two points deserve comment.

(1) For simple anions the rate order is

$$F^- < OH^- < Cl^- < Br^- < I^-$$

which is very similar to the nephelauxetic series (section 28.6), and the expected sequence of covalence in the metal-ligand bonds. This is easily understood since in more covalent systems the energy gap between the ground state M^+X^- and the excited state $M^{\cdot}X^{\cdot}$ is usually small, so that the electron-transfer contribution to the overall activation free energy is reduced.

TABLE 29.IV. *Rate constants for reaction of Cr(II) aquo complex with various Cr(III) and Co(III) complexes*

Cr(III)(H$_2$O)$_5$X X =	NCS$^-$	F$^-$	N$_3^-$	Cl$^-$	Br$^-$
k (l. mole^{-1} sec^{-1})	$1{\cdot}8 \times 10^{-4}$	$2{\cdot}6 \times 10^{-2}$	$> 1{\cdot}2$	$\sim 8{\cdot}5$	> 60
Cr(III)(NH$_3$)$_5$X X =	F$^-$	Cl$^-$	Br$^-$	I$^-$	
k (l. mole^{-1} sec^{-1})	$2{\cdot}7 \times 10^{-4}$	$5{\cdot}1 \times 10^{-2}$	$3{\cdot}2 \times 10^{-1}$	$5{\cdot}5$	
Co(III)(NH$_3$)$_5$X X =	acetate	succinate	maleate*	fumarate*	o-phthalate p-phthalate
k (l. mole^{-1} sec^{-1})	$0{\cdot}15$	$\sim 1{\cdot}0$	> 20	$0{\cdot}5$	~ 10 ~ 40

* For conjugated ligands the transition-state complex is as in Fig. 29.10.

(2) The difference in reactivity of o-phthalate and p-phthalate suggests that for a ligand with two possible ends for coordination there will be rapid electron exchange if the ligand system is conjugated, and so disposed as to permit the close approach of the reducing cation to one end of the ligand while the other end is bound to the oxidizing cation (cf. Fig. 29.10). The rate

of the Cr(II)/Co(III) reaction with succinate as a bridge is low, $k \sim 1 \cdot 0$, but that with maleate as a bridge is high, $k > 20$.

Although electron-transfer reactions involving an inner-sphere complex usually involve atom transfer too, this is not an essential feature of the mechanism. Thus the oxidation of Cr^{2+} by $[IrCl_6]^{2-}$ is thought to take place via the intermediate $[IrCl_6Cr(H_2O)_5]$, but the bridging Cl atom is not transferred from the Ir(IV) to the Cr(II).

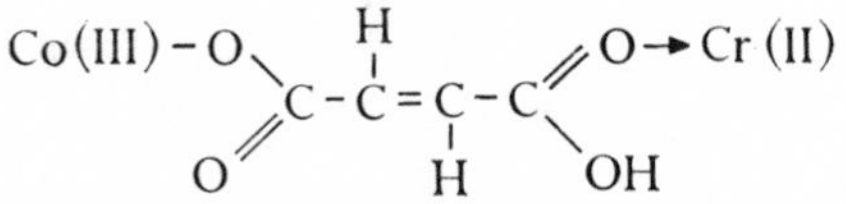

FIG. 29.10. Conjugation of one cation to another through an unsaturated ligand which may facilitate electron transport.

OUTER-SPHERE REACTIONS

The importance of conjugation can also be seen in the rates of Co(III)/Co(II) redox (exchange) reactions, which go by *outer-sphere* mechanisms.

ligands	$(phenan)_3$	$(en)_3$	$(NH_3)_6$
log k (l. mole^{-1} sec^{-1})	0·54	−3·2	−5·1

Phenanthroline is the only conjugated ligand. When ligand exchange is very slow, as, for example, when both the reducing and the oxidizing ions are low-spin, then the mechanism of the reaction could be thought of as a double bridge $M_1X...YM_2$. Thus in the reaction between $Fe(CN)_6^{4-}$ and $Fe(dipy)_3^{3+}$, it has been shown that no ligand dissociation takes place during reaction as the dipyridyl complex can be oxidized faster than it will racemize and CN^- exchange is very slow with $Fe(CN)_6^{4-}$. These facts require an outer-sphere mechanism, and since the oxidation reaction is quite rapid the movement of electrons must be *through* the coordination sphere of the ligand. Electron mobility in ligands is clearly an important contributing factor to both inner-sphere and outer-sphere redox mechanisms, and the effect of ligands upon this mobility *cannot* be related to their effect on substitution rates.

OUTER-SPHERE MECHANISM—THEORETICAL CONSIDERATIONS

Oxidation-reduction reactions are more complicated than substitution reactions, for as well as the formation of a transition-state complex there is also the actual redox, electron-transfer or atom-transfer, step to be examined:

$$M^{n+} + X^{m-} \rightarrow MX^{(n-m)+} \rightarrow M^{(n-1)+} + X^{(m-1)-} \rightarrow \text{products}.$$

In the outer-sphere mechanism no substitution in the inner coordination sphere occurs. The overall reaction is favourable, so that its oxidation-reduction potential gives no guide to the rate of electron transfer in the complex. An activation energy is observed presumably because the oxidized and reduced ions are produced in the presence of ligand atmospheres appropriate to reduced and oxidized ions respectively. This

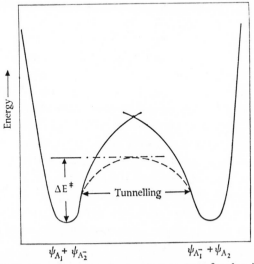

FIG. 29.11. The energy barrier to electron transfer showing the lowering of $\Delta E^{\ddagger}$ due to overlap of orbitals and the possibility of electron tunnelling.

additional relaxation energy has sometimes been called the Franck–Condon 'energy', just as the fact that an electronic excitation is fast compared with atomic vibrations is called the Franck–Condon principle. Those cations which undergo greatest loss of energy on addition of electrons *without change of chemical environment* will therefore be expected to have high activation energies for reduction. Part of this energy can be estimated in terms of a crystal-field stabilization. An example, the hexacyanoferrate(II)/hexacyanoferrate(III) exchange, illustrates the method. The crystal-field energy for the initial system is $24Dq$ $(\mathrm{Fe(CN)}_6^{4-})+20D^*q$ $(\mathrm{Fe(CN)}_6^{3-})$ and for the 'Franck–Condon' state, i.e. allowing no change of distance on electron transfer, it is $20Dq+24D^*q$ so that there is an energy change of $-4Dq+4D^*q$. The electrons are always in t_{2g} orbitals. If a reduction involves the transfer of t_{2g} electrons of one complex into the e_g orbitals of another then the theoretical activation energy of electron transfer is much higher. Particularly slow reactions should then occur with Cr(III) and Co(III) (low-spin), as indeed is found; see Fig. 29.4.

However, the observed activation energy need not relate quantitatively to the Franck–Condon barrier as 'tunnelling' through such a barrier is possible (Fig. 29.11). Tunnelling energies will be extremely sensitive both to distance and to the ligands involved. As tunnelling is less probable the higher the potential-energy barrier, a correlation with ligand-field energies may still be expected even when it is important.

INNER-SPHERE MECHANISM—THEORETICAL CONSIDERATIONS

In the inner-sphere mechanism a ligand acts as a bridge between the two cations M_1 and M_2. In this mechanism all possible activation processes normally associated with electron conduction, e.g. direct exchange of electrons between two atoms or exchange of electrons via the intermediate bridging ligand, are possible electron-transfer steps. However, the result of the electron transfer again creates the cation in an environment associated with a valence state higher or lower than its initial state. A similar Franck–Condon energy to that already described resists reaction. It may be partially overcome by the vibrations of the bridging ligand. A new energy of activation too is the energy of formation of the bridged complex. Since this process can be regarded as a substitution reaction, it is not surprising if its rate follows the rate of substitution at different cations.

The second possible mechanism for the inner-sphere electron-transfer process involves a transfer of X from M_1 to M_2. As in the transition state X must move into a position approximately half-way between M_1 and M_2, a considerable *distortion* of the coordination sphere of M_1 as well as of M_2 is involved. The ions which resist distortion of the M–X distance most strongly have d^3, d^6 (low-spin), and d^8 (high-spin) electron configurations (Table 29.II). These ions undergo slow redox reactions. Thus all possible mechanisms would suggest that d^3 and d^6 (low-spin) would undergo slow redox reactions.

We can now see several apparent reasons for the correlation between the rates of redox reactions and the rates of substitution reactions in the transition series. They may all be related to a loss of ligand-field energy: this can involve either a change of symmetry of the field (substitution) or a maintenance of a field symmetry in the presence of a change of charge and configuration accompanying electron-transfer.

ELECTRON-TRANSFER IN BIOLOGICAL SYSTEMS

The significance of metal ions in biological redox reactions has been described in Chapter 10. Most of the cations concerned—copper, iron, cobalt, molybdenum, and manganese—are probably bound to conjugated ligands such as porphyrins or to other ligands capable of oxidation or reduction such as sulphide, so that the redox reactions of the cations can go by outer-sphere mechanisms. The exact role of these reactions in biological systems is not understood.

The attack of oxygen and hydrogen peroxide on substrates employing iron- and copper-containing enzymes is a good example of atom transfer. Spectroscopic observations suggest that oxygen *atoms* rather than electrons are transferred first to the iron giving, for example, $Fe(O_2)$, $Fe(O_2H^-)$, or FeO complexes. The transfer of the oxygen atoms into the *product* molecules has been followed using ^{18}O in H_2O_2 or O_2. The action of the metal is to facilitate the breaking of the O–O link, but there need be no exchange of ^{18}O with solvent H_2O.

29.4. Atom-transfer reactions

In the reaction between Cr^{2+} and Cr^{3+} ions already discussed, atom or group transfer is coincidental with electron transfer, since an atom in the coordination sphere of one cation is transferred to the second cation through a bridged intermediate. Naturally atom or group transfer requires a bridged intermediate. Thus iron in either the divalent or trivalent state may act as a group-transferring agent:

$$[Fe(III)(H_2O)_5OH^-]^{2+}$$
$$\uparrow$$
$$[Fe(II)(H_2O)_6]^{2+}+R^{\cdot} \rightarrow [Fe(II)(H_2O)_5\dot{O}H]^{2+}+RH$$

$$[Fe(III)(H_2O)_5OH^-]^{2+}+R^{\cdot} \rightarrow [Fe(II)(H_2O)_5]^{2+}+ROH \xrightarrow{+H_2O} [Fe(II)(H_2O)_6]^{2+}$$

The intermediates in these reactions must be $Fe-OH_2-R$ and $Fe-O-R$ respectively. In the first reaction an H-atom of the ligand molecule is transferred, while in the second reaction the whole ligand is transferred.

HIGH-VALENCE STATES

As the valence state of a transition-metal in a complex is raised so the transfer of a ligand atom becomes more difficult. For example, permanganate does not easily lose an oxygen atom to another molecule and the intermediate in the attack of osmium tetroxide on a *cis*-glycol is quite stable. On heating, two moles of aldehyde are produced so that eventually atom transfer results. One of the reasons for the difficulty of atom transfer is that most high-valence transition-metal compounds involve double-bonded oxygen. However, even the Cl^- of $[IrCl_6]^{2-}$ is not lost easily. Thus the oxidation of Cr^{2+} by $[IrCl_6]^{2-}$ does not involve $Cl^{\cdot}$ atom transfer, even though a bridge mechanism is indicated by the formation of a highly-coloured intermediate,

$$Cr^{2+}(aq)+[IrCl_6]^{2-} \rightarrow [IrCl_6Cr] \rightarrow [IrCl_6]^{3-}+[Cr(H_2O)_6]^{3+}.$$
(deep blue)

In fact electron transfer is more usual than atom transfer for many reagents such as MnO_4^-, and such reagents require lower-valence transition-metal ions as intermediate one-electron catalysts. For compounds of metals in the second and third transition series, the higher coordination number of the complexes makes them weak acids and they frequently react by a hydroxyl-radical transfer which takes place much more readily than oxygen-atom transfer. This mechanism is also facile for intermediate valence states of the first transition series, for example Mn^{4+}.

REMOTE-ATOM TRANSFER

A second mechanism of atom exchange between a coordination compound and a substrate does *not* require the breaking of the metal-ligand bond, e.g. the transfer of $H^{\cdot}$ from $[Fe(H_2O)_6]^{2+}$ shown above. The nitroprusside anion $[Fe(II)(CN)_5NO]^{2-}$, which contains iron(II), reacts directly with alkali to give $[Fe(II)(CN)_5(NO_2^-)]^{4-}$:

$$[(CN)_5Fe(II)(NO^+)]^{2-}+2OH^- \rightarrow [(CN)_5Fe(II)(NO_2^-)]^{4-}+H_2O.$$

The NO_2^- group can act as an oxidizing agent while the N atom remains bound to Fe. Atoms coordinated to a central metal may be quite highly activated. In this case, the NO group has become so activated by attachment to the Fe^{3+} cation that charge is transferred in the ground state giving $Fe^{2+}NO^+$. It is this charged group, NO^+, which is so reactive to nucleophiles. Hypothetical reaction schemes of the following kind may thus be written:

$$Fe^{3+}\text{—}R^- + H_2O_2 \rightarrow \overset{\overset{\displaystyle H \quad\;\; H}{\overset{\displaystyle \diagdown\;\;\diagup}{\underset{\downarrow}{O\text{—}O}}}}{Fe^{3+}\text{—}R^-} \rightarrow \overset{\overset{\displaystyle OH^-\;\; OH}{\overset{\displaystyle |\qquad\;\; |}{}}}{Fe^{3+}\text{—}R}$$

This is a possible mechanism for biological hydroxylation, oxidation, or breakdown of H_2O_2 or O_2. Such intermediates have been postulated for catalase and peroxidase reactions *in vivo*.

Another example of this mechanism arises in some exchange reactions where a study of isotope exchange in the solid state has shown that electron transfer takes place via H-transfer. Thus the rate of the Fe^{2+}/Fe^{3+} exchange in ice is as fast as would be expected for the reaction in water at the same temperature. A transition state is required with iron atoms rigidly held far apart. One possibility may be represented by

$$(H_2O)_5Fe^{2+} \leftarrow \underset{\underset{H}{|}}{\overset{\overset{H}{|}}{O}}\!\!-\!\!\underline{H} \ldots \ldots \underset{\underset{H}{|}}{O} \to Fe^{3+}(H_2O)_5,$$

where many water molecules may be involved in the bridge shown by the dots. Transfer of the underlined H *atom* along a chain of water molecules leads to exchange. Such atom transfer could be the basis of 'electron' transfer in mitochondria and in the important iron-containing protein of photo-pyridine nucleotide reductase, ferredoxin. In both this protein and the cytochrome chain of mitochondria there are a number of iron atoms, held at a distance from one another, which change oxidation state very rapidly. The path of exchange need not be through $H^{\cdot}$ of water but could utilize $H^{\cdot}$ of phenolic OH, producing a quinonoid radical intermediate. (Coupling between oxidation and phosphorylation is easily pictured as involving cycling through phenol and quinone. The nature of this coupling is a major unsolved biochemical problem.) Similar oxidation-reduction paths are possible in the Cu^{2+}/Cu^{+} proteins, e.g. caeruloplasmin, and in proteins which contain many metal atoms such as xanthine oxidase with two molybdenum atoms and eight iron atoms. Apparently the function of all these enzymes is to oxidize substrates at a distance from the point of oxygen attack. They differ from those enzymes which incorporate oxygen into a substrate, for they require sites not only for oxygen and substrate adsorption but also for electron or $H^{\cdot}$ transfer. In mitochondria such a system of sites is highly developed. There is one site of oxygen absorption and many sites for the absorption of different substrates, the Krebs-cycle intermediates (Chapter 17). The oxidizing equivalents fan out from oxygen through a series of cytochromes (iron porphyrin complexes). There is considerable evidence that more primitive organisms use iron-sulphur complexes in a similar manner. The biological particles are not like electron semiconductors of a conventional type, for electron transport is replaced by atom transport.

29.5. Atom and electron transfer in solids

At the present time it would appear that the fundamental processes of electron transport are but partly understood. It is likely that an understanding of them will come through the study of all kinds of semiconductor materials in the solid state, in addition to that of kinetics in solution. In the solid state it is possible to separate electron *mobility* effects from the activation of charge *carriers* (for example, using measurements of the Hall effect). In some solid conductors the conduction process appears to be very similar to that in a solution reaction, i.e. mobility is slow and the electron moves by a hopping mechanism. The activation energies for these solid-state processes are often quite low and comparable with those in solution. It may be that the activation process is the vibration of the ligands of the lattice, a so-called 'relaxation' process. In many complex ions, the mobility of the electron through a bridge atom may similarly be very low indeed unless the complex is in an excited vibrational state.

PROPERTIES OF SOLIDS—CARRIER-FORMATION

It may help appreciation of the significance of solid-state phenomena in the study of the rates of redox reactions if reference is again made to spectroscopic properties. In sections 28.2 and 28.7, spectra have been described which arise from a charge transfer such as

$$Fe^{3+}{\leftarrow}NCS^- \xrightarrow{h\nu} Fe^{2+}{\leftarrow}NCS^{\cdot}$$

If this transfer occurs in a solid, the Fe^{2+} is left adjacent to a radical and either they will re-exchange electrons giving the initial state, or the excited parts of $Fe^{2+}{\leftarrow}NCS^{\cdot}$ will relax and then separate by an electron jumping from Fe^{2+} to a neighbouring Fe^{3+} ion. In the last case photoconduction may be observable. Now the creation by the absorption of light of the charge-transferred state, $Fe^{2+}NCS^{\cdot}$, sometimes referred to as carrier-formation, is only one possible way of generating carriers. It follows from the Boltzmann equation that the concentration of carriers at *thermal* equilibrium can be quite high if their excitation energy is reasonably low. Those inorganic solids which have low-lying spectroscopic charge-transfer states will also be expected to have *thermal* charge-transfer states of reasonable population at room temperature. They may well be good semiconductors. Such conductivity is obviously not expected at room temperature if A and B are so different that the carriers $\overset{\cdot\cdot}{A}\overset{\cdot\cdot}{B}$ are of very low concentration (high activation energy) compared with the ground state A^+B^-, as must be true in such crystals as Na^+Cl^-. In other solids, e.g. HgI_2, where the oxidation-reduction reaction (i.e. the process $A^+B^- \to \dot{A}\dot{B}$) is of low energy, the initial electron transfer may be achieved relatively easily. It could well be then that this part of the conduction activation energy is directly related to internal oxidation-reduction between pairs of groups in a continuous crystal.

MOBILITY

The rapid migration of electrons through solids has been discussed in terms of a molecular-orbital picture in Chapter 6. The molecular orbitals concerned are delocalized so that electron transport is easily understood. The basic picture of slow electron transport must be different and can be thought of as a series of jumps along a line of atoms

$$\overset{+}{A}\ \overset{-}{B}\ \overset{+}{A}\ \overset{-}{B}\ \overset{+}{A}\ \overset{-}{B} \xrightarrow{(1)} \overset{+}{A}\ \overset{-}{B}\ \overset{+}{A}\ \overset{\bullet}{B}\ \overset{\bullet}{A}\ \overset{-}{B} \xrightarrow{(2)} \overset{\bullet}{A}\ \overset{-}{B}\ \overset{+}{A}\ \overset{-}{B}\ \overset{+}{A}\ \overset{\bullet}{B}$$

The creation of the carrier $\overset{\bullet\bullet}{A B}$ in step (1) is followed by the transfer of the electron from $\overset{\bullet}{A}$ to a great distance from the hole $\overset{\bullet}{B}$ in step (2). This *charge-transfer* picture of electron migration is different from the one in which electrons are free to move in a crystal, for electrons are here considered to be associated with single atoms for long periods and electron mobility is low.

There is now a further energy barrier to be overcome. As each electron jumps in the crystal it moves on to an atom or ion which has a definite atmosphere. For example, in the crystal NiO the carrier could be written $Ni^+O^{2-}Ni^{3+}$, and ionization in the crystal now separates the hole and the electron so that the Ni^{3+} hole can be considered separately from the Ni^+. As the hole moves to an Ni^{2+} ion from an Ni^{3+}, it creates the new Ni^{2+} in an equilibrium oxide atmosphere of an Ni^{3+} ion and an Ni^{3+} ion in an equilibrium Ni^{2+} atmosphere. The process is energetically unfavourable and is opposed by a considerable activation energy. Thus, in order to transport an electron, either a vibrationally-excited ground state must arise before transfer, or a vibrationally-excited state will be produced on transfer. This argument follows from the Franck–Condon principle and we may call the additional 'strain' energy a Franck–Condon energy. The electron transport may also be associated with thermal vibrations of the lattice which could bring about a partial equalization of the Ni^{2+} and Ni^{3+} sites.

The above localized-electron model for conduction applies well to transition-metal compounds with incomplete $(n-1)d$ sub-shells, where the band theory is in difficulty (Chapter 6). (The hopping mechanism is not satisfactory in the discussion of metals, alloys, or many good semiconductors.)

A good illustration of the use of the model is provided by the demonstration of a connexion between magnetic properties and intrinsic electrical conductivity in some compounds. MnO, MnS, $MnCl_2$, Fe_2O_3, $FeCl_2$, CoO, NiO, and CuO are anti-ferromagnetic and their high electrical resistance falls with temperature. MnAs, MnSb, MnBi, CrTe, VCl_2, and $CrCl_2$ are ferromagnetic and their low resistance increases with temperature. Metal ions in the first group of compounds have five or more $3d$ electrons while those in the second have five or less. Electron transfer from one metal ion to the next in the ferromagnetic array maintains the spin vectors on the ions, but this is not so in the anti-ferromagnetic array. Thus the electron transfer is more strongly opposed in the first group of compounds.

Many other materials may be expected to be intrinsic semiconductors. For example, compounds in which an ion is present in two valence states, Prussian blue, molybdenum blue, Fe_3O_4, Pb_3O_4, and Cs_2SbCl_6. The tungsten bronzes $Li_x W_x^{5+} W_{1-x}^{6+} O_3$ are even metallic over some composition ranges. The electron transfer need not occur between atoms of the same kind, and substances such as $KFe(II)[Co(CN)_6]$ and $KCo(II)[Fe(CN)_6]$ are known to be moderately good semiconductors. Two examples serve to illustrate this point. Deep brown-black mixed crystals containing the anions $[CuCl_4]^{3-}$ and $[CuCl_5]^{3-}$ can be obtained by adding $[Co(NH_3)_6]^{3+}$ to the anions in solution. The electrical conductivity of these crystals rises to a maximum at the 50:50 ratio of Cu(I) to Cu(II). A study of the variation of conductivity with temperature shows that the activation energy for electron transfer is about 16 kcal. The second example is the almost black compound $(Tl^+)_3[Fe(CN)_6]^{3-}$, which is a combination of a reducing cation and an oxidizing anion. The activation energy for conduction, again associated with mobility, is 6 kcal, which suggests that a vibration is required to permit the electron jump. Electron mobility involves electron transfer from Tl^+ to the small quantities of Tl^{2+} in the lattice. A study of a large number of examples of this type of material should reveal much of importance about the transfer of electrons.

Problems

1. Werner's classical experiments on complex ions were largely carried out on complexes of Cr(III), Co(III), and Pt(IV). Comment.

2. The equilibrium constant for the reaction

$$Co(NH_3)_6^{3+} + 6H_3O^+ \rightleftharpoons Co(H_2O)_6^{3+} + 6NH_4^+$$

is almost 10^{35}, yet the hexammine Co(III) ion will keep for weeks in an acid solution. Comment.

3. In the following reaction

$$[Co(NH_3)_5CO_3]^+ + 2H_3\overset{*}{O}^+ \rightarrow [Co(NH_3)_5(H_2O)]^{3+} + 2H_2\overset{*}{O} + CO_2$$

no isotopic oxygen is found to enter the complex from the labelled water. Suggest a possible mechanism to account for this observation.

4. Explain why it is possible for hexacyanoferrate(III) to be quite poisonous while hexacyanoferrate(II) is not.

5. How far can we understand the following lability orders which have been observed experimentally for cyanide complexes?—

$$V(CN)_6^{3-} > Mn(CN)_6^{3-} \gg Cr(CN)_6^{3-} > Fe(CN)_6^{3-} \sim Co(CN)_6^{3-}$$
$$V(CN)_6^{3-} > V(CN)_6^{4-}$$

6. Using simple crystal field arguments, show that for *tetrahedral* high-spin d^n ions the reaction path via a 5-coordinate transition state (data in Table 29.II) is increasingly favoured in the order $d^2 < d^1 < d^3 < d^4$. See Tabel 24.II for details of tetrahedral crystal-field energies.

7. Crystal-field arguments exactly similar to those describing the way in which rate of reaction will vary with atomic number, show that the rate of reaction of octahedral complexes of a given metal in different valence states goes through a minimum at the d^3 and d^8 (high-spin) and at the d^6 (low-spin) ions. What other factors make it unlikely that such a simple variation of rate with valence state will be observed?

8. Supposing that the value of Dq for a square pyramidal complex is $\frac{5}{6}$ that for an octahedral complex, show that only for d^1 and d^9 cations is the 5-co-ordinate transition state favoured by crystal-field energies; see Table 29.II.

9. In the substitution reactions of $[Co(ethylenediamine)_2Cl_2]^+$ in methanol, the following sequence of reaction rates is found:

$$CH_3O^- > N_3^- > NO^- > CNS^- = Br^- = Cl^- = NO_3^-.$$

Comment.

10. The rate of the reaction

$$[Co(NH_3)_5H_2O]^{3+} + SO_4^{2-} \rightarrow [Co(NH_3)_5SO_4]^+ + H_2O$$

is nearly independent of sulphate ion concentration over a wide range. Suggest possible reasons for this.

11. Planar complexes of Ni(II) are relatively labile, those of Pd(II) fairly inert, and those of Pt(II) distinctly inert. Comment.

12. The complexes $[Cr(C_2O_4)_3]^{3-}$ and $[Co(C_2O_4)_3]^{3-}$ will not exchange oxalate with radioactive oxalate in aqueous solution under conditions in which complete racemization takes place. On the other hand, the complexes

$[Al(C_2O_4)_3]^{3-}$ and $[Fe(C_2O_4)_3]^{3-}$ exchange completely with radioactive oxalate in the time of mixing. How can these distinctions be interpreted?

13. The complex $[cis\text{-}Co(en)_2Cl_2]^+$ reacts with nitrate ion in methyl alcohol solution. The reaction rate is of zero order with respect to the nitrate, of first order with respect to the complex ion, and equal to the rate of racemization of the optically-active complex. The reaction of the same complex with hydroxide ion in aqueous solution is of first order with respect to the hydroxide and of first order with respect to the complex ion. How may these various observations be interpreted?

14. The *cis*-isomer of $Pt(NH_3)_2Cl_2$ is made by treating $[PtCl_4]^{2-}$ with ammonia, while the *trans*-isomer is made by treating $[Pt(NH_3)_4]^{2+}$ with Cl^-. Explain why this is so.

15. The two isomers of $Pt(NH_3)Cl_2$ are treated with thiourea. One forms $[Pt(thiourea)_4]^{2+}$, but the other isomer forms $[Pt(thiourea)_2(NH_3)_2]^{2+}$. Which isomer is *cis* and which *trans*?

16. Comment on the following Fe^{3+}/Fe^{2+} exchange rates $(25°)$

	k (l. mole^{-1} sec^{-1})	Activation energy (kcal)
$[Fe^{3+}(SO_4^{2-})]/Fe^{2+}(aq.)$	2.95×10^2	13.8
$[Fe^{3+}(SO_4^{2-})_2]/Fe^{2+}(aq.)$	1.75×10^4	15.6
$[Fe(C_5H_5)_2]^+/[Fe(C_5H_5)_2]$	$> 10^5$	

17. The rate constant for the one-electron redox reaction $[Os(dipy)_3]^{2+} + [Mo(CN)_8]^{3-}$ is 2×10^9 l. mole^{-1} sec^{-1}. The activation energy is about 3 kcal. Make suggestions about the nature of the rate-limiting step and thence the reason for the low activation energy.

18. The reduction of $[Fe(NCS)_6]^{3-}$ by Sn^{2+} is strongly catalysed by Cu^{2+} ions. Suggest a mechanism to account for the catalysis.

19. The rate constants (l. mole^{-1} sec^{-1}) for the formation of certain Fe^{3+} complexes are

$X^- =$	Br^-	Cl^-	NCS^-	SO_4^{2-}	F^-
$k(Fe^{3+}(aq.)+X^-)$	1	10	127	3×10^3	4×10^3
$k(Fe^{3+}(OH^-)+X^-)$	3×10^4	10^4	10^4	3×10^5	

What may be deduced about the effect of the character of the incoming ligand upon the rate of reaction?

20. The rate constant for the *trans* → *cis* conversion of $Ru(H_2O)_3Cl_3$ is 7×10^{-4} hours^{-1}, and for the reverse reaction is 2.6×10^{-3} hours^{-1}. Discuss the *trans*-effect in the light of these data.

21. The following table (after Wilkins) gives the dissociation rates of dipyridyl (dipy) and terpyridyl (trpy) complexes (in min^{-1}) and the A and E constants of the collision-theory rate equation.

Complex	spin type	10^3k	log A	E (kcal)
$[Fe(dipy)_3]^{2+}$	low	8·0	18·8	28·4
$[Ni(dipy)_3]^{2+}$	high	186	15·6	22·2
$[Fe(trpy)]^{2+}$	high	398	12·8	18·0
$[Co(trpy)]^{2+}$	high	6·3	12·6	20·2
$[Ni(trpy)]^{2+}$	high	0·001	12·0	24·2
$[Fe(trpy)_2]^{2+}$	low	0·01	16·1	28·7

Comment on these data in the light of the crystal-field theory given in section 29.2.

22. The rates of reaction of U^{4+} with Tl^{3+}, and of Sn^{2+} with Ce^{4+} are very slow although thermodynamic factors are favourable. Suggest a reason for this.

23. Chromium(III) chloride will not dissolve in water at an appreciable rate but will do so in the presence of traces of Cr(II) or Sn(II). Comment.

24. In the quantitative analysis of chromium(II) hydrazine sulphate, the chromium is first oxidized to chromium(III) by shaking in air and the hydrazine is then estimated by oxidation with potassium bromate at ice temperature. The chromium may be estimated by boiling the salt with acid potassium bromate in excess which converts it all to dichromate, the excess bromate being destroyed by boiling with an ammonium salt, and the dichromate titrated with a standard reducing agent. Comment.

25. Comment on the observation that reduction of $K_2[OsNCl_5]$ by Sn(II) chloride gives $K_2[Os(NH_2)Cl_5]$.

26. Perruthenate, Ru(VII), is reduced by OH^- but permanganate is not attacked by H_2O, despite the fact that the redox potentials favour reaction in each case. Discuss these observations in the light of the differences between the coordination chemistry of Ru(VII) and Mn(VII).

Bibliography

F. BASOLO and R. G. PEARSON, Mechanisms of Inorganic Reactions, Wiley, New York, 1958.

F. BASOLO and R. G. PEARSON, Mechanisms of Substitution Reactions of Metal Complexes, Advances in Inorganic Chemistry and Radiochemistry, vol. 3, ed. H. J. Emeléus and A. G. Sharpe, Academic Press, New York, 1961.

F. BASOLO and R. G. PEARSON, The trans Effect in Metal Complexes, Progress in Inorganic Chemistry, vol. 4, ed. F. A. Cotton, Interscience, New York, 1962.

E. F. CALDIN, *Fast Reactions in Solution*, Blackwell, Oxford, 1964.

J. O. EDWARDS, *Inorganic Reaction Mechanisms*, Benjamin, New York, 1964.

J. HALPERN, 'Mechanisms of Electron Transfer and Related Processes in Solution', *Quart. Rev. Chem. Soc.*, 1961, **15**, 207.

D. R. STRANKS, The Reaction Rates of Transition Metal Complexes, *Modern Coordination Chemistry*, ed. J. Lewis and R. G. Wilkins, Interscience, New York, 1960.

H. TAUBE, Mechanisms of Redox Reactions of Simple Chemistry, *Advances in Inorganic Chemistry and Radiochemistry*, vol. 1, ed. H. J. Emeléus and A. G. Sharpe, Academic Press, New York, 1959.

A. A. VLEČK, 'Intermediates of Electro-reduction of Transition Metal Complexes', Eighth International Conference on Coordination Chemistry, Vienna, 1964.

R. G. WILKINS and M. J. G. WILLIAMS, The Isomerism of Complex Compounds, *Modern Coordination Chemistry*, ed. J. Lewis and R. G. Wilkins, Interscience, New York, 1960.

Reactions of Coordinated Ligands and Homogeneous Catalysis, Advances in Chemistry Publication No. 37, American Chemical Society, 1963.

30 · B Metals: Atomic Structure and Valence

30.1. Introduction to B-metal chemistry

In the following three chapters we shall consider the chemistry of the B metals, i.e.

Cu	Zn	Ga	(Ge)	(As)	
Ag	Cd	In	Sn	(Sb)	(Te)
Au	Hg	Tl	Pb	Bi	(Po)

and their compounds. The position of these elements in the Periodic Table provides intriguing possibilities for comparative chemistry. They occur at the end of the three transition series, and their chemistry illustrates the culmination of certain trends, especially the increasing polarizing power of cations, which have already been emphasized in the preceding chapters. They merge gradually into non-metals, so that we begin to come back to a number of problems which were features of Part II. Finally they all exhibit a Group-valence state, in which they are thus formally analogous to the pre-transition elements. It is this last comparison which will be one of the most recurring themes in these chapters.

Because of the increase of nuclear charge across each of the transition series, the B metals are distinguished from the early A metals by their much weaker tendency to form ions or to form compounds with the non-metals. The ions themselves have high electron affinities and tend to seek out, wherever possible, polarizable anions or ligands.

This feature is particularly marked in the final row of B metals, Au, Hg, Tl, Pb, Bi, and Po, where the nuclear charge has been built up across the lanthanide as well as the third transition series. In some respects these elements might almost be classed as super-B or C metals.

In most of B-metal chemistry the d^{10} sub-shells, which have been built up across the preceding transition series, may be regarded as essentially closed. Only in the elements of Group IB, Cu, Ag, and Au, is it possible to open these sub-shells by chemical means to give rise to valence states greater than that of the Group. Cu, Ag, and Au thus provide a link between the two sets of metals, although in the next three chapters the discussion will be very largely limited to their chemistry in valence state 1. Even then the closed d^{10} sub-shells are not without chemical influence. Thus they may exhibit π-donor properties, e.g. as in the Ag-olefin complexes (section 31.1), and they make an important contribution to London energies.

For the most part, however, we shall be concerned with the ns and np valence electrons. The former are in name the same electrons as those which were relevant to the chemistry of the pre-transition series, but they are now much more firmly bound to their nuclei. Because of their greater penetration they are also held more firmly than the np electrons, and there appears what we shall call an $(N-2)$-valence state, 2 less than the Group valence. This is often called the 'inert pair' valence state because of its association with the inertness of the ns^2 electrons. However, the situation is undoubtedly more complicated than the simple involvement of pure p electrons and orbitals in bonding and the retention of the s^2 pair by the atomic core (see especially section 31.1). The valence states generally observed are listed in Table 30.I which excludes coordination valence such

TABLE 30.I. *Valence states of* B *elements* (*excluding coordination*)

Group	II	III	IV	V	VI	VII
Group valence	2	3	4	5	6	7
$(N-2)$ valence	0	1	2	3	4	5
Other						3
$(8-N)$ valence				3	2	1

as $R_3Sb{\rightarrow}M$. In addition, mercury, and to a very minor extent certain other B metals, exhibits an oxidation state one less than the Group valence, mercury(I). In this state, however, mercury is divalent, each mercury atom being covalently bound to one other, e.g. $(Hg{-}Hg)^{2+}(NO_3)_2$.

OUTLINE OF CHAPTERS 30, 31, AND 32

In order to bring out the relation between A-metal and B-metal chemistry, a scheme for the treatment of B-metal chemistry has been adopted which runs somewhat parallel to that adopted in Chapter 20 for the pre-transition metals. After a discussion of atomic structures (section 30.2), an attempt is made to relate the observed valence states to these structures, using the simplified ionic model and limiting the discussion so far as is possible to aqueous ions. Quantitative agreement between estimated and experimental Oxidation State Diagrams is now decidedly poor, although some of the same qualitative features are present in both. The discussion of the experimental diagram is left therefore until the end of Chapter 32 where it follows the treatment of solution chemistry. In this way the relationship between the B metals and the non-metals (Part II) is also stressed.

The inadequacy of the ionic model and the manner in which this model needs to be modified by allowance for other forces, especially covalence, are taken up in section 30.5. The importance of covalence is then emphasized in sections 31.1 and 31.2, where stereochemistry and related physical properties are discussed. In sections 31.3 and 31.4 the deviations from the ionic-model are then considered in the light of the thermochemical data, emphasizing the way in which these deviations are anion-dependent. Section 31.5 relates the thermochemical data to the general chemistry of B metals and their compounds. For the most part Chapter 31 is concerned with solid-state chemistry, and while it contains a very considerable amount of descriptive B-metal chemistry, this is arranged so as to bring out the nature of the binding in B-metal compounds. In Chapter 32, which is largely devoted to solubility and solution chemistry, more emphasis is laid on an ordered description of B-metal chemistry, arranged in terms of valence states in a manner analogous to that used in the discussion of the transition series. As with the transition series, the more traditional discussion in terms of Periodic Groups (as used in Part II for the non-metals) is not followed. This is done deliberately in order to bring out more general principles about the nature of B-metal chemistry, and to avoid frequent repetition of these principles.

The organometallic compounds of the non-transition elements are discussed in Chapter 33, and since the formation of organometallic compounds is particularly important with B metals, this is in the main a further chapter on B-metal chemistry.

30.2. Atomic structure

We shall be interested in the s and p electrons of the n quantum group, the d electrons of the $(n-1)$ quantum group, and the d orbitals of the n quantum group. The $(n-1)d$ electrons are particularly important in the chemistry of Cu, Ag, and Au, but in the later B elements these d electrons become part of the core and play increasingly only a minor role. On the other hand, the p electrons and the nd orbitals increase in importance along the B series. In this section the properties of these electrons and orbitals will be considered in the light of the information provided by ionization potentials and atomic spectra. These properties suggest that certain patterns will be found in the chemistries of the elements when compared with one another and with the A elements.

s ELECTRONS

Fig. 30.1 shows the differences in the ionization potentials of Groups I A and I B: in each atom an s electron is being removed, e.g. 4s in both K and

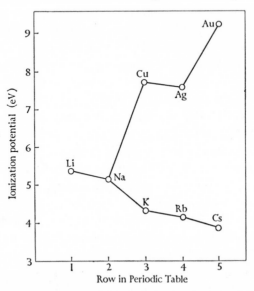

FIG. 30.1. First ionization potentials for the elements of Group I.

Cu. Between K and Cu and between Rb and Ag the nuclear charge increases by 10, and in both cases there is an increase in ionization potential of 3·4 eV. Between Cs and Au the nuclear charge increases by 24 (14 for the lanthanide series) and the corresponding increase in ionization potential is 5·3 eV. This implies that the tendency to form ionic compounds in the elements Cu and Ag will be less marked than in K and Rb, and even less marked in Au than in Cs.

The general trend from Li to Au may also be pictured as a smooth change with an 'alternation' superimposed on it such that the first, third, and fifth elements (Li, Cu, and Au) lie on the side of decreased ease of oxidation, while the second and fourth elements lie on the side of increased ease of oxidation. This effect is a very general one and appears to have important results in the chemistry of the B elements. We have already discussed it in Chapter 18 as the *alternation effect*. A related irregularity, to which we have already referred in section 20.2, occurs in the pre-transition Groups, but with a *decreased* ease of oxidation associated with the second and fourth members (Na and Rb).

A pattern similar to Fig. 30.1 is produced when the ionizations of *s* electrons are compared in other Groups, except that with increasing Group number the A/B differences are superimposed on a more sharply increasing

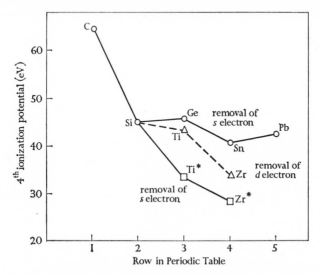

FIG. 30.2. The fourth ionization potentials for the elements of Group IV. The values marked Ti* and Zr* correspond to excited states of the Ti³⁺ and Zr³⁺ ions.

slope down from the first to the last member . The fourth ionization potentials for the elements of Group IV (the Hf value is not known) are plotted in Fig. 30.2, the values for Ti* and Zr* corresponding to the removal of *s* electrons from what are therefore excited states of Ti^{3+} and Zr^{3+}. (The normal fourth ionization potentials of Ti and Zr are connected by the broken line.) Again the differences in Fig. 30.2 between Ti* and Ge, and between Zr* and Sn are the same (12·4 eV).

p ELECTRONS

Although *np* electrons do not occur in the normal atoms of the A elements, excited states in which there are such electrons can readily be studied by atomic spectroscopy. The increases in nuclear charge across the transition and lanthanide series also lead to stronger binding of these *np* electrons, but the effect is less marked than with the more-penetrating *ns* electrons. Thus to remove the 4*p* electron from the excited state of Ca ($4s^1 4p^1$) requires

$4 \cdot 23$ eV and from Zn ($3d^{10}4s^14p^1$) $5 \cdot 34$ eV, an increase of $1 \cdot 1$ eV to be compared with an increase of $3 \cdot 3$ eV for an s electron.

In order to bring out the distinction between the different types of electrons, the ratios of ionization potential to charge left on the atom after

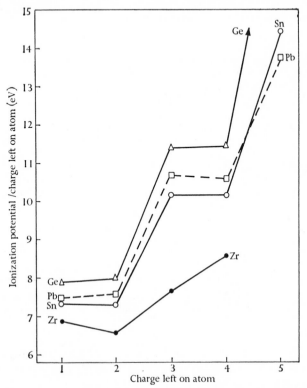

FIG. 30.3. The ratio of the ionization potential to the charge left on the atom at different charges for some elements of Group IV.

ionization (see Chapter 2) are plotted in Fig. 30.3 for the elements of Group IVB and for Zr. The sudden increase in the ratio after removal of two electrons in Group IVB brings out the greater stability of the more penetrating ns as compared with the np electrons.

This difference between s and p electrons may also be demonstrated by the figures in Table 30.II which give the excitation energies ns to np for the elements of Group I. The large differences in energy between ns and np electrons in the B elements, and particularly in the elements following Au, are associated with the phenomenon known as the *inert-pair* effect, in which to a first approximation the s electrons are often not removed under conditions where the np electrons are. It is to be noted that the inertness is associated with the s character rather than with the paired character of the electrons. Thus the nobility of Cu, Ag, and Au is in part due to the same cause (and in part due to their strong metallic binding).

TABLE 30.II. $ns \rightarrow np$ excitation energies (eV)

		Li	1·85
		Na	2·10
K	1·61	Cu	3·78
Rb	1·58	Ag	3·75
Cs	1·44	Au	5·02

$(n-1)d$ ELECTRONS

Some of the general characteristics of the $(n-1)d$ electrons are brought out by the ionization potentials plotted in Figs. 30.4 and 30.5. Most of these characteristics have also been discussed in Chapter 23. The two lower sets in Fig. 30.4 demonstrate the greater stability of the $(n-1)d$ electrons as compared with the ns electrons. These d electrons become steadily more stable from Group VIII (Ni, Pd, and Pt), through Group IB (Cu, Ag, and Au) to Group IIB (Zn, Cd, and Hg), as may be seen from Fig. 30.5 and the middle set of Fig. 30.4. (The striking change in the ionization potentials between Group IB and Group IIB is here a reflection of the much greater screening of an $(n-1)d$ electron by another $(n-1)d$ electron than by an ns electron, an effect which will be particularly marked with the non-penetrating $3d$ electrons of Cu and Zn.) At the same time the d orbitals will be contracting and thus less capable of interacting with ligands, although it is difficult to put this effect on to a quantitative basis. With increasing charge the d electrons also become more stable and the d orbitals contract. This is illustrated by a comparison of the two upper sets in Fig. 30.4, where it may also be noted that the effect is most marked for Zn and least marked for Hg. At relatively low effective charges ($+1$ or $+2$), the d electrons are most stable in the second B-metal row (e.g. Ag), while the first and third row are similar (e.g. Cu and Au). Compare thus the two sets in Fig. 30.5 where the scale of Fig. 30.4 has been changed deliberately in order to emphasize the differences. However, with increase of effective charge the first-row ionization potentials are strongly increased and the third-row ions now have much the lowest ionization potentials. Compare thus the top set in Fig. 30.4 and also the middle set, where because of the relatively ineffective screening by the ns electrons the effective charge is also approaching three.

These atomic characteristics are reflected in B-metal chemistry. The d sub-shell is broken open by chemical oxidizing agents in Cu, Ag, and Au, but in Ag only with great difficulty. It is not so broken in the B metals of

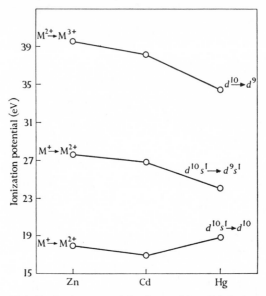

Fig. 30.4. Ionization potentials of ns and $(n-1)d$ electrons for the elements of Group IIB.

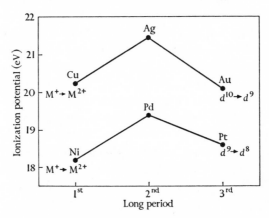

Fig. 30.5. Ionization potentials of $(n-1)d$ electrons for the elements of Group VIIIc and Group IB.

later Groups. In the higher-valence states which result, the half-empty d orbitals produced can in some circumstances overlap to form metal–metal bonds, an example of which is found in the compound $Cu_2(CH_3CO_2)_4, 2H_2O$.

The closed $(n-1)d$ sub-shells can also act by π-donation, as occurs especially in the low-oxidation-state compounds of the transition metals (Chapter 27). Monovalent Cu, Ag, and Au thus form many complexes with π-acceptors, and this type of interaction is also found to a lesser degree with the B metals of later Groups, the mercury(II) ion being a particularly important example. Mercury(II) salts are often used as catalysts for olefin and acetylene reactions. By the time Pb^{2+} is reached, the interaction has become very weak and difficult to distinguish from London effects. The large number of $(n-1)d$ electrons near the atomic surface must make a substantial contribution to the London energy, and indeed in some treatments of metallic Cu, Ag, and Au the London energies are given considerable prominence.

nd ORBITALS

As has already become apparent in Parts I and II, there is good reason to believe that nd orbitals play a role in the bonding of B elements. This appears to be particularly marked when the B element is combined with a more electronegative element, such as oxygen or chlorine. The symmetry of the nd orbitals is just right for constructive π-overlap with filled p_x and p_y orbitals (if the bond is in the z direction) on the second atom:

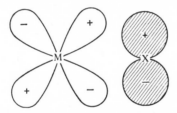

Moreover, the d orbitals contract and tend to bind more strongly as the charge on the B-atom increases. The nd orbital in the free B-atom is always less stable than the np orbital, but the difference between them gets *relatively* smaller as the charge increases. Thus the energy of the $3d$ orbitals (excited atom) is 21 per cent of the $3p$ orbital (normal atom) in P, 35 per cent in P^+, and 52 per cent in P^{2+}. (While the $3d$ orbital is less stable than the $4s$ and $4p$ in P^+ and P^{2+}, it is more stable in P^{3+} and other more highly charged ions.)

RADII

The increases of nuclear charge across the transition and lanthanide series are also reflected in decreases of atomic or ionic size. Some calculated radii for electron orbitals were given in Chapter 2 and illustrate the contraction across the first transition series. Ionic crystal radii for Group II are plotted in Fig. 30.6. As was pointed out in Chapter 5 such radii are much more anion-dependent for B-metal cations than they are for A-metal cations.

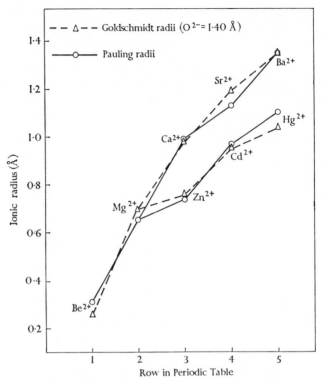

FIG. 30.6. Ionic radii for the elements of Group II.

30.3. Valence states: Group valence

THREE FEATURES IN B-METAL CHEMISTRY

There are thus three general features of B-metal chemistry which should be related to the atomic structure discussion of the previous section. (1) The much reduced affinity of B metals, as compared with the corresponding A metals, for combination with the more electronegative elements, i.e. to form 'compounds' in the sense that this term is commonly used. This tendency is particularly marked in the Group-valence compounds of the last row: Au, Hg, Tl, Pb, Bi, and Po. (2) The relatively greater affinity of B-metal ions for combination with more polarizable ligands as compared with less polarizable ones. (3) The formation of two types of valence state, the Group-valence and the $(N-2)$-valence state.

In this section we shall attempt to deal semi-quantitatively with the first and, in the next section, with the third feature, using the simplified ionic model for aqueous ions which was adopted for the pre-transition metals (section 20.3), the lanthanides (section 21.3), and the transition metals (section 23.3). We take up the second feature, the variation of ligand polarizability, in sections 31.3, 31.4, and 31.5 and it is a central theme in Chapter 32. We should stress at the outset that the ionic model is here too crude for us to expect it to predict the behaviour of B metals with any confidence, and we only use it to relate one kind of observation (atomic structure) with another (chemical behaviour). In some ways the situation is similar to that found in the chemistry of the non-metallic elements and stressed in Chapter 18. The reader who finds such discussions unhelpful may pass straight on to section 31.5 without loss.

OXIDATION STATE DIAGRAMS

The estimated Oxidation State Diagram for Mg, Zn, and Hg is given in Fig. 30.7, together with the experimental VE values for the divalent ions. The calculation method is exactly the same as that outlined in section 20.3. Pauling crystal radii have been used, and the radii of Mg^+, Mg^{3+}, Zn^+, Zn^{3+}, Hg^+, and Hg^{3+} have been assumed equal to the radii of Na^+, Al^{3+}, Cu^+, Ga^{3+}, Au^+, and Tl^{3+} respectively.

The estimated diagram agrees qualitatively with experiment in that (1) the divalent ions are predicted to be the most stable aqueous species, the monovalent ions being unstable with respect to disproportionation and the trivalent ions too strongly oxidizing, and (2) zinc is predicted to be less electropositive than Mg, and Hg less electropositive than Zn. The discrepancy between estimated and experimental values is greater for Hg^{2+} than it is for Zn^{2+} while it is zero for Mg^{2+}. This suggests that the stabilization of the M^{2+} ions by non-ionic forces increases with the electron affinity of the cation: mercury(II) compounds might be expected to be more covalent than zinc(II) compounds, and zinc(II) compounds more covalent than those of magnesium(II).

The diagram also demonstrates the difference between breaking open a noble-gas shell to form Mg^{3+}, and breaking open a filled d sub-shell to form Zn^{3+} and Hg^{3+}. Although this distinction is not reflected in the observed valence states of Mg, Zn, and Hg, it is, of course, reflected in the observed valence states of Na, Cu, and Au. In view of the crudeness of the model it is doubtful whether further discussion of the diagram is justified, but it may be of interest to note that Hg^+ is predicted to be only just unstable with respect to disproportionation. This arises in part from the low sublimation energy of Hg metal (see points at zero oxidation state in Fig. 30.7), and in part from the relatively large size of the mercury ions.

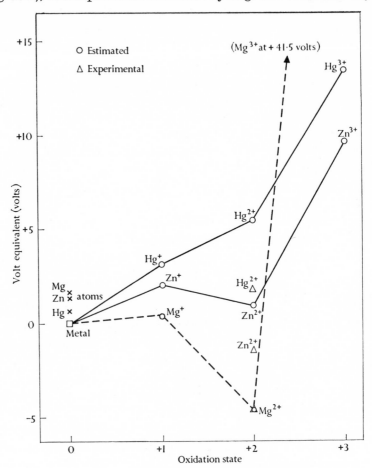

Fig. 30.7. Estimated Oxidation State Diagram for Mg, Zn, and Hg.

If an Hg^+ ion were formed then it would have an unpaired electron in a very stable ($6s$) orbital, and would be expected to combine readily with another Hg^+ ion to form a metal–metal bond. In other words, metal–metal bonding could well stabilize the +1 oxidation state even more than the zero oxidation state (with the stable $6s^2$ configuration). Along such lines it might be possible to understand the existence of the Hg_2^{2+} ion, and the absence of similar species for zinc and magnesium.

ELECTRODE POTENTIALS

The results of such calculations may be expressed in a slightly different way (see Table 30.III) by comparing estimated and experimental electrode potentials for the couples M^{2+}/M as in Fig. 30.8. This again illustrates

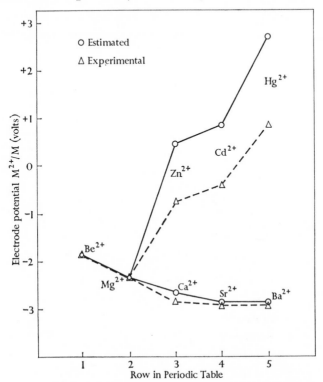

FIG. 30.8. Estimated and experimental electrode potentials for Group II.

TABLE 30.III. *Estimation of electrode potentials, M^{2+}/M, using the simplified ionic model of section 20.3*

Metal	Ionization-potential sum, (I+II) (eV)	Sublimation energy (eV)	Ionic radius (Å)	'Hydration' energy (eV)	Estimated electrode potential† (volts)
Ca	18·0	2·0	0·99	—25·3	—2·7
Sr	16·7	1·7	1·13	—24·1	—2·8
Ba	15·2	1·8	1·35	—22·7	—2·8
Zn	27·4	1·4	0·74	—27·8	+0·5
Cd	25·9	1·2	0·97	—25·4	+0·9
Hg	29·2	0·6	1·10	—24·4	+2·7

† Estimated electrode potential $= \frac{1}{2}$(ionization-potential sum+sublimation energy+ 'hydration' energy).

two of the distinctions between the A subgroups and B subgroups, namely the greater electropositive character and better fit with the ionic model of the former. These distinctions are brought out generally by a comparison between the estimated potentials in Fig. 30.9 and the experimental

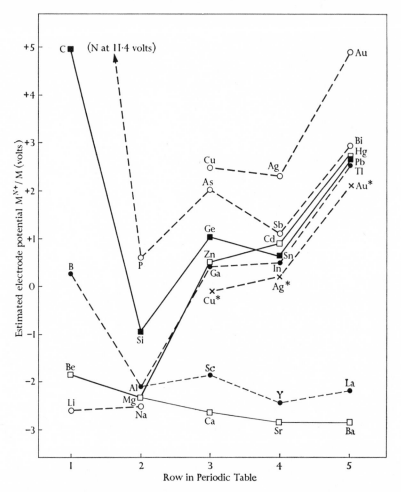

FIG. 30.9. Estimated electrode potentials in Groups I to V. Group-valence ions. See text for significance of lower set of values for Cu, Ag, and Au.

potentials of Fig. 30.10. It will be seen again that many of the general qualitative features of the experimental diagram are predicted correctly, while the quantitative agreement is very poor. The general trends of Figs. 30.9 and 30.10 may be summarized as follows.

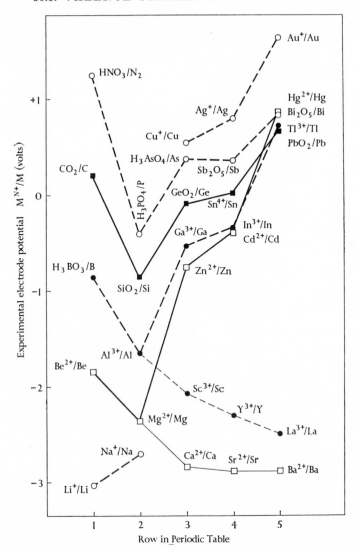

FIG. 30.10. Experimental electrode potentials in Groups I to V. Group valence. (Many of the experimental potentials do not correspond to Group-valence ions, but to more stable species, e.g. oxides. In these cases the experimental values for ions must correspond to more positive potentials than those plotted in Fig. 30.10.)

(1) B elements are less readily oxidized to their Group-valence states than are the corresponding A elements. The differences are related to differences in ionization potentials, but are smaller than these differences in absolute terms.

(2) Oxidation to the Group-valence state tends to become more difficult in succeeding Groups. An exception to this rule is provided by the elements of Group IB, where the unusually high nobility of the metals arises largely because of their high sublimation energies. In Fig. 30.9, values for Cu*, Ag*, and Au* are also plotted to represent the estimated electrode potentials if the sublimation energies of Cu, Ag, and Au were only the same as K, Rb, and Cs respectively. It will be seen that these lower values then fit in quite well with the general rule.

(3) The greatest changes along a row are found in the early rows, the values for electrode potentials in the last row (Hg to Bi) being remarkably similar. Correspondingly there is a change from a sequence of A (e.g. Be and Mg), B (e.g. Zn to Cd), and 'super-B' character (e.g. Hg) in the early Groups to an 'alternation' in later Groups. These changes have already been discussed as a postscript to non-metal chemistry in Chapter 18.

30.4. Valence states: $(N-2)$-valence

OXIDATION STATE DIAGRAMS

Estimated Oxidation State Diagrams for Pb and Zr (Pauling radii 0.84 Å for Pb^{4+} and 0.80 for Zr^{4+}) are plotted in Fig. 30.11 and for Sn and Si in Fig. 30.12, together with the known experimental VE values. In each case the method of section 20.3 has been used; thus the radii of Sn^{3+}, Sn^{2+}, and Sn^+ have been taken as equal to the Pauling crystal radii for In^{3+}, Cd^{2+}, and Ag^+ respectively. The diagrams predict that the stable aqueous valence states of Sn and Pb will be 2 and 4, although Pb(IV) should be very strongly oxidizing. For Zr and Si only the tetravalent state should be stable, the lower states being expected to disproportionate, as should the 1 and 3 states of Sn and Pb. The general patterns once again reflect the ionization-potential data (compare thus Fig. 30.3) and bring out the poor quantitative predictions of the ionic model for the B metals. It may also be noted, see values for sublimation energies plotted at zero oxidation state in Figs. 30.11 and 30.12, that part of the relative stability of the 2-valent state in Sn and Pb may be attributed to the relatively low binding energies in the elemental forms of these two elements.

The qualitative predictions are in agreement with general chemical observations, so that it is reasonable to associate the $(N-2)$-valence state with the inert pair of atomic s electrons. It is clear, however, that, on these simple ionic arguments, anything like a complete account of the so-called 'inert-pair' effect cannot be given. Other considerations, particularly of covalent bonding, must be introduced. This will also become apparent when we consider the structures of compounds in which B metals exhibit their $(N-2)$-valence (section 31.1). Sn^{3+} has been detected in the oxidation of Sn^{2+} compounds by trisoxalatocobaltate(III) ions in aqueous solution,

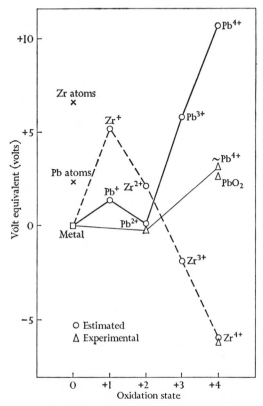

FIG. 30.11. Estimated Oxidation State Diagram for Pb and Zr.

but normally the $(N-2)$- and the Group-valence states are the only stable ones. At high temperatures, when entropy considerations become more significant, divalent silicon compounds can be obtained, e.g.

$$\left.\begin{array}{l} SiO_2 + Si \to 2SiO \\ \text{compare } AlCl_3 + 2Al \to 3AlCl \end{array}\right\} \text{volatile at high temperatures,}$$

but at low temperatures SiO disproportionates.

REDOX POTENTIALS

To conform to the pattern of the previous section, estimated redox potentials for the Group-valence $(N)/(N-2)$-valence couples are plotted in

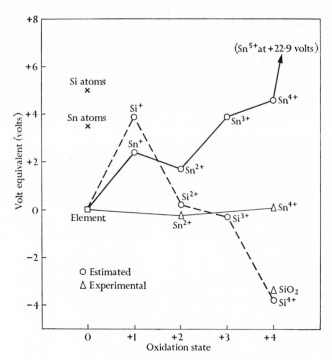

FIG. 30.12. Estimated Oxidation State Diagram for Sn and Si.

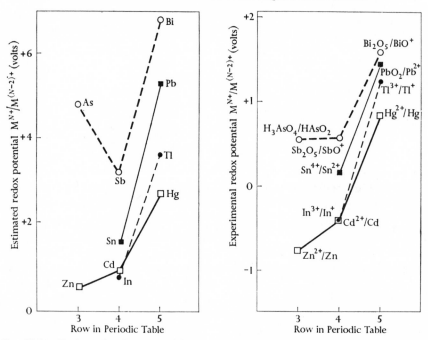

FIG. 30.13. Estimated redox potentials for the Group-valence/$(N-2)$-valence couples.

FIG. 30.14. Experimental redox potentials for the Group-valence/$(N-2)$-valence couples.

Fig. 30.13, and corresponding experimental values in Fig. 30.14. Again there is an overall qualitative relation between the two figures, but no quantitative agreement. It will be noted that oxidation from the $(N-2)$-valence state to the Group-valence state becomes harder in general along each row, and that oxidation is particularly difficult in the last row, so that the 'inert-pair' effect is especially associated with 'super-B' character.

DEVIATIONS FROM THE IONIC MODEL

It is also of interest to note that the differences between the experimental electrode potentials and those calculated for B-metal ions tend to fall into the three main classes shown in Table 30.IV. In view of the approximate nature of the estimates, too much weight should not be placed on the numerical values, but they do fit quite well with the observed patterns of B-metal behaviour, in which the characteristic B properties are usually more marked in the 'super-B' ions and less marked in the 'inert-pair' ions.

TABLE 30.IV. *Differences between estimated and experimental electrode potential* M^{n+}/M *(volts)*

Simple B ions

Cu^+	Zn^{2+}	Ga^{3+}	
(2·0)	1·2	1·0	
Ag^+	Cd^{2+}	In^{3+}	Sn^{4+}
(1·5)	1·3	0·8	1·1

'Super-B' ions

Au^+	Hg^{2+}	Ti^{3+}	Pb^{4+}
(3·2)	1·9	1·8	1·9

'Inert-pair' B ions

		In^+	Sn^{2+}
		$\sim 0·4$	1·0
		Tl^+	Pb^{2+}
		0·3	0·2

30.5. Choice of model

For many of the compounds of the B metals, especially those formed with elements differing rather little in electronegativity, the bond and the band models are the most useful. The bond approach is particularly illuminating in the discussion of stereochemical problems (section 31.1) and organo-metallic chemistry (Chapter 33), while the band model is as usual most appropriate to the discussion of alloy-like systems with other metals or with metalloids (Chapter 19). In these respects the B metals show their similarity to the more electropositive non-metals which were treated at the end of Part II.

We now wish to consider what sort of model is likely to prove most useful in the discussion of the compounds of B metals with non-metals. As the last two sections have suggested, and as the next two chapters will further demonstrate, the simple ionic model is quite inadequate. This situation might have been expected from our earlier considerations of the chemistry of the later transition metals. In general it would appear that the most instructive approach to this type of B-metal chemistry is that which makes use of a combination of the ionic and bond models. In this, the formation of B-metal ions is first considered, and then the way in which these interact covalently with their chemical environment. These interactions give rise to deviations from the ionic predictions. *Ceteris paribus*, e.g. equal ionic radii, these deviations are larger for B-metal ions of high electron affinity and larger for combinations with more polarizable ligands.

The position is complicated by the nature of the non-ionic energies. σ-bonding appears to be the most important, but this may take place involving s, p, or hybrid sp B-metal orbitals. There may also be π-bonding involving either the filled $(n-1)d$ orbitals or the empty nd orbitals. In addition the filled d orbitals will tend to increase the value of the repulsive exponent n in the ionic equation, and will make a considerable extra contribution to the London energy. The distinction between London and other energy contributions is particularly difficult in B-metal compounds, as we have already indicated in Chapter 5.

PHYSICAL EVIDENCE FOR COVALENT BONDING

The various physical techniques which may provide evidence for covalent bonding have already been discussed in connexion with transition-metal chemistry. Those involving incompletely filled electron sub-shells (e.g. the spectroscopic and magnetic methods) are not normally applicable to B-metal problems, but those which depend upon interactions of atomic nuclei with electron fields are. In special cases free radicals containing B-elements can be trapped in a lattice or generated in the gas phase. In such cases, e.g. XeF, the covalence of molecules can be investigated by ESR. B-metals can also be studied as substituents in organic radicals.

The electron distribution in normal B-metal compounds can be determined from three properties of nuclei. (1) The Mössbauer effect. This is applicable mainly to Sn. (2) The nuclear magnetic resonance spectra, so far mainly applied to ^{205}Tl. (3) The nuclear quadrupole coupling constants of nuclei such as ^{35}Cl, ^{79}Br, and ^{127}I or ^{129}I. This last method is the most general.

Table 30.v gives the Mössbauer shifts, δ, for a series of Sn^{4+} compounds showing that covalence decreases in the usual order: $I^- > Br^- > Cl^- > F^-$, and $S^{2-} > O^{2-}$. The results for Sn^{2+} compounds are more complicated as the shift is affected by s/p mixing, involving the s^2 'inert' pair as well as the bonding pairs.

TABLE 30.v. *The Mössbauer shifts, δ, in some Sn(IV) compounds*

System	δ	% ionic character from δ	% ionic character from nuclear quadrupole coupling
SnF_4	−2·5	..	..
$SnCl_4$	−1·3	50	38
$SnBr_4$	−1·0	38	28
SnI_4	−0·3	12	17
SnO_2	−2·2	..	..
SnS_2	−0·8	..	..
Sn metal	0	0	..

After Cordey-Hayes, *J. Inorg. Nucl. Chem.*, 1964, **26**, 915.

TABLE 30.vi. *Nuclear magnetic resonance.* ^{205}Tl *chemical shifts, δ*

$TlNO_3$	1·7	TlCl	6·3
Tl_2SO_4	2·6	TlBr	11·0
Tl(I) acetate	7·8	TlI	21·5

From Hafner and Nachtrieb, *J. Chem. Phys.*, 1964, **40**, 2891. δ is measured relative to an extrapolated value for the free Tl^+ ion.

The NMR spectral shift has been studied in a number of Tl^+ compounds (Table 30.vi) and found to follow the order $I^- > Br^- > Cl^- > NO_3^-$, with an estimated 10 per cent covalence in TlI and ~ 1 per cent in $TlNO_3$. Covalence is probably more marked in Tl^{3+} compounds.

TABLE 30.vii. *Nuclear quadrupole resonance frequencies of ^{35}Cl, ^{79}Br, and ^{127}I, the covalent character of metal-ligand bonds, and the net charge on the central metal atom (after Nakamura, Ito, and Kubo)*

Compound	(Mc/sec)[†]	Covalence[‡][§]	Net +ve charge on B-metal atom
M_2SnBr_6	129	0·40	1·60
M_2SeCl_6	20·7	0·45	1·30
M_2SeBr_6	174	0·53	0·82
$(NH_4)_2TeCl_6$	15·137	0·32	2·08
M_2TeBr_6	136	0·42	1·48
M_2TeI_6	153	0·52	0·88

† The value at liquid-nitrogen temperature unless otherwise noted.
‡ The extent of s character in the bonding orbital of halogens was assumed to be 0·15.
§ Vanishing asymmetry parameters were assumed.

The more extensive data (Table 30.VII) on the quadrupole resonance frequencies of ^{35}Cl, ^{79}Br, and ^{127}I have confirmed the general order of covalence $I^- > Br^- > Cl^-$ and, in any given halide, have led to the order $Sn^{4+} \leqslant Te^{4+} < Se^{4+} < Pd^{4+}$. The complex bromides of these elements all have bonds with some 40–50 per cent covalent character. The covalence in Sn^{4+} compounds estimated from this method and from the Mössbauer shifts are compared in Table 30.V and shown to be in reasonable agreement.

The above evidence suggests that even the most ionic cation of the B metals, Tl^+, should be regarded as up to 10 per cent covalent while the least ionic cations, e.g. Hg^{2+} and Sn^{4+}, may be more than 50 per cent covalent. In such circumstances the ionic model can only be a rough guide to our thinking.

CHANGE OF METAL OR VALENCE

We have already commented several times on the relation between the strength of covalent bonding and the magnitude of ionization potentials. The considerations of section 30.2 would therefore lead us to suppose that deviations from the ionic model would be increasingly marked in the series: pre-transition A-metal cations, $(N-2)$-valence B-metal cations, Group-valence B-metal cations, Group-valence 'super-B' metal cations. In general this distinction is observed in the experimental data, although as we shall see in section 31.4, the $(N-2)$-valence B-metal cations are more like A metals with some ligands and more like B metals with others.

On the other hand, deviations from the ionic model frequently tend to become *relatively* less marked as the ionic forces become more important, that is with increase of charge or decrease of ionic radius. Some guide to the magnitude of the various effects may be obtained from Fig. 30.15, where the ratio of the ionization-potential sum to the square of ionic charge is plotted as a function of ionic radius. This figure may be compared with a number of thermochemical comparisons made in section 31.5.

CHANGE OF LIGAND

The deviations from the ionic model are reflected chemically in a preference by B-metal cations for polarizable ligands. The relative polarizability of ligands is most simply demonstrated by comparing the chemistry of two ions, such as Ca^{2+} and Cd^{2+}, which have the same formal charge and almost identical ionic radii, so that the ionic considerations would not distinguish between them. We shall consider this type of comparison in some detail in the next chapter, concentrating our attention on systems in which the ligand is an anion in a solid compound. In this way we free

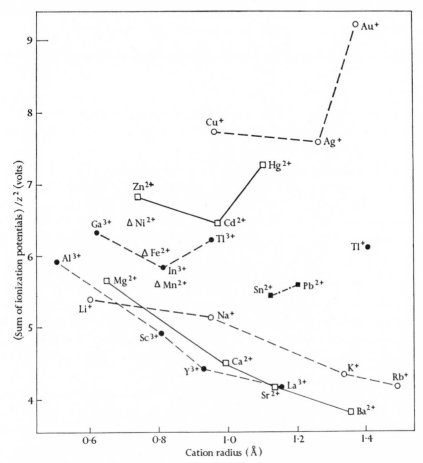

Fig. 30.15. (Sum of ionization potentials)/(charge)^2 as a function of cation radius. It is suggested that this plot may indicate, approximately, where deviations from the ionic model are to be expected, see Figs. 31.13–31.16.

ourselves from some of the complicating features, especially entropy considerations, which are also present in equilibria involving solutions (Chapter 32). Before we consider chemical equilibria, however, we shall discuss the structures (section 31.1) and related physical properties (section 31.2) of B-metal compounds, as these provide some clear indications of the importance of covalent bonding.

Problems

1. Plot (as a function of the row in the Periodic Table) the first ionization potentials of the elements of Group II (typical, A, and B), and comment on the features of your plot. (Ionization potentials required for this and the following problems are given at the end of Chapter 2.)

2. Compare the ratios of the second and first ionization potentials for the elements of Group II. Comment on the significance of the differences between IIA and IIB.

3. Plot the sum of the first two ionization potentials for the elements C, Si, Ge, Sn, and Pb. Compare your plot with a similar plot for the sum of the third and fourth ionization potentials.

4. Plot the fifth ionization potentials for the elements N, P, As, Sb, and Bi, and comment on the result. Compare with the ionization potentials of the excited V^{4+} ion (Ar core. $4s^1$) and the excited Nb^{4+} ion (Kr core. $5s^1$), which may be estimated as approximately 46·9 and 40·7 eV respectively.

5. For each of the following elements (compare Fig. 30.3) plot the ratio of ionization potential to charge left on the atom after ionization as a function of charge: Cu, Zn, Ga, Si, Ti. Comment on your results.

6. Determine the difference in the ionization potentials of Pb and Sn for each of the first five ionization potentials, of Tl and In for each of the first four ionization potentials, and of Hg and Cd for each of the first three ionization potentials. Comment on your results.

7. The following are the excitation energies (kcal per g atom) for promoting one ns electron to an np orbital (e.g. Mg, $3s^2$ to $3s^1 3p^1$): Be 63, Mg 62, Zn 93, Cd 87, Hg 112. How may these values be explained, and how far are the changes along the series reflected in the general chemistry of the elements?

8. Comment on the changes in the ionic radii of trivalent ions between Sc and Ga, Y and In, and La and Tl.

9. Fluorides of xenon and krypton are now known and compounds of trivalent silver have also been prepared. What do you think are the chances of preparing compounds of Cd(III)?

10. Nearly all the compounds of B metals are diamagnetic. Comment on the relevance of this observation to the valence states exhibited by B metals.

11. How far is it possible to explain the fact that Sn^{2+} is a more powerful reducing agent than Pb^{2+}?

12. $PbBr_4$ and PbI_4 have not been prepared. $PbCl_4$ decomposes easily. How may these observations be interpreted ?

13. Explain why it is that above 1100 °C silicon can be transported in a stream of $SiCl_4$, and aluminium in a stream of $AlCl_3$.

14. Before reading Chapters 31 and 32, try to predict—in as much detail as you can—the general chemistry of the B metals. Later compare your predictions with the experimental observations.

15. How may Fig. 30.15 be related to the 'a' and 'b' classification of cations (see especially Fig. 32.2) ?

Bibliography

C. E. MOORE, *Atomic Energy Levels*, Circular of the National Bureau of Standards No. 467, Washington, D.C., 1949 (vol. 1), 1952 (vol. 2), and 1958 (vol. 3).
W. M. LATIMER, *The Oxidation States of the Elements and their Potentials in Aqueous Solutions*, 2nd ed., Prentice-Hall, Englewood Cliffs, N.J., 1952.

31 · B Metals: Solid-State Chemistry

31.1. The stereochemistry of B-metal compounds

In discussing the structures found in B-metal compounds, it will be illuminating to relate the general trends which are observed experimentally against the predictions which might be expected from the various models. Regular crystal structures would be expected on the simple ionic model, with an increase in cation coordination number as the cation size increases.

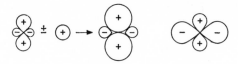

FIG. 31.1. $(d_{z^2}-s)$ hybrid orbitals (after Dunitz and Orgel).

Irregular structures can occur if the cations are not truly spherical (e.g. the Jahn–Teller type distortion (section 24.3) which is of particular significance in the stereochemistry of Cu(II)). At first sight Group-valence ions (d^{10}) and $(N-2)$-valence ions $(d^{10}s^2)$ should all be quite spherical. However, it has been suggested that in the first group of ions there may be some hybridization of $(n-1)d$ and ns orbitals, especially when the two are particularly close in energy as in Au and Hg (see Dunitz and Orgel), while in the second group some 'admixture' of ns and np orbitals may be important. Both effects could lead to non-symmetrical ions. Thus if the Hg^{2+} ion is to be regarded as $(d,s)^{10}$, rather than simply $(d)^{10}$, it would be a spherical ion with a hole in it corresponding to some empty ds hybrid orbital. A linear hybrid involving one d and the s orbital would then give rise to a hole of shape shown in Fig. 31.1. As with transition-metal ions, similar stereochemical results can be derived from a formally-similar treatment using molecular orbitals.

Strong London forces should in general lead to an increase in coordination number, but they will introduce no directional character to the structure. On the other hand, covalent interactions will tend to favour structures of low coordination number related to the number of available and energetically-useful bonding orbitals. The contribution of an orbital will depend upon its radial distribution (overlap) and its energy. These properties of the orbitals also affect the relative importance of sp^3 (tetrahedral), sp^2 (planar), and sp (linear) combinations. Where covalence is dominant, bond lengths will be shorter than those expected from ion-size considerations.

GROUP-VALENCE IONS

The coordination number of pre-transition ions generally increases down any Group (e.g. BeF_2 to BaF_2, section 20.4). This is not found with the B metals. Thus LiI and NaI both crystallize with 6:6 structures, but CuI and AgI form 4:4 tetrahedral crystals while AuI has been assigned a chain structure with 2:2 coordination. More generally the important coordination numbers for Cu, Ag, and Au are (with the most important underlined)

Cu 2 and $\underline{4}$; Ag 2, 4, and 6; Au $\underline{2}$ and 4,

as is brought out by the examples given in Table 31.I. Au exhibits in this way its 'super-B' properties, and its preference for 2-fold coordination could be attributed to a tendency to mix s (here strongly stabilized) with as little p as possible. Alternatively or in addition the $(d, s)^{10}$ hybridization argument outlined above may be used. It should be noted that the extra energy contribution from covalent bonding need not necessarily be very large, for we have already seen (Chapter 5) that the differences in ionic lattice energy between different structures are often quite small.

Other coordination numbers are also found. Thus in AgCuS where Cu is presumably monovalent, it is surrounded by three S atoms in a plane. Copper sulphide of deceptively simple formula CuS is probably best written as

$$Cu_4^+ Cu_2^{2+} (S_2)_2 S_2$$

with the copper(I) ions in a tetrahedral coordination, and the copper(II) ions at the centre of an equilateral triangle of sulphur atoms.

Similar structural features are found in Group II (see Table 31.II) with a slight tendency to increase the coordination number from Zn^{2+} to Cd^{2+} while there is a marked decrease at Hg^{2+}.

In keeping with their less ionic character, these B-metal compounds have a somewhat greater tendency than A-metal compounds to adopt a layer-type lattice. Thus $CaCl_2$ and $CaBr_2$ occur in deformed rutile structures, while $CdCl_2$ and $CdBr_2$ crystallize in a layer structure ($CdCl_2$ structure). However, both CaI_2 and CdI_2 have layer structures.

TABLE 31.I. *Stereochemistry of compounds of 1-valent B metals*

	Linear	Tetrahedral	Octahedral	Other structures
Cu(I)	$Cu(NH_3)_2^+$, Cu_2O	$CuCl$, $CuBr$, CuI, $[CuI(AsR_3)]_4$, $Cu(CN)_4^{3-}$, $Cu(o\text{-phenanthroline})_2^+$, $Cu(thioacetamide)_4^+$		$AgCuS$ (see text), $Cu_2Cl_2 \cdot N_2(CH_3)_2$, $KCu(CN)_2$, $[Cu(diazoaminobenzene)]_2$
Ag(I)	$Ag(NH_3)_2^+$, $Ag(CN)_2^-$, Ag_2O	AgI, $(AgI_3^{2-})_n$, $Ag(S_2O_3)_2^{3-}$, $Ag(o\text{-phenanthroline})_2^+$, $Ag(thioacetamide)_4^+$	AgF, $AgCl$, $AgBr$, $Ag(dioxan)_3ClO_4$	$AgSCN$ (non-linear), $Ag(PR_3)_2I(?)$
Au(I)	$AuCl_2^-$, $Au(CN)_2^-$, $Au(thioacetamide)_2^+$, $AuI(PR_3)$, $Au(NH_3)_2^+$	$Au(S_2O_3)_2^{3-}(?)$		

R = organic group such as methyl.

TABLE 31.II. *Stereochemistry of compounds of 2-valent B metals*

	Linear	Tetrahedral	Octahedral	Other structures
Zn		$[ZnCl_4]^{2-}$, $Zn(NH_3)_2Cl_2$, ZnO, ZnS, ZnSe, ZnTe, $Zn_4O(acetate)_6$, $[Zn(NCS)_4]^{2-}$, $[Zn(NH_3)_4]^{2+}$	$ZnCl_2$, etc. (solid), $Zn(H_2O)_6^{2+}$, $Zn(oxinate)_2,2H_2O$, $[Zn(dipyridyl)_3]^{2+}$	$Zn(terpy)Cl_2$, $Zn(AcAc)_2,H_2O$ (both 5-coordinate)
Cd		$CdCl_4^{2-}$, $Cd(SCN)_4^{2-}$, CdS, CdSe, CdTe	CdO, $[Cd(H_2O)_6]^{2+}$, $[Cd(NH_3)_6]^{2+}$	$Cd(SCN)_2$
Hg	$HgCl_2$, $[Hg(NH_3)_2]^{2+}$, HgO, HgS(cinnabar)	$[HgCl_4]^{2-}$, etc, $[Hg(SCN)_4]^{2-}$, $HgI_2(linked(\beta))$, HgS, HgSe, HgTe	$(HgCl_3^-)_n$ chains	HgF_2 (8-coordinate), NMe_4HgBr_3 (3-coordinate)

Terpy is terpyridyl and AcAc is the acetylacetonate ion.

Zn also exhibits 5-fold coordination, as in $Zn(acetylacetonate)_2,H_2O$

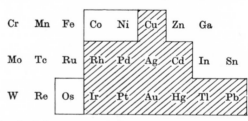

and $Zn(terpyridyl)Cl_2$.

Similar differences between A subgroups and B subgroups are seen again in Groups III and IV. Whereas the trivalent and tetravalent compounds of the A subgroups show very high coordination numbers, 9, 8, and 7 being quite common, lower values are found in the B subgroups. Thus with the heavier halides Ga and In are 4-coordinate; the complex ions have the formulae MX_4^-, and are tetrahedral. The halides and hydrides of Ge, Sn, and Pb are best considered with the molecular halides of the non-metals. In common with Al and B, the methyls and hydrides of Ga and In are electron-deficient and based on tetrahedral coordination around the metal. The oxides of Group IV are structurally related to SiO_2 rather than to fluorite, cf. ZrO_2, and those of Group III to Al_2O_3 rather than to the lanthanide oxides. In general the lower coordination number in the B subgroups can be rationalized in terms of sp^3 hybridization rather than hybridization involving nd orbitals also.

The dependence of coordination number upon the ligand is quite curious. The highest coordination numbers are found with fluoride, e.g. 8 in HgF_2. The lowest coordination numbers are found with the ligands of intermediate polarizability, e.g. 2 in $Ag(NH_3)_2^{2+}$ and $HgCl_2$. Ligands of greater polarizability lead to higher coordination, e.g. 4 in HgSe and $[Cu\{S=C(NR_2)_2\}_4]^+$. Unsaturated ligands such as cyanide and pyridine also give higher coordination numbers than ammonia.

TABLE 31.III. *Structures of thiocyanates*

Cr	Mn	Fe	Co	Ni	Cu	Zn	Ga
Mo	Tc	Ru	Rh	Pd	Ag	Cd	In	Sn
W	Re	Os	Ir	Pt	Au	Hg	Tl	Pb

The metals in the shaded area give M–SCN complexes and M–SCN–M polymers. The metals in the enclosed unshaded areas form M–NCS and M–SCN complexes, depending upon the other ligands present, and M–SCN–M polymers. Other metals form M–NCS complexes. The metal cations which form M–SCN compounds usually form sulphite and thiosulphate complexes with M binding to S. The low-valence states of the metals show a greater preference for S than the higher-valence states.

In such compounds as thiocyanates where there is a choice of a polarizable sulphur atom or polar nitrogen atom in the same ion (see Table 31.III) heavier B metals choose the polarizable end.

π-COMPLEXES

The d^{10} ions, Cu^+, Ag^+, and Hg^{2+} (compare also Pt^0 and the low-spin Pt^{2+}) are able to form compounds with unsaturated hydrocarbons (olefins, acetylenes, and aromatics). Most of these compounds are rather unstable and some are possibly important as reaction intermediates. They are thought to involve a 'synergic' type of interaction with electron donation of a σ-type from the double bond of the unsaturated hydrocarbon to the metal ion, coupled with back-donation of a π-type from the metal ion to the ligand (see Fig. 31.2). The structures of $AgClO_4, C_6H_6$, and of the compound of $AgNO_3$ with *cyclo*-octatetraene $AgNO_3, C_8H_8$ have been studied. In both compounds, columns of Ag^+ ions and organic molecules are formed, with each Ag^+ ion closely associated with *one* double bond of the organic ring.

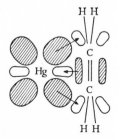

Fig. 31.2. Postulated bonding between Hg^{2+} and ethylene.

METAL–METAL BONDING

Metal–metal bonding is found in compounds of cadmium $\{Cd_2(AlCl_4)_2\}$, and gallium (GaS), and especially with Hg, the well-known mercury(I) compounds. In the mercury(I) halides, e.g. Hg_2Cl_2, the Hg atoms appear to form two (sp) collinear bonds, one to halogen and one to the other Hg atom, and to have four other halogen atoms as next-nearest neighbours to form a distorted octahedral group. In passing from fluoride to iodide, the Hg–Hg distance increases, the apparent ionic 'radius' to the nearest halogen decreases, while the apparent ionic radius to the next four halogens remains approximately constant, as is shown by the figures in Table 31.IV.

TABLE 31.IV. *Interatomic distances and apparent ionic 'radii' in mercury(I) halides* (Å)

	Hg—Hg	Hg—X	Hg—X *minus ionic radius of* X^-	Hg *to* 4X	Hg *to* 4X *minus ionic radius of* X^-
Hg_2F_2	2·42	2·31	0·95	2·69	1·33
Hg_2Cl_2	2·53	2·52	0·71	3·17	1·36
Hg_2Br_2	2·58	2·57	0·62	3·32	1·37
Hg_2I_2	2·69	2·68	0·52	3·51	1·35

Metal–metal bonding involving two different metals one of which is a B metal is also quite common. $SnCl_3^-$ and SnR_2 can combine with a number of transition-metal ions in low oxidation states, e.g. Pt, Ir, and Mn. The basis of one colorimetric analysis procedure for Pt depends on the yellow complex of Pt^{4+} and Sn^{2+} in a chloride medium. Other examples of M′—M″ bonds are found in such compounds as $(R_3P)AuMn(CO)_5$ and $RHgFe(CO)_4$. Presumably Pb^{2+}, like Bi^{3+}, forms few M—M bonds since the 'inert' pair of electrons occupies a 'purer' s orbital than it does in Sn^{2+} and Sb^{3+}.

$(N-2)$-VALENCE IONS

Apart from Cu, Ag, and Au, which exhibit characteristic transition-metal valence states (e.g. copper(II)), the B metals appear to have only two valence states, the Group valence and the $(N-2)$ or 'inert-pair' valence state. We have already discussed one class of *apparent* exceptions to this rule, in which there is metal–metal bonding: thus mercury(I) is not monovalent but divalent. Another class is formed by compounds in which the element is found in both valence states. Thus $GaCl_2$ (diamagnetic) does not contain the Ga^{2+} ion (which would give rise to paramagnetism), but it has been shown by a number of measurements (e.g. Raman, X-ray) to consist of equal quantities of monovalent Ga^+ and trivalent Ga as $GaCl_4^-$. Similar mixed-valence states are found, e.g. in $In_2Cl_3(In_3^+InCl_6^{3-})$, TlS, and Pb_3O_4. In Tl_2Cl_3, which has a very complex and as yet incompletely understood structure, the presence of both Tl^+ and Tl^{3+} has been demonstrated by NMR spectroscopy, which shows two peaks in the [205]Tl resonance of relative intensities 1 and 3, and by the fact that the Tl^{3+} readily undergoes radioactive exchange with [204]$TlCl_3$. Radioactive exchange between Tl^+ and Tl^{3+} is known to be slow in solution. The crystal structure of $TlBr_2$ shows it to be $Tl(I)[Tl(III)Br_4]$.

$(N-2)$-valence ions generally crystallize in structures with a somewhat higher coordination number than is the case with ordinary Group-valence B-metal ions. This is in keeping with their somewhat greater electropositive character, to which we have already referred. It is also accentuated by the fact that $(N-2)$-valence ions are most common with the larger elements, e.g. Tl^+, Pb^{2+}, and Bi^{3+}. There is in fact therefore a very marked distinction in these elements in their two valence states, one less and one (super-B) more polarizing than the 'normal' B-metal ions. Thus in TlS Tl^+ is surrounded by eight S atoms (at 3·32 Å), and Tl^{3+} with only four S atoms (at 2·60 Å). TlCl, TlBr, and the red form of TlI all crystallize in the 8:8 CsCl structure in striking contrast to the behaviour of gold(I), where a coordination number of 2 is commonly preferred. However, the normal yellow form of TlI has a 5:5 structure which may be regarded as derived from a NaCl structure with one anion missing from the octahedral coordination around each Tl^+ ion. Table 31.v gives the structures for the

TABLE 31.v. *Crystal structures of some* Ge(II), Sn(II), *and* Pb(II) *compounds*

	Oxide	Sulphide	Selenide	Telluride
Ge(II)	?	O	O	O and N
Sn(II)	T	O	O	N
Pb(II)	T+R	N	N	N

N   NaCl structure   O distorted (orthorhombic) NaCl structure
T   tetragonal PbO structure   R   rhombic PbO structure

oxides, sulphides, selenides, and tellurides of Ge(II), Sn(II), and Pb(II). The first point of interest is that the regular NaCl structure tends to occur with the larger anions, in direct contrast to the behaviour of Cd. In GeS and SnS, for example, the following distances are found:

$$\text{Ge} \begin{cases} 1\ \text{S at } 2\cdot47\ \text{Å} \\ 2\ \text{S} \quad\ 2\cdot64 \\ 1\ \text{S} \quad\ 2\cdot91 \\ 2\ \text{S} \quad\ 3\cdot00 \end{cases} \qquad \text{Sn} \begin{cases} 1\ \text{S at } 2\cdot62\ \text{Å} \\ 2\ \text{S} \quad\ 2\cdot68 \\ 2\ \text{S} \quad\ 3\cdot27 \\ 1\ \text{S} \quad\ 3\cdot39 \end{cases}$$

The tetragonal forms of SnO and PbO have the structure shown in Fig. 31.3, in which four oxygen atoms in a plane lie to one side of the metal atom, while the other side is presumably occupied by the 'inert' electron pair. Rhombic PbO is essentially a puckered version of tetragonal PbO. This type of distortion, in which the 'inert pair' apparently occupies a stereo-chemical position in the lattice, occurs in a number of structures, e.g. $SnCl_2,H_2O$; K_2SnCl_4,H_2O; $KSbF_4$; $(NH_4)_2SbCl_5$; and Bi_2O_3. In the latter compound a simple cubic lattice may be formed in which it appears that each Bi atom has six oxygen neighbours arranged at the corners of a cube, the remaining two (diagonally-opposed) corners being unoccupied. These remarkable distortions suggest some bonding with hybridized *sp* orbitals, the 'inert pair' also occupying a similar hybrid orbital. This type of structure is particularly marked with smaller anions, and we shall find in section 31.4 that these structural effects are paralleled by thermochemical irregularities in oxides.

The regular NaCl structures found with PbS, PbSe, and PbTe (i.e. with the largest of the 'cations' in Table 31.v) are in marked contrast to the behaviour of the Group IIB elements, where Hg^{2+} shows the greatest preference for a small coordination number. In these divalent compounds of lead the 'inert pair' is stereochemically inert. Another example of what must be presumed to be a 'pure' s^2 'inert pair' is the symmetrical structure of $[SbCl_6]^{3-}$.

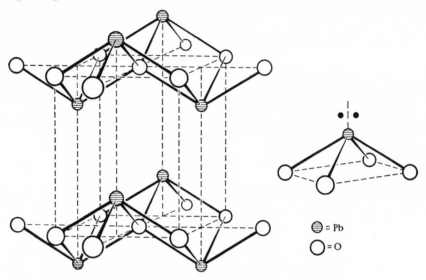

FIG. 31.3. The structure of PbO (after Wells).

BOND DISTANCES

In Chapter 5 comment was made upon the short bond distances in B-metal compounds. With any one anion a part of the bond contraction is due to the low coordination number which must be taken into account in any strict comparison with the A-metal compounds. A simpler way of bringing out the magnitude of the bond contractions is to examine the bond distances with a series of anions. Thus the absolute size of the mercury(II) 'ion' can be estimated from the fluoride lattice (CaF_2 structure) distance, Hg–F 2·40 Å, which makes Hg^{2+} about the same size as Ca^{2+}. In HgS, however, the Hg^{2+} 'ion' has about the same effective size as Mg^{2+}. The situation is very much the same in complex ions. The distances Hg^{2+}–CN⁻ (1·98 Å) and Hg^{2+}–NH_3 (2·07 Å) are very close to those in the corresponding Zn^{2+} complexes, and the Ag^+–ligand distances are often nearly as short as the corresponding Li^+–ligand distances.

The $(N-2)$-valence cations of the B metals are much larger, and the ionic radii are more consistent. Table 31.VI shows that in the solid phase Tl–X distances are similar to those of K–X: the distances in the gas-phase molecules, however, make the Tl^+ ion considerably smaller. In both the gas and the solid state the distances do not increase from Cl⁻ to I⁻ with Tl⁺ as much as they do with K⁺. Unfortunately detailed comparisons are made difficult by the distortions from simple geometry in the crystals.

TABLE 31.VI. *Interatomic distances in thallium(I) and potassium halides* (Å)

	gas	solid		gas	solid
TlCl	2·55	3·15	KCl	2·67	3·14
TlBr	2·68	3·29	KBr	2·82	3·29
TlI	2·87	3·47	KI	3·05	3·53

The data for the solid thallium halides are for crystals grown with the NaCl structure.

31.2. Some physical properties of B-metal compounds

BOILING-POINTS

Boiling-point data for B-metal compounds are less complete than for the corresponding A-metal compounds: this is largely a result of the relatively easy decomposition of B-metal compounds. B-metal halides, however, provide a useful series for discussion. The boiling-points of the halides of Groups IIA and IIB are plotted in Fig. 31.4. With pre-transition cations (compare the alkali halides, section 20.4) boiling-points reflect lattice energies, so that the highest boiling-points are in general found with the smallest ions. Exceptions to this general rule can be explained in terms of anion-contact effects, and polarization effects in the gaseous molecules. The latter may account for the anomalously low values for the Mg halides. The B-metal halides lie much lower in Fig. 31.4 than the halides of the corresponding A metals. Thus Cd halides have very considerably lower boiling-points than the Ca halides, although Ca^{2+} and Cd^{2+} have almost exactly equal ionic radii so that any argument on the basis of an ionic model would lead to similar results in both cases. It is reasonable to assume that this difference is associated with the greater polarization or tendency to covalent bonding in the Cd-halide than in the Ca-halide vapours. In the next section we shall discuss in some detail the extent to which such polarization energies contribute to the binding in *solid* B-metal compounds: here we must note that it increases in absolute magnitude on passing from the continuous lattice of the solid to the molecules in the vapour. Covalent forces would thus be expected to be very important in Cd-halide molecules.

We may put this on a more quantitative basis, e.g. for CdF_2 and CaF_2. The lattice energy of CaF_2 is calculated to be 622 kcal mole⁻¹, while the experimental value (Born–Haber cycle) is 624 kcal mole⁻¹. For CdF_2 the values are calculated 634, and experimental 662 kcal mole⁻¹, so that by comparison with CaF_2 taken as a 'pure' ionic compound, the CdF_2 lattice gains about 26 kcal 'polarization energy'. The latent heats of fusion of CaF_2 and CdF_2 are relatively small (7·1 and 5·4 kcal mole^{-1} respectively), but the latent heats of vaporization are 74 kcal (CaF_2), and 52 kcal (CdF_2). Thus in the process of changing from solid lattice to vapour molecules, CdF_2 gains (i.e. loses less binding energy) over CaF_2 by about another 24 kcal. In rough

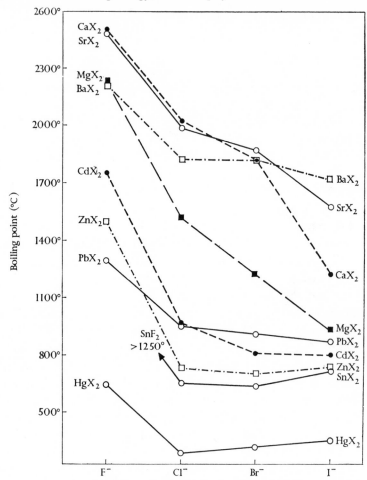

FIG. 31.4. The boiling-points of the halides of Group II, Sn(II), and Pb(II).

terms we may therefore say that the polarization energy gain in the CdF_2 molecules compared with CaF_2 is about twice what it is in the solid lattice. A similar argument for the iodides gives an extra polarization energy of about 62 kcal in solid CdI_2 as against solid CaI_2, and a further gain by CdI_2 of about 27 kcal mole^{-1} on passing from the solid to the molecular (vapour) state.

Apart from the uniformly lower values, the pattern of boiling-points in Fig. 31.4 for the Zn, Cd, and Pb halides is comparable with that found for the Mg, Ca, and Ba halides, as might be expected in terms of ionic sizes. On the other hand, the Hg halides all have very low boiling-points.

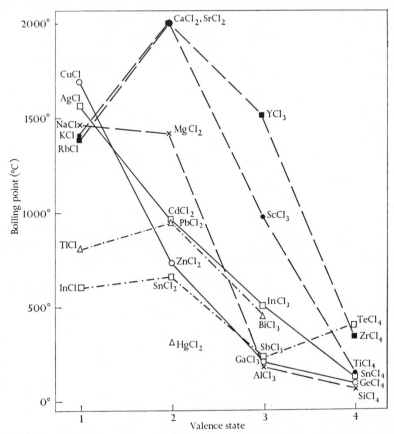

FIG. 31.5. The boiling-points of some chlorides as a function of the metal valence.

We may attribute this to the very pronounced tendency of mercury(II) to form covalent molecular species in keeping with its 'super-B' character. The mercury(II) halides also follow the boiling-point sequence of

fluoride $\gg$ chloride $<$ bromide $<$ iodide

which we have discussed in Chapter 12. Compare also the Sn, Zn, and to some extent the Pb halides.

Boiling-points for chlorides of both A metals and B metals with valence states from 1 to 4 are plotted in Fig. 31.5. Again the general pattern of higher boiling-points in the A-metal than in the B-metal compounds is observed. There are, however, two exceptional groups. The first comprises

CuCl and AgCl, which have surprisingly high boiling-points (the value quoted for CuCl is for the temperature at which there will be one atmosphere of CuCl vapour: in practice CuCl volatilizes also as Cu_3Cl_3 polymer so that the normal experimental boiling-point is about 100° lower with an abnormally low entropy of vaporization (Trouton constant) of 4·3 entropy units). We do not know why this should be so, but it may possibly be connected with large contributions from London forces which will be very roughly proportional to the number of near neighbours. Thus for AgCl, Mayer calculates a London contribution of 29 kcal (see Chapter 5). If most of this energy were lost in forming AgCl molecules from the 6:6 solid lattice, then, from the experimental entropy of vaporization (23 e.u.) we would estimate that this London energy would give rise to an increase of the order of

$$29,000/23 \simeq 1300°$$

in the boiling-point. The Ag halides incidentally form a curious series for their boiling-points are AgF 1150°; AgCl 1564°; AgBr 1540°; AgI 1505 °C. This would appear to be the only case where a metal fluoride has a lower boiling-point than that of the other halides: CuF disproportionates on heating. The second exceptional group is typified by the case of $TeCl_4$. Here the high boiling-point may be attributed at least in part to the non-tetrahedral nature and consequent polar character of the molecule (contrast, for example, $TiCl_4$).

Somewhat similar general considerations would appear to apply to the boiling-points of other B-metal compounds. Thus while CdO sublimes at 1497° and PbO boils about 1470°, CaO boils around 3500° and SrO around 3200 °C.

MELTING-POINTS

Melting-points are rather more difficult to interpret. The same overall considerations would appear to apply as with boiling-points (compare, for example, Fig. 31.6 with Fig. 31.4), but added complications arise because of the possibility of alternative structures. Especially low melting-points will be expected when the difference in energy between one type of co-ordination and another is small. This latter consideration could perhaps account for the long liquid ranges found, for example in AgCl, AgBr, and AgI compared with NaCl, NaBr, and NaI.

ELECTRICAL CONDUCTIVITY

At first sight it might be expected that, because of their marked departure from the ionic model, B-metal compounds would show lower electrical conductivities in the solid and molten forms than do their A-metal counterparts. In fact, however, the activation energy for ion diffusion is usually a more controlling factor than ionic character. Thus the α or high-temperature solid form of AgI (i.e. the form stable above 145·8 °C) has the very high

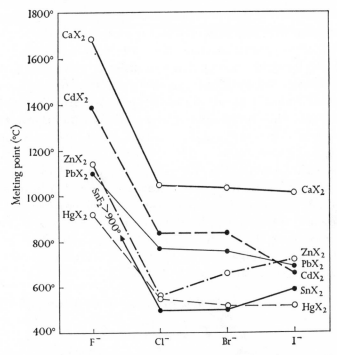

FIG. 31.6. The melting-points of some halides of Group II, Sn(II), and Pb(II).

electrical conductivity of 1·3 ohm^{-1} cm^{-1} at 146°, while at the same temperature samples of solid NaCl have conductivities of only 10^{-8} to 10^{-12} ohm^{-1} cm^{-1}, depending on the particular specimen. The current through solid NaCl is carried virtually entirely by the Na$^+$ ions at this temperature (transport number of Na$^+$ is 1·00), and these ions have great difficulty in pushing their way through the rigid lattice. On the other hand, the α-AgI crystal has locations of 2-, 3-, and 4-fold coordination for Ag$^+$ in the lattice and these enable Ag$^+$ to move fairly freely. Ag$_2$HgI$_4$ and CuI have similar high conductivities, but it is not clear to what degree these conductivities are due to ion migration.

A number of other B-metal compounds, e.g. Cu$_2$O and ZnO, are good semiconductors, the electrical conductivity sometimes being a function of non-stoicheiometry. Their conductivity is electronic in origin rather than ionic. This is true too of some heavy-metal halides (e.g. HgI_2), sulphides (e.g. PbS), selenides, and tellurides, and many arsenides and antimonides. The IIIB–VB compounds, e.g. InSb, form an especially well-studied series: these semiconductors have been described in Chapter 17.

COLOUR

Colour is more common in B-metal compounds than in the corresponding compounds of the pre-transition metals. In a general way we may associate this with the increased ease of charge transfer from a given anion to the B-metal ion with its high affinity for electrons. Thus while the oxides and sulphides of Group IIA are all white, CdO is brown, HgO (the stable form) is red, SnO exists in olive-green, red, and black forms, PbO exists in yellow and red forms, CdS is orange, HgS is black, SnS is black (the precipitate is brown), and PbS is black.

The polarizing power of the cations is also shown in the absorption-band shifts which they induce in such anions as arsenate and dichromate. These colours are of use in analytical procedures, e.g. silver arsenate and silver chromate, and in paints, e.g. lead(II) chromate. There is an interesting correlation between the colours and the interatomic distances in the oxy-anion salts of silver (Table 31.VII). The polarization of the charged oxygen is likely to be very sensitive to this distance.

TABLE 31.VII. *Colour and interatomic distance in silver salts (after Helmholz)*

Compound	Ag–O mean distance (Å)	Colour
$AgClO_3$	2·51	Colourless
Ag_2SO_4	2·50	,,
$KAgCO_3$	2·42	,,
Ag_3PO_4	2·34	Yellow
Ag_3AsO_4	2·34	Deep red
Ag_2CO_3	2·30	Yellow
Ag_2O	2·06	Black

Colourless	Yellow or red	Black
$AgNO_3$	$AgNO_2$	Ag_2S
Ag_2SO_3	$Ag_2N_2O_2$	
$AgReO_4$	$AgClO_2$	
AgC_2O_4	$Ag_2S_2O_3$	
AgCN		

MIXED-VALENCE COMPOUNDS

A surprisingly large number of B-metal compounds are known which contain ions of both the Group valence and the $(N-2)$-valence. Some examples are included in Table 31.VIII. The compounds are to be compared

TABLE 31.VIII. *Some mixed-valence compounds*

I$_B$	III$_B$	IV$_B$	V$_B$
$[Co(NH_3)_6]_2^{3+}[CuCl_5]^{3-}[CuCl_4]^{3-}$	$GaCl_2$	Pb_3O_4	K_2SbCl_6
	GaS	$K_3[PbCl_6]$	$(NH_4)_2SbBr_6$
	InS		
$[Cu(I)]_4[Cu(II)]_2[S_2]_2S_2 \ (\equiv CuS)$	$TlCl_2$		
	$TlBr_2$		
	TlS		
$Cs_2Au(I)Au(III)Cl_6$	$TlSe$		
	$TlSO_4$		

with the mixed-valence transition-metal compounds. Like them they are strikingly coloured. The colour has been attributed to electron transfer from the $M^{(N-2)+}$ to the M^{N+} ion. This transition is not simply related to the electronic conductivity of the solids for $K_2[SbCl_6]$, containing Sb^{3+} and Sb^{5+} ions, is deeply coloured but is virtually an insulator. It is not yet known whether the phase diagrams for binary systems such as Pb/O contain a number of discrete phases with little variation of composition, or whether there are large regions of continuous variation of composition. PbS exists over a small composition range on either side of the ideal formulation. Above 700 °C the range extends from $PbS_{0\cdot9996}$ to $PbS_{1\cdot00025}$. The variation is probably due to excess Pb atoms and Pb-ion vacancies at the two extremes. The treatment of structures such as these in terms of ionic models and point defects breaks down as the binding becomes more metallic and the composition ranges become broader, e.g. in PbTe (see Chapter 8).

31.3. Thermochemistry: Group valence

The remaining sections of this chapter will be primarily concerned with the heats of formation of a number of compounds of the B metals. Much of the discussion parallels the discussion of Oxidation State Diagrams in the previous chapter. The analogous compounds of the A subgroups have already been discussed in terms of an ionic model (Chapter 20). Here comparison with the A subgroups will be made in order to emphasize the deviations from the simple ionic model. As was seen in section 30.2, B metals have considerably higher ionization potentials than the corresponding A metals. It follows therefore that compounds of B metals in which the metal plays an electropositive role should be formed less readily than those of the corresponding A metals. This is generally true. There are, of course, a number of other factors to be taken into consideration. The binding energies of Cu, Ag, and Au are very considerably greater than those of K, Rb, and Cs, so that the extreme nobility of Group I$_B$ is in part due to the high ionization potentials of the atoms, and in part due to the high binding energies of the metals. Thus if we compare the formation of Cu^+ and K^+ from their metals, the first stage (atomization) requires 60 kcal more for Cu than for K, while the second stage (ionization) requires 78 kcal more (3·38 eV). The metal binding energies of B metals other than the

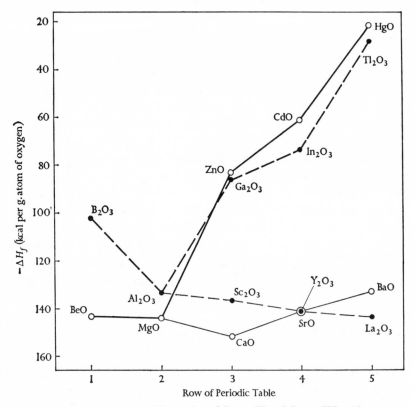

FIG. 31.7. The heats of formation of Group II and Group III oxides.

metals of Group I are somewhat lower than those of the corresponding A metals.

In general, however, B metals are somewhat less noble than the high ionization potentials might have led one to expect, for although B-metal ions are harder to form than A-metal ions, the lattice energies of their compounds are greater than would be given on an ionic model. The additional energy may be regarded as a measure of the covalent contributions arising from the increased electron affinity of the cations. The comparison of A-metal and B-metal thermochemistry may be summarized by saying that while qualitatively the differences in heats of formation may be largely linked with the ionization-potential differences, such differences in practice are not as great as would be expected on an ionic model.

The ionization-potential increases are most marked in the last B series (Au, Hg, Tl, Pb, and Bi). The chemistry of these elements correspondingly

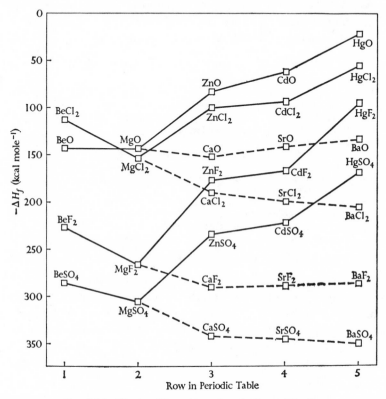

Fig. 31.8. Heats of formation of some Group II salts.

differs more distinctly from that found in the A series. We may note this in the extra-low heats of formation of their compounds, e.g. as demonstrated in Figs. 31.7 and 31.8, or the corresponding electrode potentials, Fig. 30.8. The zigzag pattern down such Groups as Be–Mg–Zn–Cd–Hg tends, in the later Groups of the Periodic Table, to be superimposed on a more rapidly changing background. This leads to the characteristic pattern of the later B elements already discussed in Chapter 18 under the title of the 'alternation' effect.

LIGAND POLARIZABILITY

We shall now proceed to make a more detailed comparison of heats of formation in A-metal and B-metal compounds by selecting pairs of ions (one A and one B) of the same charge and of very similar ionic radii. In such cases the lattice energies calculated on the simple ionic model will be very similar. B-metal ions cannot be assigned constant radii to the same extent that this is possible for A-metal ions, but the consequences of this, although significant, are largely another illustration of the effects we wish to demonstrate. Suitable pairs of ions are Ca^{2+} and Cd^{2+} (Pauling

TABLE 31.IX. *Lattice energies of* CaO *and* CdO

	Ca	Cd	Difference Cd−Ca
Sum of ionization potentials (I+II), (kcal mole^{-1})	+413	+596	
Metal sublimation energy (kcal mole^{-1})	+46	+27	
Thus ΔH_f M^{2+} (kcal mole^{-1}) . .	+459	+623	+164
Experimental ΔH_f MO crystal (kcal mole^{-1})	−152	−61	+91
Experimental lattice energy (kcal mole^{-1}) (ΔH_f O^{2-} = 217 kcal mole^{-1}) .	−828	−901	−73
Interatomic distance in MO crystal (Å)	2·40	2·35	
Repulsive exponent, n . . .	8	8½	
Calculated ionic lattice energy, MO (kcal mole^{-1})	−842	−866	−24

ionic radii 0·99 and 0·97 Å), Sr^{2+} and Hg^{2+} (1·13 and 1·10 Å), and somewhat less satisfactorily Na^+ and Ag^+ (interatomic distance in NaCl, 2·81 Å, 2·77 Å in AgCl, but note the variability of the apparent radius of the Ag^+ ion—see Chapter 5). The first pair will illustrate the simple A–B relationship, the second pair the enhanced effects found in the Au–Hg–Tl–Pb–Bi series, while a comparison of the Ca/Cd case with the Na/Ag case will help to bring out the effects of charge. We begin with CaO and CdO both of which crystallize in the NaCl structure. The relevant data are given in Table 31.IX.

The heat of formation of the gaseous Cd^{2+} ion is seen to be greater than that of the Ca^{2+} ion by 164 kcal mole^{-1}. In view of their similar radii, we should expect on an ionic model that the heats of formation of the crystalline oxides would have a very similar difference, but experimentally this is only 91 kcal. Part (24 kcal) of the 73 kcal discrepancy arises from the slightly different 'interionic' distances in CaO and CdO, but there still remains an extra 49 kcal. That is, although the heat of formation of CdO is less exothermic than that of CaO, we should on the ionic model have expected CdO to be even less exothermic. We may say that the Cd^{2+} ions, with their greater electron affinity, polarize or bond in part covalently to the O^{2-} ions. This tendency to polarize the anions may be seen thus in terms of the difference between 164 kcal and 91 (more strictly 91+24) kcal. The effect is illustrated in Fig. 31.9, not only for CaO and CdO, but for a series of Ca and Cd compounds, and also for a series of compounds of the Sr–Hg pair, and the Na–Ag pair.

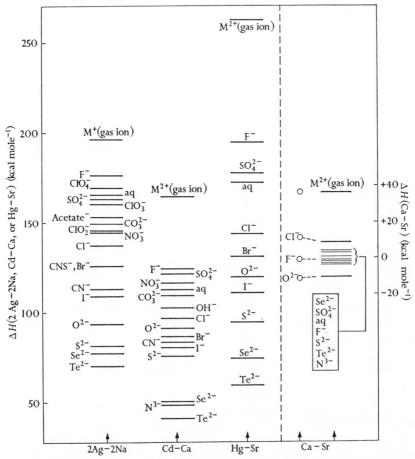

FIG. 31.9. Differences between the heats of formation of A-metal and B-metal compounds for cations of very similar size and the same formal charge. See text for further details.

Now for Ca and Cd it will be seen that the deviation from the gas-ion prediction is least for the heats of formation of CaF_2 and CdF_2 and greatest for CaTe and CdTe. In fact the observed sequence

$$F^- < SO_4^{2-} < NO_3^- < \text{hydrated ion} < CO_3^{2-} < OH^-$$
$$< Cl^- < O^{2-} < Br^- < I^- < S^{2-} < Se^{2-} < Te^{2-}$$

forms a reasonable series of increasing polarizability. This may be expressed in another way for the data merely represent the fact that, in double-decomposition reactions, Ca^{2+} ions will tend to combine with early members of the series, while Cd^{2+} ions will tend to combine with later members.

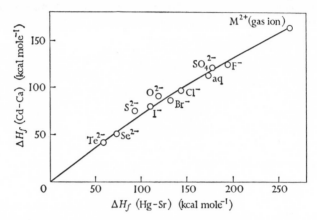

Fig. 31.10. The relation between the polarizability sequence established on the basis of differences in the heats of formation of Cd and Ca compounds with that established from Hg and Sr compounds.

This relative preference of Cd^{2+} for Cl^- rather than F^-, or S^{2-} rather than O^{2-}, has already been demonstrated in the thermochemical comparisons of fluorides and chlorides (Chapter 12) and of oxides and sulphides (Chapter 16).

The polarizability sequence for the Sr/Hg pair is almost exactly the same as for Ca and Cd, except that Br^- has moved up relative to oxide. This is shown in Fig. 31.10 where the Ca/Cd differences are plotted against the Sr/Hg differences, all the points lying close to the smooth curve. However, the sequence is now much more spread out (i.e. the gradient of Fig. 31.10 is a good deal less than 1), and the divergence from the predicted gas-ion difference (262 kcal) even greater. This may be taken as a reflection of the increased difference in ionization potential, i.e. the much greater polarizing power of the Hg^{2+} ion compared with Sr^{2+}. Again in double-decomposition reactions with Sr^{2+}, Hg^{2+} will trade F^- for Cl^-, or O^{2-} for S^{2-}, but even more exothermally than Cd^{2+} does with Ca^{2+}.

The Na/Ag pair may similarly be compared with the Ca/Cd pair (the former values in each case corresponding to 2 metal atoms so as to compare the same number of anions or charges). Again a broadening of the sequence of values may be noted, and in general it would appear that polarization or covalence effects are *relatively* more important with ions of lower charge. With increase of charge the ionic effect increases more sharply.

At the right-hand side of Fig. 31.9, a comparison is made between two A-metal ions, Sr^{2+} and Ca^{2+} (radii 1·13 and 0·99 Å). Here the difference in radii is much greater than in any of the A/B pairs with which we have been concerned. However, the differences between one anion and another are now a good deal smaller; moreover, these differences agree very well with values calculated on the basis of the differences in ionic size. The theoretical predictions given by ionic lattice-energy calculations are shown as circles to the left of the Sr/Ca points.

Since the pairs in Fig. 31.9 have been chosen so that the purely ionic contributions to the lattice energy would be very similar, some correlation of the data with the Pauling electronegativity scale might be expected. Thus for the Ca/Cd pair (electronegativities Ca 1·0, Cd 1·7) we should calculate for the difference in heats of formation with anion X (see Chapter 4)

$$2 \times 23[(x_X - 1 \cdot 0)^2 - (x_X - 1 \cdot 7)^2],$$

i.e. $(64x_X - 87)$ kcal mole^{-1}, and similarly $(83x_X - 120)$ kcal mole^{-1} and $(92x_X - 129)$ kcal per two gram moles respectively for the Sr/Hg and Na/Ag pairs. Rough agreement is in fact obtained between calculated and experimental values, although in the case of oxide this is very poor (see Table 31.x).

TABLE 31.x. *A/B comparison (see Fig. 31.9) and electronegativity predictions (kcal mole^{-1} or per 2 g mole for Na/Ag)*

Anion	F$^-$	O^{2-}	Cl$^-$	Br$^-$	I$^-$	S^{2-}	Se^{2-}	Te^{2-}
Electronegativity	4·0	3·5	3·0	2·8	2·5	2·5	2·4	2·1
Ca/Cd { Calculated	169	137	105	92	73	73	67	47
Ca/Cd { Experimental	124	91	97	86	80	75	50	41
Sr/Hg { Calculated	212	170	129	112	87	87	79	54
Sr/Hg { Experimental	194	119	143	131	110	94	74	59
2(Na/Ag) { Calculated	239	192	147	128	101	101	92	64
2(Na/Ag) { Experimental	176	93	137	125	108	81	77	70

31.4. Thermochemistry: $(N-2)$-valence ions

In the discussion of ions showing the 'inert-pair' effect, e.g. Tl^+, Sn^{2+}, Pb^{2+}, and Bi^{3+}, it has been suggested that the B character of these ions is less marked than that found in the 'normal' B-metal ions such as Ag^+, Cd^{2+}, and In^{3+}. Such a conclusion was derived partly from a consideration of electrode potentials (Table 30.iv). A similar conclusion might also have been arrived at from Fig. 30.15, where, for example, Sn^{2+} and Pb^{2+} are seen to lie between the Zn^{2+} and Cd^{2+} positions and the positions occupied by the alkaline-earth ions. In general the conclusion is a fairly useful rough guide to the chemistry of the B metals in their $(N-2)$-valence states. However, it obscures many important details. Thus Sn^{2+} and Pb^{2+} have a particular preference for combination with oxide. We shall now try to examine such details more closely.

In Fig. 31.10 the polarizability sequence as measured by the Ca/Cd difference in heats of formation was plotted against the polarizability sequence as measured by the Sr/Hg difference. A good correlation was found between the two. The experimental plot was not quite a straight line, which we might interpret by saying that the 'super-B' ion Hg^{2+} was relatively a little more successful at extracting electrons from the least polarizable ions (such as F^-), but in general the extra 'covalent' energy in Hg^{2+} compounds as against Cd^{2+} compounds appears to be just a function of the extra energy required to form the Hg^{2+} ion.

A similar comparison between the difference in the heats of formation of Sr^{2+} and Pb^{2+} compounds and the difference in the heats of formation of Ca^{2+} and Cd^{2+} compounds is made in Fig. 31.11. That is, the polarizability sequence shown by the $(N-2)$-ions is compared with that shown by the 'normal' B-metal ions. The same type of result is achieved in Fig. 31.12 by comparing the differences in the heats of formation of K^+ and Tl^+ compounds with the difference between the heats of formation of Na^+ and Ag^+ compounds. (The Pb^{2+} ion is a little larger than the Sr^{2+} ion: the Sr^{2+}/Sn^{2+} comparison would have been better, but the data for Sn^{2+} are not so extensive as those for Pb^{2+}. Again the Tl^+ ion is a little larger than the K^+ ion and is better compared with an average of K^+ and Rb^+ (Tl^+ ionic radius is 1·40, K^+ 1·33, Rb^+ 1·48 Å), but the results obtained are essentially the same as for the Tl^+/K^+ comparison.)

Two main points emerge from Figs. 31.11 and 31.12. The first is that, by comparison with Fig. 31.10, the curvatures are much more pronounced. Thus it would appear that with anions of low polarizability $(N-2)$-valence ions are relatively inefficient at drawing back electrons. In other words, the ionic model would appear to be moderately satisfactory for the chemistry of Pb^{2+} and Tl^+ with fluoride, sulphate, water, nitrate, etc. We may note, for example, the insolubility of PbF_2 and $PbSO_4$ (compare Sr^{2+} and contrast Cd^{2+}). On the other hand, Pb^{2+} and Tl^+ begin to show considerable deviations from the ionic model with the more polarizable ions such as sulphide and selenide, and in fact behave very much more like B-metal ions (e.g. the insolubility of PbS; contrast SrS which is hydrolysed,

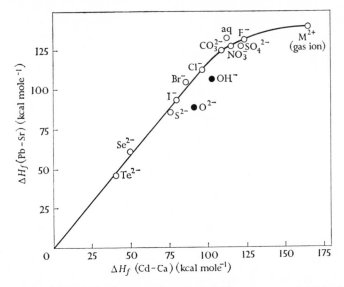

FIG. 31.11. The relation between the polarizability sequence established on the basis of differences in the heats of formation of Pb(II) and Sr compounds with that established from Cd and Ca compounds. Figs. 31.11 and 31.12 when compared with Fig. 31.10 illustrate the relation between the Group- and the $(N-2)$-valence state.

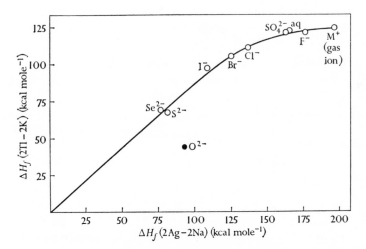

FIG. 31.12. The relation between the polarizability sequence established on the basis of differences in the heats of formation of Tl(I) and K compounds with that established from Ag and Na compounds.

but compare CdS). Thus the simple model based on the aqueous ion behaviour will be rather misleading when we are concerned with strongly-polarizable ligands, for with these ligands $(N-2)$-valence ions are able, as it were, to demonstrate superior polarizing power.

The second point is that oxide falls well below the line in both cases (compare also OH⁻ in Fig. 31.11; there are no data for AgOH). In fact the comparison between Sr^{2+} and Sn^{2+} (ionic radii 1·13 and 1·12 Å) shows that the difference in the heats of formation of their oxides (73 kcal mole⁻¹) is actually less than that between their sulphides (83 kcal mole⁻¹), suggesting at first sight that Sr^{2+} is a more polarizing ion than Sn^{2+}! It would be more plausible to suspect that the $(N-2)$-valence ions have unusually strong bonding to oxide. There is some evidence for this in the structures of SnO, PbO, and Bi_2O_3, in the amphoteric nature of SnO and PbO (which demonstrates the ease of combination with further O^{2-}), and in the existence of BiO^+ and SbO^+ compounds somewhat reminiscent of the oxocations formed by the early transition metals. With transition-metal ions this effect was associated with π-donation of the oxide electrons into vacant d orbitals. In the $(N-2)$-valence ions it may be that a similar binding occurs (O^{2-} radius 1·40 Å, compare the ionic radii of Tl^+, Sn^{2+}, and Pb^{2+}—the empty p orbitals would presumably be somewhat larger), using, however, the vacated np orbitals, or as the structures clearly suggest partly-hybridized sp orbitals. There would appear to be a similar, though less pronounced, effect in fluorides: thus we may note the unusual structures of TlF and $KSbF_4$ (see, for example, Wells). The effect may also be associated in part with the contractions of the $(n-1)d$ core. This could lead to a decreasing affinity for π-acceptor ligands (to which class O^{2-} and F^- do not belong) or to an increase in affinity for small anions due to a decrease in the repulsive exponent n. Finally, the effect may simply be a result of combining a highly-polarizing *anion* with a highly-polarizable cation.

31.5. Résumé: chemistry and thermodynamic data

In the previous two sections we have discussed the thermodynamic data for many B-metal compounds largely in relation to the type of binding and in particular as a reflection of the polarization of anions by B-metal cations. In so doing we have, however, implicitly covered a good deal of B-metal chemistry, and it will be the purpose of this section to highlight some of the general chemical features which may have been obscured by the more theoretical discussion of the thermodynamic data.

DECOMPOSITION REACTIONS

The first general feature which distinguishes B-metal compounds (at least those with the more electronegative elements) from those of the A metals is their lower stability. B-metal compounds are much more readily decomposed to give the metals or lower-valence compounds. This may be seen, for example, from the heats of formation of the Group II oxides which were plotted in Fig. 31.7, HgO being very readily decomposed on heating. The importance of this in the extraction of the elements has been emphasized in Chapter 7. The chief extraction methods are summarized in Table 31.XI. Ease of decomposition to the element or a lower-

TABLE 31.XI. *The main extraction procedures for the B metals*

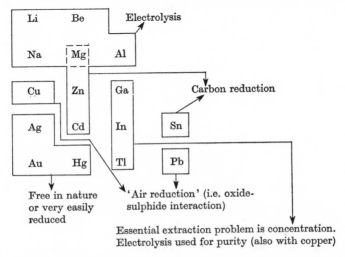

valence state is especially associated with the elements of the last row, Au, Hg, and—when they are exhibiting the Group valence—Tl, Pb, and Bi, e.g.

$$\begin{array}{ll} & \Delta H \text{ at } 25\,^\circ\text{C} \\ 2\text{HgO} \rightarrow 2\text{Hg} + \text{O}_2 & +43\text{·}4 \text{ kcal mole}^{-1} \\ \text{Tl}_2\text{O}_3 \rightarrow \text{Tl}_2\text{O} + \text{O}_2 & +42\text{·}0 \quad ,, \\ 2\text{PbO}_2 \rightarrow 2\text{PbO} + \text{O}_2 & +27\text{·}4 \quad ,, \\ (\text{cf. } 2\text{BaO} \rightarrow 2\text{Ba} + \text{O}_2 & +266\text{·}0 \quad ,, \quad) \end{array}$$

Bi_2O_5 is very unstable, and it is doubtful if it can be obtained pure. Au, Ag, and Cu are particularly 'noble' because of the additional contribution from their high metal-binding energies. It may be noted in passing that all the metals used by ancient man are to be found in this region of the Periodic Table.

This distinguishing feature is also brought out in detail by Fig. 31.9, for with each A-metal/B-metal pair an A-metal compound is always formed more exothermally than the corresponding compound of the B metal. The difference is greatest with the least polarizable ligands, so that B-metal

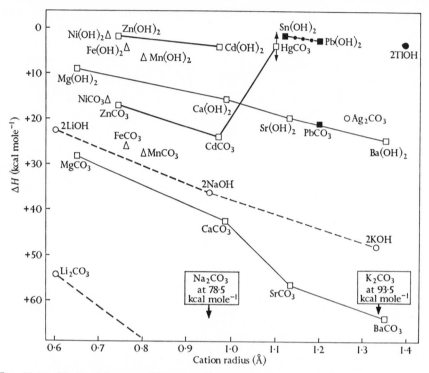

FIG. 31.13. Heats of decomposition to oxide of carbonates (per g molecule of CO_2) and hydroxides (per g molecule of H_2O) as a function of cation radius.

compounds are not only more unstable than are A-metal compounds with respect to the metal, but also with respect to compounds containing more polarizable ligands. It is also generally true that highly-charged simple anions are more polarizable than complex anions. Thus carbonate lies higher than oxide in Fig. 31.9, so that B-metal carbonates are more readily decomposed to oxide and CO_2 than are carbonates of A-metal cations of comparable size. (For a discussion of the thermodynamics of carbonate decomposition see Chapter 7.) In Fig. 31.13 the energies (ΔH) required to decompose various carbonates are plotted as a function of cation size. For the A metals (e.g. Mg to Ba) the energy required increases and the carbonates become more stable with increase in cation size, in keeping with the arguments of a simple ionic model (section 20.5). However, the B-metal carbonates lie markedly higher than their A-metal counterparts. Data for Ag_2CO_3, $ZnCO_3$, $CdCO_3$, and $PbCO_3$ are plotted in Fig. 31.13. $HgCO_3$ is unstable and so far only known as a basic salt; it is therefore

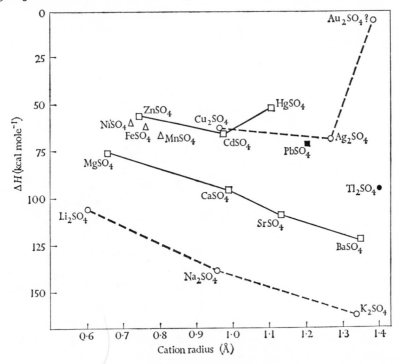

FIG. 31.14. Heats of decomposition to oxides of sulphates (per g molecule of SO_3) as a function of cation radius.

represented in the figure by an approximate point. There is no information on the carbonates of monovalent Cu or Au. The transition from A to B character is illustrated by the values for $MnCO_3$, $FeCO_3$, and $NiCO_3$, and similarly for other compounds of Mn^{2+}, Fe^{2+}, and Ni^{2+} in the following figures.

Also plotted in Fig. 31.13 are similar values for the energy required to decompose hydroxides. Since H_2O is a weaker acid than CO_2, these values all lie higher, i.e. less energy is required to decompose hydroxides than carbonates, but it will be seen that there is again the same distinction between A-metal and B-metal compounds, the hydroxides of the latter being more readily decomposed. The ΔH values for the reaction $MSiO_3 \rightarrow MO + SiO_2$ are very similar to those for $M(OH)_2 \rightarrow MO + H_2O$.

The hydroxides of mercury(II), copper(I), silver(I), and gold(I) are too unstable to be isolated. With a stronger acid such as SO_3, the data for B-metal compounds are more complete. Fig. 31.14 plots the heats of reaction for the decomposition of sulphates (note the change of scale). Table 31.XII provides a list of some of the anions which readily decompose in the presence of B-metal cations.

TABLE 31.XII. *Some anions readily decomposed by B-metal cations*

Group IV	Group V	Group VI	Group VII
CO_3^{2-}	N_3^-	SO_3^{2-}	I_3^-
$C_2O_4^{2-}$	NO_3^-	O_2^{2-}	ICl_4^-
Fulminate	NO_2^-	$S_2O_3^{2-}$	ClO_3^-
CNO^-		RS_2^-	

DOUBLE DECOMPOSITIONS

The decomposition of thiosulphates, in which B metals such as Ag, in contrast to the A metals, tend to form sulphides rather than oxides, leads us on to the second feature of distinction between A-metal and B-metal compounds which we wish to bring out here. That is the tendency for B metals to combine with the more polarizable ligand in all kinds of double-decomposition reactions. We have already commented on this feature in connexion with the F/Cl (Chapter 12) and O/S (Chapter 16) plots, and in Chapter 34 we shall show how the same feature dominates the behaviour of B-metal cations in qualitative analysis (virtually all B-metal cations being precipitated as sulphides in weakly-acid solutions), and in their occurrence in nature (only B metals and later transition metals are found as sulphide ores). In the next chapter we shall see how the stable complexes of B metals are those with the more polarizable ligands.

Free energies for the aqueous-solution reaction

$$M^{2+} + S^{2-} \rightarrow MS\downarrow$$

or $$2M^+ + S^{2-} \rightarrow M_2S\downarrow$$

are plotted in Fig. 31.15. (The pattern for the heats of reaction is not substantially different: there are no data for Li_2S and Au_2S.) The similarity with Figs. 31.13 and 31.14 and the marked difference between the A-metal and B-metal sulphides may be noted. Similar trends may be observed for other polarizable anions, e.g. chloride, bromide, and especially iodide. This relative preference for polarizable anions as against water molecules is also demonstrated by the fact that hydrated salts are less common in B-metal chemistry than in A-metal chemistry.

In Figs. 31.13 and 31.14, the position of the $(N-2)$-valence compounds (i.e. of Sn^{2+}, Pb^{2+}, and Tl^+) is in general more in line with their being typical Group-valence B-compounds than intermediate between A and B, as our preliminary discussion suggested (section 31.1). This variation in behaviour

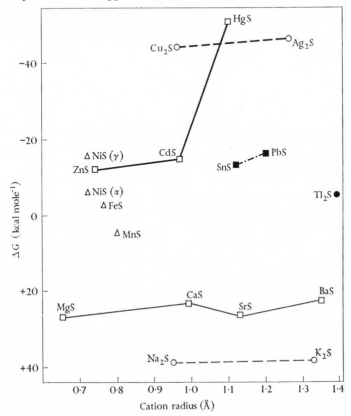

FIG. 31.15. Free energies of precipitation of sulphides from aqueous solution (e.g. $M^{2+}+S^{2-} \rightarrow MS\downarrow$) as a function of cation radius.

is associated largely with the curious position of oxide in Figs. 31.11 and 31.12, for in both Figs. 31.13 and 31.14 oxide has been taken as the more polarizable anion, and this, as we have seen, is rather peculiarly polarized by Sn^{2+}, Pb^{2+}, and Tl^+. This effect may be further demonstrated by Fig. 31.16 where the heats of formation of oxides and sulphides are compared. Here oxide is the less polarizable anion, and although the same general pattern reappears between Groups IIA and IIB, the position of Pb^{2+} is now very close to that of a IIA metal, and Sn^{2+} even lies below the IIA line.

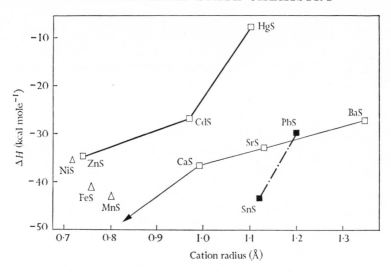

FIG. 31.16. ΔH for the reaction $MS + \frac{1}{2}O_2 \rightarrow MO + S$ as a function of cation size.

IONIZATION POTENTIALS, IONIC CHARGES, AND RADII

Our whole discussion of the thermochemistry of B-metal compounds with more electronegative elements has suggested that a useful approach lies in a combination of the ionic model together with a consideration of an additional binding energy resulting largely from polarization of the anions by the B-metal cations. Ionic forces increase in proportion to the square of charges, while a very rough approximation to the polarizing power of a cation may be made by taking the energy (the ionization-potential sum) required to produce it from the metal atom. This suggests that the ratio

$$\frac{\text{sum of ionization potentials}}{(\text{charge on cation})^2}$$

might give some guide to the effects we have been discussing. In Fig. 30.15 this ratio was plotted against ionic radius. It is suggested that the reader compare Fig. 30.15 with Figs. 31.7 and 31.8, and particularly with Figs. 31.13, 31.14, 31.15, and 31.16.

Problems

1. ZnO crystallizes with the wurtzite (4:4) structure, CdO with the NaCl (6:6) structure, and HgO with two structures in both of which the Hg atom has only two nearest oxygen neighbours. Comment.

2. Apart from oxocations such as $(UO_2)^{2+}$ the coordination number of 2 is most commonly found in compounds and complexes of Cu^+, Ag^+, Au^+ and Hg^{2+}. How may this observation be interpreted?

3. All known compounds of mercury(I) and of gallium(II) appear to be diamagnetic. Comment on the structural consequences of this observation.

4. The structures of AsI_3, SbI_3, BiI_3, and BiF_3 suggest that the VB atoms are in octahedral holes. As_2O_3, Sb_2O_3, and $[Sb_2F_7]^-$ have irregular structures. Discuss the stereochemical influence of the 'inert pair' in these compounds.

5. 'Melting-points are more structure-sensitive than boiling-points.' Quote some examples of this generalization, selected if possible from compounds of a wide range of metals.

6. The difference between the melting-point and the boiling-point (°C) is given below for each of the Group IIB halides

	F^-	Cl^-	Br^-	I^-
Zn	630°	405°	355°	285°
Cd	640°	390°	300°	405°
Hg	5°	25°	80°	100°

What deductions can you draw?

7. Discuss the properties (especially colour) and character of the compounds Pb_3O_4, K_2SbCl_4, InS, and $GaCl_2$.

8. Tl(I) salts unlike Group IA salts are often coloured, e.g. TlOH (yellow), Tl_2O (black), Tl_2S (black), TlI (yellow), and $Tl_3Fe(CN)_6$ (brown-black). How can this be explained?

9. How many *distinct* lines of evidence can you think of which suggest that Ca compounds are more ionic than Cd compounds?

10. Compare the polarizability sequences of section 31.3 with (a) the Pauling electronegativity scale and (b) polarizabilities obtained from refractive-index measurements (Table 24.XII). Comment on your comparison.

11. Using Pauling crystal radii calculate the (ionic-model) lattice energies for PbS and BaS, both of which crystallize in the NaCl structure. Compare your results with the Born–Haber cycle values obtained using the ionization potentials (given at the end of Chapter 2) and the following data:

ΔH_f: S^{2-} +152, Pb (gas atoms) +46, Ba (gas atoms) +42, PbS −22·5, BaS −106 (kcal mole^{-1}).

12. Why was it that most of the metals first used by man were B metals?

13. Comment on the fact that the only important ore of Hg is cinnabar (HgS), while Zn and Cd occur as sulphide, carbonate, silicate, and oxide.

14. From Fig. 30.15 estimate where In_2S_3 and TlS might be expected to appear in Fig. 31.16. Compare with the experimental values based on the following heats of formation: In_2S_3 −107·2, In_2O_3 −221·5, Tl_2S −20·8, Tl_2O −42·5 (kcal mole^{-1}).

15. Look up the Pauling electronegativity values (Chapter 4) for the elements given in Fig. 30.15. Plot these also against ionic radius. Compare your plot with Fig. 30.15, and with various related figures in this chapter. Comment on your comparisons.

Bibliography

J. D. DUNITZ and L. E. ORGEL, Stereochemistry of Ionic Solids, *Advances in Inorganic and Radiochemistry*, vol. 2, ed. H. J. Emeléus and A. G. Sharpe, Academic Press, New York, 1960.

D. GRDENIĆ, 'The Structural Chemistry of Mercury', *Quart. Rev. Chem. Soc.*, 1965, **19**, 303.

W. N. LIPSCOMB, 'The Reactions of Mercury(I) Compounds with Ammonia' *Analyt. Chem.*, 1953, **25**, 737.

R. G. PEARSON and H. B. GRAY, 'Partial Ionic Character of Metal-Chlorine Bonds', *Inorg. Chem.*, 1963, **2**, 358.

A. F. WELLS, *Structural Inorganic Chemistry*, 3rd ed., Oxford University Press, 1962.

32 · B Metals: Solid-Solution and Complex-Ion Equilibria

32.1. Introduction

In sections 32.2–32.5 the solution and complex-ion chemistry of the B metals will be examined taking their valence states one at a time. To some extent this cuts across the usual Group classification, for, although elements of a Group in one valence state such as Cu(I), Ag(I), and Au(I) will be taken together, their properties will also be contrasted with those of the same valence state in elements of a different Group, e.g. Ga(I), In(I), and Tl(I). The chemistry of some elements will therefore appear in two places, e.g. thallium under valence states of I and III. The discussion of the relative stability of the valence states has already been treated in Chapter 30 and will be returned to in section 32.6. The advantages of this procedure are: (1) comparison between B-subgroup and A-subgroup elements becomes easier when there are no valence-state problems to confuse the discussions; (2) attention is drawn to the character of the $(N-2)$-valence state as somewhat intermediate between those of the A and B subgroups, i.e. Tl(I) resembles both K(I) and Cu(I) in its chemistry; (3) ligands which combine to give complexes with particular valence states and not with others can be discussed once, instead of repetitively under each element. In order to make this point clear a short survey of the general features of the complex-ion chemistry will be given before describing the chemistry of the valence states individually.

There are considerable changes in general chemistry in passing from the Group IB metal, copper, to the IIIB metal, gallium. Thus copper forms almost every kind of complex ranging from those usually associated with transition metals, e.g. carbonyls, nitrosyls, and cyanides, to those typical of strongly-polarizing cations, e.g. phosphines, ammines, thioethers, and thiocyanates. It also forms very stable complexes with the heavier halides, but much weaker complexes with oxyanions. On the other hand gallium(III) behaves more like an A-metal cation. Its aqueous-solution chemistry is largely restricted to oxyanions, fluoride, and chloride complexes, although in non-aqueous media or in aqueous solutions of very high ligand concentration it does give a much wider range of complexes, e.g. ammines and bromides. Between copper(I) and gallium(III), zinc(II) behaves in an intermediate way.

On passing from the first to the second B-metal row there is a considerable increase in the sizes of the cations but no increase in their electron affinities as measured by the ionization potentials of the metals. The overall result is a marked strengthening of B-metal character. Thus cadmium forms more complexes with sulphur ligands than does zinc, and indium binds iodide as readily as fluoride. On passing to the third B-metal row there is a smaller increase in the size of the cations, but now the ionization potentials of the atoms rise very greatly. There develops a close similarity between the halide complex-ion chemistry of Au(I), Hg(II), and Tl(III), all of which show extreme B-metal behaviour. However, the ability of these cations to form ammines and cyanides decreases from Group I to Group III while the stability of their hydroxide complexes increases. On going to higher valence the oxygen, oxide/hydroxide, chemistry dominates until in Group V the only Bi(V) chemistry which it is possible to study in water is oxygen chemistry.

In the compounds of the $(N-2)$-valence states the situation is different again. The monovalent cation, Tl^+, behaves very like an A-metal cation, forming a few weak complexes and having but few insoluble salts. Sn(II) and more so Pb(II) behave rather like zinc and cadmium, i.e. in an intermediate manner, while Bi(III) behaves more like a 'super'-B metal. This is brought out especially in the halide chemistry but is less noticeable in the ammines or cyanides. The change in character with increasing valence is not due to changes in ionization potential alone. In the $(N-2)$-valence state of the B metals there is also, compared with the A-cation contraction,

	Rb^+	Sr^{2+}	Y^{3+}	Tl^+	Pb^{2+}	Bi^{3+}
Ionization-potential sum (eV)	4·18	16·72	39·1	6·11	22·44	∼50·0
Ionic radius (Å)	1·48	1·13	0·93	1·40	1·20	1·00

a smaller change in the size of the cation with increase of formal charge. It is in part the *relative* change in the terms 1/(ionic radius) and ionization potential which decide the change in character of the elements. A quantitative consideration of complex-ion equilibria in solution, mostly aqueous solution, illustrates these generalizations in detail. When it is clear which ligands stabilize which valence states (Table 32.1), the general effect of ligands on redox potentials (section 32.6), is largely understood. The method we have adopted for treating the B metals requires a separate section (section 32.4) for 'abnormal' cations such as Hg_2^{2+}.

TABLE 32.I. *Ligands forming strong complexes with B-metal ions*

Group valence

1	2	3	4	5
CN^-, NH_3, CO, C_2H_4	CN^-, NH_3, OH^- weak-acid oxyanions	OH^-, O^{2-} weak-acid oxyanions F^-	OH^-, O^{2-}, F^-, RO^-	OH^-, O^{2-}
Cl^-, Br^-, I^-	(Cl^-, Br^-, I^-)	(Cl^-, Br^-, I^-)		

$(N-2)$ *valence*

1	2	3
virtually none	OH^-, (Cl^-, Br^-, I^-)	OH^-, F^-, Cl^-, Br^-, I^-

Parentheses are placed around those ligands for which stability is strongly dependent on the *element* in a particular Group, e.g. the halides in Group IIB.

32.2. Valence state 1

HYDRATION AND HYDROLYSIS

A full treatment of cation hydration for the B metals is no more possible than a full treatment of lattice energies for the compounds of these elements. A simple ionic model is clearly inadequate, but it is difficult to find out how to improve upon it in a quantitatively reliable fashion. The IB cations undoubtedly have higher heats of hydration than IA cations (Table 32.II), but it would appear from the few types of hydrate they form, e.g. $AgClO_4$, $2H_2O$, $Cu(acetate),H_2O$, AgF,H_2O, that the number of nearest-neighbour water molecules is always small. The hydrolysis constants show that the IB cations also polarize the water molecule more effectively, and whereas the Cu^+ and Ag^+ ions are rather weak bases, the Tl^+ ion is a fairly strong base (Table 32.II), intermediate in character between the IB and IA cations though rather more like the IA. Raman-spectra measurements have failed to detect covalent character in the Tl—OH bonds.

TABLE 32.II. *Heats of hydration and stability constants of hydroxide complexes (25 °C)*

	Cu^+	Ag^+	Tl^+	Na^+	K^+
Heat of hydration ($H^+ = -257$) (kcal mole^{-1})	-138.3	-109.9	-74.2	-93.2	-73.0
Log K (l. mole^{-1})	~ 4.0	~ 4.0	0.8	< 0.0	0.0
Pauling ionic radius (Å)	0.96	1.26	1.40	0.95	1.33

SOLUBILITY

Table 32.III gives the solubility products of some IB and thallium(I) salts. The insolubility of the iodides and sulphides is particularly marked. Unlike the IA metals, the IB metals form their most soluble salts with such anions as nitrate, perchlorate, chlorate, sulphate, and even fluoride. However, with the oxyanions of phosphorus(V), carbon, and boron the salts of the IB cations are insoluble. Thus, with the exception of fluorides, the soluble inorganic salts are derived from the anions of strong acids. The problem of the relative solubilities of the metal halides will be discussed with the compounds of the divalent and trivalent B metals in section 32.5. The silver salts are usually anhydrous, in contrast to sodium bromide and iodide. However, silver fluoride is hydrated while sodium fluoride, the most insoluble sodium halide, is not.

TABLE 32.III. *Solubility products* (log[S.P.] *values*) *of* 1-*valent salts* (25 °C)

	Cu^+	Ag^+	Au^+	Tl^+
Chloride	-6.0	-10.0		-4.0
Bromide	-8.0	-12.5		-5.5
Iodide	-11.5	-16.0		-7.5
Thiocyanate	-10.0	-12.0	All highly insoluble	-4.0
Cyanide	-20.0	-13.0		soluble
Hydroxide	-10.0	-8.0		soluble
Carbonate		-11.3		soluble
Oxalate	insoluble			soluble
Sulphide	-50.0	-50.0		-22.0

The insolubility of the chloride of silver and the iodide of copper(I) are utilized in standard determinations of silver and copper. The insolubility of silver thiocyanate and cyanide are also of great analytical importance. The wide range of solubility and colour of silver salts explains the use of silver nitrate as a general reagent for anions in qualitative analysis (Table 32.IV). Thallium(I) follows the general trends exhibited by silver and copper(I), but to a smaller degree (e.g. compare the halides), with two marked exceptions. The cyanide of thallium(I) is soluble and the thiocyanate is more soluble than a comparison with the halides would have suggested. This shows that Tl^+ does not behave like a transition-metal ion to the same degree as do Cu^+ and Ag^+. Thallium(I) carbonate, hydroxide, and oxalate, all salts of oxyanions, are also more soluble than expected. With these anions thallium(I) behaves more like a pre-transition element. It is generally true that the $(N-2)$-valence state of a B metal only shows strong B-metal character in combination with elements of the second and later rows of the Periodic Table.

TABLE 32.IV. *Qualitative analysis of anions from the solubility of their silver salts*

Soluble	fluoride, chlorate, perchlorate, sulphate, nitrite, nitrate, acetate.
Soluble in acid	orthophosphate, pyrophosphate, arsenite, arsenate, oxalate, tartrate, citrate, borate, chromate.
Soluble in dilute ammonia	chloride, bromate, iodate, cyanide, thiocyanate, hexacyanoferrate(III), hexacyanocobaltate(III).
Insoluble	iodide, sulphide, hexacyanoferrate(II)

Underlined anions may be identified by the colours of their silver salts. Ag_2S is formed from silver thiosulphate. Silver bromide is soluble in conc. ammonia.

A comparison of the solubilities of Cu(I), Ag(I), and Au(I) salts shows that Ag(I) is only sometimes intermediate in character between the other two cations (alternation effect). Properties in B subgroups, unlike those in A subgroups, do not always show continuous trends down the Groups. The effect is a reflection of the ionization-potential variations.

COMPLEX STABILITY

The generalizations we have put forward in discussing solubility apply also to complex formation in aqueous solution. Stability data are given in Table 32.V. There are the following differences between A-metal and B-metal cations.

TABLE 32.V. *Stability constants,* $\log K_1$ *(l. mole^{-1}) at 25 °C*

	Cu^+	Ag^+	Au^+	Tl^+
Fluoride	?	~ 0.0		~ 0.1
Chloride	3.0	3.5	~ 6.0	0.5
Bromide	> 3.0	4.1	> 6.0	1.0
Iodide	8.8	12.0		1.0
Thiocyanate	10.0	10.0	22.0	1.0
Cyanide	24.0	21.0	~ 40.0	no complex
Ammonia	5.9	3.4	12.0	-1.0
Dipyridyl	14.2	(6.8)		

Because of the variety of conditions and methods used in their determination, the values cannot be considered to be very comparable, but the orders of the values are not likely to be affected. See A. E. Martell and L. G. Sillén, *Stability Constants*, Special Publication No. 17, Chemical Society, London, 1964.

(1) B-metal cations, with the possible exception of thallium(I), form very weak fluoride complexes. Although the fluoride complexes are feeble in Group IA, they are formed to a larger degree than with the IB elements.

(2) The other halides form strong complexes with IB cations and weak complexes with thallium(I), but they do not form complexes with IA cations.

(3) Thallium(I) and IA cations do not form stable cyanide, dipyridyl, or thiocyanate complexes. These complexes are relatively strong with transition metals and IB and IIB metals, but are much weaker in the later B subgroups.

(4) Aliphatic oxyanion complexes, e.g. of oxalates, have not been reported with thallium(I). These complexes are weak in Group IA, but quite strong in IB. Tl^+, however, forms stronger complexes with acetyl-acetonate and salicylate ions than do the A metals. The last two ligands are much stronger bases than oxalate.

(5) Ammines are formed by Cu^+, Ag^+, and Au^+, but not by Tl^+ or IA cations.

(6) With some ligands Ag^+ is intermediate in complex stability between the other two IB cations and with other ligands not. With ligand atoms from the first row of the Periodic Table the order is usually $Au^+ > Cu^+ > Ag^+ > Tl^+$, but the order changes to $Au^+ > Ag^+ > Cu^+ > Tl^+$ for heavier non-metal ligand atoms.

Cu^+, Ag^+, and Au^+ also form complexes with a great number of organic derivatives of sulphur, selenium, phosphorus, and arsenic. Tl^+, unlike IA cations, does form a number of such complexes, but they are of lower stability. At the moment interest in these compounds largely centres on stereochemical problems. The differences between the cations, in so far as they have been studied, are due to differences in heats (rather than entropies) of complex formation and may be attributed to covalence.

Many copper(I) and silver(I) complexes catalyse homogeneous hydrogenation reactions. It has been shown that the catalysis is increased as the strength of the anion as a base increases and a plausible transition state involving heterolytic fission is

$$\begin{array}{ccc} M^+ & \cdots & X^- \\ | & & | \\ H^- & \cdots & H^+ \end{array}$$

Copper(I) forms a moderately stable hydride, CuH.

COORDINATION NUMBERS IN COMPLEX IONS

The evidence available, both from crystal structures and from step-wise equilibria in solution, shows that the B-metal cations are remarkably specific in their coordination numbers with different ligands. 2-coordinate complexes, e.g. $Ag(NH_3)_2^+$, are usually found with saturated monodentate nitrogen and oxygen donors and even with saturated chelating agents such as ethylenediamine, but unsaturation in the ligand leads to higher coordination numbers. The best examples are those with chelating ligands such as $Cu(o\text{-phenanthroline})_2^+$. More-polarizable neutral ligands such as those of phosphorus and sulphur also give higher coordination numbers,

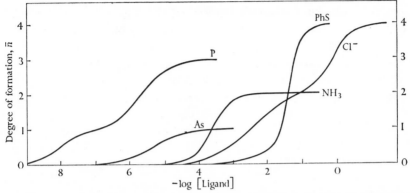

FIG. 32.1. The average coordination numbers, $\bar{n}$, of the Ag^+ ion with different ligands as revealed by formation curves in aqueous solution. $P = 3\text{-}PPh_2C_6H_4SO_3^-$, $As = As(3\text{-}C_6H_4SO_3^-)_3$, $PhS = 4\text{-}SPhC_6H_4SO_3^-$ (after Chatt).

usually 3 or 4 (Fig. 32.1): this may arise from the availability of acceptor orbitals. In partial confirmation of this, simple anions, such as halides and cyanide, readily give complex anions with two anions bound to the cation but much less readily go on to give 3- and 4-coordination. The stability of the linear 2-coordination relative to the tetrahedral 4-coordination seems to increase as the size of the cation increases. The same trend is found in Group IIB where mercury(II) has a strong preference for linear 2-coordination which is not found in zinc or cadmium chemistry.

SPECTROSCOPIC PROPERTIES

With ligands which can act as electron acceptors, e.g. pyridine and *ortho*-phenanthroline, copper(I) complexes are strongly coloured as a result of charge-transfer excitation from Cu^+ to the ligand. The corresponding Ag^+ complexes are not coloured. The explanation for this difference presumably lies in the higher ionization potential of the Ag^+ than the Cu^+ cation, M^+ to M^{2+}, Cu^+ 20·29 eV, Ag^+ 21·48 eV.

32.3. Valence state 2

HYDRATION AND HYDROLYSIS

The hydration energies of the divalent cations of Group IIB and Group IVB exceed those of ions of equal size from Group IIA. The stronger interaction with water also leads to an increased acidic behaviour of the cations,

$$[M(H_2O)]^{2+} \rightarrow [MOH]^+ + H^+.$$

The acidity of the ions is much more marked than in Group IB, and this restricts the pH region in which complex formation may be studied. The importance of hydrolysis increases as charge is further increased, much as it does in A subgroups, largely because of the increasingly-unfavourable entropy of the hydrated cations. The general problem of this hydrolysis will be discussed in this section.

The B metals also have very insoluble hydroxides, but many of these hydroxides redissolve in excess alkali. This amphoteric behaviour is not simply explained. The series of equilibria involved are

$$M^{n+} + H_2O \rightleftharpoons M(OH)^{(n-1)+} + H^+ \qquad *K_1$$
$$\text{(or polymers)}$$
$$M^{n+} + nOH^- \rightleftharpoons M(OH)_n \text{ (solid)} \qquad \text{Solubility Product}$$
$$M(OH)_n + H_2O \rightleftharpoons M(OH)_{n+1}^- + H^+.$$
$$\text{solid} \qquad \text{(or polymers)}$$

Thus amphoteric character can only be shown when a cation is a weak base, when the hydroxide formed is not extremely insoluble, and when the cation can readily bring about further ionization of protons from the bound water or hydroxyl ions so that the hydroxide is an acid. Table 32.VI gives some information about the hydrolytic equilibrium constants for a variety of cations. Hydrolysis clearly increases with valence state. The hydroxides which redissolve in excess alkali are not those which are the most easily precipitated in more dilute alkali and have therefore the smallest solubility products, nor are they derived from the cations which are most readily hydrolysed to hydroxide complexes, large $\log *K_1$. Thus amphoteric character does not depend simply upon the polarizing power of the cation, although it is clear that only cations which are strongly polarizing, i.e. the B-metal cations, the cations of typical elements such as Be and the rather high-valence A-subgroup cations, give rise to amphoteric hydroxides. A second factor controlling the re-solution of the hydroxide in alkali would appear to be the ease of change of coordination number. Those cations which are almost invariably 6-coordinate with oxygen anions, e.g. copper(II), cadmium(II), and thallium(III) are not amphoteric, although they form insoluble hydroxides. Those cations which can readily form oxyanion complexes of both high and low coordination, e.g. both 6 and 4, or 4 and 3, are Zn^{2+}, Ga^{3+}, and Al^{3+} (amongst those in the table) and Be^{2+}, As^{3+}, and Sb^{3+} (not in the table). These cations are most prominently amphoteric. It would appear too that this factor explains why it is that

TABLE 32.VI. *Amphoteric character*

Cation	Stability constant of hydroxide, $\log K_1$ (25°C)	$-\log$ (solubility product) (25°C)	Character
Cu$^+$	~4·0	10·0	not amphoteric
Ag$^+$	~4·0	8·0	not amphoteric
Zn^{2+}	~5·5	16·5	amphoteric
Cd^{2+}	5·0	14·0	not amphoteric
Hg^{2+}	10·3	25·5	not amphoteric
Ga^{3+}	~11·5	35·0	amphoteric
In^{3+}	9·6	34·0	not strongly amphoteric
Tl^{3+}	12·9	45·0	not amphoteric
Sn^{2+}	10·1	25·0	amphoteric
Pb^{2+}	~6·0	16·0	amphoteric
Bi^{3+}	12·4	~30·0	slightly amphoteric
Cu^{2+}	(6·0)	18·5	slightly amphoteric
Al^{3+}	~9·5	31·5	amphoteric
Sc^{3+}	8·9	~28·0	not amphoteric
Fe^{3+}	10·9	37·0	not amphoteric

A large number for $\log K_1$ represents easy hydrolysis. Values of *hydrolysis* constants are often given as $\log {}^*K_1$ where ${}^*K_1$ is related to K_1 by the equation

$$\log K_1 \simeq 14\cdot0 + \log {}^*K_1.$$

The values quoted are from W. Feitknecht and P. Schindler, 'Solubility Constants of Metal Oxides, Metal Hydroxides and Metal Hydroxide Salts in Aqueous Solution', *Pure Appl. Chem.*, 1963, **6**, 130.

the lighter rather than the heavier elements in both A and B subgroups are amphoteric. The smaller the cation the less energy difference there is likely to be between the low-coordinate anionic and soluble hydrolysis products and the higher-coordinate hydroxide (oxide) lattice. Ready change of coordination number also affects melting, a not altogether dissimilar process from solution.

SOLUBILITY

The solubilities of some 2-valent salts are given in Table 32.VII. The solubility pattern for the halides changes from one in which the fluoride

TABLE 32.VII. *Solubilities of some* M^{2+} *salts at* 25°C

	Zn^{2+}	Cd^{2+}	Hg^{2+}	Sn^{2+}	Pb^{2+}
F$^-$	insoluble	insoluble	hydrolysed	insoluble	insoluble
Cl$^-$	soluble	soluble	soluble	soluble	insoluble
Br$^-$	soluble	soluble	insoluble	soluble	insoluble
I$^-$	soluble	soluble	insoluble	soluble	insoluble
S^{2-}(log(S.P.))	$-23\cdot0$	$-28\cdot0$	$-53\cdot0$	-27–28	$-29\cdot0$
OH$^-$(log(S.P.))	$-16\cdot5$	$-14\cdot0$	$-25\cdot5$	$-25\cdot0$	$-16\cdot0$
SO$_4^{2-}$	soluble	soluble	soluble	rather insoluble	insoluble
CrO$_4^{2-}$	soluble	soluble	rather insoluble	soluble ?	insoluble

is the most insoluble, zinc, cadmium, and A metals, to one in which it is the most soluble, mercury(II). This pattern is discussed under the 3-valent elements. With other anions the solubilities conform roughly to the rule that the salts of strong-oxyacid anions are soluble, e.g. nitrate, perchlorate, chlorate, and sulphate, though lead sulphate is exceptional, while the weak-oxyacid anion salts are insoluble, e.g. oxalate, phosphate, carbonate, and borate. The strong-acid anion salts are usually heavily hydrated while those of the weak acids are not. Certain oxyanions present a cation with a choice of neighbour, e.g. NO_2^- (N or O) and SO_3^{2-} (S or O). In such cases the lighter B-cations prefer oxygen while the heavier cations prefer N or S (see Chapter 14).

COMPLEX FORMATION

The 2-valent B-metal cations form many complexes in solution. Table 32.VIII gives some of the relevant stability data. As with the 1-valent cations the following points may be noted and discussion reserved until the 3-valent ions have been considered.

TABLE 32.VIII. *Stability constants of M^{2+} complexes*

Ion	Zn^{2+}	Cd^{2+}	Hg^{2+}	Sn^{2+}	Pb^{2+}
Pauling radius, (Å)	0·74	0·97	1·10	1·12	1·20
F^-, log K_1	0·7	0·5	∼1·0	∼3·0	0·5
Cl^-, log K_1	0·0	2·0	7·0	1·5	1·5
Br^-, log K_1	v. small	2·0	9·0	0·8	1·5
I^-, log K_1	v. small	2·5	13·5	?	2·0
NH_3, log β_2	4·8	4·6	17·5	..	..
Ac^-, log K_1	1·0	1·5	large	..	2·5
Dipy, log β_2	16·0	14·0	?	?	?
CN^-, log β_4	17·5	17·5	41·5	low	10·0 ?
Glycine, log β_2	10·0	8·5	19·2	..	8·9
En, log β_2	11·0	10·2	23·0	..	..
$EDTA^{4-}$, log K_1	16·2	16·5	22·0	..	17·5
Thioglycollate, log β_2	14·4	∼15·0	45·0	..	15·0
SCN^-, log K_1	0·5	1·5	∼10·0	1·2	1·0

The constants are dependent on ionic strength and temperature. The orders of the constants are certainly as given, but an exact comparison is not justifiable without reference to the conditions of measurement. See A. E. Martell and L. G. Sillén, *Stability Constants*, Special Publication No. 17, Chemical Society, London, 1964.

(1) The cations, with the probable exception of Sn^{2+}, form only weak fluoride complexes.

(2) The order of the stability of the halide complexes is $I^- > Br^- > Cl^-$ for Hg^{2+} and Pb^{2+}, as for the 1-valent B-metal cations, but the reverse of this for Zn^{2+}, and presumably Ge^{2+} and Sn^{2+}.

(3) Whereas Zn^{2+}, Cd^{2+}, and Hg^{2+} form dipyridyl and cyanide complexes, the complexes of these π-acceptor ligands are weak with the $(N-2)$ cations, much as they are with the A-subgroup cations. This is an indication of the transition-metal (π-donor) character of the B-metal cations.

(4) Oxyanion complexes are common for all the divalent cations. They are stronger with B-subgroup than with A-subgroup cations.

(5) Ammines are formed by the Group-valence cations, but not to any marked degree by Sn^{2+} and Pb^{2+}. The study of such complexes of the last two cations in aqueous solution is largely prevented by the anomalously high affinity for OH^- which leads to ready hydrolysis.

(6) With coordinating atoms of the first row, oxygen, nitrogen, and carbon, Cd^{2+} is not intermediate between Zn^{2+} and Hg^{2+} in its complex-forming ability but is intermediate with the larger coordinating atoms and ions. The Hg^{2+} cation forms complexes which are more stable than those of almost any other 2-valent cation.

(7) The stability constants of Pb^{2+} with all classes of ligand follow those of Cd^{2+} very closely.

(8) The Hg^{2+} ion also forms complexes with olefins. It is much used in the catalysis of the reactions of these compounds.

The importance of the polarizable anions as partners for the B metals is seen in the ligands used in analytical procedures for the determination of these elements. Common analytical reagents are thiocyanate, sulphide, 8-hydroxyquinoline, dithizone, many semicarbazides, and dithiol. These reagents coordinate either through nitrogen or sulphur. The most common reagents for the A-subgroup metals, phosphate, oxalate, sulphate, and perchlorate, have only oxygen to bind directly to the cation.

THERMODYNAMIC DATA

Some thermodynamic properties of B-metal complexes are listed in Tables 32.IX and 32.X. The entropy of complex-ion formation is rarely very far from the value expected on the basis of the ionic charge and size. The heat terms show considerable differences which may be attributed to covalence. For a ligand such as NH_3 the heats are in the numerical order $Zn^{2+} \simeq Cd^{2+} \ll Hg^{2+}$, accounting for the alternation in stability in Group IIB. For larger ligands such as $EDTA^{4-}$ and the halides, this order changes to $Zn^{2+} < Cd^{2+} \ll Hg^{2+}$, probably as a result of steric hindrance. The variations in ΔH for the $[M(NH_3)_2]^{2+}$ complexes and the $[M(NH_3)_4]^{2+}$ complexes are very different, reflecting the stereochemical idiosyncrasies of the cations. Zinc changes from an octahedral hydrate to a tetrahedral

TABLE 32.IX. *Heats of formation of ammines in aqueous solution at 25 °C (kcal mole^{-1})*

	$[M(NH_3)_2]^{2+}$	$[M(NH_3)_4]^{2+}$	$[M(NH_3)_6]^{2+}$
Zn^{2+}	$\sim-6\cdot5$	$\sim-15\cdot0$	not known
Cd^{2+}	$-7\cdot0$	$-12\cdot5$	$\sim-15\cdot0$
Hg^{2+}	$-24\cdot7$	$-28\cdot5$	not known

TABLE 32.X. *Thermodynamic properties for the formation of EDTA^{4-} complexes in aqueous solution at 20 °C*

	$\Delta G°$ (kcal mole^{-1})	$\Delta H°$ (kcal mole^{-1})	$\Delta S°$ (cal deg^{-1} mole^{-1})
Zn^{2+}	$-22\cdot13$	$-4\cdot85$	$59\cdot0$
Cd^{2+}	$-22\cdot07$	$-9\cdot05$	$44\cdot4$
Hg^{2+}	$-29\cdot23$	$-18\cdot9$	$35\cdot5$
Pb^{2+}	$-24\cdot19$	$-13\cdot2$	$37\cdot5$

ammine, the stereochemical change probably occurring on the addition of one or two NH_3 ligands: cadmium remains octahedral throughout, while mercury(II) prefers 2-coordination. The similarities between the free energy of formation of complexes in the different tables frequently arises from a compensation between $T\Delta S°$ and $\Delta H°$ differences. This is of very great importance in the comparison between the Group-valence and the $(N-2)$-valence cations, e.g. Cd^{2+} and Pb^{2+}. Thus the similar stability of the EDTA complexes of these metals arises from a larger $\Delta S°$ for Cd^{2+} and a larger $-\Delta H°$ for Pb^{2+}. The differences in the thermodynamic functions are probably due to cation size.

TABLE 32.XI. *Thermodynamic functions for the formation of ammonia, ethylenediamine, and cyanide complexes in aqueous solution at 25 °C*

	$\Delta H°$ (kcal mole^{-1})	$T\Delta S°$ (kcal mole^{-1})
$Cd^{2+}+2NH_3$	$-7\cdot0$	$-0\cdot9$
$Cd^{2+}+en$	$-7\cdot5$	$-0\cdot9$
$Cd^{2+}+4NH_3$	$-12\cdot5$	$-2\cdot6$
$Cd^{2+}+2en$	$-13\cdot5$	$+0\cdot6$
$Zn^{2+}+trien$	$-8\cdot9$	$+7\cdot0$
$Zn^{2+}+tren$	$-13\cdot8$	$+6\cdot0$
$Cd^{2+}+2CN^-$	$-25\cdot0$	$+9\cdot0$
$Hg^{2+}+4CN^-$	$-60\cdot0$	$-5\cdot0$

Heat and entropy data for some other complexes are included in Table 32.XI. Entropy changes alone, as might have been anticipated from the simplest interpretation of the chelate effect, do not account for the differences between ethylenediamine and ammonia. The entropy effect obviously stabilizes the complexes of triethylenetetramine (trien),

$$H_2NCH_2CH_2NHCH_2CH_2NHCH_2CH_2NH_2$$

as much as it stabilizes those of nitrilotriethylamine (tren),

$$N(CH_2CH_2NH_2)_3.$$

Here the heat term differences indicate the preference of Zn^{2+} for tetrahedral as opposed to planar or octahedral geometry. The heat and entropy data for CN^- in the same table show that its complexes are formed with very great heat evolution. Presumably the extreme polarizability of CN^- accounts for this. A different indication, kinetic rather than thermodynamic, is shown by the stability of $[CH_3Hg]^+$ and $[(CH_3)_2Tl]^+$ in water. These ions, section 32.4, behave like Ag^+ in their ability to form complex ions.

The heats of complex formation in aqueous solution are not a guide to the absolute strength of bonds, but are a measure of differences between water binding and ligand binding. It should be noted that these differences involve the heats of hydration of water and of the ligand. The stretching frequencies of comparable symmetrical molecules provide more information about bond character. Table 32.XII gives the frequencies for several comparable tetrahedral species and clearly shows the alternation expected down a B subgroup.

TABLE 32.XII. *Symmetrical stretching frequencies of tetrahedral species* (cm^{-1})

M	$[M(NH_3)_4]^{2+}$	$[MCl_4]^{2-}$	$[MBr_4]^{2-}$
Zn	427	285	172
Cd	350	259	166
Hg	410	273	168

32.4. Mercury(I) and other unusual cations

Although the Cd_2^{2+} ion has been stabilized in certain solids, and metal–metal bonds as in GaS are found elsewhere in the Periodic Table, the mercury(I) ion is the only stable cation of its kind. It will be considered here for the formal reason that it carries two positive charges. The Hg_2^{2+} cation appears always to be bound covalently to two ligands, which may be anions, such as halides or carboxylates, or even two water molecules. The two ligands are thought to be placed so that there is always a straight line of four atoms.

The Hg_2^{2+} cation can be regarded as an Hg^{2+} ion bound to an Hg atom. The equilibrium in water

$$Hg(\textit{hydrated atom in water}) + Hg^{2+} \rightleftharpoons Hg_2^{2+},$$

which is set up rapidly in the presence of Hg metal, is strongly in favour of the Hg_2^{2+} cation. This may be expressed by saying that the Hg^{2+} complex with the ligand Hg is very stable. There would seem to be no good theoretical reason why a second Hg atom should not be bound to give $[Hg_3]^{2+}$, but no evidence for this species has yet been found.

A number of other examples of metal–metal bonds in complexes are now known, e.g. $Fe(CO)_4Hg$, and Sn(II) is quite a good donor to low-valence cations of Ir, Pt, and Mn. (Lewis, Plenary Lecture, 'Metal–Metal Bonds', *Eighth International Conference Coordination Chemistry*, Vienna, 1964.)

There are two points of theoretical interest about the mercury(I) ion. (1) The bonding in the cation itself. The Hg–Hg distance is quite short, 2·5 Å as compared with 3·1 Å in the metal, despite the presence of the charges. The simplest explanation of the structure is that it is based on overlap between the $6s$ orbitals giving a 2-electron bond. The energy of the $6p$ orbital suggests that mixing with it will be poor. The closest parallel in the Periodic Table is then the H_2 molecule. (2) The ability of the Hg_2^{2+} ion to bind only two further groups. The Cu(I), Ag(I), and Au(I) cations also generally prefer two linear bonds over any other arrangement, but unsaturated donors particularly increase their coordination numbers to 4, showing that in extreme circumstances all three p orbitals can be used in bonding. There is no evidence that this is the case in mercury(I). The restriction to two bonds is probably the cause of some of the peculiarities of the Hg_2^{2+} ion.

CHEMICAL PROPERTIES

The Hg_2^{2+} ion forms soluble salts with very few anions, notably ClO_4^-, NO_3^-, and ClO_3^-. These solid salts are hydrated. All the other salts are insoluble and usually anhydrous. Of particular interest are the insoluble acetate and chloride, which are used in electrodes. The insolubility and the inability of the cation to form higher anionic complexes with anions such as Cl^-, Br^-, I^-, CN^-, CNS^-, N_3^-, and carboxylates have prevented the study of Hg_2^{2+} complexes in solution. Fluoride has been examined but the complexes are excessively weak. The 'b'-class character of the cation, as shown by the large increments in the insolubility sequence $I^- > Br^- > Cl^- > F^-$, is comparable with that of Au^+ and greater than that of Ag^+.

The cations CH_3Hg^+ and $(CH_3)_2Tl^+$ behave somewhat like the Hg_2^{2+} cation. They are both class 'b' cations (see, e.g., Table 32.XIII) and coordinate to only one further group. In their reactions the CH_3^- anion is not displaced. The 'b'-character of these cations is, however, much less than that of Hg^{2+}. As such alkyl cations are very large their restriction to two coordination should make it possible to study the *trans*-effect amongst B-subgroup metals. As Table 32.XIII shows, some of the replacement reactions of CH_3Hg^+ are relatively slow, but it is not yet possible to make a comparison with data for other HgX^+ species.

TABLE 32.XIII. *Stability and rate constants for the reactions of* CH_3Hg^+

Ligand	Stability† constant	Rate‡ constant k_1	Rate‡ constant k_{-1}
F^-	1·55	..	..
Cl^-	5·30	$1·1 \times 10^4$	$1·5 \times 10^8$
Br^-	6·67	$2·2 \times 10^5$	$1·2 \times 10^8$
I^-	8·66	$7·0 \times 10^6$	$4·1 \times 10^7$
$CH_3CO_2^-$	3·90	..	..
OH^-	9·42	..	..
SCN^-	6·10	$2·0 \times 10^5$	$5·0 \times 10^8$
SO_3^{2-}	8·16	$2·5 \times 10^5$	$5·0 \times 10^6$
NH_3	7·65	..	..
CN^-	14·0	..	..

† 20 °C, ionic strength 0·1. For the reaction $CH_3Hg(H_2O)^+ + L^- \rightleftharpoons CH_3HgL + H_2O$.

‡ The rate constants (litre mole^{-1} sec^{-1}) are for the reactions

$$CH_3Hg(OH) + L^- \underset{k_{-1}}{\overset{k_1}{\rightleftharpoons}} CH_3HgL + OH^-.$$

From Eigen, Geier, and Kruse, *Essays in Coordination Chemistry*, eds. Schneider, Anderegg, and Gut, p. 164, Birkhäuser, Basel, 1964.

The cation following $(CH_3)_2Tl^+$ in the sequence of the Periodic Table would be $(CH_3)_3Pb^+$, but this does not appear to have been extensively studied. The structures of compounds of $(CH_3)_3Sn^+$, such as the acetate and nitrate, apparently contain 5-coordinate Sn, the nitrate and acetate acting as bridging groups, while complexes of such formulae as $[Sn(CH_3)_3(NH_3)_2]^+$ have been prepared. Trimethyl tin chloride is an extremely poisonous material affecting oxidative phosphorylation. Phenyl mercury(II) acetate is used to block active RS^- groups of enzymes, for the 2-coordination of $[PhHg]^+$ makes it very stable to replacement. Inhibition of an enzyme by phenyl mercury(II) acetate is often taken to mean that an RS^- group is involved at the active site.

32.5. Valence state 3

SOLUTION CHEMISTRY OF 3-VALENT IONS

The hydrolytic equilibria for these ions have been discussed in section 32.3. In this section, the differences between 1-, 2-, and 3-valent cations in their behaviour towards halide ions will be a major theme. The reactions of the 3-valent ions with many other anions and neutral molecules are inhibited in water by the stability of the hydrolysed species. The cations can be precipitated by fluoride but readily dissolve in excess as anionic complexes. Chloride, bromide, and iodide give anionic complexes which may be extracted in ethers. It is also possible to form complex anions with polydentate ligands such as oxalate. The preferred organic reagents for precipitation or extraction into an organic solvent contain the RO^- group. 8-hydroxyquinoline and acetylacetone derivatives are most commonly used for quantitative analysis, but phenolic azo-dyes are used in 'lake-forming' reactions.

In organic solvents and in the vapour the compounds MX_3 act as acceptors, when $M = Ga$, In, or Tl, and as donors when $M = As$, Sb, or Bi. The character of the acceptor changes down the series such that $GaMe_3$ and $GaCl_3$ have a higher affinity for the more polar ligands while $TlMe_3$ and $TlCl_3$ have a high affinity for the more polarizable ligands.

TABLE 32.XIV. *Stability constants*, $\log K_1$, *of the trivalent ions in aqueous solution* ($l.\ mole^{-1}$)

	Ga^{3+}	In^{3+}	Tl^{3+}	Sb^{3+}	Bi^{3+}
F^-	5·0	3·7	~3·0 ?	~3·0 ?	~3·0 ?
Cl^-	−0·6	2·3	6·2	small	2·0
Br^-	<0·0	2·0	9·5	small	2·0
I^-	<0·0	1·5	large	small	~2·0
SCN^-	small	2·5	large	small	1·0
$EDTA^{4-}$	20·3	25·0	..	..	..
Acetyl acetonate	9·5	8·0	..	..	..

See note at the bottom of Table 32.VIII for conditions.

Table 32.XIV collects together the available information on the stability constants of the other complexes of the trivalent cations. There are very few quantitative data outside the strong-acid anions, for the easy hydrolysis of all the complexes of weak-acid anions prevents their study. The stability orders place Tl^{3+} with Hg^{2+}, Ga^{3+} and probably Sb^{3+} with Zn^{2+} and In^{3+}, and probably Bi^{3+} with Cd^{2+}. The step-wise stability constants for some of the halide complexes should reveal the changes in coordination number during complex formation, for although many of the hydrates are octahedral, Ga^{3+}, In^{3+}, and Tl^{3+}, the halide complexes $[GaX_4]^-$ and $[InX_4]^-$ are tetrahedral for $X = Cl$, Br, and I^-. On the other hand, the fluorides are octahedral, and Tl^{3+} can give octahedral chloride and bromide species.

THE '*a*'/'*b*' CLASSIFICATION OF CATIONS†

There are a number of cations (Fig. 32.2) which form stronger complexes *in water* with iodide than with bromide, chloride, and fluoride in this order. These cations, which include those of the heavy B metals, form sparingly-soluble halides which show the order of insolubility $I^- > Br^- > Cl^- > F^-$. In a given valence state they are the cations for which the differences in heat of formation between the solid fluoride and the iodide are smallest. They also form very insoluble sulphides, which are precipitated even from strongly acidic hydrogen sulphide solutions, they give complexes with

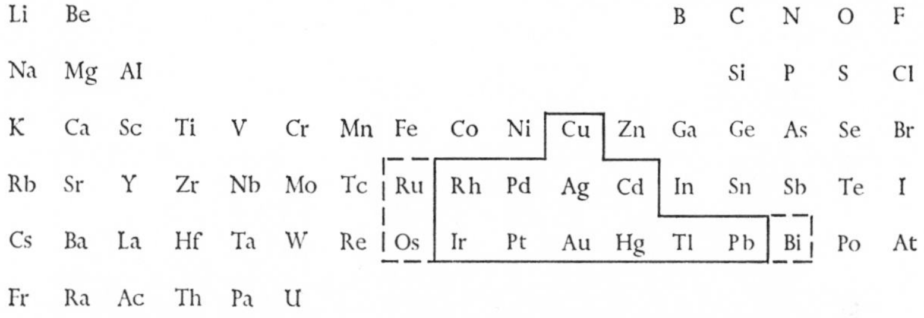

```
Li  Be                                          B   C   N   O   F

Na  Mg  Al                                      Si  P   S   Cl

K   Ca  Sc  Ti  V   Cr  Mn  Fe  Co  Ni |Cu| Zn  Ga  Ge  As  Se  Br

Rb  Sr  Y   Zr  Nb  Mo  Tc |Ru  Rh  Pd  Ag  Cd| In  Sn  Sb  Te  I

Cs  Ba  La  Hf  Ta  W   Re |Os  Ir  Pt  Au  Hg  Tl  Pb |Bi| Po  At

Fr  Ra  Ac  Th  Pa  U
```

FIG. 32.2. The '*b*'-class metals (see Ahrland, Chatt, and Davies).

sulphur and to some extent phosphorus donors, and they prefer to bind to the sulphur rather than to the nitrogen or oxygen atom of thiocyanate and sulphite respectively. However, B-metal ions in water do not necessarily form either strong ammine complexes or very strong complexes with any unsaturated ligands such as cyanide and dipyridyl. In this they are readily distinguishable from the cations of the later transition metals, which they otherwise resemble strongly. In common with these later transition-metal ions they are good electron acceptors, but they differ from them in that they are not good π-electron donors. Often they are also much larger ions.

THERMODYNAMIC DATA

The underlying causes of the relative magnitudes of the equilibrium constants can only be appreciated by careful consideration of thermodynamic data. Table 32.xv lists the heats and entropies of formation of some halide complex ions. In Table 32.xvi the heats of solution of some anhydrous halide salts in aqueous solution are given. The reverse of the solution process, like the complex-ion formation, is of the type

$$M(H_2O)^{m+} + L^- \rightarrow ML^{(m-1)+},$$

where the hydration of the complex is often unknown but is less than that

† This classification is related to the distinction between 'soft' and 'hard' acids and bases suggested by Pearson (*Chem. Eng. News*, 1965, **31**, 90).

TABLE 32.XV. *Thermodynamic data for the formation of complexes in aqueous solution at 25 °C*

Complex-forming reaction	$\Delta G°$(kcal mole^{-1})	$\Delta H°$(kcal mole^{-1})	$\Delta S°$ (cal deg^{-1} mole^{-1})
$Ag^+ + Cl^-$	$-4\cdot5$	$-2\cdot7$	$+6$
$+ 3I^-$	..	$-29\cdot2$	..
$+ IO_3^-$	$-1\cdot13$	$+5\cdot14$	$+20\cdot3$
$Tl^+ + OH^-$	$-1\cdot12$	$+0\cdot37$	$+5\cdot1$
$+ Cl^-$	$-0\cdot93$	$-1\cdot43$	$-1\cdot7$
$+ Br^-$	$-1\cdot20$	$-2\cdot45$	$-4\cdot2$
$+ NO_3^-$	$-0\cdot45$	$-0\cdot65$	$-1\cdot0$
$+ CNS^-$	$-1\cdot09$	$-2\cdot96$	$-6\cdot4$
$+ N_3^-$	$-0\cdot53$	$-1\cdot33$	$-2\cdot7$
$Zn^{2+} + SO_4^{2-}$	$-3\cdot25$	$+4\cdot01$	$+24\cdot4$
$Cd^{2+} + Cl^-$	$-2\cdot67$	$+0\cdot98$	$+12\cdot2$
Br^-	$-2\cdot93$	$-0\cdot32$	$+8\cdot8$
I^-	$-3\cdot34$	$-2\cdot05$	$+4\cdot3$
$Hg^{2+} + 2Cl^-$	$-18\cdot2$	$-13\cdot4$	$+16\cdot0$
$+ 4Br^-$	$-29\cdot0$	$-25\cdot9$	$+10\cdot3$
$+ 4I^-$	$-38\cdot9$	$-43\cdot0$	$-13\cdot7$
$Sn^{2+} + Cl^-$	$-1\cdot6$	$+2\cdot6$	$+14\cdot0$
Br^-	$-1\cdot0$	$+1\cdot4$	$+8\cdot0$
$Pb^{2+} + NO_3^-$	$-1\cdot62$	$-0\cdot57$	$+3\cdot5$
Cl^-	$-2\cdot20$	$+1\cdot25$	$+11\cdot6$
Br^-	$-2\cdot53$	$+0\cdot30$	$+9\cdot4$
I^-	$-2\cdot62$	$-0\cdot30$	$+7\cdot8$
$Ga^{3+} + F^-$	$-7\cdot9$	$+1\cdot7$	$+32$
$In^{3+} + F^-$	$\sim-5\cdot0$	$\sim+2\cdot5$	$\sim+25$

TABLE 32.XVI. *Heats of solution of anhydrous salts in water at 25 °C (kcal mole^{-1})*

	Chloride	Bromide	Iodide
Zinc	$-17\cdot1$	$-16\cdot1$	$-13\cdot2$
Cadmium	$-4\cdot4$	$-0\cdot7$	$+4\cdot0$
Mercury(II)	$+3\cdot2$	$+12\cdot4$	$+30\cdot0$
Tin(II)	$-1\cdot6$	$+1\cdot6$	$+5\cdot8$
Lead(II)	$+6\cdot2$	$+8\cdot8$	$+15\cdot5$
Magnesium	$-37\cdot1$	$-44\cdot5$	$-51\cdot5$
Barium	$-3\cdot2$	$-6\cdot0$	$-9\cdot4$
Nickel(II)	$-19\cdot9$	$-18\cdot9$	$-21\cdot5$

of M^{m+}. In the reaction there is some neutralization of charge. It is expected that entropy terms will favour the reaction more the greater the hydration of the ions. In so far as the data are known this expectation is borne out. The entropy changes strongly favour the formation of fluoride complexes by the smallest cations. It is this term which controls the formation of the complexes of A-subgroup cations. The inversion of the stability and solubility sequences amongst the halides of the heavier B metals is then seen to be solely due to the effect of the heat terms. Thus any explanation of these solubility orders should relate bond or lattice heats to heats of hydration. The hydration of the anions is common to all the series of equilibria and need not be considered in seeking *differences* between '*a*'- and '*b*'-character in water.

The absolute bond energies of the halide compounds and complexes are very generally in the order $F^- > Cl^- > Br^- > I^-$, for both A- and B-subgroup cations. The heats of hydration of the anions are also in the numerical order $F^- > Cl^- > Br^- > I^-$.

The fact that the order of stability of $-\Delta H_f$ for the metal halide complexes is found to be $I^- > Br^- > Cl^- > F^-$ with some cations means, therefore, that the increments along the absolute series of bond energies MF > MCl > MBr > MI have become smaller than the increments in the hydration of the anions. Now the increments in the absolute heats of the halide complexes diminish (1) as the cation gets larger and of lower charge (ionic model), (2) as the cation becomes more polarizing (covalent model) where bond energy is related to the polarizability of the anion, $I^- > Br^- > Cl^- > F^-$, and possibly (3) as the cation becomes a better π-electron donor. In a comparison between A cations and B cations factor (3) is not usually important. It is also clear that changes in size alone do not produce class '*b*' characteristics for even the largest A-metal ions do not have this character. Thus the main factor determining class '*b*' character in aqueous solution is high polarizing power (see Chapter 5 B). As an estimate of this power, the function

$$\text{(ionization-potential sum)}/(z^2/r)$$

has been suggested. The character of a complex cation is also dependent on the nature of the ligands. Thus $[Co(CN)_5H_2O]^{2-}$ is of '*b*'-character while $[Co(NH_3)_5H_2O]^{3+}$ is of '*a*'-character. The last observation is contrary to the predicted effect of factor (3) above.

SOLVENT EXTRACTION OF HALIDES

Another feature of the solution chemistry of these B elements which it is convenient to discuss here is the ease of extraction into non-aqueous solvents. Technically and analytically these processes are extremely important. On the whole, A-subgroup compounds do not extract easily into organic solvents such as ether, higher alcohols and ketones, or benzene. Particularly is this so for the lower-valence cations of Groups IA and IIA. The cations of Group IIIA, especially the heavier ions, can be extracted by nitrate, thiocyanate, and by the half-esters of some phosphates, into solvents such as *tert*-butyl phosphate or ethyl methyl ketone. Even more readily extractable are the 4-valent cations and the oxocations MO_2^{2+}. However, none of these A metals extract readily as halide complexes.

TABLE 32.XVII. *Per cent extraction of metal chlorides from* $6N$ HCl *into ether*

Zn(II)		Ga(III)			Ge(IV)	As(III)	As(V)
0·2		97			40–60	68	2–4
Cd(II)		In(III)	Sn(II)	Sn(IV)		Sb(III)	Sb(V)
0		trace	15–30	17		66	81
Hg(II)	Tl(I)	Tl(III)	Pb(II)			Bi(III)	
0·2	0	90–95	0			0	

From Irving, *Quart. Rev. Chem. Soc.*, 1951, **5**, 200.

On the other hand, very many B metals are readily extracted from strongly *acidic* aqueous solutions of the halogen acids, as well as from acidic nitrate and thiocyanate solutions, for example Table 32.XVII. The ease of extraction is dependent upon complex formation with the halide anion. However, if complex formation occurs to such an extent that the complex becomes highly negatively charged, the complex remains in the aqueous phase. The complexes usually extracted are the hydrated acids $H_9O_4^+[MX_4]^-$, while $[MX_6]^{3-}$ complexes are not extracted. Thus the sequential step-wise equilibria, which are themselves specific for each cation, lead to selective ranges of halogen-acid concentration over which each individual cation can be extracted (Chapter 15). This kind of selectivity is the basis of those separation procedures which utilize solvent extraction of metal halides and other inorganic salts. The anionic halide complexes can also be absorbed in an anion-exchange resin so that chromatographic separations are easily devised, utilizing the same selectivity of complex-forming ability.

The solubility of the anhydrous B-metal halides in organic solvents—mercury(II) iodide is much more soluble in benzene than in water—has also made it possible to use them as catalysts or dehydrating agents in a variety of organic reactions, e.g. the Friedel–Crafts' reaction ($AlCl_3$, $GaCl_3$, $FeCl_3$) and condensations ($ZnCl_2$). Mercury(II) halides are used in the mercuration of diazo-compounds and carbonyls. The activity is probably related to the ability of these halides to form addition compounds with ethers, ketones, alcohols, and amines in the absence of water. Cu(I) halides also catalyse the decomposition of diazo-compounds.

OXOCATIONS

As has already been shown in section 31.4, many of the B-metal cations have a high affinity for oxide. In the chemistry of the early transition metals such an affinity leads to the formation of oxocations with very short M—O bond distances. There would not appear to be similar cations in the hydrolysed solutions of the B-metal compounds, although many solid oxyhalides are formed by the $(N-2)$-valence states. The oxyhalides of Sb(III) and Bi(III) are particularly interesting in that they are insoluble, and it is tempting to think of them as salts of SbO^+ and BiO^+. These cations could then be likened to the Group Ib cations which also give insoluble halides. The crystal structures of the Group V salts do not support this comparison for they indicate little evidence of true oxocation formation. Basic salts are also common with the B metals. One important example is the basic lead chromate which is used in the paint industry.

32.6. Redox equilibria

This section is essentially a résumé of experimental data for aqueous solution, many of which have already been discussed in relation to atomic structure in sections 30.3 and 30.4. It is convenient at this stage to reconsider and enlarge on the redox-potential data, now that the solution and some solid-solution equilibria have been discussed in detail. It is also suggested that the reader may find it instructive to compare the Oxidation State Diagrams for the B metals with those for the non-metals treated in Part II.

OXIDATION STATE DIAGRAMS

The Oxidation State Diagram for the first two B-metal rows is given in Fig. 32.3, and for the last B-metal row in Fig. 32.4. The couples span a wide range of potentials. The general trends in acid solution have already been noted in Chapter 30. They include: (1) the general increase in the oxidizing power of the Group-valence state along the first two rows, Cu and Ag being exceptional on account of their large metallic binding energies. (Compare similar trends in the transition series (Chapter 23) and in the non-metals (Chapter 18).) (2) The similarity between the first and second rows (the second row giving rise to slightly more oxidizing couples, which could be in part explained by the ionic model in terms of larger ionic radii), and the much greater oxidizing potentials in the third B-metal row when the elements are exhibiting their Group valence. This latter observation is readily explicable in terms of the higher ionization potentials in the third row elements. (3) The relatively low oxidizing power of the $(N-2)$-valence states, and their marked stability with respect to disproportionation.

These states are more pronounced in the third than in the other two B-metal rows.

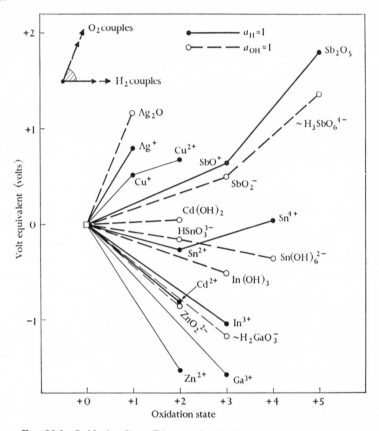

FIG. 32.3. Oxidation State Diagram for the first two rows of B metals.

Most of the valence states are relatively weak bases, so that in general the alkaline VE values lie higher than the acid values, but less than the $0.83z$ volts higher which would correspond to a strong base. The base strength normally decreases with increase of valence state, as is commonly observed throughout the Periodic Table; compare thus the acid and alkaline positions of Cd, In, Sn(IV), and Sb(V) in Fig. 32.3. Some high-valence states are acidic, e.g. Sn(IV), Sb(III), and Sb(V). In alkaline solution the $(N-2)$-valence states therefore become relatively less stable with respect to the Group-valence states; see, for example, Sn in Fig. 32.3 and Tl or Pb in Fig. 32.4. The Group-valence compounds are often prepared under alkaline conditions.

Valence states with VE values below zero should be formed in aqueous solution directly from the metal, even in the absence of an oxidizing agent such as atmospheric oxygen. Thus (see Fig. 32.3) Zn, Sn, and Ga will

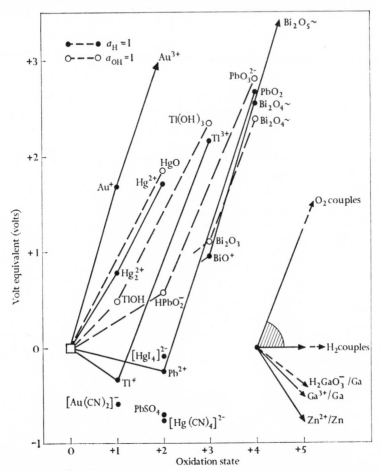

FIG. 32.4. Oxidati   te Diagram for the third row of B metals.

dissolve in acid or alkali with evolution of hydrogen. So should In, but, although it is attacked by acids, it is apparently unaffected even by boiling concentrated solutions of caustic potash. This passivity is presumably due to the formation of an insoluble oxide film. In a similar manner, as a result of the insolubility of a $PbSO_4$ surface film, Pb is not attacked by sulphuric acid and may be used for handling sulphuric acid on an industrial scale. Fig. 32.4 demonstrates that Pb will also dissolve in water (acid, alkaline, or neutral) in the presence of oxygen. This can be a considerable danger when lead piping is used for water. If the water is hard, protective films of carbonate or silicate are formed, but with soft water, particularly moorland water containing organic acids, sufficient lead can dissolve to make the water poisonous.

EFFECTS OF LIGANDS ON THE M^{n+}/M POTENTIALS

The OH^- ion is just one example of a host of ligands which can very materially alter the redox potentials because of their complexing power with metal cations. The potentials of a silver electrode in equilibrium with various Ag(I) species are given in Table 32.xviii. It will be seen that

TABLE 32.XVIII. E° (or VE) values for the couples (Ag$^+$ complex)/Ag (unit activity of ligand), and solubility products or dissociation constants (after Latimer)

Substance or complex	E° or VE, (volts)	Solubility product or dissociation constant
Ag^+(aq.)	0·799	
Ag_2SO_4	0·653	$1·24 \times 10^{-5}$
$Ag(CH_3CO_2)$	0·643	$2·3 \times 10^{-3}$
Ag_2CO_3	0·47	$8·2 \times 10^{-12}$
$Ag(NH_3)_2^+$	0·373	$5·9 \times 10^{-8}$
$AgCl$	0·222	$1·7 \times 10^{-10}$
$AgCNS$	0·09	$1·0 \times 10^{-12}$
$AgBr$	0·03	$5·0 \times 10^{-13}$
$AgCN$	$-0·017$	$1·6 \times 10^{-14}$
AgI	$-0·151$	$8·5 \times 10^{-17}$
$Ag(CN)_2^-$	$-0·31$	$1·8 \times 10^{-19}$
Ag_2S (α)	$-0·69$	$5·5 \times 10^{-51}$

in the presence of strongly-complexing ligands such as cyanide or sulphide the silver becomes quite electropositive, and will be thermodynamically capable of dissolving with the evolution of hydrogen. In practice such solution is very materially assisted by the presence of atmospheric oxygen. Cyanide is used in the extraction of Ag and Au, and the sulphide tarnishing of silver is a familiar household inconvenience. The reader may wish to compare the sequence of potentials in Table 32.xviii with the polarizability sequence provided by heats of formation (Fig. 31.9).

The effect of ligands on stability may also be represented in the Oxidation State Diagrams. Thus the potential of the couple represented by

$$Hg(CN)_4^{2-} + 2e^- \rightleftharpoons Hg + 4CN^-$$

is $-0·37$ volts, so that the corresponding VE value is $-0·74$ volts, as plotted in Fig. 32.4. The considerable stabilization of Hg^{2+} by cyanide is clearly demonstrated by the different positions of Hg^{2+} and $[Hg(CN)_4]^{2-}$ in this diagram. The marked effect of ligands on redox potentials is often used in polarography, a technique for which B metals are particularly suited. Two polarographic waves which occur at almost the same potential may frequently be differentiated by addition of a suitable selectively-complexing ligand.

The higher-valence states, particularly those of the last row B metals, are in general limited to ligands which are not readily oxidized. The chemistry is largely dominated by the oxides and fluorides. Thus if PbO_2 is treated with cold concentrated HCl, $PbCl_4$ and H_2PbCl_6 may be isolated, but they readily decompose on heating. The disproportionation of Pb(IV) and Pb to Pb(II) is the basis of the lead accumulator. When fully charged this contains as one electrode a plate of spongy lead and as the other electrode a plate impregnated with lead dioxide. The electrolyte is sulphuric acid so that the two basic electrode reactions are

$$PbO_2 + SO_4^{2-} + 4H^+ + 2e^- \rightarrow PbSO_4 + 2H_2O, \quad E^\circ = +1\cdot685 \text{ volts,}$$

and
$$PbSO_4 + 2e^- \rightarrow Pb + SO_4^{2-}, \quad E^\circ = -0\cdot356 \text{ volts,}$$

acting in opposition so as to give an overall E° of $2\cdot041$ volts. The same potential may be derived from Fig. 32.4, by joining Pb and PbO_2 and measuring the vertical distance above $PbSO_4$ to this line. The actual voltage of an accumulator depends on the acid concentration and will fall off on discharge when the acid concentration drops. It also varies with the current taken from the accumulator, for the cell is only operating reversibly and at its thermodynamic potential at very low currents.

Fig. 32.4 shows that in aqueous solution the Hg_2^{2+} ion is only just stable with respect to disproportionation to Hg and Hg^{2+}. Furthermore, the ion can only be produced over a very restricted range of redox potentials between those which are sufficient to oxidize it to Hg^{2+} and those which will reduce it to Hg. In practice this range is usually achieved by carrying out the oxidation in the presence of an excess of mercury. Since most ligands complex more strongly with Hg^{2+} than with Hg_2^{2+}, disproportionation of Hg_2^{2+} is favoured by complexing, e.g.

$$Hg_2^{2+} + OH^- \rightarrow HgO + Hg$$
$$Hg_2^{2+} + SH^- \rightarrow HgS + Hg$$
$$Hg_2^{2+} + CN^- \rightarrow Hg(CN)_2^- + Hg.$$

This is one reason why so little is known about the 'non-ionic' compounds of mercury(I).

EFFECT OF LIGANDS ON THE $M^{N+}/M^{(N-2)+}$ POTENTIALS

In this sub-section the relative stability constants of complexes of one metal in different valence states will be considered. Figs. 32.5, 32.6, and

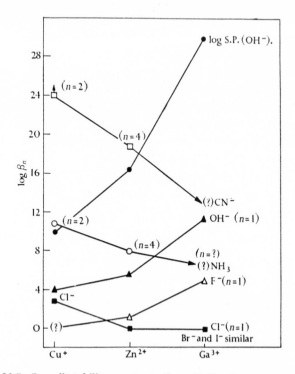

FIG. 32.5. Overall stability constants ($\beta_n = K_1 K_2 ... K_n$) for the Group-valence ions of the first row of B metals. Note the different values of n in the complexes ML_n.

32.7 give schematically the changes in stability constants with valence state for (1) the Group and (2) the ($N-2$)-valence states along series such as (1) Cu^+, Zn^{2+}, and Ga^{3+} (Fig. 32.5) or Au^+, Hg^{2+}, and Tl^{3+} (Fig. 32.6) and (2) Tl^+, Pb^{2+}, and Bi^{3+} (Fig. 32.7). This information can be used to predict the effect of ligands on redox potentials where direct evidence about both of the valence states of a given couple is lacking. The data must be treated with caution, as must any statement about the effect of ligands upon redox potentials for these metals. There are two reasons for this. (1) The metal ions have very different coordination numbers, and data are given for specific values of n in the complex ML_n. Where n is not the same for two valence states, the couple $M^{N+}/M^{(N-2)+}$ will have a potential which varies with ligand concentration. For a weak-acid ligand this means that it will vary with pH. (2) The formation of some complexes leads to the precipitation of ML_n. The insolubility of a complex is equivalent to a very high

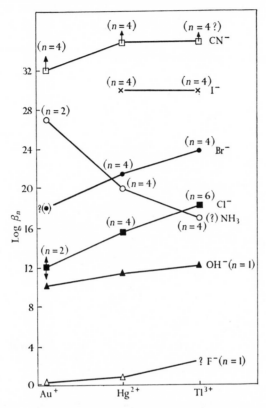

FIG. 32.6. Overall stability constants ($\beta_n = K_1 K_2 \ldots K_n$) for the Group-valence ions of the third row of B metals. Note the different values of n in the complexes ML_n.

stability constant for this complex. The combination of these two factors has already been seen in the effect of OH^- concentration upon the redox potentials M^{N+}/M or $M^{(N-2)+}/M$. High-valence states are invariably stabilized by increase in pH; see the positive slopes of all three hydroxide plots (Figs. 32.5 to 32.7). For very high valence states, such as AsO_4^{3-} (not shown in the figures), the very great affinity for OH^- or O^{2-} virtually eliminates all other complex-ion formation, so that all other ligands can only favour the lower valence state. Thus As^{3+} forms F^-, Cl^-, Br^- complexes in aqueous solution, but As^{5+} does not.

Those couples which involve two lower-valence states are more specifically affected by ligands. The simplest example is the thallium(III)/(I) couple. Tl^+ behaves like an A-subgroup cation and all ligands stabilize the Tl(III) state. An apparent contradiction is the reduction of Tl(III) by I^-,

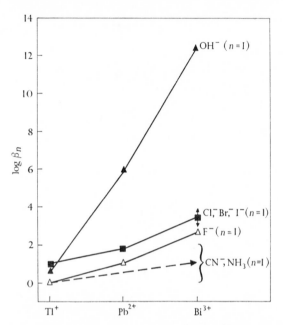

FIG. 32.7. Overall stability constants ($\beta_n = K_1 K_2 ... K_n$) for the $(N-2)$-valence ions of the third row of B metals. Note the different values of n in the complexes ML_n.

but in such a case it is not just the Tl(III)/Tl(I) couple which is of significance, but its potential relative to that of the oxidizable ligand I^-. No other (III)/(I) couple can be readily examined, but Figs. 32.5 and 32.6 suggest that Ga(III)/Ga(I) would not be affected by ligands in a similar way to Tl(III)/Tl(I), for Ga(III) is rather like an A-subgroup metal in oxidation state III, e.g. Al(III). Thus the effect of ligands such as I^-, CN^-, or RS^- would be much less.

Of the M(IV)/M(II) couples, both the tin and lead systems can be examined experimentally. However, even in weakly-acid solution, the IV state of both elements is extensively hydrolysed to MO_2. The only simple ligand which keeps these ions in solution in such circumstances is F^-. Many other ligands such as Cl^-, Br^-, I^-, and CNS^- form complexes, though not very strong complexes, with the M^{2+} ion, and thus the oxidizing power of the couples is slightly increased. It is convenient to use Sn(II) as a reducing agent in strong HCl where no precipitate appears since Sn^{4+} forms a halide complex. The reaction

$$SnO_2 + 6HCl \rightleftharpoons [SnCl_6]^{2-} + 2H_2O + 2H^+$$

stabilizes the Sn(IV) state slightly, but the potential Sn(IV)/Sn(II) is little altered by chloride because of the simultaneous formation of $[SnCl_3]^-$ and $[SnCl_4]^{2-}$. Pb(IV) is used as an oxidizing agent either as PbO_2 in suspension or as lead tetraacetate. The latter reaction is thought to go via the unstable Pb(III), for radicals are produced.

In the M(V)/M(III) couples the $(N-2)$-valence state has now developed some class 'b' character. As mentioned above, all ligands stabilize the lower-valence state for the higher-valence state is almost invariably bound to OH^- or O^{2-}.

A feature of all the couples is the small part played by weak-acid ligands such as NH_3 and CN^- which were a major centre of interest in the transition series. The reason for this can be seen in Figs. 32.5 to 32.7. The complexes with CN^- and NH_3 are only very stable in the Group-valence state in Groups I and II. Elsewhere, that is either in Groups III to V in the Group-valence state or in Groups III to V in the $(N-2)$-valence state, these complexes are too unstable relative to OH^- or too weak absolutely to shift potentials markedly.

Problems

SECTION A

1. Comment on the following experimental observations:

(a) In contrast to the metals of Group IB, thallium forms a monovalent hydroxide, TlOH, which is a strong base, very soluble in water.

(b) AgI is less soluble in water than is AgF, but LiI is more soluble than LiF.

(c) Ag_2S is produced when equimolar quantities of a silver salt and sodium thiosulphate are mixed in aqueous solution.

(d) Silver(I) forms few chelated complexes.

2. Aqueous TlOH with cyclopentadiene, C_5H_6, gives an insoluble precipitate. What are the plausible structures of the compound, TlCp? Consider σ-bond, ionic, and π-bond formulations.

3. Compare and contrast the chemistry of the Ca, Sr, and Ba series with the chemistry of the Zn, Cd, and Hg series.

4. Discuss the following stability constants given as $\log K_1$

	F^-	Cl^-	Br^-	I^-
Zn^{2+}	0·76	$\sim 0·0$	$-0·5$	very small
Cd^{2+}	0·50	2·0	2·0	2·5

5. Cadmium fluoride is more insoluble than zinc fluoride, but mercury(II) fluoride is relatively soluble. Discuss.

6. The step-wise formation constants of Cd^{2+} halide complexes decrease with increasing numbers of halide ions bound, but this is not true for Zn^{2+} halide complexes. Comment.

7. Lead sulphate is an insoluble anhydrous salt (solubility product $1·3 \times 10^{-8}$), but tin(II) sulphate crystallizes as $SnSO_4,2H_2O$ and is quite soluble. $PbCl_2$ is also anhydrous and insoluble, but the tin(II) salt has the formula $SnCl_2,2H_2O$ and is rather soluble. Compare this behaviour with that of Group IIA cations.

8. Comment on the following:

(a) While both Zn and Al salts dissolve in alkaline solution, they may be distinguished by passing H_2S into the alkaline solution, when only ZnS is precipitated.

(b) $Cd(OH)_2$ is more basic than $Zn(OH)_2$, which is amphoteric; but $Hg(OH)_2$ is a very weak base.

(c) $PbSO_4$ is soluble in strong aqueous solutions of sodium acetate.

(d) The chlorides, bromides, and iodides of Zn and Cd are soluble in organic solvents such as alcohol and acetone.

(e) The solubilities (in g moles per litre of water at 25 °C) of $HgCl_2$, $HgBr_2$, and HgI_2 are 0·269, 0·0171, and 0·00013 respectively. HgF_2 is very soluble in water, but is at once hydrolysed to HF and the black oxide.

9. How may the following experimental observations be explained?

(a) The cyanide complexes of Zn^{2+}, Cd^{2+}, and Hg^{2+} are normally written $[M(CN)_4]^{2-}$, but cyanide complexes of the divalent transition-metal cations are commonly octahedral.

(b) The ratio of the step-wise stability constants, K_3/K_2, is anomalously low for the ethylenediamine complexes of Zn^{2+}.

(c) The ratios of the step-wise stability constants, K_3/K_2, are anomalously low for the halogen complexes of Hg^{2+}.

10. For a solution of an ionized mercury(I) salt in equilibrium with metallic mercury, the fraction of the dissolved mercury present as mercury(II) is

independent of the concentration of mercury(I) ions. What does this suggest about the nature of the mercury(I) ion?

11. Why is it that in the traditional scheme of qualitative analysis (see Chapter 34) nearly all the B metals are precipitated as chlorides in group I or as sulphides in group II?

12. Show how the solubility products and dissociation constants quoted in Table 32.xviii may be derived from the corresponding electrode potentials.

13. Show that the following solubility products (concentrations in moles litre^{-1} units) are in conformity with the data plotted in Figs. 32.3 and 32.4:

$$PbSO_4 \; 1 \times 10^{-8}, \quad Cd(OH)_2 \; 2 \times 10^{-14}, \quad TlOH \; 7 \times 10^{-1}, \quad Tl(OH)_3 \; 10^{-44}.$$

(Hint: For a hydroxide compare the plotted alkaline value with the acid value plus $0.83z$ volts.)

14. Comment on the following observations in relation to Fig. 32.4:

(a) Tl dissolves in acids but not in alkalis.

(b) Bi will only dissolve in hydrochloric acid if oxygen is present. No hydrogen is evolved. Bi will, however, dissolve easily in nitric acid.

(c) $Hg_2(NO_3)_2$ is formed by the action of cold dilute nitric acid on an excess of mercury, while $Hg(NO_3)_2$ is obtained from mercury and hot concentrated nitric acid.

(d) Hg_2Cl_2 reacts with ammonia gas at room temperature largely according to the equation

$$Hg_2Cl_2 + 2NH_3 \rightarrow Hg + [Hg(NH_3)_2]Cl_2.$$

15. The Hg^{2+}/Hg_2^{2+} couple ($E^0 = +0.92$ volts) is more powerfully oxidizing than the Fe^{3+}/Fe^{2+} couple ($E^0 = +0.77$ volts). Hg_2^{2+} may be detected by its ability to reduce Fe^{3+} to Fe^{2+} in the presence of CNS^-. How may these two apparently contradictory statements be reconciled?

16. In terms of redox potentials which member of each of the following pairs is the most powerful reducing agent: Hg and Hg_2^{2+}(aq.), Pb and Pb^{2+}(aq.), Zn and Zn^+(hypothetical aqueous ion)? Comment on your conclusions.

17. How would you establish whether or not such compounds as $[Tl_2Cl_9]^{3-}$ (compare $[W_2Cl_9]^{3-}$) had M—M bonds?

18. Despite the fact that As(III), Sb(III), and Bi(III) form more insoluble sulphides than Cr(III), Co(III), and Fe(III), they do not form ammines. What explanation can be offered for this distinction?

19. Some halogen compounds of the Group- and $(N-2)$-valence compounds are said to undergo ionization of the kind

$$2AsF_3 \rightleftharpoons AsF_4^- + AsF_2^+,$$

while others ionize normally

$$PBr_5 \rightleftharpoons PBr_4^+ + Br^-.$$

What factors might control these different equilibria? Consider the stability of 4- and 6-coordinate anions in the different periods.

20. Make a plot of the heats of formation of B-metal oxides as a function of valence state. Comment on the relation of this plot to the Oxidation State Diagrams, Figs. 32.3 and 32.4.

SECTION B. (*Experimental*)

Carry out the following test-tube reactions and any further related reactions which you feel might be of interest. Note carefully what you observe. Comment on your observations and the light which they throw on B-metal chemistry.

1. Silver nitrate solution and strong KI solution.

2. Silver nitrate solution, dilute KI solution, and an excess of KCN *or* $Na_2S_2O_3$ solution.

3. Silver nitrate solution and $Na_2S_2O_3$ solution.

4. Silver nitrate solution and a starch–iodine solution.

5. Silver nitrate solution and metallic copper.

6. Thallium(I) sulphate solution and dilute HCl.

7. Thallium(I) sulphate solution and strong KI solution.

8. Thallium(I) sulphate solution and H_2S, followed by the addition of dilute HNO_3.

9. Thallium(I) sulphate solution and metallic zinc.

10. Thallium(I) sulphate solution and an acidified solution of dilute $KMnO_4$.

11. Copper(II) sulphate solution and KBr solution.

12. Copper(II) sulphate solution and KI solution.

13. Copper(II) sulphate solution and KCN solution.

14. Copper(II) sulphate solution and benzidine (dissolved in acetic acid), followed by KCN solution.

15. Copper(II) sulphate solution and metallic zinc.

16. Zinc sulphate solution and ammonia solution.

17. Zinc sulphate solution and H₂S, followed by the addition of dilute HCl.

18. Zinc sulphate solution, a drop of CCl₄, and a solution of KI and potassium hexacyanoferrate(III).

19. Mercury(II) chloride solution and KI solution.

20. Mercury(II) chloride solution and tin(II) chloride solution.

21. Mercury(II) chloride solution and Na₂S₂O₃ solution in the presence of methyl-orange indicator.

22. Mercury(II) chloride solution and metallic copper.

23. Mercury(I) nitrate solution and KI solution.

24. Mercury(I) nitrate solution and tin(II) chloride solution.

25. Mercury(I) nitrate solution and H₂S.

26. Tin(II) chloride solution and strong NaI solution, followed by the addition of solid NaF, followed by the addition of solid boric acid.

27. Tin(II) chloride solution and NaOH solution, followed by the addition of bismuth(III) nitrate solution (dissolved in the least quantity of dilute HNO₃).

28. Tin(II) chloride solution and metallic zinc.

Bibliography

S. AHRLAND, J. CHATT, and N. R. DAVIES, 'The Relative Affinities of Ligand Atoms for Acceptor Molecules and Ions', *Quart. Rev. Chem. Soc.*, 1958, **12**, 265.

I. R. BEATTIE, 'The Acceptor Properties of Quadripositive Silicon, Germanium, Tin, and Lead', *Quart. Rev. Chem. Soc.*, 1963, **17**, 382.

N. N. GREENWOOD, The Chemistry of Gallium, *Advances in Inorganic Chemistry and Radiochemistry*, vol. 5, ed. H. J. Emeléus and A. G. Sharpe, Academic Press, New York, 1963.

R. G. PEARSON, 'Hard and Soft Acids and Bases,' *J. Am. Chem. Soc.*, 1963, **85**, 3533.

33 · Organometallic Compounds: Non-Transition Metals

33.1. Types of organometallic compound

The more electropositive pre-transition metals tend to form organo-metallic compounds which may be loosely described as ionic. The organo-metallic compounds of the transition metals have already been treated in Chapter 27. The B metals form organometallic compounds which are very similar in character to the analogous compounds of the non-metals, and, since the division between metal and non-metal is here of relatively little significance, we shall include in this chapter many examples of alkyl and aryl derivatives of such non-metals as B, Si, Ge, P, and As. All these compounds may be classed together as covalent compounds, although the bond polarities will vary considerably from one element to another. These distinctions, and their relation to the Periodic Table, resemble in a general way those made in Chapter 11 for the hydrides of the elements.

IONIC COMPOUNDS

The compounds of the more electropositive alkali and alkaline-earth metals (Na to Cs, Ca, Sr, and Ba) are markedly ionic. They tend to be colourless (except where the metal atom is combined with an aromatic nucleus or a system of conjugated double bonds) non-volatile solids (especially with lower alkyl groups), insoluble in hydrocarbon solvents, and on heating to decompose without melting. The remaining elements of Groups IA and IIA—Li, Be, and Mg—form derivatives which have some ionic character, but which are best regarded as being predominantly covalent. Their structures resemble those of the electron-deficient hydrides, e.g. of Be, B, etc., with bridging alkyl groups between the metal atoms. They are thus polymeric, and consequently are less volatile than the simple covalent alkyls and aryls of Groups IVB to VIIB. Alkyls of Al, Ga, and In also tend to dimerize or polymerize through bridging alkyl groups. In contrast to the hydrides, boron alkyls are all monomeric, BR_3.

TRANSITION-METAL COMPOUNDS

Organometallic compounds of the transition metals include a variety of types, so that even a single organic group such as cyclopentadienyl forms compounds which are either essentially ionic, σ-bonded, or both σ- and π-bonded. The role of the metal d orbitals is particularly significant in the compounds of the transition metals with unsaturated organic molecules (olefins, cyclopentadiene, benzene, etc.). Simple organometallic compounds in which carbon is σ-bonded to the metal are relatively rare and are generally rather unstable (e.g. TiMe$_4$, CrPh$_3$,3THF where THF = tetrahydrofuran). However, the discovery of the vitamin B$_{12}$ coenzyme with a Co(III)—C σ-bond has led to a re-examination of the possibility of stabilizing such compounds through the mutual interaction of all the coordination groups; see the discussion of *cis*- and *trans*-effects in section 29.2. Similarly, several σ-bonded alkyls of transition-metal carbonyls are known, e.g.

$$(\pi\text{-}C_5H_5)M(CO)_3(\sigma\text{-}CH_3) \quad (M = Cr, Mo, or W),$$

of which the tungsten compound seems to be stable indefinitely in air. With Pd and Pt such compounds become important, e.g. (Et$_3$P)$_2$PdMe$_2$, and σ-bonded organic derivatives are by far the most important in the B elements (e.g. RHg$^+$ and R$_2$Tl$^+$ may be studied in aqueous solution).

σ-BONDED (COVALENT) COMPOUNDS

The organic derivatives of the B elements are, for the most part, simple alkyls and aryls. In these the organic group may be regarded as bonded to the B element by a normal 2-electron bond, predominantly covalent in character. Their properties depend largely on the electronegativity difference between M and C (per cent ionic character), and on the donor and/or acceptor power of the central atom M.

As in so much of inorganic chemistry, the divisions between the classes are not all clear cut. We shall see below that d orbitals also play a role among the B-element derivatives, while the ionic or polar character of the M—C bond must be regarded as changing continuously, roughly in accordance with the electronegativity of M.

FORMULA TYPES

The formulae of the alkyls and aryls are, for the most part, very similar to those of the corresponding hydrides. Thus in Group VB they are of the type MR$_3$, although there are some 5-valent compounds such as

PPh$_5$, AsPh$_5$, SbPh$_5$, BiPh$_5$, R$_4$SbX, and LiSbPh$_6$.

For these organometallic compounds, clearly, the general electronegativity rule of Chapter 4 ($x_A - x_B = 0.4$ for octet expansion) no longer holds. In Group IVB the stable compounds are all of the type MR_4, although a few compounds of apparently divalent Sn and Pb have been described: these are probably all polymeric and contain metal–metal bonds (see below) with tetravalent Sn or Pb. This adoption of the highest valence, which is also apparent in the hydrides, is in sharp contrast to the *salts* of Sn and especially Pb. On account of the easy cleavage of Pb—Pb bonds, the reaction of $PbCl_2$ with methyl magnesium iodide yields not 'dimethyllead' but a mixture of lead and tetramethyllead. Hexamethyldilead can also be isolated under suitable conditions:

$$2MeMgI + PbCl_2 \rightarrow (1/n)[PbMe_2]_n + MgI_2 + MgCl_2$$

$$(3/n)[PbMe_2]_n \rightarrow Me_3Pb \cdot PbMe_3 + Pb$$

$$2Me_3Pb \cdot PbMe_3 \rightarrow 3PbMe_4 + Pb.$$

Dialkyl and diaryltins, however, are less susceptible to disproportionation, and may be isolated from the reaction between tin(II) chloride and a Grignard reagent. Degradation by bromine, which cleaves only the Sn—Sn bonds, yields a mixture of R_3SnBr, R_2SnBr_2, and $RSnBr_3$, showing the presence of both straight and branched chains of tin atoms.

In Group IIIB the compounds are all of the type MR_3, but, as they are electron-deficient, there is a tendency to polymerize (compare the hydrides), which is particularly strong among the alkylaluminiums. There is some evidence for the transient existence of monovalent thallium compounds, e.g. TlPh. The compound Tl(cyclopentadiene), however, is remarkably stable, and is regarded as a salt.

MR_2 is the formula for alkyls and aryls of Group IIB, but extensive polymerization occurs in the Be and Mg compounds, akin to the electron-deficient behaviour found in Al.

Many catenated alkyl and aryl compounds are known. In Groups IVB and VB the range of such compounds is quite large (e.g. Si_nMe_{2n+2}, Ge_2Ph_6, Ge_3Ph_8, Sn_2Me_6, Pb_2Me_6). The compounds may be linear, e.g.

$$Me_3Si(SiMe_2)_4SiMe_3,$$

or cyclic, e.g. $(SiMe_2)_6$ and $(SnBu_2^t)_4$. The tendency towards catenation in general decreases down any Group. Substitution of hydrogen in hydrides by alkyl or aryl decreases the reactivity of the catenated compounds to disproportionation, oxidation, etc. Thus while silicon and germanium hydrides are readily oxidized in air, the former being spontaneously inflammable, the corresponding methyls are stable to distillation at 300 °C and to attack by air and water.

Related structural types in Group VB include the cyclotetraphosphines

$$\begin{array}{ccc} R & & R \\ \diagdown & & \diagup \\ & P\!\!-\!\!P & \\ & | \quad | & \\ & P\!\!-\!\!P & \\ \diagup & & \diagdown \\ R & & R \end{array} \qquad R = \text{alkyl, aryl,} -CF_3$$

and arsenobenzene

$$\begin{array}{ccccc} & & Ph & & \\ & & | & & \\ Ph & & As & & Ph \\ \diagdown & \diagup & \diagdown & \diagup & \\ & As & & As & \\ | & & & & | \\ & As & & As & \\ \diagup & \diagdown & \diagup & \diagdown & \\ Ph & & As & & Ph \\ & & | & & \\ & & Ph & & \end{array}$$

The latter, the parent compound of the salvarsan drugs, has been shown by X-ray diffraction to possess a puckered six-membered ring, and not to have the structure $PhAs\!\!=\!\!AsPh$, as was previously believed. Although PH_3 and P_2H_4 are the only known hydrides of phosphorus (apart from ill-defined polymeric hydrides), organic derivatives of triphosphine, e.g.

$$CF_3\!\!-\!\!P\!\!\begin{array}{c}\diagup P(CF_3)_2 \\ \diagdown P(CF_3)_2\end{array}$$

as well as of these two hydrides are known.

The compound $Me_2Sb\!\!-\!\!SbMe_2$ may be formed by reacting an Sb mirror with methyl radicals produced by the pyrolysis of $PbMe_4$. The corresponding Bi compound is probably produced in a similar reaction. Cacodyl, $Me_2As.AsMe_2$, has been known for nearly 200 years.

Mixed compounds, e.g.

$$Ph_2BOCOCH_3, \quad Me_3PbH, \quad Me_2TlOH, \quad MeSnCl_3,$$

are also of importance, but we shall refer to them only in passing. The silicones (see Chapter 17) belong to this class.

Although we shall be concerned in the main with σ-bonding, π-interactions do occur between B metals and organic compounds or groups. Copper(I) forms complexes with olefins and with CO, some of which are used in gas analysis. Similar interactions are found with Ag^+, and many Ag salts may be dissolved in aromatic solvents, e.g. $AgClO_4$ in benzene. The interaction between the Hg^{2+} ion and olefins or acetylenes is of importance in a number of catalytic processes, e.g. the conversion of acetylene to acetaldehyde. There is here, however, some evidence that addition across the double bonds takes place, e.g. to give

$$HO—CH_2—CH_2—Hg—X$$

or

$$MeO—CH_2—CH_2—Hg—OCO.CH_3,$$

although a π-bonding intermediate may first be formed. It is tempting to regard such interactions as an indication that the filled $(n-1)d$ orbitals still play some role in bonding, especially in Groups IB and IIB. This is in line with other evidence, e.g. the formation of cyanide, carbonyl halide, dipyridyl, and *ortho*-phenanthroline complexes.

π-interactions with unfilled nd orbitals may also occur. Thus *para*-substituted-$SiMe_3$ lowers the base strength of aniline and dimethylaniline and raises the acid strength of phenol. This may be interpreted in terms of contributions from such resonance structures as

in which the $3d$ orbital of the Si interacts with the π-electron system in the aromatic ring. The opposite effects occur, though weakly, with *meta*-substituted-$SiMe_3$, as the σ-bond between C and Si will place a slight negative charge on the C (the inductive effect).

ALKALI-METAL AROMATIC COMPOUNDS

An unusual group of compounds are formed by the interaction of alkali metals with aromatic hydrocarbons containing two or more aromatic rings, which may be joined as in biphenyl, fused as in naphthalene or anthracene, or conjugated as in 1,4-diphenylbutadiene, $PhCH:CH.CH:CHPh$. Reaction takes place without evolution of hydrogen and involves essentially the transfer of an electron to form an alkali-metal ion (the reaction goes more readily, e.g. in an ether solvent, presumably due to solvation of such ions) and a hydrocarbon ion in which the electron may be pictured as entering the lowest unoccupied π molecular orbital. The hydrocarbon anions, e.g. $C_{10}H_8^-$ from naphthalene, are paramagnetic and coloured, and their structures have been studied by electron spin resonance. Low concentrations of anions may similarly be obtained from benzene, toluene, or xylene by reaction with potassium in ethylene glycol dimethyl ether at $-80°$. Aromatic hydrocarbons of high electron affinity may be titrated potentiometrically with the alkali compound of a hydrocarbon of lower electron affinity. Thus when anthracene is titrated with biphenylsodium two end-points may be observed, corresponding to the formation of the anthracene⁻ and the anthracene²⁻ ions. Solutions of these compounds are strong reducing agents. $CoCl_2$ may be reduced in stages (in tetrahydrofuran solvent) to colloidal cobalt. Halogen from any organic halide is converted into halide ion, e.g.

$$C_{12}H_{10}^- + RX \rightarrow C_{12}H_{10} + R^\cdot + X^-$$

even fluorine being removed from the chemically-unreactive fluorocarbons. Such a reaction may thus be used for the determination of halogen in organic compounds.

33.2. Thermochemistry and bonding

In general, as with organic chemistry, kinetic are more important than thermodynamic considerations in the chemistry of organometallic compounds. In Table 33.I are given the heats of formation (from element,

TABLE 33.I. ΔH_f *of monomeric gases* ($kcal\ mole^{-1}$)
(*after Long, Pure and Appl. Chem.*, 1961, **2**, 61)

	MMe₂		MMe₃		MMe₄		MMe₃
Be	..	B	−29·8	C	−39·7	N	−4·1
Mg	..	Al	−13·9	Si	−49·5	P	−23·2
Zn	+13·3	Ga	−9·1	Ge	..	As	+3·7
Cd	+26·4	In	..	Sn	−11·2	Sb	+9·2
Hg	+20·8	Tl	..	Pb	+32·6	Bi	+45·8

graphite, and hydrogen) of the monomeric gaseous methyls, so far as they are known. The general decrease of stability down any Group (e.g. N to Bi) is similar to that found with the hydrides (e.g. heats of formation $NH_3 - 11\cdot0$, $PH_3 + 1\cdot3$, $AsH_3 + 15\cdot9$, $SbH_3 + 34\cdot7\ kcal\ mole^{-1}$). While some of the methyls have negative heats of formation and are thus stable with respect to their elements, they will all be unstable with respect to such reactions as

$$MMe_2(gas) \rightarrow M(solid) + C_2H_6$$

(the heat of formation of C_2H_6 is $-20\cdot2\ kcal\ mole^{-1}$, so that BMe_3 is just on the borderline of thermodynamic stability), and all are very unstable with respect to attack, e.g. by oxygen. The 'alternation' effect is shown in the N–P–As–Sb–Bi series.

In Table 33.II are quoted the heats calculated (per methyl radical produced) for decomposition of the gaseous monomer into methyl radicals and free atoms of the element. Such values provide a clearer picture of the variation in bond-strength, M—C, in the various methyls. A similar picture is provided by the stretching-force constants for the M—C bond (Table 33.III).

TABLE 33.II. ΔH reaction $(1/n)[MMe_n \rightarrow M + nMe^\bullet]$, taking ΔH_f $CH_3^\bullet$ as 32·5 kcal mole^{-1} (after Long, Pure and Appl. Chem., 1961, **2**, 61)

	MMe$_2$		MMe$_3$		MMe$_4$		MMe$_3$	
Be	..	B	87·5	C	85·3	N	71·5
Mg	..	Al	62·9	Si	71·1	P	65·3
Zn	41·5	Ga	57·5	Ge	..	As	51·5
Cd	32·8	In	..	Sn	53·3	Sb	49·7
Hg	29·5	Tl	..	Pb	35·9	Bi	33·7

TABLE 33.III. Stretching-force constants $(10^5 \times dyne\ cm^{-1})$

CMe$_4$	4·84	NMe$_3$	4·68
SiMe$_4$	3·38	PMe$_3$	2·99
GeMe$_4$	2·96	AsMe$_3$	2·63
SnMe$_4$	2·39	SbMe$_3$	2·18
PbMe$_4$	1·95	BiMe$_3$	1·82

33.3. Preparative methods

Preparative methods are described in detail, for example by Eisch, Jones and Gilman, and by Eisch and Gilman. We shall comment only on the following general methods.

(1) INTERACTION OF A METAL AND AN ALKYL (ARYL) HALIDE

The main driving force for these reactions may be considered to be the reaction between a halogen and an electropositive metal. The reaction therefore proceeds readily with the more electropositive metals such as Li and Mg. Either an ether or a hydrocarbon solvent may be used to prepare organolithium or Grignard reagents in this way:

$$RX + 2Li \rightarrow LiR + LiX$$

$$RX + Mg \rightarrow RMgX \text{ (Grignard reagents)}$$

$$RI + Zn \rightarrow RZnI \xrightarrow{heat} ZnR_2 + ZnI_2$$

$$CH_3I + Be \rightarrow CH_3BeI$$

Similarly, aluminium reacts with alkyl halides to yield alkylaluminium sesquihalides,

$$3RX + 2Al \rightarrow R_3Al_2X_3,$$

which may be reduced by sodium or magnesium to trialkylaluminium,

$$R_3Al_2X_3 + 3Na \rightarrow AlR_3 + Al + 3NaX.$$

The alkylaluminiums are important as polymerization catalysts for olefins (see below). However, with the most electropositive metals of all, e.g. Na to Cs, the metal alkyl first formed reacts with alkyl halide very readily (Wurtz–Fittig reaction), and thus cannot be prepared in this way:

$$RX + 2Na \rightarrow NaR + NaX$$

$$RX + RNa \rightarrow R\text{—}R \text{ (etc.)} + NaX.$$

With the less electropositive metals the driving force for the simple reaction may disappear. Thus

$$2CH_3Br(l) + 2Hg \rightarrow HgMe_2(l) + HgBr_2(s)$$

would be endothermic to the extent of 17 kcals. The Hg alkyls may, however, be prepared, e.g. by using a Na amalgam. Sometimes it is necessary to use the alkyl iodide, e.g. in the preparation of alkylzincs, even though the chloride or bromide reaction would be thermodynamically favoured. Similarly in the removal of Pb from internal combustion engines (arising from the use of $PbEt_4$ as an anti-knock) ethylene dibromide may be only partly replaced by the chloride.

The reaction between several non-metals or metalloids with alkyl halides is catalysed by copper and other metals. The most important example of this is the reaction between methyl chloride and a silicon-copper alloy at 300–400 °C, to give the methylchlorosilanes, Me_nSiCl_{4-n}, as the major products. These substances are intermediates in the manufacture of silicones. The reaction

$$Si + 2CH_3Cl(g) \rightarrow (CH_3)_2SiCl_2$$

is strongly exothermic. Similar reactions, also catalysed by copper, occur between alkyl halides and Ge, Sn, P, As, and Sb. It is very likely that the unstable CuMe is an intermediate, and that this decomposes to copper and methyl radicals, which then attack the non-metal to give methyl derivatives. At 250 °C the half-life of methylcopper is only about 0·002 sec.

Trifluoroiodomethane reacts with many elements to give trifluoromethyl derivatives, many of which have interesting properties (see Lagowski, *Quart. Rev. Chem. Soc.*, 1959, **13**, 233):

$$CF_3I + Mg \xrightarrow[\text{ether}]{-70°} CF_3MgI$$

$$CF_3I + As \xrightarrow{200°} As(CF_3)_3 + (CF_3)_2AsI + (CF_3)AsI_2$$

$$CF_3I + Hg \xrightarrow{260°} CF_3HgI$$

cf. $$CH_3I + As \longrightarrow [As(CH_3)_4]I.$$

(2) METAL EXCHANGE

e.g.

$$2\text{Na amalgam} + \text{HgR}_2 \xrightarrow[\text{ether}]{\text{petroleum}} 2\text{NaR} + \text{Hg}$$

$$2\text{Al} + 3\text{HgPh}_2 \rightarrow 2\text{AlPh}_3 + 3\text{Hg}$$

$$\text{MgR}_2 + 2\text{Li} \rightarrow 2\text{LiR} + \text{Mg}.$$

As will be seen from the thermodynamic data given in Table 33.1, heavy-metal alkyls (and similarly aryls) should be particularly prone to lose their organic groups. Dialkylmercury and diarylmercury compounds are thus often used for syntheses. In fact, the reaction between an alkylmercury and an alkali metal provides the only satisfactory method for the preparation of alkali-metal alkyls in a pure state. In addition, the reactions proceed satisfactorily with the alkaline-earth metals, zinc, aluminium, gallium, tin, lead, antimony, bismuth, selenium, and tellurium, but reversible equilibria occur with Cd, In, and Tl. In some of these cases (e.g. Bi), the formation of a metal amalgam may assist the reaction to proceed. The reactions

$$\text{SbPh}_3 + \text{As} \rightarrow \text{AsPh}_3 + \text{Sb}$$

and

$$\text{AsPh}_3 + \text{P} \rightarrow \text{PPh}_3 + \text{As}$$

are of the same type.

The reaction of an alkali metal with the alkyls or aryls of more electronegative elements, e.g. Ge, Sn, Pb, P, As, Sb, and the elements of Groups VIB and VIIB, can lead to cleavage of one alkyl or aryl group, forming an alkali-metal derivative, e.g.

$$\text{GePh}_4 + 2\text{Na} \xrightarrow[\text{NH}_3]{\text{liquid}} \text{Na}.\text{GePh}_3 + \text{NaPh}$$

$$\text{PbEt}_4 + 2\text{Na} \xrightarrow[\text{NH}_3]{\text{liquid}} \text{Na}.\text{PbEt}_3 + \text{C}_2\text{H}_6 + \text{NaNH}_2$$

$$\text{PPh}_3 + 2\text{Na} \xrightarrow{\text{dioxan}} \text{Ph}_2\text{P}.\text{Na,dioxan} \downarrow + \text{NaPh}$$

cf.

$$\text{PhCl} + 2\text{Na} \xrightarrow[\text{solvent}]{\text{hydrocarbon}} \text{NaCl} + \text{NaPh}.$$

The alkali-metal derivatives of the elements of Groups IVB and VB resemble organometallic compounds in some ways, and they are useful in preparing derivatives containing bonds between different elements, e.g.

$$\text{Na}.\text{PPh}_2 + \text{Me}_3\text{SiCl} \rightarrow \text{Ph}_2\text{P}.\text{SiMe}_3 + \text{NaCl}$$

$$3\text{Na}.\text{PPh}_2 + \text{CrCl}_3,3\text{THF} \rightarrow \text{Cr}(\text{Ph}_2\text{P})_3 + 3\text{NaCl} + 3\text{THF}.$$

(3) ALKYL-HALOGEN EXCHANGE

e.g.
$$2ZnMe_2 + GeCl_4 \rightarrow GeMe_4 + 2ZnCl_2$$
$$2RMgX + CdCl_2 \rightarrow CdR_2 + MgX_2 + MgCl_2$$
$$ZnMe_2 + 2Me_3C.Cl \rightarrow 2CMe_4 + ZnCl_2$$
$$AlR_3 + BF_3 \rightarrow BR_3 + AlF_3$$
$$2LiR + HgCl_2 \rightarrow 2LiCl + HgR_2.$$

As might be expected, the net effect is usually to combine halogen with the more electropositive element and the organic radical with the element of greater electronegativity. Thus Hg alkyls may be prepared from Li alkyls by this type of reaction, while Li alkyls may be prepared from Hg alkyls by reaction (2). The general decrease of reactivity, e.g. Li alkyl > Grignard reagent > Cd alkyl, is made use of in organic syntheses. Thus the reaction of acid chlorides, RCO.Cl, stops at the ketone stage with Cd alkyls. The Cd alkyls are prepared *in situ* without isolation by addition of anhydrous $CdCl_2$ to a Grignard reagent.

On account of their ease of preparation, organolithium or organomagnesium compounds are used whenever possible for the alkylation or arylation of the halides of other elements. Where the required product is not attacked by water, it may be isolated by hydrolysis of the reaction mixture (e.g. BR_3 from BF_3; SiR_4, GeR_4, and SnR_4 from MX_4; PR_3, AsR_3, SbR_3, and BiR_3 from MX_3). Where hydrolysis of the product occurs, organolithium reagents are to be preferred, as lithium halides can be easily filtered off, whereas magnesium halides are rather soluble in ethers as complexes, making the isolation of products difficult. By use of the appropriate proportions of metal halide and organometallic reagent, partial substitution of halogen may sometimes be achieved, but often a mixture of products results. Thus

$$HgCl_2 + RMgCl \rightarrow RHgCl + MgCl_2,$$

and the RHgCl can be obtained free from HgR_2, as the latter reacts rapidly with $HgCl_2$
$$HgR_2 + HgCl_2 \rightarrow 2RHgCl.$$

A reaction between $SiCl_4$ and $2PhMgBr$ gave $PhSiCl_3$ (22 per cent), Ph_2SiCl_2 (56 per cent), and Ph_3SiCl (22 per cent).

To achieve stepwise replacement of halogen atoms, it is often better to use a less reactive organometallic compound as the alkylating agent, e.g.

$$2BCl_3 + SnR_4 \rightarrow R_2SnCl_2 + 2RBCl_2$$
$$BCl_3 + SnR_4 \rightarrow R_2SnCl_2 + R_2BCl$$
$$PCl_3 + PbEt_4 \rightarrow EtPCl_2 + Et_3PbCl.$$

(4) METAL-HYDRIDE AND OLEFIN ADDITION

e.g.
$$(AlH_3)_n + 3nC_2H_4 \rightarrow nAl(CH_2CH_3)_3$$

$$4C_2H_4 + LiAlH_4 \xrightarrow[\text{pressure}]{100°} LiAl(C_2H_5)_4.$$

This reaction is of interest in connexion with the polymerization of olefins by Ziegler catalysts (see below).

The addition of diborane to olefins occurs under very mild conditions, e.g. at room temperature in a solvent (often diethylene glycol dimethyl ether), to yield trialkylborons

$$B_2H_6 + 6RCH{=}CH_2 \rightarrow 2(RCH_2CH_2)_3B.$$

This reaction is termed 'hydroboration', and has been studied in great detail, especially with reference to its applications in organic chemistry (Brown, *Hydroboration*, Benjamin, New York, 1962). Oxidation of the trialkylboron by alkaline hydrogen peroxide gives an alcohol

$$B(CH_2CH_2R)_3 + 3H_2O_2 \rightarrow 3RCH_2CH_2OH + H_3BO_3.$$

Similarly, hydrides of Group IVB add to olefins:

$$Bu_3^n GeH + CH_2{=}CHCN \rightarrow Bu_3^n GeCH_2CH_2CN.$$

Silicon hydrides usually require heating under increased pressure in the presence of a catalyst, and some polymerization of the monomer often occurs. However, the addition of alkyltin or aryltin hydrides to olefins occurs under mild conditions, requires no catalyst, and gives practically quantitative yields, e.g.

$$Ph_3SnH + C_6H_{13}CH{=}CH_2 \rightarrow Ph_3SnC_8H_{17}.$$

(5) METHYLENE-INSERTION REACTION

Diazoalkanes can sometimes be used to produce M—C bonds, e.g.

$$SiCl_4 + CH_2N_2 \xrightarrow[\text{ether}]{-50°} Cl_3Si.CH_2Cl + N_2.$$

These chloromethylsilanes are important intermediates in the production of silylmethylene polymers. They are usually made commercially, however, by the photochemical chlorination of methylchlorosilanes or of SiMe$_4$,

$$SiMe_4 + Cl_2 \rightarrow Me_3SiCH_2Cl + HCl.$$

(6) THE REACTION BETWEEN ARYL DIAZONIUM SALTS AND METAL
     HALIDES OR OXIDES IN AQUEOUS SOLUTION

This is sometimes used to form M—C bonds. A well-known example is the Bart reaction

$$As(OH)_3 + PhN_2X \rightarrow PhAsO(OH)_2 + N_2 + HX,$$

cf. $$Sb(OH)_3 + PhN_2X \rightarrow PhSbO(OH)_2 + N_2 + HX.$$

This method is only suitable where the products are stable to hydrolysis and the element M is susceptible to electrophilic attack.

33.4. Chemical properties

The M—C bond is readily transformed into MX, MO, and MN bonds on the one hand, and into C—C, C—H, C—O, and C—X bonds on the other, so that organometallic compounds are for the most part highly reactive. Many are spontaneously inflammable in air, hydrolyse very readily, and decompose on mild heating. Compounds of the alkali and alkaline-earth metals are particularly reactive, while relatively low reactivity is shown by the compounds of Group IVB. Thus $SnMe_4$ is not readily attacked by air or water, in contrast to, for example, $InMe_3$ and $SbMe_3$, both of which inflame in air. This must be a kinetic problem, and is probably to be associated with the absence of a vacant orbital (as in $InMe_3$) or a lone pair (as in $SbMe_3$).

(1) REACTION WITH SOME NON-METALS

The transfer of organic groups in the reaction of organometallic compounds with metals has been mentioned above (section 33.3(2)). Here the reactions with non-metals, especially with oxygen and the halogens, are discussed.

(a) *Oxygen*

All organometallic compounds combine exothermally with oxygen. Many are spontaneously inflammable in air, especially the lower alkyls of the alkali and alkaline-earth metals, Be, Mg, Zn, Cd, B, Al, Ga, In, and Tl. This is also true for some donor elements in Group VB—P, As, Sb, and Bi. Under controlled conditions, compounds of Groups IA, IIA, and IIIA form alkoxides, e.g.

$$RMgX \rightarrow ROMgX$$

$$AlEt_3 \rightarrow Al(OEt)_3.$$

In the oxidation of trimethylboron, a peroxide $MeOOBMe_2$ is an intermediate. Group VB derivatives, however, are oxidized from the trivalent to the pentavalent state, without cleavage of the X—C bond:

$$2PR_3 \text{ (AsR}_3, \text{ or SbR}_3) + O_2 \rightarrow 2R_3PO \text{ (R}_3AsO, \text{ or } R_3SbO).$$

(b) Sulphur and selenium

Similarly, sulphur and selenium can insert their atoms into the M—C bond. They react less readily than oxygen, so that their reactions are more easily controlled. Reaction is most favoured, as with oxygen, among the compounds of Groups IA to IIIA,

e.g.
$$BR_3 + S \xrightarrow{170°} R_2B.SR$$

$$RMgX + Se \xrightarrow{35°} RSeMgX \xrightarrow{H_2O} RSeH + MgX(OH)$$

$$SnPh_4 + S \xrightarrow{300°} (Ph_2SnS)_3 + Ph_2S.$$

The alkyls and aryls (MR_3) of Group VB, however, merely add S or Se,

e.g.
$$R_2P\text{—}PR_2 + 2S \rightarrow R_2P\text{—}PR_2$$
$$\underset{\displaystyle S}{\overset{\displaystyle \|}{}} \quad \underset{\displaystyle S}{\overset{\displaystyle \|}{}}$$

$$AsR_3 + S \rightarrow R_3AsS$$

(c) Halogens

Halogens often cleave the metal-carbon bond, forming metal halides. The reaction occurs most readily with the alkyls and aryls of the most electropositive elements, e.g.

$$RMgX + X_2 \rightarrow RX + MgX_2.$$

Partial cleavage can often be achieved in order to prepare alkyl metal halides, e.g.
$$R_2Ar_2Pb + 2I_2 \rightarrow R_2PbI_2 + 2ArI$$

$$GeEt_4 + 2Br_2 \xrightarrow{AlBr_3} Et_2GeBr_2 + 2EtBr.$$

These reactions are catalysed by Lewis acids such as the aluminium halides. The trialkyls and the triaryls of P, As, and Sb, and the triaryls of Bi, add halogens rather than undergo cleavage. Trimethylbismuth, however, reacts by substitution

$$BiMe_3 + Br_2 \rightarrow Me_2BiBr + MeBr,$$

as do the pentaphenyls,

e.g.
$$SbPh_5 + I_2 \rightarrow Ph_4SbI + PhI$$

$$Ph_4SbI + I_2 \rightarrow Ph_4SbI_3.$$

(2) REACTION WITH PROTONIC HYDROGEN

Organometallic compounds undergo typical reactions with compounds which contain protonic hydrogen, i.e. which act as acids towards them, e.g. NH_3, RNH_2, H_2O, ROH, H_2S, RSH, $HHal$, and $R.COOH$. Of these reactions, hydrolysis is one of the most important. The reaction is violent with the alkyls of Groups IA, IIA, and IIIA, e.g.

$$AlEt_3 + 3H_2O \rightarrow 3C_2H_6 + Al(OH)_3,$$

although boron alkyls do not react below 170 °C, and even then only one alkyl group is removed:

$$BBu_3^n + H_2O \rightarrow Bu_2^n B.OH + C_4H_{10}.$$

Alkyls and aryls of Groups IVB and VB withstand hydrolysis under normal conditions. Trifluoromethyl derivatives of P, As, and Sb, in contrast, are hydrolysed by alkali, giving fluoroform. The strongly electron attracting $—CF_3$ groups impart some acceptor properties to the central atom.

Hydrogen halides, either gaseous or in aqueous solution, cleave many organometallics, e.g.

$$SnPh_4 + HX \xrightarrow{\text{aq.}} Ph_3SnX + PhH$$

$$BBu_3^n + HCl \xrightarrow{110°} Bu_2^n BCl + C_4H_{10}$$

$$BBu_3^n + 2HCl \xrightarrow[\text{catalyst}]{AlCl_3} Bu^n BCl_2 + 2C_4H_{10}.$$

Stepwise cleavage is, as here, often possible. These reactions are catalysed by Lewis acids, e.g. aluminium halides. The reaction

$$Me_3Si.SiMe_3 + H_2SO_4 \xrightarrow[\text{after allowing to stand}]{\text{add } NH_4Cl} Me_3Si.SiMe_2Cl + CH_4$$

shows that in hexamethyldisilane the Si—C bond is cleaved by cold concentrated sulphuric acid in preference to the Si—Si bond, perhaps an unexpected result. The strong tendency for the alkyls of trivalent antimony to attain the pentavalent state is well illustrated by the reaction

$$SbMe_3 + 2HCl \rightarrow Me_3SbCl_2 + H_2.$$

To illustrate the reactions with other compounds containing acidic hydrogen, some examples from boron and aluminium chemistry are listed below. Similar reactions, well known in organic chemistry, occur with

Grignard and organolithium reagents, etc. In every case a hydrocarbon is eliminated.

$$BBu_3^n + ROH \xrightarrow{180°} Bu_2^n B.OR + C_4H_{10}$$

$$BBu_3^n + RSH \xrightarrow[\text{temp.}]{\text{room}} Bu_2^n B.SR + C_4H_{10}$$

$$BBu_3^n + PhNH.NH_2 \xrightarrow{180°} Bu_2^n B.NH.NHPh + C_4H_{10}$$

$$BBu_3^n + CH_3COOH \xrightarrow[\text{temp.}]{\text{room}} Bu_2^n B.OCO.CH_3 + C_4H_{10}$$

$$\xrightarrow{60°} \underset{\underset{OCOCH_3}{|}}{Bu^n B} \text{---} O \text{---} \underset{\underset{OCOCH_3}{|}}{BBu^n}$$

$$4AlPh_3 + 4PhNH_2 \longrightarrow (PhAl.NPh)_4 + 8C_6H_6.$$

The product in the last example appears to have a structure related to that of cubane, Fig. 33.1.

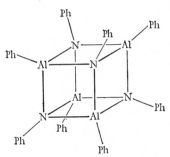

Fig. 33.1. Proposed structure for [PhAl.NPh]₄ (Idris Jones and McDonald, *Proc. Chem. Soc.*, 1962, 366).

When a Grignard or organolithium reagent reacts in this way with an 'acid', a new reagent, of organometallic type, is produced which may be useful in synthesis. This is especially true of the hydrogen compounds of N, P, and As, e.g.

$$2EtMgBr + PhPH_2 \rightarrow PhP(MgBr)_2 + 2EtH$$

$$\left\{ \begin{array}{l} LiPh + R_2AsH \rightarrow LiAsR_2 + PhH \\ LiAsR_2 + R_2AsCl \rightarrow R_2As.AsR_2 + LiCl \end{array} \right.$$

Although boron–hydrogen bonds generally react with Grignard reagents as if they contained hydridic hydrogen (see section 33.4(3)), decaborane gives a Grignard-type reagent, from which substituted decaboranes may be prepared:

$$B_{10}H_{14} + MeMgBr \rightarrow B_{10}H_{13}MgBr + CH_4$$

$$B_{10}H_{13}MgBr + RCl \rightarrow B_{10}H_{13}R + MgBrCl.$$

An important special case is the 'hydrogen-metal exchange' reaction, in which a reactive organometallic compound (usually an organolithium reagent) attacks an acidic C—H group in an organic compound. The method is valuable in preparing new lithium reagents for use in synthesis, e.g.

$$RC{\equiv}CH + LiPh \rightarrow RC{\equiv}CLi + PhH$$

$$[Me_4\overset{\oplus}{N}]Cl^- + LiPh \rightarrow [Me_3NCH_2Li]^+Cl^- \rightarrow [Me_3N{\rightarrow}CH_2].$$

Another important example of the last type is the preparation of a phosphine-methylene,

$$PPh_3 \xrightarrow{CH_3Br} [Ph_3PCH_3]^+ . Br^- \xrightarrow{LiPh} Ph_3P{=}CH_2,$$

which converts a ketone $R_2C{=}O$ into an olefin $R_2C{=}CH_2$ (Wittig reaction),

$$Ph_3P{=}CH_2 \atop {+} \atop O{=}CR_2 \longrightarrow {Ph_3P \atop \|\atop O} + {CH_2 \atop \| \atop CR_2}$$

(3) REACTION WITH HYDRIDIC HYDROGEN

Certain reactive organometallic reagents, e.g. alkyllithiums or Grignard reagents, can substitute an organic group for hydrogen in the hydrides of elements such as B, Si, or Sn, e.g.

$$B_2H_6 + 6EtMgCl \rightarrow 6HMgCl + 2Et_3B$$
$$Ph_3SiH + LiMe \rightarrow Ph_3SiMe + LiH.$$

These reactions may be compared with the common reactions between organometallic reagents and metal or non-metal halides (section 33.3(3)). Triphenylgermane, however, reacts as if it contains protonic hydrogen. This has been cited as evidence that Ge is more electronegative than either Si or Sn (an example of the 'alternation' effect):

$$Ph_3GeH + LiMe \rightarrow LiGePh_3 + CH_4.$$

(4) REACTION WITH HYDROGEN

Again the metal–carbon bond is split, e.g.

$$Al(C_2H_5)_3 + H_2 \rightarrow HAl(C_2H_5)_2 + C_2H_6.$$

The method has been applied to the preparation of boron hydrides, using hydrogen under pressure (c. 100 atm) in the presence of amines (to give boron hydride amine complexes) at 200 °C.

$$BR_3 + 3H_2 + NR_3' \rightarrow H_3B.NR_3' + 3RH.$$

In the absence of amines the reaction is more complex, and alkylboron hydrides as well as olefins and paraffins are produced.

(5) PYROLYSIS

The thermal decomposition of unstable alkyls, e.g. of Cr, Cu, Ag, Pb, or Bi, leads to the production of radicals. This reaction forms the basis of the anti-knock properties of $PbEt_4$, and is said to take place homogeneously and to be practically complete in 12 hours at 275 °C. Reference to Table 33.II shows that radical production will be most ready with the alkyls of the heavier elements (thus $SnMe_4$ is stable to 400 °C). Measurements on the breakdown of HgR_2 seem to show that the primary step is to give two R· radicals rather than R· and Hg—R·. Within a row of the Periodic Table thermal stability is in general higher the more electronegative the element.

Pyrolysis may also lead to the production of a hydride and an olefin, a reaction found with the more reactive alkyls, e.g.

$$LiC_4H_9 \rightarrow CH_3CH_2CH{=}CH_2 + LiH$$

$$Al(\textit{iso}\text{-butyl})_3 \xrightarrow{150\text{--}80°} HAl(\textit{iso}\text{-butyl})_2 + \textit{iso}\text{-butylene}.$$

These reactions frequently give very complex mixtures of products on account of rearrangements and polymerizations of the olefins first produced. As boron and aluminium hydrides add to olefins, the reactions are reversible. Therefore a high-boiling olefin can displace a volatile olefin from a boron alkyl on heating,

$$B(C_4H_9^i)_3 + 3\ \textit{iso}\text{-octene} \rightarrow B(C_8H_{17}^i)_3 + 3\ \textit{iso}\text{-butene}.$$

Some unusual heterocyclic compounds are sometimes formed by pyrolysis. Thus the compounds

are reported in the products of the thermal decomposition of tetramethyl-silane. Again a free-radical mechanism is postulated.

(6) EXCHANGE REACTIONS

Apart from the exchange of groups which occurs between an organo-metallic compound of one element and the halide of another (section 33.3(3)), exchange of groups between two derivatives of the same element often occurs. The simplest case of this is between two alkyls MR_n and MR'_n, where the groups R and R' become redistributed. Thus the apparent molecular weight of tri*iso*octylaluminium dissolved in tri*iso*butylaluminium is one-third of the formula weight, because each tri*iso*octylaluminium molecule is converted into three di*iso*butyl*iso*octylaluminium molecules by reaction with the solvent:

$$AlOct_3^i + 2AlBu_3^i \rightarrow 3Oct^iAlBu_2^i.$$

Here exchange can take place through bridging alkyl groups—

Exchange of alkyl groups between two alkylborons is catalysed by alkyl-aluminiums, and presumably involves a similar complex.

Similarly, when two Group IVB alkyls, e.g. $SiEt_4$ and $SiPr_4^n$, are heated together at their boiling-point with traces of aluminium chloride as catalyst, redistribution occurs to give all five possible species $SiEt_xPr_{4-x}^n$ ($x = 0$ to 4).

Redistribution is also observed between an alkyl or aryl and a halide, alkoxide, etc., of the same element. These reactions are very important in organoboron chemistry, and are catalysed by boron hydrides, which presumably effect the exchange through H-bridged intermediates (cf. Al alkyls above)

$$BR_3 + BX_3 \rightarrow R_2BX + RBX_2 \quad (X = F, Cl, OR, SR, NR_2, \text{etc.}).$$

Alkyls and aryls of silicon and germanium undergo similar exchange with their halides; $AlCl_3$ catalysis is advisable, so that the reaction proceeds at a sufficiently low temperature. Alkyltins, however, react very readily with $SnCl_4$ or $SnBr_4$, and alkyltin halides are generally prepared by mixing the stoicheiometric quantities of SnR_4 and $SnCl_4$ and heating if necessary

$$3SnR_4 + SnCl_4 \xrightarrow{\;0°\;} 4R_3SnCl$$

$$SnR_4 + SnCl_4 \xrightarrow{\;200°\;} 2R_2SnCl_2.$$

(7) COMPLEX FORMATION

The organometallic compounds of Groups III and II can act as electron acceptors and thus form complexes with amines, ethers, halide ions, and carbanions. By comparing heats of dissociation of $R_3M \leftarrow NR_3$ complexes, and by correlating dipole moments of solutions of R_3M in donor solvents, the sequence of acceptor character has been found to be

$$B < Al > Ga > In > Tl.$$

Steric hindrance has been invoked to explain the boron-aluminium relation. The Group II pattern appears to be similar, i.e.

$$Be < Mg > Zn > Cd > Hg.$$

While $AlMe_3$ and $GaMe_3$ clearly belong to the class 'a' type acceptor ($N > P > As$; $O > S$), $HgMe_2$, $TlMe_3$, and rather surprisingly BMe_3 show some class 'b' character (e.g. $S > O$).

The following illustrate further types of complex formation:

$$BPh_3 + KCN \rightarrow K^+[Ph_3BCN]^-$$

$$BPh_3 + NaOR \rightarrow Na^+[Ph_3BOR]^-$$

$$BPh_3 + LiH \rightarrow Li^+[Ph_3BH]^-$$

$$BPh_3 + NaPh \rightarrow Na^+[Ph_4B]^-.$$

$Na(Ph_4B)$ is used as a quantitative precipitant for K^+ in aqueous solution. Cf. also

$$BPh_3 + Na \rightarrow Na^+[Ph_3B^\cdot]^-.$$

The organometallic compounds of Group VB can show either donor or acceptor properties. The use of the alkyls and aryls as donors, especially to transition metals, is well known, e.g. PPh_3 and

are typical ligands. In contrast, however, $Sb(CF_3)_3$ lacks donor character, but acts as an acceptor in forming a pyridine complex, $(CF_3)_3Sb \cdot NC_5H_5$. This is explained by the very strong electron-attracting nature of the trifluoromethyl groups.

33.5. Some synthetic applications

Because of their reactive nature, organometallic compounds have been widely used as synthetic agents in both organic and organometallic chemistry. We cannot hope to do more than touch on a few examples from a very large field. Thus addition of an organometallic may take place across $C=O$, $C=C$, or $C\equiv N$. By comparing rates of reaction, it has been found that the orders of activity are

$$CsR > RbR > KR > NaR > LiR, \quad CaR > MgR > BeR,$$
$$LiR > BeR > BR, \quad ZnR > CdR > HgR,$$
$$LiR > CuR, \quad and \quad BeR > ZnR,$$

so that within a Group the least active of the A-element alkyls is more reactive than the most reactive of the B-metal alkyls. Such trends are in general keeping with what one might expect on grounds of bond polarity, and it is even possible, as is shown in Table 33.IV, to draw up an approximate border line for a given type of reaction in terms of the electronegativity of the metal.

TABLE 33.IV. *Approximate division between reacting and non-reacting methyl and ethyl derivatives of metals on the basis of Pauling electronegativities*

Reaction with	Limiting electronegativity	Reacting	Not reacting
Ethers	0·9	Na	Ba
$Ph_2C=CH_2$	1·1	Ca	Mg
CO_2	1·5	Be, Al	Zn, Cd
$RC\equiv N$	1·55	Zn and Cd slowly	
RCOCl	1·7	Ga, In	Hg, Tl, B

In such reactions the alkyl group attaches itself to carbon, and the metal to the electronegative atom if present, e.g.

$$R—C{\overset{H}{\underset{O}{\big\langle}}} + RMgX \longrightarrow {\overset{R}{\underset{R}{\big\rangle}}}C{\overset{H}{\underset{OMgX}{\big\langle}}}$$

$$O{=}C{=}O + NaR \longrightarrow R—C{\overset{O}{\underset{\overset{-}{O}\overset{+}{Na}}{\big\langle}}}$$

The reaction may be regarded as taking place via an R^- nucleophilic attack on the carbon (contrast formation of R^+ cations with $AlCl_3$ and RCl).

Li and Al alkyls add across ethylenic double bonds, e.g.

$$Ph_2C{=}CH_2 + LiR \rightarrow Ph_2CLi . CH_2R.$$

Displacement reactions may also occur (see also section 33.4(5)):

$$RCH{=}CH_2 + R'CH_2CH_2M \rightarrow R'CH{=}CH_2 + RCH_2CH_2M.$$

In the case of the alkylaluminiums, the growth reaction to give long alkyl chains has been very considerably investigated, especially by Ziegler and his co-workers, in connexion with the commercial polymerization of ethylene and propylene, for which it is now extensively used. These polymerizations can be greatly accelerated by various catalysts (e.g. Ti chlorides, Ziegler–Natta process). They are often stereospecific giving, for example, crystalline oriented polypropylene.

An indication of the types of inorganic catalyst which can be used in these polymerizations was given at the end of Chapter 10. The catalyst $TiCl_4/AlEt_3$ is found to be less successful than many others, in marked contrast with the results in the polymerization of ethylene. The general specificity of the catalysts is quite remarkable, and it is unlikely that any single theory of their action can account for the variation in products. It seems that the reaction is usually heterogeneous, although in some cases homogeneous stereospecific polymerizations are established. Again while alkylaluminiums and titanium halides form red complexes, the nature of these compounds is not yet fully understood, nor is it known whether they are required for catalysis. In other theories the titanium atom acts as the propagation centre, and π-complexes are invoked between the titanium atom and the unsaturated monomers.

The production of new organometallic derivatives from R—M and acidic C—H compounds has been mentioned above (section 33.4(2)). Another reaction, of great importance in organic chemistry, is the halogen-metal exchange reaction,

$$LiBu^n + RX \rightarrow Bu^nX + LiR \quad (X = Br, I).$$

It provides a useful method for obtaining organolithium reagents which cannot be prepared by direct reaction between lithium and the halide. Lithium becomes attached to the more electronegative organic radical. Some examples are given below. Organolithium reagents may also be prepared in this way from aromatic halides containing —OH, —SH, —NH$_2$, etc. These groups are regenerated on hydrolysis; they are 'protected' during any reaction at the carbon centre, as they are converted by LiBu^n to the Li derivative.

$$C_3F_7I + LiCH_3 \xrightarrow{-78°} LiC_3F_7 + CH_3I$$

The use of tetrahydrofuran (THF) as solvent promotes these reactions, but accelerates even more the coupling reactions in which lithium halide is eliminated. Thus methyllithium cannot be prepared from lithium and methyl iodide in tetrahydrofuran, as the coupling reaction

$$CH_3I + LiCH_3 \rightarrow CH_3CH_3 + LiI$$

is so rapid. The preparation of 2,2′-dibromobiphenyl from o-dibromobenzene and n-butyllithium in THF at −78° illustrates both metal-halogen exchange, and coupling:

33.6. Physical properties and structures

BOILING-POINTS AND MELTING-POINTS

With the exception of the ionic compounds (e.g. the alkali and alkaline-earth metal alkyls and aryls), organometallic compounds have boiling-points similar to organic compounds of comparable molecular weight.

TABLE 33.V. *Boiling-points of chlorides and ethyls compared*

X	NaX	MgX_2	AlX_3	SiX_4	PX_3	SX_2
Cl	1465°	1418°	180°	58°	75°	59°
Et		infusible solids	186°	153°	128°	92°

There is likewise a useful comparison with the boiling-points of the halides, as is shown in Table 33.V. The compounds of Group IVB form a particularly simple series, and the boiling-point and density of $SiEt_4$ were predicted accurately by Mendeleeff, fifteen years before it was first prepared. In Groups III and II there are, however, complications from polymerization. All the boron compounds are monomeric both in the vapour state and in solutions in inert solvents such as benzene. With Al, however, there is a strong tendency to dimerize. The ease of dissociation of the dimer seems to depend on the size and extent of branching of the alkyl groups, i.e. on a steric effect. Thus for AlR_3, when R = Me, Et, or Pr^n, the compounds are dimeric in benzene solution, but a monomer $\rightleftharpoons$ dimer equilibrium exists in the vapour. When R = Pr^i and Bu^i, however, the alkyls are monomeric both in solution and in the vapour. The heat of dissociation of Al_2Me_6 to two moles of monomer is 20·2 kcal. The Tl alkyls appear to be monomers both in vapour and in solution, while Ga and In alkyls are sometimes polymerized and sometimes not, depending upon the compound and its physical state. $BeMe_2$ is highly polymerized (as is also $MgMe_2$), but the alkyls of Zn, Cd, and Hg appear to be monomeric. The variation in polymerization is reflected in melting-points and boiling-points. Fig. 33.2 shows some values for compounds of Group IIIB elements, with distinct maxima at Al and (less marked) at In. These variations may be connected with the extent of association between the molecules in the solid or liquid states. That this is not the only effect is suggested by the fact that a similar alternation in boiling-point occurs for the series $ZnMe_2$ (44°), $CdMe_2$ (105°), and $HgMe_2$ (92 °C). There is no evidence of association in any of these compounds; for instance, the Trouton constants are all normal—$ZnMe_2$ (21·6), $CdMe_2$ (21·8), $HgMe_2$ (21·3 entropy units). CdR_2 compounds are in general less volatile than their Hg analogues.

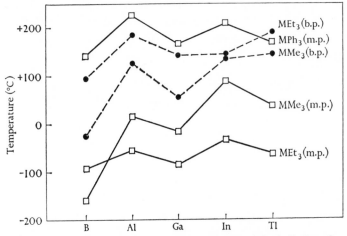

Fig. 33.2. Some melting-points (□) and boiling-points (●) of alkyls and aryls.

STRUCTURES

As has been mentioned above, the alkyls and aryls of the alkali metals, apart from lithium, are non-volatile salts insoluble in light petroleum or benzene. On the other hand, the alkyls and aryls of Groups IVB to VIIB are volatile simple-covalent derivatives. The alkyls of Group IVB all have regular (sp^3) tetrahedral structures. The barriers to rotation of the methyl groups in MMe_4 decrease down the Group as follows:

$$C = 4\cdot8; \quad Si = 1\cdot1-1\cdot5; \quad Ge = 0\cdot4; \quad Sn = 0; \quad Pb = 0 \text{ (kcal mole}^{-1}\text{)}.$$

The methyls of Group VB, like the hydrides, are pyramidal. The angles C–M–C are given in Table 33.vi and compared with the angles C–M–C in the trifluoromethyls and the angles H–M–H in the hydrides. The angles fall sharply from a near tetrahedral angle in the N, to nearer a right angle in the P, As, and Sb compounds. In their hydrides sp^3 hybridization is probably used by N, and largely p^3 bonding by P, As, and Sb. The wider valence angle at P, As, or Sb in the methyls and trifluoromethyls may be explained (1) by greater steric repulsion between the CH_3 and CF_3 groups compared with that between H atoms, and/or (2) by better orbital overlap

TABLE 33.vi. *A comparison of bond angles (see text)*

M	$M(CH_3)_3$	$M(CF_3)_3$	MH_3
N	$108\pm4°$	..	$107\cdot3\pm0\cdot2°$
P	$99\cdot1\pm0\cdot2°$	$99\cdot6\pm2\cdot5°$	$93\cdot3\pm0\cdot2°$
As	$96\cdot5\pm5°$	$100\cdot1\pm3\cdot5°$	$91\cdot8\pm0\cdot3°$
Sb	..	$100\cdot0\pm3\cdot5°$	$91\cdot3\pm0\cdot3°$

with the fourth sp^3 C orbital which is achieved when some s character is present in the bonding orbitals of the central atom. A similar difference in bond angle is found between the hydrides and methyls of Group VIʙ, Table 33.vɪɪ.

TABLE 33.vɪɪ. *A comparison of bond angles (see text)*

M	$M(CH_3)_2$	$M(CF_3)_2$	MH_2
O	$111\pm3°$	..	$104\cdot5°$
S	$105\pm3°$	$105\cdot6°$	$92\cdot1°$
Se	..	$104\cdot4°$	$91°$

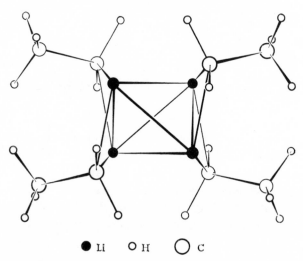

● Li   ○ H   ◯ C

FɪG. 33.3. The structure of ethyllithium (after Dietrich, *Acta Crystallogr.*, 1963, **16**, 681).

The organic derivatives of the elements lying between those giving the largely ionic and the largely covalent types have interesting structures. As mentioned above, these compounds are electron deficient and they tend to polymerize. A similar situation exists in the hydrides of some of these elements. Although lithium hydride forms an ionic crystal, the alkyllithiums have electron-deficient structures, with bridging alkyl groups between the metal atoms. Thus ethyllithium is associated in benzene $(LiEt)_n$ with $n = 4$ to 6. Its crystal structure has recently been determined, and consists of $(LiC_2H_5)_4$ units, running through the crystal, with the lithium atom in an approximately tetrahedral arrangement. The —CH_2— units of the ethyl groups form symmetrical bridges between the lithium atoms (Fig. 33.3). Solid $BeMe_2$ has a similar type of structure, as does the trimethylaluminium dimer. X-ray analysis of the former shows that there

are long chains of

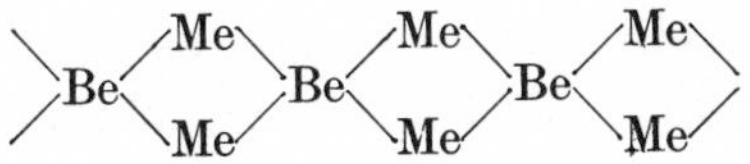

with the angle Be–C–Be = 66° and the angle C–Be–C = 114°. The low volatility of dimethylmagnesium indicates that it is polymeric, and its structure may well be similar. The trimethylaluminium dimer has the structure:

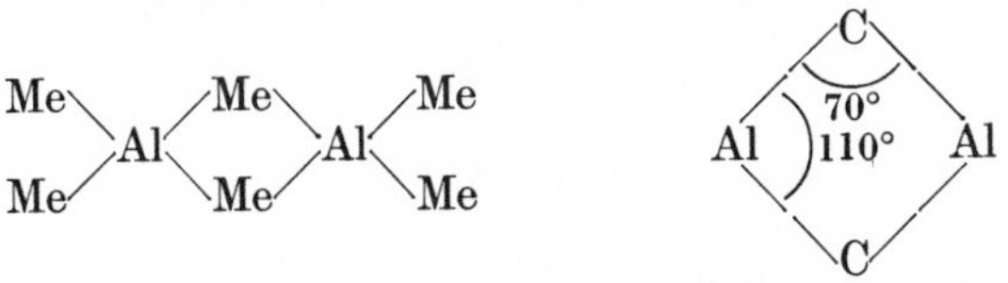

which has been obtained by X-ray diffraction, and is supported by the infra-red spectrum. The bonding in the bridge may be interpreted in terms of a three-centre orbital between Al (sp^3), C (sp^3), and Al (sp^3):

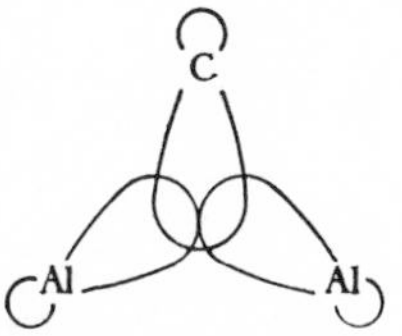

If each of the orbitals were the same size and contributed equally, then the three atoms would be expected to lie at the corners of an equilateral triangle, i.e. the Al–C–Al angle would be 60°. An alternative explanation, involving the use of carbon $3d$ orbitals has been proposed (see Wells, *Structural Inorganic Chemistry*, 3rd ed., p. 759, Oxford University Press, 1962).

Crystalline InMe$_3$ is also polymerized through bridging Me groups. X-ray analysis shows a network of tetramer units, held together by long 'partial' bonds. Bridging methyl groups are again involved in this structure, but here they are unsymmetrically disposed in relation to the In atoms (In–C distances = 2·1 and 3·1 Å), and the In–C–In bridge is almost linear.

The monomeric alkyls of Group IIIB are all planar (sp^2). A point of contrast occurs here between the hydrides and the alkyls. Whereas boron hydrides, e.g. B$_2$H$_6$ are polymerized through H-bridges, boron alkyls, e.g. BMe$_3$ are monomeric under all circumstances.

The problem of the structure of Grignard reagents has invited much work and speculation, and a great deal still remains to be clarified. Their composition in ethereal solution corresponds to the formula RMgX (an

X-ray study of the structure of $C_6H_5MgBr.2Et_2O$ has been carried out by Stucky and Rundle). Addition of dioxan to the ether solution precipitates MgX_2 as a dioxan complex, and the dialkyls MgR_2 may be isolated from the solution. No ready equilibration of the type

$$2RMgX \rightleftharpoons MgR_2 + MgX_2$$

can exist, as there is very little exchange between radioactive $\overset{*}{M}gBr_2$ and $MgEt_2$. Solutions prepared from a mixture of $MgEt_2$ and $MgBr_2$ seem to

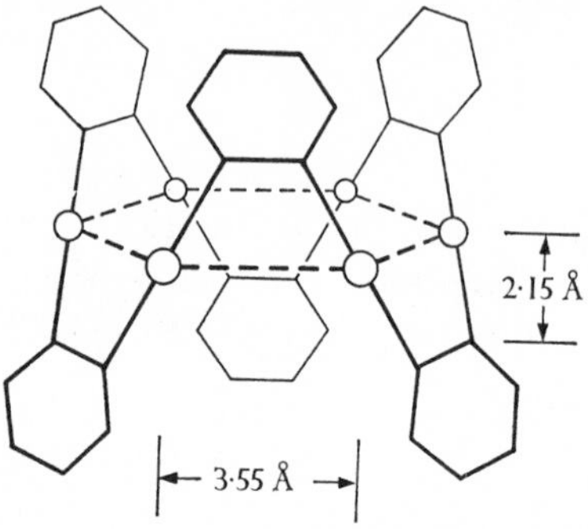

Fig. 33.4. o-phenylene mercury (after Grdenić, *Chem. Ber.*, 1959, **92**, 232).

be identical with those of the Grignard reagent prepared from Mg and EtBr. These conclusions are supported by nuclear magnetic resonance spectra, viscosity measurements, rates of reactions, etc. Thus while there are appreciable differences in the chemical shifts of the CH_3— and —CH_2— groups between $Hg(C_2H_5)_2$ and C_2H_5HgCl, the values observed for $Mg(C_2H_5)_2$, and 'C_2H_5MgBr' (prepared from Mg and EtBr) are almost the same. This would suggest that the Grignard reagent may be better formulated as $MgX_2.MgR_2$ than as RMgX. Grignard solutions tenaciously retain ether on concentration, indicating that the ether is chemically combined. Molecular-weight determinations indicate association in ethereal solution. Studies on the electrolysis of Grignard solutions show that ions are present, and that both cations and anions contain magnesium.

The monomeric alkyls of Group II have the linear structure (*sp*). An interesting example of this is o-phenylene mercury, which has been shown to be hexameric with the structure given in Fig. 33.4 and not

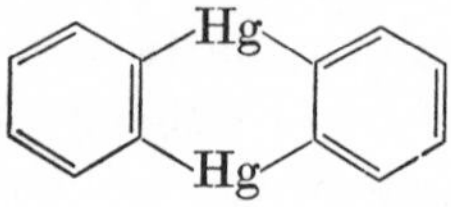

which would involve a bent C—Hg—C bond.

There are considerable shifts of the proton nuclear magnetic resonance lines of ethyl and methyl groups in metal alkyls as compared with ethane and methane. The shifts are closely related to the electronegativities of the metals, which lends support to the use of this parameter in descriptions of bond properties (Allred and Rochow, *J. Inorg. Nucl. Chem.*, 1958, **5**, 269).

Problems

1. The following points are observed in the electrolysis of LiEt dissolved in $ZnEt_2$ solution. Zinc is produced at the cathode in the quantities required by Faraday's law. At the anode a gas is normally evolved, which analysis shows to be approximately ethylene 40 per cent, ethane 40 per cent, butane 17 per cent, propane 3 per cent, but if a lead anode is used no gas is evolved and $PbEt_4$ is produced in almost the correct Faradaic quantity. Suggest explanations for these observations.

2. It is found that aryl bromides tend to react with alkyllithiums to give aryllithiums and alkyl bromides, rather than the reverse. Suggest a possible explanation for this observation.

3. Suggest methods which might be used for the synthesis of the following compounds: LiR, $NaC_{10}H_8$, $HgMe_2$, $AlEt_3$, $AlPh_3$, $R_3Al_2Cl_3$, Me_2SiCl_2, Cl_3SiCH_2Cl, R_2SnCl_2, Pb_2Me_6, Ph_2PSiMe_3, Sb_2Me_4. In each case at least one synthetic route is mentioned in the text.

4. Give examples of the synthetic applications of the following organo-metallic compounds: $LiPh$, $EtMgBr$, $CdEt_2$, $HgPh_2$, $AlEt_3$.

5. The Wurtz–Fittig reaction

$$ArX + RX + 2Na \rightarrow ArR + 2NaX$$

gives much higher yields than the Wurtz reaction

$$R'X + RX + 2Na \rightarrow R'R + 2NaX.$$

How can this be explained?

6. Why is $(Li^+)_2(dipyridyl^-)_2$ a useful reagent for the reduction of transition metal dipyridyls to very low oxidation states, e.g. -1?

7. Comment on the following dissociation constants (measured at $25°$ in 60 per cent ethanol) for the acids *para*-R_3M—C_6H_4—COOH:

M	*Pauling electronegativity*	$10^6 \times K_a$ R *is* Me	$10^6 \times K_a$ R *is* Et
C	2·5	0·70	0·71
Si	1·8	1·11	1·13
Ge	1·8	1·07	1·08
Sn	1·8	1·05	1·17

8. Comment on the fact that the silicon analogue of acetone is a high-polymeric substance $(Me_2SiO)_n$.

9. How can you explain the differences in the hydrolysis reactions of $SnCl_4$ and $SnMe_4$?

10. Suggest a possible explanation for the fact that the electrical conductivity of $NaF,2AlEt_3$ is about 100 times that of $NaF,AlEt_3$.

11. Ziegler has observed that the absorption rate of ethylene by dissolved aluminium triethyl to form butyldiethylaluminium increases when more solvent is added. The rate of absorption is proportional to the square root of the total volume. What does this observation suggest about the possible nature of the reacting species?

12. The alkali-metal salts of phenylacetylene react with benzonitrile. Under the same conditions the following times for reaction have been found:

	Li	Na	K	Rb	Cs	(MgBr)
Hours	60	6·8	5·0	4·7	3·8	86

Comment.

13. Comment on the following series of boiling-points: $BeMe_2$ 217° (extrapolated), $BeEt_2$ 194° (extrapolated), $ZnMe_2$ 44°, $ZnEt_2$ 117°, CMe_4 9°, CEt_4 146°, $SiMe_4$ 27°, $SiEt_4$ 154°, $GeMe_4$ 43°, $GeEt_4$ 164 °C.

14. Beryllium *bis*-cyclopentadiene is apparently isomorphous with ferrocene, yet it has a large dipole moment. Electron diffraction studies indicate that the beryllium atom is on the central axis of the molecule 1·4 Å from one ring and 2·0 Å from the other. How could this be accounted for by ionic or covalent binding?

15. In Cu(I) benzene and Ag(I) benzene compounds the metal atom lies under two carbon atoms rather than under the centre of the ring. Compare these structures with that of $Cr(benzene)_2$ and discuss the types of bonding which may be involved.

16. Phenylcopper is stable to 70° while phenylsilver decomposes below 0°. What are the probable reasons for this difference?

17. The reaction of a diazonium salt RN_2Cl with a copper(I) salt, CuX, gives RX. The product of the reaction of RN_2Cl with $HgCl_2$ in the presence of copper is RHgCl. Can you account for this distinction?

18. In general divalent organometallic compounds of tin and lead are not stable to disproportionation but both the tin and lead *bis*-cyclopentadiene compounds (MCp_2) are known. Comment.

19. The species $Zn(CH_3)_2$ and $ZnCl_2$ can be dissolved in organic solvents but give no $Zn(CH_3)Cl$. Compare this with observations on the *trans*-effect in transition-metal compounds (Chapter 29).

20. Although $[Zn(C_6H_5)_3]^-$ is thought to exist it is generally true that anions $[MR_n]^{m-}$ are unstable. Why should this be the case when anionic halide complexes are so common?

21. Silicon and germanium alkyls may be readily separated and analysed by gas-liquid chromatography. For a given column temperature and

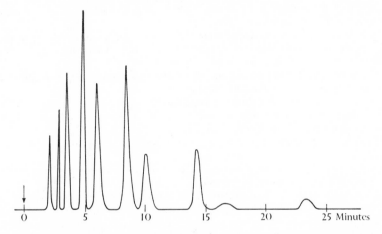

Fig. 33.5. Gas-liquid chromatogram of products from reaction of $SiEt_4$ and $GePr_4^n$.

column liquid, an individual alkyl may be characterized by its *relative retention time*, which is a measure of the time the alkyl is retained in the column liquid during its passage through the column. The retention time is thus proportional to the solubility of the gaseous alkyl in the column liquid. After each of the following compounds, its retention time (relative to the retention time of mesitylene, for a column at 100 °C containing the hydrocarbon squalane as column liquid) is given in parentheses:

$$GeEt_4 \ (0.87), \quad GeEt_2Pr_2^n \ (2.63), \quad GePr_4^n \ (7.76).$$

Can you see an approximate relation between these values, and how can this relation be accounted for?

Estimate relative retention times for

$$GeEt_3Pr^n \ (1.51), \quad GeEtPr_3^n \ (4.57), \quad GeBu_4^n \ (70.8), \quad GePr_2^nBu_2^n \ (24.0),$$

and compare with the experimental values, again given in parentheses.

When $SiEt_4$ (relative retention time 0·63) is refluxed with $GePr_4^n$ and catalytic quantities of $AlCl_3$, a reaction takes place. On gas-chromatographic analysis of the product (under the same conditions as above), ten 'peaks' are observed in the chromatogram (Fig. 33.5). Their retention times are 0·63, 0·87, 1·12, 1·51, 1·91, 2·63, 3·31, 4·57, 5·60, and 7·76. To what compounds might these peaks correspond?

Bibliography

G. E. COATES, *Organometallic Compounds*, 2nd ed., Methuen, London, 1960.

J. J. EISCH, *Organometallic Syntheses*, vol. 2, *Non-transition Metal Compounds*, Academic Press, New York, 1966.

J. EISCH and H. GILMAN, Organometallic Compounds, *Advances in Inorganic Chemistry and Radiochemistry*, vol. 2, ed. H. J. Eméleus and A. G. Sharpe, Academic Press, New York, 1960.

R. G. JONES and H. GILMAN, 'Methods of Preparation of Organometallic Compounds', *Chem. Rev.*, 1954, **54**, 835.

R. KÖSTER, and P. BENGER, Organoaluminium Compounds, *Advances in Inorganic Chemistry and Radiochemistry*, vol. 7, ed. H. J. Eméleus and A. G. Sharpe, Academic Press, New York, 1965.

F. G. MANN, 'Stereochemistry of N, P, As, Sb, and Bi', *Prog. Stereochem.*, 1958, **2**, 196.

E. G. ROCHOW, D. T. HURD, and R. N. LEWIS, *The Chemistry of Organometallic Compounds*, Wiley, New York, 1957.

F. G. A. STONE, 'The Role of Organometallic Compounds in the Development of Coordination Chemistry', Eighth International Conference on Coordination Chemistry, Vienna, 1964.

F. G. A. STONE and W. A. G. GRAHAM, *Inorganic Polymers*, Academic Press, New York, 1962.

G. STUCKY and R. E. RUNDLE, 'The Constitution of the Grignard Reagent, Phenylmagnesium Bromide Dietherate', *J. Am. Chem. Soc.* 1964, **86**, 4825.

K. ZIEGLER, *New Aspects of Some Organometallic Complex Compounds*, Special Publication No. 13, Chemical Society, London, 1959.

Advances in Organometallic Chemistry, ed. F. G. A. Stone and R. West, Academic Press, New York, 1964–.

Metal–Organic Compounds, Advances in Chemistry Series No. 23, American Chemical Society, Washington, D.C., 1959.

34 · Postscript to the Metals: Qualitative Analysis and Occurrence

34.1. General comparison of metals

The purpose of this last chapter on the metals is not the same as that served by the survey chapter on the non-metals (Chapter 18). At the end of the discussion of non-metal chemistry, we wished to summarize the atomic properties of non-metals in relation to the chemistry which had just been described in Chapters 11 to 17. In the treatment of metal chemistry the significance of the atomic properties has been emphasized in the individual chapters. Here we wish to discuss two particularly general chemical problems in order to draw together the chemistries of different kinds of metals which have so far been treated in separate chapters of the book. We have chosen to discuss (Part A) the traditional methods of qualitative analysis, as we believe that the series of reactions used in this analysis form a good experimental introduction to the aqueous solution chemistry of metals, and (Part B) the occurrence and extraction of the elements, as an example of metal chemistry in largely non-aqueous circumstances. We shall also attempt to show how in both analysis and in extraction procedures the methods used are dictated by the general chemical considerations already discussed in the preceding chapters. Thus the difficulties in understanding the seemingly complicated analytical tables and descriptive accounts of occurrence and extraction may to some degree be reduced.

Table 34.1 lists the main features of three major classes of metals. Because of their relative 'rarity' the lanthanides and actinides are deliberately omitted. Here we wish to establish the principal differences between these three classes and generalize at the risk of over-emphasis. From the pre-transition A-subgroup metals to the B-subgroup metals there is a large change in the polarizing power of the cation. The result of this change is to increase the relative affinity of the B metals for more polarizable ligands. Thus the B metals form complexes and insoluble compounds with the heavier rather than the lighter halide ions, and give ammines and

TABLE 34.I. *General distinctions in the chemistry of the three major types of metallic elements*

	Pre-transition metals	Transition metals	B metals
Valence	Constant	Variable	Group and $(N-2)$
Colour	Colourless	d–d and charge transfer	Charge transfer
Oxides	Readily hydrated, basic	Not readily hydrated, often amphoteric or acidic: valence-dependent	Often amphoteric or acidic: valence dependent
Halide complexes (stability)	$F^- > Cl^- > Br^- > I^-$	Intermediate and valence-dependent	$I^- > Br^- > Cl^- > F^-$ for heavier ions
Sulphides	Readily hydrolysed	Insoluble	Insoluble
Oxyanion salts, e.g. carbonate	Stable for low valences	Sometimes unstable	Sometimes unstable
Ammine complexes	Unstable to water	Stable	Stable
Cyanides, nitrosyls, and CO complexes	Unstable	Especially stable in lower valences	Unstable except for cyanides in the early Groups
Phosphorus and sulphur complexes	Unstable	Especially stable in lower valences	Mainly stable in the early Groups
Hydrides	Stable in all periods	Unstable especially in first row	Unstable
Methyls, etc.	Unstable	Unstable especially in first row	Stable at least kinetically in certain cases, e.g. $[TlMe_2]^+$
Ethylene and arene complexes	Unstable	Stable in low oxidation states	Unstable except for Group IB and Hg^{2+}
Carbides and nitrides	Stable	Unstable in later Groups	Generally unstable
Phosphides, silicides, and borides	Not as stable as carbides	More stable than carbides	More stable than carbides

complexes with sulphur and phosphorus ligands in aqueous solution. In a comparable valence state the transition metals represent a somewhat intermediate position between these extremes. However, the change from pre-transition metal behaviour to B-metal behaviour is not entirely continuous across a transition series: the exposed d electrons and orbitals considerably affect the properties of the transition-metal cations, as has been described in Chapters 24, 25, and 26. The effects are pronounced in lower valences, and especially in the later transition-metals where many d electrons are present, and are then particularly significant in compounds with unsaturated ligands such as cyanide, CO, and benzene. They may also be marked in the higher valences and especially in the earlier transition metals, where there are many empty d orbitals, for example in combination with oxide and fluoride.

The detailed analysis of these effects was the subject of Chapters 20 to 33. As we shall now illustrate, the changing polarizing power of the cations is one of the two major factors controlling separation procedures. The second factor is a feature of the transition and B metals which is not common to the pre-transition metals. The valence state of the former may be altered by a control of the oxidation conditions in the solution. Thus the character of a transition metal such as iron or chromium can be made more like that of a B metal, e.g. Fe(II) compare Zn(II), or more like that of a pre-transition metal of Group III, e.g. Fe(III) compare Al(III), or even more like that of a non-metallic element, for example Cr(VI) is like Se(VI).

Finally physical properties, especially colour, may be used for the direct identification of compounds and hence elements. A transition, lanthanide, or actinide metal is usually coloured in its compounds because of internal d–d or f–f transitions, but the resulting colours are much more sensitive to the anion in the transition-metal compounds than in the other two series. In addition both B-metal and transition-metal compounds are often coloured through charge-transfer absorption.

PART A

34.2. Qualitative analysis: group separation

GENERAL PRINCIPLES

During the course of the usual group analysis, the different metal cations are passed through a variety of equilibria. These equilibria are examined successively by changing the conditions in the solution under observation. Thus either the pH is changed, and thereby the amount of a given anion readily available to a cation, or else the concentration of a given anion is changed virtually from nothing, by adding it to the solution in relatively large quantities. All cations are examined together until the separation into groups has been achieved. Thus the study of qualitative-analysis procedures provides a convenient demonstration of the different ways in which metal ions react with different anions. In many ways an examination of the occurrence and distribution of elements is a similar study. Here, however, we can only observe in general the total result of a series of changes over geological times, and from this attempt to deduce why the particular partition of an element took place. It is assumed that the slow cooling of the earth initially permitted an approximate equilibrium to be set up, so that cations and anions were paired in the most stable way. The competitive equilibria involved, e.g. between oxide and sulphide, are not so very different from those used in qualitative analysis, e.g. between hydrates and sulphides.

In qualitative analysis careful use is made of both homogeneous and heterogeneous equilibria. For simple mechanical reasons the heterogeneous equilibria, precipitation, distillation, extraction, and selective solution of a mixture of solids can be used to separate one substance from another, whereas the homogeneous equilibria can only be used to aid heterogeneous separations and in actual identification, e.g. by colour tests. The formation of a separate phase can also be used in identification, but more often than not a group of elements will be precipitated under similar conditions. Further identification within the group then requires re-solution and a more or less specific test based on a homogeneous reaction.

SOLUTION

The common form of analysis table starts with a solution of the material to be analysed. This is analysis in the 'wet' way as opposed to dry tests. The process of obtaining a solution in water, in hydrochloric acid, or in some oxidizing acid solution is not in itself very useful for separation purposes, although certain materials such as silica and titanium dioxide may well be left undissolved. In order to get these more intractable solids into solution, alkali, carbonate, or peroxide fusions may be employed.

The difficulty found in dissolving many metal salts is partly a reflection of the properties of the corresponding oxides (Fig. 34.1). The pre-transition metal oxides are basic, so that they and their salts are usually soluble in acid if not water. The salts of the later transition metals and of the early B metals, which have low-valence oxides only, are also usually readily soluble in acids despite the fact that these oxides are less basic than the oxides of the pre-transition metals. The very high valence oxides of the non-metals are soluble as anions, e.g. sulphate. It is the salts of the early transition metals and of the non-metal elements such as silicon, all having valences of around 4, which are the most difficult to obtain in aqueous solution. In Chapter 14 it was shown that these are the elements close to the amphoteric oxide lines in the Periodic Table. The oxides are not strong enough as bases to be readily dissolved by acids, yet they are such weak acids as to be soluble in alkali only with difficulty. The early transition metals are usually easier to handle than the non-metals, such as silicon and

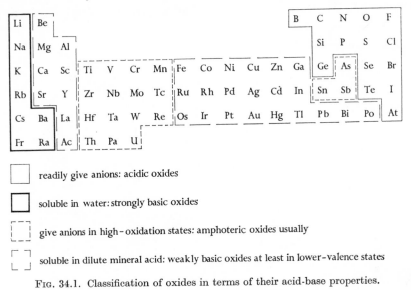

readily give anions: acidic oxides

soluble in water: strongly basic oxides

give anions in high-oxidation states: amphoteric oxides usually

soluble in dilute mineral acid: weakly basic oxides at least in lower-valence states

FIG. 34.1. Classification of oxides in terms of their acid-base properties.

germanium, for they often give still higher valence oxides under oxidizing conditions. These oxides are readily soluble in alkali for they are quite strong acids.

ANION CONTROL

Three main types of anion are used in group analysis. They are (1) a strong-acid polarizable anion, chloride, (2) a weak-acid highly polarizable anion, sulphide, and (3) a series of oxyanions of both weak and strong acids, less polarizable than either chloride or sulphide—e.g. hydroxide, carbonate, sulphate, and phosphate. The availability of the anions to the cations is controlled by the pH of the solution and by the order of their addition to the solution. The principles of pH control of the anion concentration are outlined in Fig. 34.2. Hydrochloric acid is added to the initial acid solution in group I until it is about one molar. Since chloride is the anion of a strong acid, its concentration is relatively independent of the pH and remains roughly the same in all the analytical procedures. Hydroxide is also present in all the solutions, but its concentration is changed from about 10^{-14} in groups I and II to 10^{-8} in groups III and IV. The change is brought about by adding ammonia. Fig. 34.2 shows the effect of pH on the logarithm of the hydroxide concentration. Sulphide is only added to the system in group II. Because it is the anion of a weak *dibasic* acid, its concentration is very low in acid media, but increases very rapidly with pH. Carbonate can only be used as a precipitant in alkaline solution for obvious reasons. It is not added until group V.

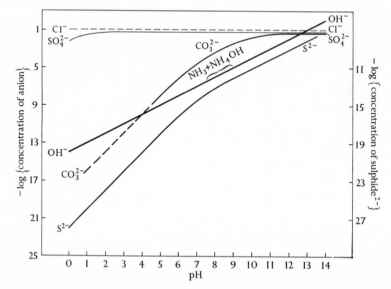

Fig. 34.2. The effect of pH upon the concentration of anions for $M/10$ solutions at pH 14, except for sulphide which is plotted for $M/10^6$ solution at pH 14. These are the approximate concentrations usually encountered in analytical procedures.

The control of the anion concentrations allows the solubility products of a limited number of metal salts to be exceeded under a given set of group-analysis conditions. The main separation stages following solution in strong acid are then as follows.

GROUP SEPARATIONS

I. Hydrochloric acid is added and the acid solution is brought to a pH of about 1 (e.g. blue colour with brilliant cresyl blue, about 0·25 to 0·3 M in HCl). Under these conditions the elements of group I are precipitated as chlorides. All the elements which have a high affinity for chloride are found in a particular 'triangle' of the Periodic Table (Fig. 34.3), but some of them also have a high coordination number so that they form anionic chloride complexes which remain soluble. Thus the group I procedure removes from the solution some of the highly-polarizing cations, e.g. Ag^+ and Pb^{2+}, while leaving others, e.g. Hg^{2+} and Pt^{2+} or Pt^{4+} in the filtrate together with all the less polarizing cations.

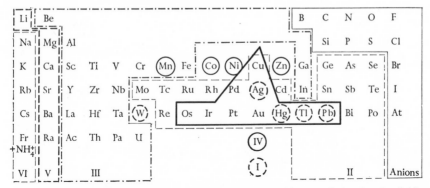

FIG. 34.3. 'Triangle' of elements giving strong chloride complexes (or insoluble chlorides) in aqueous solution. The other elements are divided in accordance with the groups in which they occur in qualitative analysis.

Li	Be													B	C	N	O	F
Na	Mg	Al													Si	P	S	Cl
K	Ca	Sc	Ti	V	Cr	Mn	Fe	Co	Ni	Cu	Zn	Ga		Ge	As	Se		Br
Rb	Sr	Y	Zr	Nb	Mo	Tc	Ru	Rh	Pd	Ag	Cd	In		Sn	Sb	Te		I
Cs	Ba	La	Hf	Ta	W	Re	Os	Ir	Pt	Au	Hg	Tl		Pb	Bi	Po		At
Fr	Ra	Ac	Th	Pa	U													

FIG. 34.4. The elements which precipitate as sulphides in group II of the analysis tables.

II. H_2S is passed into the acid solution and throws down the rest of the extremely polarizing cations as sulphide precipitates (see Fig. 34.4). Except for Zn, Ga, In, and Tl all B metals are removed, but the slightly less polarizing metals of the first transition-metal series, i.e. Mn to Ni, remain behind with the pre-transition metals. However, some of the second- and third-row transition metals such as Pd, Pt, and even Mo are also removed. The reason for this separation is shown in Fig. 34.5 which gives the solubility products of the sulphides. Sulphide is a large anion and even on an ionic model it is expected to show some preference for large cations (Chapter 16). However, the extra polarization energy provided by the cations of the B metals and the later or second and third series of transition metals is required if precipitation as sulphide is to occur in acid media.

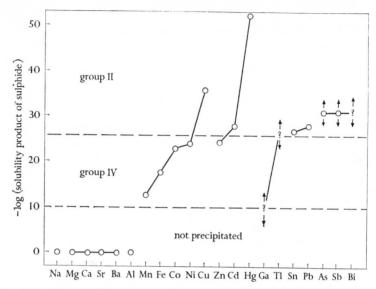

Fig. 34.5. The solubility products of some sulphides in relation to the groups in which they occur in qualitative analysis. Values are appropriate to those valence states normally encountered in analysis. Elements are plotted in order of the Periodic Groups.

The second analytical group now contains a very large number of cations, and a splitting of the group is achieved by redissolving many of the cations as complex sulphides. This may be compared with the procedure producing group I, where a division is made between cations giving insoluble chlorides and those giving higher chloride complexes. A similar division is used in splitting group III into basic and amphoteric hydroxides.

III. The sulphide-precipitation procedure of group II reduces transition-metal ions to their lower valence states. In order to make the next major subdivision of the cations in solution, the precipitation of hydroxides, the oxidation potential in the solution must be deliberately increased so that, for example, iron is in the trivalent state. The oxidation is carried out with strong nitric acid. Ammonium hydroxide is then added to the solution and the pH adjusted to about 7·0 with ammonium chloride: the metals precipitated are illustrated in Fig. 34.6. The alkali-metal, alkaline-earth-metal, and Mn^{2+} hydroxides are soluble at this pH. Furthermore, the high concentration of ammonia in the solution leads to the formation of soluble ammine complexes with the more polarizing cations, e.g.

Co^{2+}, Ni^{2+}, and Zn^{2+}, while Fe^{3+}, Cr^{3+}, and Al^{3+} are precipitated. The hydroxide solubility products and ammine stability constants are shown in Fig. 34.7. The higher-valence metals of the A subgroups such as Ti(IV), Zr(IV), Hf(IV), Ce(III), and U(VI) also come down as hydroxides. The insolubility of the tungsten(VI) hydroxide is such, however, that it precipitates in group I with the chlorides, i.e. at an acidity of around pH 1·0.

Li	Be												B	C	N	O	F
Na	Mg	Al												Si	P	S	Cl
K	Ca	Sc	Ti	V	Cr	Mn	Fe	Co	Ni	Cu	Zn	Ga		Ge	As	Se	Br
Rb	Sr	Y	Zr	Nb	Mo	Tc	Ru	Rh	Pd	Ag	Cd	In		Sn	Sb	Te	I
Cs	Ba	La	Hf	Ta	W	Re	Os	Ir	Pt	Au	Hg	Tl		Pb	Bi	Po	At
Fr	Ra	Ac	Th	Pa	U												

FIG. 34.6. The elements which precipitate as hydroxides in group III of the analysis tables.

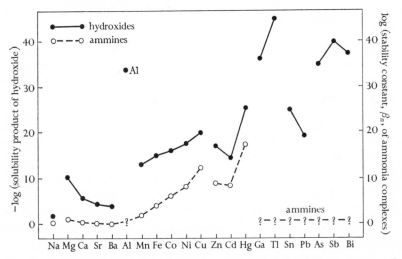

FIG. 34.7. The solubility product of hydroxides and the stability constants of ammines. Values are appropriate to those valence states normally encountered in analysis. Elements are plotted in order of the Periodic Groups.

Thus the third group separates the cations of the early transition-metals, which are precipitated as hydroxides, from the cations of the later first-row transition-metals, which are held in solution as ammines together with the cations of the pre-transition metals.

IV. The separation of the more-polarizing metal cations from those of the pre-transition metals is now readily accomplished by reverting to a more concentrated (i.e. alkaline) solution of sulphide, the polarizable anion used in group II. All the remaining B metals and transition metals are thrown out of solution by H_2S and ammonia (see Fig. 34.8).

Li	Be												B	C	N	O	F
Na	Mg	Al											Si	P	S	Cl	
K	Ca	Sc	Ti	V	Cr	|Mn|	Fe	|Co Ni|	Cu	|Zn|	Ga	Ge	As	Se	Br
Rb	Sr	Y	Zr	Nb	Mo	Tc	Ru	Rh Pd	Ag	Cd	In	Sn	Sb	Te	I
Cs	Ba	La	Hf	Ta	W	Re	Os	Ir Pt	Au	Hg	Tl	Pb	Bi	Po	At
Fr	Ra	Ac	Th	Pa	U										

FIG. 34.8. The elements which precipitate as sulphides in group IV.

The rest of the analysis table makes use of the ionic equilibria already described for the pre-transition metals in section 20.6.

V. Addition of carbonate, a weak-acid oxyanion, separates the divalent from the monovalent cations, apart from lithium which comes down with the former.

VI. The larger monovalent cations may now be identified by precipitation reactions, for example, using very large complex anions. Thus sodium tetraphenylborate, hexachloroplatinate(IV), pyroantimonate, or hexanitritocobaltate(III) can be used to precipitate potassium.

The ammonium ion and substituted ammonium cations also find their way into this last analytical group.

RELATION TO THE PERIODIC TABLE

The group-separation scheme is shown in relation to the Periodic Table in Fig. 34.9. The chemical separation procedures used do not divide the elements in strict accordance with the Groups and rows of the Periodic Table, although there is a reasonably close parallel between analytical groups and Periodic Table Groups. The differences between the two arise, despite the rather regular changes from one Periodic Group to another, because small energy differences can affect chemical equilibria very considerably. For example, it is not at first sight easy to see why the metals chromium, molybdenum, and tungsten should come down in the analytical groups III, II, and I respectively. However, from Fig. 34.5 it is clear why copper behaves differently from the other first-row transition metals, and why the early and later transition metals are found in different analytical groups. In analytical chemistry it is often easier to see why a given procedure has worked *after* it has been devised, and it is dangerous to expect to predict everything from elementary theory. This point becomes clearer in the next sections where the methods used to split the major analytical groups into smaller subgroups are examined. At the same time we can quickly appreciate the major differences between the metals of different parts of the Periodic Table by reference to their behaviour in the analysis tables.

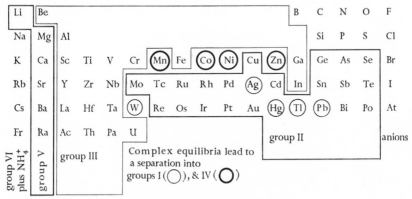

FIG. 34.9. A full group-analysis scheme.

34.3. Separations within analytical groups

GROUP I

The procedure of group I gives insoluble chlorides of silver, thallium(I), mercury(I), and lead(II). Tungsten(VI) also appears as an insoluble hydroxide. Copper(I) and gold(I) chlorides would also have come down in this group but for their ease of oxidation to a higher valence state, where interaction with chloride is either (*a*) too weak (copper(II), compare other *small* (first-row) transition-metal cations), or (*b*) too strong (gold(III), compare other *large* (second-and third-row) transition-metal cations), so that anionic complexes are formed in place of precipitates. The separation of the precipitated chlorides from one another uses the same principles as in the major group separations. First ammonia is added to the chloride precipitate, when silver chloride and tungsten hydroxide dissolve. They are easily distinguished in the filtrate, as addition of iodide yields a silver iodide precipitate while tungsten remains unaffected. Tungsten is a high-valence element of '*a*' character, and shows its strong preference for oxygen by remaining as a tungstate anion in alkaline solution. Silver(I) has '*b*' character and shows a preference for polarizable groups, $I^- > NH_3 > Cl^- > H_2O$. Thus in order to separate the two elements which occur together in analysis more or less by accident, controlled additions of the polarizable neutral molecule, NH_3, and of the polarizable anion, I^-, are used.

The addition of ammonia to the precipitate dissolves two and leaves three metals as precipitates. Of the latter, mercury(I) undergoes a specific solid-state reaction in the presence of ammonia; it disproportionates into mercury(II) and free mercury which turns the precipitate black. The reaction is complex and may be represented by the following equations, the importance of each varying according to the circumstances.

$$Hg_2Cl_2 \rightleftharpoons Hg + HgCl_2$$

$$HgCl_2 + 2NH_3 \rightarrow Hg(NH_3)_2Cl_2\downarrow$$

$$HgCl_2 + 2NH_3 \rightarrow HgNH_2Cl\downarrow + NH_4^+ + Cl^-$$

$$2HgCl_2 + 4NH_3 + H_2O \rightarrow Hg_2NCl,H_2O + 3NH_4^+ + 3Cl^-$$

Thallium(I) and lead(II) can now be removed from the mercury by washing the solid with hot water. This solubility is an example of the more 'a'-like character of the $(N-2)$-valence compounds (Chapter 33). Thallium and lead may be separated subsequently by treating them as though they were typical pre-transition elements, e.g. Cs and Ba. Lead gives an insoluble sulphate and chromate, compare barium, while thallium(I), compare caesium, does not.

GROUP II

The second group is also split into subgroups by a change of conditions, rather than by the use of a new set of reagents. The main method is the re-solution of the sulphides in alkaline ammonium polysulphide. Gold, platinum, molybdenum, selenium, tellurium, arsenic, antimony, and tin give anionic thiocomplexes which are soluble, but copper, lead, mercury, bismuth, and cadmium sulphides do not so redissolve. The parallel between this amphoteric character of the sulphides and the amphoteric character of the oxides is quite strong, as was indicated in Chapter 16. The two subgroups of metals are less easily separated further.

The sulphide complexes, e.g. the thiostannates(IV), can be reprecipitated as sulphides by the addition of dilute hydrochloric acid. If this precipitate is heated with concentrated hydrochloric acid then two of the sulphides, antimony and tin, dissolve as their complex chlorides, while the rest remain undissolved. Antimony and tin can be identified separately later. The other sulphide precipitates require oxidizing conditions to dissolve them. On treatment with potassium chlorate in concentrated hydrochloric acid, they all dissolve as complex chlorides or oxyacid anions. From this solution, the platinum complex chloride, K_2PtCl_6, can be crystallized.

It is important to realize what is being achieved in these series of reactions. Under acid reducing conditions, the affinity of the $(N-2)$-valence ions of tin and antimony for sulphide is not sufficiently high relative to their ability to form chloro-complexes. On the other hand, the heavier and more polarizing cations have a much higher relative affinity for sulphide than chloride. The sulphur is removed from them only by oxidation to SO_2, when they dissolve either as complex chlorides and may be crystallized as such, e.g. Pt, or as complex oxyanions of the high-valence states of the elements. Thus a change of valence state is utilized at this stage of the analysis.

One of the oxidized anions, arsenate, can be specifically removed by the addition of ammonia and magnesium, when magnesium arsenate precipitates. The remaining metals in solution as anions are Au, Mo, Se, and Te. They can be separated in the order of their nobility as elements, for under different reducing conditions the elemental metals can be selectively precipitated leaving only molybdenum in solution. The elements which come out of solution on reduction have typical colours (see Chapter 6). Such colour reactions always help very greatly in the identification of elements. The ease of reduction is related to the position of the elements in the electrochemical series (see Chapter 9), although account must be taken of the formation of complex ions and of the pH of the solution under consideration. The precipitation of the elementary metals is another example of a change of valence. Separation by changing valence state is thus represented in this group by three different reactions, reduction by $H_2S \rightarrow$ sulphide of low or intermediate valence; oxidation $\rightarrow$ high valence; strong reduction $\rightarrow$ metal.

GROUP III

The hydroxides precipitating in group III may be divided into two subgroups, those of Fe, Ti, Zr, Th, and Ce on the one hand and those of Cr, V, Al, and U on the other. The two subgroups differ in that Cr, V, and U in their higher valence states and aluminium in valence state III are more strongly acidic and therefore dissolve in alkaline solution. The separation procedure is to add sodium hydroxide and hydrogen peroxide, converting Cr to chromate, V to vanadate, U to peroxyuranate, and Al to aluminate, while keeping the other metals as hydroxide precipitates. After filtration, addition of a lead salt to the solution brings down lead chromate and vanadate, leaving only aluminium and uranium in solution. The individual metals in the pairs are readily identified by their colour reactions; see below.

Colour reactions are also the basis of further differentiation in the group of alkali-insoluble hydroxides. Fe^{3+} gives a colour with a wide range of reagents, while the 4-valent ions do not. The elements from the subgroup Ti, Zr, Th, and Ce are much more difficult to separate from one another, and for details the reader must consult a treatise on analytical chemistry.

In each of the first three major groups, a close control of conditions allows a separation between those metals which form anionic complexes with excess reagent, i.e. with Cl^-, $SH^-(S_n^{2-})$, and OH^-, and those which do not. It is the more strongly acidic elements which dissolve in each case. The subdivision may be represented as in Table 34.II.

TABLE 34.II. *Main separations in analytical groups* I, II, *and* III

	group I Very polarizing cations plus chloride	*group* II Moderately polarizing cations plus sulphide	*group* III More weakly polarizing cations plus hydroxide
Low-valence or large metal ions which give precipitates	Ag(I), Hg(I), Tl(I), Pb(II)	Cu(II), Cd(II), Hg(II), Pb(II), Bi(III)	Ce(IV), Ti(IV), Zr(IV), Th(IV), Fe(III), Cr(III)
High-valence metal ions, which give complexes only or dissolve in excess anion	Pt(IV), Au(III), Hg(II)	Mo(IV), Pt(IV), Sn(IV), As(III), Sb(III), Se(IV), Te(IV)	Al(III), V(V)

Acidic character develops towards the upper right-hand corner (non-metals) of the Periodic Table and in high-valence states.

GROUPS IV, V, AND VI

In group IV the procedure of group II is reversed. The sulphides which were precipitated in alkaline media are dissolved in acid. Of the four, manganese and zinc redissolve but cobalt and nickel do not. This insolubility of the cobalt and nickel sulphides has been the cause of much speculation, as these sulphides are not, of course, precipitated under acid conditions (group II). It has been suggested that polymorphic changes occur in the precipitate to give less soluble forms, but the most likely explanation is that in the presence of air the precipitates are oxidized. In support of this, is the observation that CoS remains soluble in acid indefinitely if air is excluded. Identification of the individual metals within the separated pairs is quite readily achieved, see below.

Separations in groups V and VI are based on the selective pairing of large anions with large cations and of small anions with small cations as was stressed in section 20.6.

34.4. Identification of metals

At the next stage of an analysis the number of possible unknowns will have been reduced to a very few: for example, in group IV there could be a precipitate of either nickel or cobalt sulphide. Clearly either some even more refined precipitation method is needed or a direct and, at this level, specific test. Colour tests are usually chosen as they are quick and simple. Here we shall indicate the reasons for the use of certain types of reagent.

GROUP I

Both mercury and lead give coloured iodide precipitates. HgI_2 is red and PbI_2 is golden with a characteristic crystalline form which is seen as 'spangles'. The silver cation can be identified by the blood-red silver chromate precipitate. The lead(II) and mercury(II) tests are based on the charge-transfer of electrons to the oxidizing cation from the reducing anion. The $(N-2)$-valence B-metal cations, Tl^+ and Pb^{2+}, have a lower electron affinity than the similar N-valence B cations Ag^+ and Hg^{2+}, and the former therefore do not give strongly coloured precipitates with polarizable anions such as iodide. The peaks of their absorption bands are in the ultra-violet. The very strong colour of silver chromate is probably due to the opposite charge transfer, i.e. of an electron from Ag^+, which could also explain the deep colours of thallium(I) hexacyanoferrate(III) and silver hexachloro-iridate(IV).

GROUP II

The colours of the sulphides of the metals in this group have been described in Chapter 16. The charge-transfer bands are not sufficiently characteristic to distinguish between tin and arsenic sulphides, yellow-brown, and copper and bismuth sulphides (black). On the other hand, use can be made of the chocolate colour (charge-transfer band) of copper(II) hexacyanoferrate(II), or of the fairly strong blue colour (d–d transition) of copper(II) in ammonia. Possibly both CuI_2 and BiI_3 are black (charge-transfer) but copper(II) oxidizes iodide to iodine which can easily be recognized. Bismuth iodide is soluble as a yellow BiI_4^- anion. Arsenic is identified by the action of copper(II) salts on an arsenite which produces a green precipitate. The green colour is due to absorption of both red (copper(II) d–d band) and blue (charge-transfer band).

In group IIb there are some eight elements. We have already shown how reduction to the metal can be used to identify Au, Se, and Te. Platinum, which is separated as potassium hexachloroplatinate(IV), is also easily identified for this complex reacts with iodide to give a deep red-brown complex. The formation of such a coloured complex is typical of metals with 'b' character. In the reaction, iodide displaces chloride for the stability sequence of halide complexes is $I^- > Br^- > Cl^- > F^-$, the reverse of that found for class 'a' metals. The colour is due to electron transfer to the central cation. Molybdenum is identified by its colour reaction with thiocyanate in reducing solutions (e.g. in the presence of $SnCl_2$). The colour is reminiscent of that of iron(III) thiocyanate complexes and is due to electron transfer to the central oxidizing Mo(V). An alternative test is the precipitation of molybdenum blue on adding reducing agents to a molybdate solution. The blue colour has the same origin as prussian blue—charge transfer between different oxidation states of the same element, here Mo(V) and Mo(VI). An analogous test is also used for tungsten.

Lastly, arsenic, antimony, and tin must be distinguished from one another. The subgroup has already been split in two by the greater stability of the halide complexes of the heavier metals. Arsenic can be confirmed either by precipitation as magnesium arsenate, by the colour of its sulphide (not very satisfactory), or by Marsh's test. This test uses the fact that arsenic forms a moderately-stable volatile hydride which can be readily destroyed in a hot tube to give a 'metallic' mirror. The mirror is soluble in oxidizing agents such as hypochlorite giving arsenate. The corresponding test with antimony differs from the arsenic test only in the last stage—the antimony mirror does not dissolve in hypochlorite. Tin and antimony can be distinguished either by the reducing action of tin(II) salts on mercury(II) chloride or by the colours of the sulphides. The reduction of $HgCl_2$ by tin(II) and not by antimony(III) illustrates how the relative stability of the N- and $(N-2)$-valence states is changing among the B metals, Hg (Group II and last row in the Periodic Table), Sn (Group IV), and Sb (Group V).

Both d–d and charge-transfer transitions may therefore be used to identify cations. It is worth noting that the positions of these bands are very dependent upon the ligand bound to the cation. The band position of a d–d transition is related to the spectrochemical series, and the band position of a charge-transfer band to the redox properties of the ligand. Only transition-metal cations give the rather weak colours due to d–d

transitions, while both B-metal and transition-metal cations give rise to charge-transfer spectra.

GROUP III

Here again the simple colour tests are most effective. Chromium can be oxidized to chromate (yellow) (note that the higher oxidation states of molybdenum and tungsten are virtually colourless), and iron in the iron(III) state reacts with reducing groups such as hexacyanoferrate(II) (blue), thiocyanate (red), and phenolate (red) to give a whole series of highly characteristic charge-transfer colours. Aluminium is usually identified through its amphoteric character. To confirm the presence of this cation, which shows no charge-transfer bands of any utility in any of its complexes, the element is precipitated with a phenolate dye and a characteristic lake produced. Lake formation is a general reaction of small and high-valence cations. Lakes owe their colours to internal transitions of the dye-stuff. Thus such a 'spot' test cannot be used in the presence of Ti, Zr, Th, or Ce, which also gives lakes readily with phenolate dyes. However, interference from these elements has already been prevented by the group-separation procedures. In fact confusion can only occur with uranyl(VI), but UO_2^{2+} has many other colour reactions, e.g. with hexacyanoferrate(II), and is easily distinguished from aluminium.

Chromium may be distinguished from vanadium because peroxychromates (blue) are soluble in ethers while peroxyvanadates (red) are not. The intense colours are again due to electron transfer from the peroxide anion to the central metal. No such easy tests distinguish between the metals Zr, Ti, and Th, which are more stable in their higher oxidation states, and similar colours are not formed with the heavy elements of either Group V or Group VI, i.e. Nb, Ta, Mo, and W. Another example of the change in colour of complexes down Group V is provided by the tannin complexes: V, dark precipitate as with many phenolates, e.g. 8-hydroxyquinoline; Nb, pale yellow-brown; and Ta, nearly colourless. The colours of the complexes are due to electron transfer from the reducing phenolate group, and the bands move to a shorter wavelength as the oxidizing character of the cation falls. Oxidizing strengths, Chapter 23, follow the orders V > Nb > Ta; Cr > Mo > W; Ti > Hf and Zr. The heaviest elements give few colour reactions.

GROUP IV

The elements in group IV are manganese, zinc, cobalt, and nickel. Two transition-metal cations have been separated from the series Mn^{2+}, Fe^{2+},

Co^{2+}, Ni^{2+}, Cu^{2+}, and Zn^{2+} by using the high polarizing power of one of them, Cu^{2+} (group II), and by using the ease of oxidation of the other, Fe^{2+} to Fe^{3+} (group III). It now remains to distinguish between the two elements which form black sulphide precipitates, cobalt and nickel, and between the two which form very weakly coloured or colourless precipitates, manganese and zinc. Again advantage is taken of the same two properties, polarizing power and ease of oxidation. Thus the hydroxide of zinc is amphoteric while that of manganese is not. This distinction may be associated with the higher polarizing power of the divalent B-metal cation relative to that of the divalent cation with a half-filled d sub-shell and formed from an element in the middle of the first transition series. Zinc has very few colour reactions in solution: it has no possibility of d–d transitions and the charge-transfer bands are at high energy, because of the low stability of both $Zn(I)$ and $Zn(III)$ relative to $Zn(II)$. Solid ZnO changes from colourless to yellow on heating, but this is thought to be due to the production of defects in the zinc oxide lattice: zinc oxide is a moderate semiconductor. Manganese(II) hydroxide, even without heating, turns brown due to its ready oxidation to a higher valence state, here $Mn(IV)$. Oxidation with bismuthate to a still higher oxidation state (VII) yields the purple permanganate. Its colour is probably due to charge transfer. The heavier elements in Group VII, e.g. rhenium, do not have such highly coloured oxyanions.

Cobalt and nickel are also readily distinguished once their sulphides have been oxidized and the metals obtained as simple hydrated cations. The test solution, presumed to contain either or both nickel(II) and cobalt(II), is made alkaline with ammonia, which in excess precipitates neither hydroxide, as was found in group III. In the presence of air much of the cobalt in solution will be converted to cobalt(III) ammines. On addition of dimethylglyoxime a red precipitate of the nickel chelate is formed if nickel is present, but if only cobalt is present there is no precipitation although the solution goes yellow. Large quantities of cobalt interfere with the nickel test and may be effectively removed by the formation of the very stable hexacyanocobaltate(III) ion.

The specificity of this action has been brought about by a combination of the properties introduced by the different electron structures of cobalt and nickel. Cobalt is easier to oxidize and $Co(III)(dimethylglyoximate)_2$ is a singly-charged cation soluble in water. On the other hand, the nickel complex, $Ni(II)(dimethylglyoximate)_2$, is uncharged with but weak coordination either above or below the plane of the complex. It is a low-spin nickel complex so that solvent molecules are not strongly bound to it at right angles to the molecular plane. The precipitate is insoluble, the insolubility being increased by a slight Ni—Ni interaction between molecules in the lattice. Its colour is also due to the change of spin state. High-spin nickel(II) ions have charge-transfer bands far in the ultra-violet, corresponding to electron transfer from ligand to metal ion. Both Ni(I) and Ni(III) are very unstable relative to the high-spin cation. On the other hand, low-spin nickel(II) is in a promoted electron state on its way toward Ni(III). Charge-transfer of an electron from this high energy state *to the ligand* is now possible with the absorption of energy just on the edge of the visible. Nickel dimethylglyoxime, like a number of other low-spin nickel complexes, is red. It can be further oxidized by hypochlorite to a soluble Ni(III) or Ni(IV) complex.

Cobalt is precipitated as Co(III) by α-nitroso-β-naphthol. The precipitate is brown. It is distinguished from the corresponding nickel precipitate by its insolubility in HCl. It is extremely fortunate, both for the utility of this test and that for nickel using dimethylglyoxime, that iron has already been removed. Iron(II) reacts with nitrosophenols to give an intense green colour and it reacts with dimethylglyoxime in solution to give an intense red colour. Both colours are examples of electron transfer from the cation to an unsaturated ligand. The higher energies of the colours of Ni(II) ($\lambda_{max} \leqslant 450$ mμ) and Co(III) ($\lambda_{max} < 400$ mμ) indicate the greater difficulty of oxidizing them as compared with Fe(II) ($\lambda_{max} > 500$ mμ).

A more highly specific colour test for cobalt uses the lower oxidation state. As was pointed out in Chapter 24, cobalt(II) complexes readily go over into a tetrahedral geometry. A tetrahedron has no centre of inversion so that the d–d transitions become of greatly heightened intensity. If a cobalt(II) salt is dissolved in concentrated hydrochloric acid, an intense blue $[CoCl_4]^{2-}$ complex is formed. Again addition of concentrated thiocyanate solution to cobalt(II) salts gives the intense blue $[Co(CNS)_4]^{2-}$, which is readily precipitated as blue $HgCo(CNS)_4$. Neither nickel nor iron give similar colour tests, though Fe^{3+} interferes as it forms an intensely red solution with thiocyanate (charge-transfer from the reducing thiocyanate anion to the oxidizing Fe^{3+} cation).

GROUPS V AND VI

Identification of pre-transition metals can hardly depend upon specific colour reactions, for both higher and lower oxidation states than that of the Group are very inaccessible (no visible charge-transfer bands), and

there are no internal transitions such as those in compounds of the lanthanides (f–f) and transition metals (d–d), which make it so easy to follow
the latter. Some of the complexes are coloured due to the colour of the
anion. For example, the rhodizonates of Ba^{2+} and Sr^{2+} are red-yellow
while rhodizonic acid itself is yellow. In general, selective precipitation is
the main means of separation and identification. Fortunately there is a fair
selectivity of action even with oxyacid anions, so that the problem is not
too difficult. Magnesium precipitates with weak-acid anions such as hydroxide, while its salts with sulphate and chromate, anions of strong acids,
are soluble. The sulphates of strontium and barium are more insoluble
than that of calcium, while the chromate of barium is distinctly more insoluble than that of strontium. A suitable form of group analysis can be
based on these tests. Most of the precipitates are colourless. Where colour
is produced, as in the hexanitritocobaltate(III) and the hexachloroplati-
nate(IV) tests for potassium, this is due to the d–d transitions of the central
cation inside the anion. These transitions are not markedly perturbed by
the alkali-metal cations.

34.5. Organic reagents for metals

SELECTIVE FORMATION OF COMPLEXES

Various organic reagents may also be used to distinguish metals by
selective precipitation, extraction, or elution from a chromatographic
column. 8-hydroxyquinoline (8-quinolinol) is an example of a fairly general
precipitation reagent. Its low selectivity is illustrated in Figs. 34.10 and
34.11, which also demonstrate the additional selectivity which can be
achieved by adjustment of pH. Cupferron is an example of a much more
selective reagent as is shown by its behaviour as a precipitant, summarized
in Fig. 34.12. Thus 8-hydroxyquinoline is a more useful 'scavenger' reagent
than cupferron, while cupferron is of more value when one metal is to be
estimated in the presence of a lot of others.

In Table 34.III reagents are listed according to their selectivity. The
obvious feature of the table is the increasing selectivity achieved by increase
in the polarizability of the coordinating atoms. Roughly the order is

$$R{-}S^- > R{-}NH^- > R{-}NH_2 \geqslant RO^- > RCO_2^-.$$

Very high selectivity is observed in the reaction of the Sn(II) complex,
$SnCl_3^-$, as a donor to the extreme acceptor cations such as Pt^{4+}. The low
selectivity of RCO_2^- is probably due to the dependence of the free energy
of formation of its complexes on entropy changes, the selectivity resting

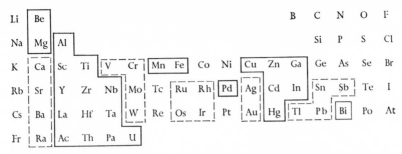

FIG. 34.10. Elements completely (inside full lines) or partially (inside dotted lines) precipitated by 8-hydroxyquinoline from a solution of pH ~ 5.

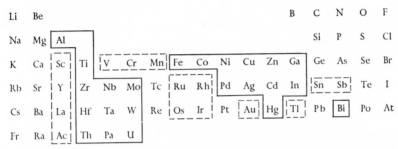

FIG. 34.11. Elements completely (inside full lines) or partially (inside dotted lines) precipitated by 8-hydroxyquinoline in ammonia solution, pH ~ 8.

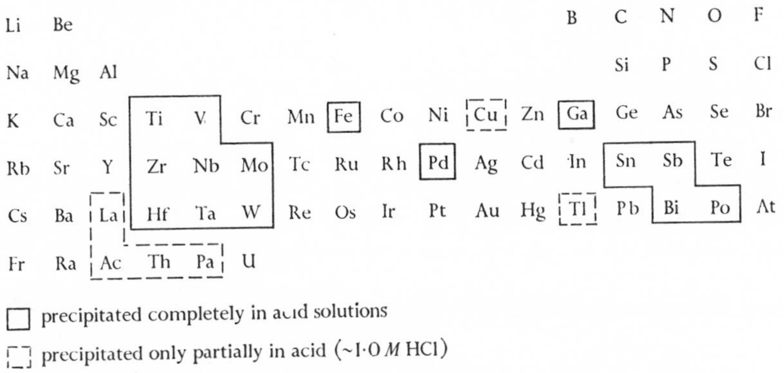

Li	Be											B	C	N	O	F
Na	Mg	Al										Si	P	S	Cl	
K	Ca	Sc	Ti	V	Cr	Mn	Fe	Co	Ni	Cu	Zn	Ga	Ge	As	Se	Br
Rb	Sr	Y	Zr	Nb	Mo	Tc	Ru	Rh	Pd	Ag	Cd	In	Sn	Sb	Te	I
Cs	Ba	La	Hf	Ta	W	Re	Os	Ir	Pt	Au	Hg	Tl	Pb	Bi	Po	At
Fr	Ra	Ac	Th	Pa	U											

☐ precipitated completely in acid solutions

☐ precipitated only partially in acid (~1·0 M HCl)

FIG. 34.12. Elements precipitated by cupferron ($C_6H_5N(NO)ONH_4$).

in the heat term being low. Entropy changes are very closely related to the charges and sizes of cations, but changes in these parameters alone do not lead to such selectivity as arises from changes in electron affinities.

Apart from the gross changes in the immediate coordinating atoms of a ligand, organic chemistry readily makes it possible to introduce subtle

TABLE 34.III. *Organic reagents in increasing order of selectivity*

Reagent	Coordinating atoms	Elements
EDTA	4O, 2N	most metals (pre-transition, transition, or B)
Acetylacetone	2O	most metals (pre-transition, transition, or B)
8-hydroxyquinoline (oxine) . .	O, N	most metals (pre-transition, transition, or B)
Oximes	2N	Ni, Pd, Cu, Fe, and many other transition metals
Nitrosophenols	N, O	Co, Pd, Cu, Fe, and many other transition metals
Cupferron ($C_6H_5N(NO)ONH_4$) .	N, O	Fe, V, Ti, Zr, Sn, U, and other transition metals
Thionalide ($C_{10}H_7.NH.CO.CH_2.SH$)	S, N	Cu, Ag, Hg, Bi, Ru, Tl
Dithizone ($C_6H_5.NH.NH.CS.N{:}N.C_6H_5$).	S, N	Pb, Cu, Zn, Hg, Tl, Cd
Thiocarbamates	S, N	Cu, Bi, Zn, Pb

changes in the character of these atoms themselves. Nitrogen as a co-ordinating partner is very different in the following groupings:

$$R_3N \text{ (amines)}, \qquad {>}N \text{ (pyridines)}, \qquad {=}N{-}OH \text{ (oximes)},$$

$$R{-}NO \text{ (nitroso groups)}, \qquad R{-}\overset{\displaystyle NO}{N}{-}OH \text{ (nitroso-hydroxylamines)},$$

$$R{-}N{=}N{-}R \text{ (azo groups)}, \qquad {-}C{\overset{\displaystyle S}{\underset{\displaystyle NH_2}{}}} \text{ (thio-amides)}.$$

Selectivity is also introduced by the ability of the unsaturated reagents to act as acceptors as well as donors. Thus, in general, the unsaturated ligands combine preferentially with transition-metal ions. The combination with a transition-metal ion can be exceedingly selective for the following reasons. (1) The interaction may force certain cations into low-spin states, e.g. dipyridyl forces Fe^{2+} into the diamagnetic configuration t_{2g}^6, but does not have the same effect on Ni^{2+}. (2) The geometry of the resulting complex may be a more or less specific property of a very small group of cations, e.g. Ni^{2+} goes into a *planar* 4-coordinate low-spin complex with dimethyl-glyoxime. This complex coordinates only extremely weakly with out of plane (z-axis) ligands. As a consequence the complex is insoluble. The selectivity is increased by metal–metal bonding in the crystal.

Selectivity for polarizing metal ions is readily achieved in organic reagents by using polarizable ligand atoms. Selectivity for highly-charged cations can also be achieved by using relatively weakly polarizable ligand atoms, L, provided that the ligand acid HL has a low acid dissociation constant. Only highly-charged cations will then be able to react with the ligand in acid solution for they alone will form sufficiently stable complexes. The main reagents involved are polyphenols.

Organic reagents can also be designed to take advantage of the selectivity introduced by steric hindrance. An example illustrates the general principle. *Ortho*-phenanthroline reacts with Fe^{2+} and Cu^+ to give deeply coloured complexes. If the reaction of one of the cations can be prevented then the other can be estimated without interference. The geometry of the complexes are: $[Fe(phenan)_3]^{2+}$ octahedral, $[Cu(phenan)_2]^+$ tetrahedral. As the Cu^+ ion is also much larger than the Fe^{2+} ion, the packing in the coordination sphere of the former is much less dense. Introduction of methyl groups into the 2 and 9 positions in phenanthroline (I) or better the use of diquinolyl (II) increases steric hindrance near the cation, so that

(I)   (II)

only the Cu^+ complex forms. Thus diquinolyl is a specific reagent for copper in the presence of iron.

SPECIFIC COLORIMETRIC REAGENTS

The formation of precipitates or of complex ions is a selective property. A maximum in the absorption of light at a given wavelength is virtually a specific property of a particular complex. In Chapter 29 it was stressed that there were three types of transition of inorganic complexes which could lead to intense absorption. (1) Certain internal transitions of the organic ligand. The colour of the cobalt(III) α-nitroso-β-naphthol complex is due to such a transition. (2) Internal *d–d* transitions of complexes which do not have a centre of inversion, e.g. tetrahedral complexes. The transitions are particularly intense in covalent complexes and when the *d–d* bands are close in energy to charge-transfer transitions. The colour of the blue $Co(py)_2Cl_2$ is due to such a transition. (3) Certain charge-transfer transitions. These are probably the most important.

Unsaturated nitrogen ligands, e.g. dipyridyl, oximes, and nitroso compounds, are the most common electron-acceptor reagents. The colours of the complexes can be related to the energy of certain transitions of the central-metal ions involved. This is shown in Fig. 34.13 where the energy required

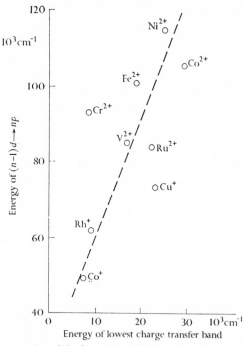

FIG. 34.13. The energies of the lowest $(n-1)d$ to np (*gas-ion*) transitions plotted against charge-transfer band energies of dipyridyl complexes.

to excite a d electron from the ground state of the free gas ion appropriate to the complex to the lowest-lying p orbital is plotted against the energy of the charge-transfer band. The p orbital overlaps and is stabilized by the π^* orbitals of the ligand. Colour is thus produced by the ability of the ligand (1) to force the cation into a low-spin configuration, e.g. t_{2g}^6 for Fe^{2+}, and (2) to offer a low-lying acceptor orbital. While inorganic ligands such as CN^- are effective in producing the required ground state they do not offer low-lying π^* orbitals. Reagents which act as electron donors can be discussed in very similar terms.

OTHER CONFIRMATORY TESTS

A number of solid-state reactions are carried out either as preliminary or confirmatory tests. An example is the borax-bead test, in which metal cations are dissolved in molten borax in either an oxidizing or a reducing flame. The change from oxidizing to reducing conditions alters the oxidation state of the cation in the melt so that there are two distinct colour tests. Cobalt is an example where no colour change is observed on change of conditions; it always gives a deep-blue borax bead. The colour implies that the cobalt is trapped in a tetrahedral hole. In this symmetry Co^{3+} ions are exceedingly unstable, and no doubt this explains why it is that oxidizing conditions in the flame do not convert the element to Co(III). Iron is quite different. In the reducing flame it gives a very pale-green colour, but in oxidizing conditions a deeper brown coloration is observed. Here there is a change from a weak d–d transition in iron(II) to a charge-transfer transition in the iron(III) complex: the d–d transitions in high-spin Fe^{3+} are spin-forbidden. A simple test for copper is very similar. In the oxidizing flame it is present as Cu^{2+} and gives a bead which is green from absorption of both blue (charge-transfer) and red (d–d spectrum). In the reducing flame the copper bead is colourless due to the absence of transitions in copper(I) oxide complexes, or red due to the formation of copper metal.

Charcoal-block reduction is merely a test of the ability of carbon to reduce a metal oxide at a temperature below about 1000 °C. The thermodynamics of this type of reaction has already been discussed in Chapter 7. Only the more noble metals such as lead and mercury can be detected in this way. Simple flame tests in which a metal is volatilized in a Bunsen flame are of little use, as few compounds are sufficiently volatile to give good tests. Moreover, many elements give flames of somewhat similar appearance. However, by the use of flame photometers, involving very high-temperature flames, it is possible to make this apparently clumsy qualitative testing into an excellent quantitative method.

PART B

34.6. Occurrence of the metals—major constituents

THE MAJOR PARTING

The elements near the surface of the earth are distributed very largely between different solid phases. There is a gas phase of relatively small mass which consists mainly of N_2 and O_2 and a large liquid phase which is mostly water. However, although the gas and liquid phases are of enormous importance in other parts of chemistry, the essential problem of occurrence is one of the solid phases. It is customary to regard it as basically a thermodynamic problem, in which the observed distribution of elements in different combinations is a result of the relative free energies of their reactions at some unspecified temperature and at an early state in the formation of the earth. This equilibrium distribution has been modified, not necessarily at equilibrium, by changes mostly of temperature with time. Thus if we are to understand the crust of the earth we need to discover the history of the earth's formation.

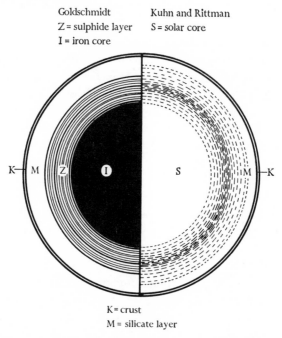

FIG. 34.14. Possible layers of material in the earth (after Gibson).

In detail this is an impossible task. There is as yet even no general agreement about the composition of the interior of the earth. Two possibilities which have been suggested are illustrated in Fig. 34.14. One of them is based on an iron core, the other on a solar H/He core at very high pressure. The first is the more probable. However, both descriptions agree that around the core there is a moderately-deep silicate layer and then the earth's crust. As the problem to be considered is the occurrence and distribution of the elements *available* to us, it is the crust with which we are concerned and not the earth as a whole. The composition of the earth's crust is given in Table 34.IV. The first phase of development of the crust was probably the formation of a mixed molten silicate phase, with some sulphide present in solution or as a dispersed liquid phase. As there was little free oxygen, but both water and sulphide were present, the solution must have been moderately reducing, so that it is probable that there would also be present a small molten-metal phase of the more noble metals. As the total mass cooled the different phases, silicate, sulphide, and metal, separated. This division is the major 'parting' or division of minerals.

TABLE 34.IV. *Relative abundances in the earth's crust by weight (after Gibson)*

O	50%	K	2·4
Si	26	Mg	1·9
Al	7·5	H	0·9
Fe	4·7	Ti	0·6
Ca	3·4	Cl	0·2
Na	2·6	P	0·1

The abundances of the remaining elements are conveniently expressed in g/ton (1 kg/ton = 0·1 per cent) of crustal rock: less than 1 kg/ton: Mn, C, S, Ba, Cr, N, F, Zr, Zn, Ni, Sr, V; less than 100 g/ton: Cu, Y, W, Li, Rb, Hf, Ce, Pb, Th, Nd, Co, B; less than 10 g/ton: Mo, Br, Sn, Sc, Be, La, As, Ar, Ge; less than 1g/ton: Se, Nb, Sb, U, Ta, Ga, In, Tl, Cd; mg/ton: I, Pt metals, Ag, Bi, Hg, Te, Au, noble gases; mg/1000 tons: Ra, Ac, Po.

That such a division could take place has been demonstrated in the laboratory. Furthermore, in the laboratory experiments individual metals choose to go largely into the silicate, the sulphide, or the metal phase roughly in agreement with their parting in nature. The preferential concentration of the elements is shown in Fig. 34.15. For the reaction

$$M'S + M''\text{silicate} \leftrightharpoons M''S + M'\text{silicate}$$

the order of $\Delta G°$ seems to parallel fairly closely the electrochemical series. Elements more electropositive than iron in the series occur largely in the silicate phase, while elements less electropositive occur largely either in the sulphide or in the metallic phase. The silicates formed are extremely difficult to use for the extraction of the elements. The main economic sources of metals have been produced by erosion. From the 5 per cent of the igneous silicate rock which has suffered weathering comes something like 90 per cent of the minerals which are readily workable. A number of metals are extracted from ores of the sulphide phase.

OCCURRENCE AND EXTRACTION

We shall now discuss the occurrence of individual elements in more detail, examining extraction processes simultaneously. The metals will be considered in the order of the Periodic Groups, that is, in almost the opposite order from that in the analytical tables.

The elements of Group IA are the most difficult to obtain free from water or anions, and in general, across the Periodic Table from Group IA, the methods of extraction used become less and less powerful. The Group IA metals either occur as simple chlorides, NaCl, KCl, and RbCl (strong-acid anion), or in silicates such as pollucite (Cs) and lepidolite (Li). The Group IIA metals are generally found as phosphates, carbonates, or silicates (weak-acid anions). However, the larger cations also occur with strong-acid anions, e.g. witherite, $BaSO_4$. Quite generally these elements can be

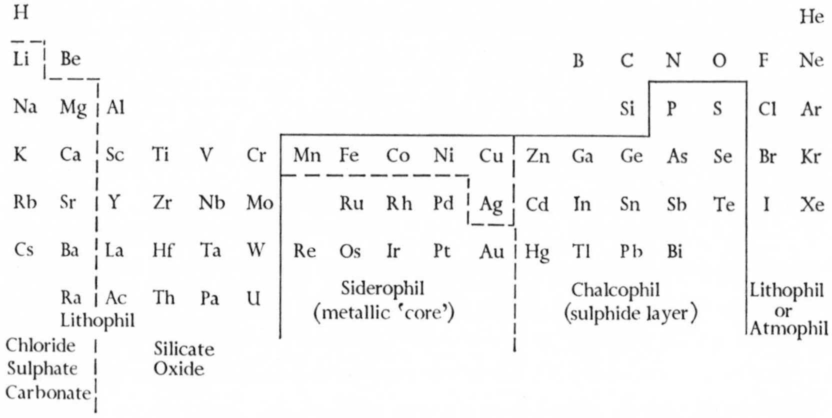

FIG. 34.15. Distribution of the elements.

obtained from a suitable conducting halide melt once acid extraction has removed the aluminium and silicon. The electrolysis must be carried out in the absence of water because of the reactivity of the metals. It is possible to use metals in Groups II and III to displace anions from metals of Groups I and II respectively.

e.g.
$$2RbCl + Ca \rightarrow 2Rb + CaCl_2,$$

and
$$3BaO + 2Al \rightarrow Al_2O_3 + 3Ba.$$

In Groups III to VIIA of the Periodic Table none of the metals is found as a carbonate and the most usual anions are now phosphate and silicate. However, two other classes of compound occur with the metal (1) in an anion, and (2) in an oxide. Well-known examples are (1) borates, alumino-silicates, vanadates, chromates, molybdates, and tungstates, where the element is found in the oxyanion, and (2) pitchblende (U), thorite (Th), ilmenite (Ti), zircon (Zr), chromite (Cr), and pyrolusite (Mn), where the element is found as a cation in a simple oxide. In monazite the lanthanides occur as cations in a phosphate. The elements are extracted from these ores by electrolysis or by displacement of the anion from the metals by a pre-transition metal or by carbon (see Chapter 7). Many of the oxides must be converted to chlorides with acid before either extraction procedure can be made satisfactory.

These remarks cover about half the elements in the Periodic Table. All these elements tend to occur as oxides, oxyacid anions, or with oxyacid anions. In analysis the same elements are generally found either in group III as hydroxides, group V as carbonates and sulphates, or in group VI as residual soluble cations. That the soluble cations are found as chlorides in nature is not surprising for these deposits developed from the evaporation of aqueous solutions. They are the 'residual' elements in solution just as in analytical procedures. It is the small high-valence cations, Al^{3+}, V^{5+}, and W^{6+}, which occur as anions, while the lower-valence cations of elements in both immediately earlier and later Groups in the Periodic Table occur as simple oxides. The former are separated from the latter in group analysis by using these amphoteric properties. While the most electropositive cations from the beginning of each row occur with oxyanions as salts, the less electropositive cations following Groups VIA and VIIA occur increasingly as sulphides.

In the analysis tables, most B metals and most of the later metals in all three transition series are precipitated as sulphides. These are the elements which also occur as sulphides, e.g. Fe, Co, Ni, Cu, Zn, Cd, and Hg. There are but two major exceptions. Much tin occurs as the oxide, cassiterite, and the platinum metals occur native in the alloy osmiridium. The platinum metals together with gold are of extreme nobility. All these elements are very easily obtained from their ores, for sulphur can be removed by roasting and the oxide can be reduced by heating with carbon. In detail some processes must differ greatly from others due to the temperature required for the reactions to take place, or because of the level of purity required. In order to obtain extremely pure metals it is frequent practice to use an electrolytic procedure.

During crystallization of the different phases there must have been a further segregation of the elements. Thus a fractionation would occur on separation of the numerous solid silicates from their more or less homogeneous melts. The fractionation of the major constituents, Fe, Al, Ca, Na, Mg, and K, was largely based on the ease of isomorphous replacement. Ions of approximately the same size, e.g. Mg^{2+}, Fe^{3+}, Al^{3+}, and (Si^{4+}), can readily be taken into the same lattice site in a silicate. Larger ions are taken up either in different structures or different lattice sites of the same structure, e.g. such ions as Ca^{2+}, Na^+, and K^+. It is probable that fractionation did not only occur in melts but also in the cooling of aqueous silicate solutions. Silica and silicates are soluble in water under high pressure and at a temperature high but below its critical point. The order of solubility would largely control selective deposition in this case. The problem of the distribution of trace elements in, for example, the silicates is taken up in the following section.

EROSION

We have already mentioned (Chapter 17) that many phosphate, carbonate, carbon (coal), sulphur, and nitrate deposits are due to the cycle of chemicals in living organisms. It is possible that all the oxygen of the air has this origin too. Even greater effects have been produced by weathering. In general weathering selectively extracts the more basic ions, Na^+, Ca^{2+}, Fe^{2+}, Mg^{2+}, and leaves the more acidic (insoluble oxides) in the rock, e.g. Ti^{4+}, Fe^{3+}, and Al^{3+} silicates. The process, which is reminiscent of the solution of material at the beginning of analysis, is outlined in Fig. 34.16.

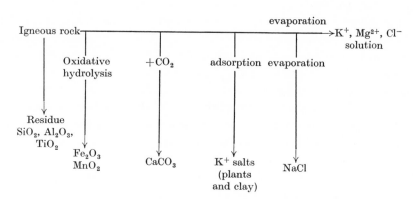

FIG. 34.16. Chart of weathering of minerals.

The scheme shows that erosion effects a partial separation of the elements. It is this separation which makes the deposits formed from the erosion of rock of such value. In particular the elements, silicon, aluminium, and titanium, which make extraction processes troublesome and all of which are quite common, are removed from such elements as iron, manganese, calcium, and sodium.

34.7. Trace-element distribution

IN SILICATES

Perhaps the most detailed investigation of the fractionation of trace elements during the deposition of a mineral is that carried out on the basic magma of the Skaergaard intrusion, Greenland (Wager and Mitchell, *Geochim. Cosmochim. Acta*, 1951, **1**, 129). We shall consider the formation from the melt of the solid silicate phase of this magma, examining the inclusion of trace elements. The time sequence of the solidification is fairly well established. Thus the deposition of trace elements is illustrated in Figs. 34.17 and 34.18. A downward curvature to a line represents preferential removal of the element or a partition coefficient of that element favouring the solid rather than the liquid. The orders of deposition include:

$$Ni^{2+} > Co^{2+} > Mn^{2+} > Fe^{2+} > Cu^{2+}$$

and
$$Cr^{3+} > V^{3+} > Sc^{3+} > Ga^{3+} > Fe^{3+}.$$

The ions normally go into octahedral holes in the silicate. We can give the following explanation of these orders.

The uptake of an ion into a crystal from a melt can be thought of as being characterized by (1) an increase in average coordination number to a fixed value for all the atoms, and (2) a decrease of the interatomic distances. The two terms are consistent with a greater bond energy, lower heat content, on formation of the solid phase. This is generally observed. The change in heat content can be further analysed. An element which is particularly stabilized in an octahedral coordination site will be expected to gain somewhat in stability (ligand-field energy) on passing from a melt of irregular coordination number to a regular solid which provides such an octahedral hole. Again, ions which have the largest ligand-field energies will gain most in energy on transfer from the liquid to the solid phase due to the shortening of interatomic distances. Ligand-field energies are very dependent upon these distances. Now it has been established in Chapter 24 that the ligand-field energies of d electrons are important in the stabilization of transition-metal ions in certain coordination symmetries rather than in others. In an octahedral site these energies are in the orders:

$$Ni^{2+} > Co^{2+} > Fe^{2+} > Mn^{2+} \geqslant Ca^{2+}, \quad Ni^{2+} > Cu^{2+} > Zn^{2+},$$

and
$$Cr^{3+} > V^{3+} > Sc^{3+} = Ga^{3+} = Fe^{3+}.$$

These orders are almost exactly those found for the selective uptake of the ions into the Skaergaard intrusion silicates.

We conclude that selective uptake is based upon ligand-field energies which are highly dependent upon hole symmetry and interatomic distances.

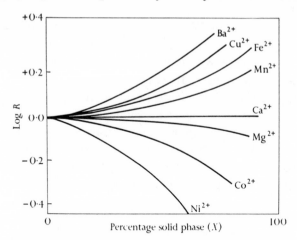

FIG. 34.17. The uptake of divalent ions into a silicate.
R is the ratio of the concentration of the element in the liquid after X per cent solidification to the concentration of the element in the initial liquid (after Williams).

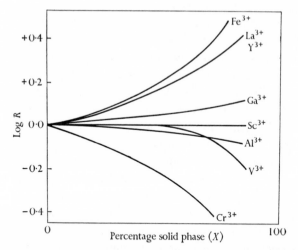

FIG. 34.18. The uptake of trivalent ions into a silicate (R and X as in Fig. 34.17) (after Williams).

We expect that the same trace elements will be accumulated preferentially in silicates generally. This might explain the absence of nickel and chromium in biological systems. It is worth noting that the divalent ions and trivalent ions which accumulate most readily are those with the highest melting oxides. In section 25.2 these high melting-points were interpreted as an indication of high ligand-field stabilization energies. In minerals providing holes of quite other symmetry, the order of uptake will be different again.

OTHER RARE ELEMENTS IN OXYANION MINERALS

The elements of the first transition series are all to be found in silicates in the divalent and trivalent states. The elements in the second and third transition series show a greater diversity of behaviour. The early elements go very readily to high-valence states and occur as their oxyanions in combination with divalent cations, for example, Nb as niobite (columbite), $Fe(NbO_3)_2$, Ta as $Fe(TaO_3)_3$ in tantalite, Mo as wulfenite, $PbMoO_4$, and W as scheelite, $CaWO_4$. Similar minerals are known for but few of the first row elements, e.g. Cr in crocoite, $PbCrO_4$. At the end of the second and third transition series, the elements are so noble that they occur even in the alloy osmiridium, which includes Ru and Os, Rh and Ir, and Pd and Pt. This illustrates the rapid change in character of the elements in the second and third transition series.

The B-subgroup elements generally occur in sulphides, see below, but in the $(N-2)$-valence state they may also occur with oxyanions. In this way the $(N-2)$-valence state shows similarity with the A-subgroup elements, much as in their general chemistry. Thus Tl(I) is found with Rb(I) in micas and in pollucite. Pb(II) occurs in molybdates and chromates much as Ca(II) occurs in scheelite $CaWO_4$. The IIA cations are also found in sulphates and carbonates and these minerals sometimes contain considerable quantities of Pb(II).

TRACE ELEMENTS IN SULPHIDES

The $(N-2)$-valence state in the later B subgroups, Groups VB and VIB, increasingly resembles the Group-valence state of Groups IIIB and IVB, respectively. Both series of elements occur in sulphide ores. A major source of the latter elements is zinc blende, ZnS, which contains small quantities of Ga(III), In(III), Tl(III), and Ge(IV) in place of the Zn, and of Se and Te in place of S. The extraction of these elements then depends on the volatility of the elements or their compounds at one stage or another of the working-up of the metals. Cadmium distils off before zinc and many of the other elements are trapped in furnace flues. The flue dust is a particularly valuable source of germanium. Selenium and tellurium are recovered from anode sludges in the electrolytic refining of copper.

Another rare element found in sulphide ores is rhenium. It occurs, twenty parts per million, in molybdenite, MoS_2. The curious stability of high-valence sulphides early in the second and third transition series has been mentioned in previous chapters.

TRACE ELEMENTS IN BIOLOGY

Elements are differentially accumulated by living organisms. Just as industrial refinement requires work, so living cells expend free energy in their enrichment of elements with respect to the environment. The most familiar example of this enrichment is that of iodine in seaweeds, which have been used as a source of the element. Other examples are the accumulation of vanadium in sea cucumbers and of potassium generally in plant life. Apart from the separation of elements between different living organisms, the different organs of one plant or animal have very different trace-element contents. Little cadmium is found in the body of the horse except in its kidney. The eyes of some animals and fish contain crystalline zinc cysteinate and of course blood cells contain considerable amounts of iron as haemoglobin. In fact erythrocytes are not unlike a crystalline phase of haemoglobin. Again the concentration of magnesium, as chlorophyll, in chloroplasts is very high. The chloroplasts also contain traces of iron, copper, and manganese all of which are essential for activity. Molybdenum, which is an essential part of xanthine oxidase, is found in the liver of rats. The reasons for these and many other cases of specific associations of metal-containing compounds with particular functional parts of living things have been little explored.

Problems

1. What are the advantages of OH^- as against PO_4^{3-} as a selective precipitant? (Consider the cases of Al^{3+}, Fe^{3+}, Zn^{2+}, and Mg^{2+}.) Pyrophosphate, but not hydroxide, is a good precipitant in the quantitative determination of many metals. Why?

2. Show that the behaviour of Bi^{3+}, Pb^{2+}, and Tl^+ in the analysis groups is in accordance with the rule that the higher the Group of an $(N-2)$-valence B-metal cation the more 'b' character it shows.

3. Yellow ammonium sulphide is used to redissolve some sulphides in group II. Explain the use of this reagent, comparing its acid-base function with that of NaOH and its oxidizing function with that of sodium peroxide.

4. How would you analyse Ag_2WO_4 qualitatively? Explain the procedure you select.

5. What use is made of ammonia in analysis? Explain its reactions.

6. Comment on the difference between Figs. 34.10 and 34.11 in terms of competitive complexing by ammonia and 8-hydroxyquinoline. Which elements do you think will be precipitated at pH 2·0 by 8-hydroxyquinoline?

7. The only metals which are precipitated by cupferron (see Fig. 34.12) in the presence of EDTA and citrate (pH 5·0) are Ti, Zr, Hf, lanthanides, V, Nb, Ta, Al, Fe, and Sn. Which of these precipitates would you expect to be strongly coloured?

8. What are the causes of the relative selectivity of two reagents one of which contains the grouping

and the other the grouping

9. The reagent thenoyltrifluoroacetone,

is much used to extract elements from aqueous solution into benzene. What are the functions of the different groups in the reagent? Compare it with dithiol

10. Which is likely to be the more selective organic reagent

Dithizone or α-Picolinic acid ?

11. Why is thiocyanate a usual colorimetric reagent yet cyanide is not?

12. A soluble nitrate, X, gives a black precipitate with H_2S. The precipitate dissolves in 1:2 nitric acid, but on neutralizing this solution with

ammonia a white precipitate, Z, is formed. Z dissolves in concentrated HCl but dilution of this solution again gives a white precipitate. The last precipitate turns black on treatment with sodium stannite. What is the metal in X and what are the different white precipitates?

13. Although analytical group separation methods place Pb and Tl in group I and Mn in group IV, it is a relatively common observation to discover Pb in group II, Tl in group IV, and Mn in group III. Can you explain these facts?

14. A white nitrate, M, gives an insoluble carbonate, a phosphate which is only insoluble above pH about 10 and a somewhat insoluble hydroxide. Its chromate is insoluble in neutral solution but soluble in acetic acid and its sulphate is insoluble even in relatively strong acid solutions. What is the metal involved? Comment upon the solubility of the salts of oxyacid anions as revealed by these facts.

15. Describe the methods for the separation of Cu and Cd, and of Ni and Co. Refer to Chapter 26 B for a discussion of the stabilities of the various valence states involved.

16. A substance, Q, gives a *yellow-brown* precipitate in group II, which is not very soluble in ammonium carbonate solution. The precipitate dissolves in *yellow* ammonium sulphide, but on addition of acid a *yellow-brown* precipitate is again formed. The precipitate now dissolves in ammonium carbonate, but once again addition of acid to this solution gives a *yellow-brown* precipitate. Oxidation of the precipitate with concentrated nitric acid followed by neutralization of the *colourless* solution, gives, on addition of silver nitrate, a *brown* precipitate. Explain the reaction sequence and the colours observed.

17. What geochemical factors have caused the relatively easy accessibility of iron as compared with titanium?

18. In the light of Fig. 34.1 discuss the occurrence of B in borax, Al in bauxite, Si in silicates, V in lead vanadate, Cr in chromite, and W in tungstates.

19. Carnallite is $KCl,MgCl_2,6H_2O$. What is the origin of this double salt? Why do K and Mg occur together, rather than Li and Mg as would be suggested by the diagonal relationship? How does Li occur?

20. Comment on the observations that the main sources of gallium are from ZnS and Al_2O_3 ores, while the main sources of indium are from ZnS and SnO_2 ores.

21. If cobalt had been stable as Co^{3+} and chromium as Cr^{2+}, would they have been expected to occur in trace quantities in late or early solid fractions of magma?

22. The main elements, which occur naturally are the noble gases, N_2, O_2, carbon, sulphur, Group IB, and the platinum metals. Why is this?

23. Can you suggest experiments which might distinguish between the alternative theories of the earth in Fig. 34.14? Consider possible chemical model systems as well as physical methods of investigation.

24. The main source of Pb is PbS and the main source of Sn is SnO_2, yet both elements are readily precipitated in group II of the analysis tables. Explain.

EXPERIMENTAL PROBLEMS

No experimental problems have been set in this chapter although much of the material in Part A is particularly suitable to experimental verification. Experiments are omitted because there already exist numerous excellent texts on qualitative analysis. It is our view that these texts should be used to teach inorganic chemistry and not analysis. Perhaps the best way of doing this is to give the student unknown *single* substances and to test his powers of observation and interpretation of the reactions as seen in group analysis.

Bibliography

L. H. AHRENS, *The Distribution of Elements on our Planet*, McGraw-Hill, New York, 1965.

J. BJERRUM, G. SCHWARZENBACH, and L. G. SILLÉN, *Stability Constants of Metal Ion Complexes*, Parts I and II, Special Publications Nos. 6 and 7, Chemical Society, London, 1958; revised by A. E. Martell and L. G. Sillén, 1964.

G. CHARLOT, *Qualitative Inorganic Analysis*, Methuen, London, 1954.

V. V. CHERDYNTSEV, *Abundance of Chemical Elements*, Chicago University Press, 1961.

C. D. CURTIS, 'Applications of Crystal Field Theory to the Inclusion of Trace Transition Elements in Minerals during Magmatic Differentiation', *Geochim. Cosmochim. Acta*, 1964, **28**, 389.

R. M. DIAMOND and D. G. TUCK, Extraction of Inorganic Compounds into Organic Solvents, *Progress in Inorganic Chemistry*, vol. 2, ed. F. A. Cotton, Interscience, New York, 1960.

F. FEIGL, *Specific, Selective, and Sensitive Reactions*, Academic Press, New York, 1949.

H. FREISER and Q. FERNANDO, *Ionic Equilibria in Analytical Chemistry*, Wiley, New York, 1963.

O. W. GAMOW, *Biography of the Earth*, Macmillan, London, 1964.

R. M. GARRELS, *Mineral Equilibria*, Harper, New York, 1960.

D. T. GIBSON, 'The Terrestrial Distribution of the Elements', *Quart. Rev. Chem. Soc.*, 1949, **3**, 263.

V. M. GOLDSCHMIDT, *Geochemistry*, Oxford University Press, 1954.

I. MAY and L. SCHUBERT, Reactive Groups as Reagents—Inorganic Applications, *Treatise on Analytical Chemistry*, ed. I. M. Kolthoff and P. J. Elving, Part I, Vol. 2, p. 833, Interscience, New York, 1961.

G. H. MORRISON and H. FREISER, *Solvent Extraction in Analytical Chemistry*, Wiley New York, 1957.

D. D. PERRIN, *Organic Complexing Reagents*, Interscience, New York, 1964.

F. C. PHILLIPS, 'Oceanic Salt Deposits', *Quart. Rev. Chem. Soc.*, 1947, **1**, 91.

G. SCHWARZENBACH, The General, Selective, and Specific Formation of Complexes by Metal Cations, *Advances in Inorganic Chemistry and Radiochemistry*, vol. 3, ed. H. J. Emeléus and A. G. Sharpe, Academic Press, New York, 1961.

G. SCHWARZENBACH, *Die komplexometrische Titration*, Enke, Stuttgart, 1956. (English edition by H. Irving, Methuen, London, 1957).

R. J. P. WILLIAMS, 'Deposition of Trace Elements in Basic Magma', *Nature, Lond.*, 1959, **184**, 44.

A. I. VOGEL, *A Textbook of Qualitative Chemical Analysis*, 4th ed., Longmans, London, 1954.

35 · Atomic Nuclei

35.1. Introduction

OUTLINE OF CHAPTER

In the rest of this book, the atomic nuclei have been very largely treated as though they possessed only two properties, charge and mass. It has also been pointed out that other properties such as nuclear quadrupoles, nuclear spins, and phenomena such as the Mössbauer effect may be used to investigate electron fields near nuclei, while from time to time reference has been made to the use of isotopes in following reactions. The discussion of occurrence in the previous chapter naturally raises questions about the abundance of the elements, a problem which can only be tackled in terms of nuclear stability, both 'thermodynamic' and 'kinetic'. There are also many other ways in which nuclear properties impinge upon inorganic chemistry, and indeed much of the present revival of interest in inorganic chemistry is associated with work undertaken in connexion with atomic-energy programmes. It is therefore appropriate to devote this final chapter to a very brief and simple outline of nuclear structure and nuclear properties, emphasizing those aspects which are likely to be of most interest to inorganic chemists.

Section 35.2 is concerned with nucleon interactions and nuclear binding energies, and concludes with a short account of the way fusion and fission processes may be used to provide controlled releases of atomic energy. Section 35.3 discusses radioactivity and related nuclear properties. The cosmic abundances of the elements and the theories which set out to account for these abundances are treated in section 35.4. The final section, section 35.5, gives a brief description of the electric quadrupole and magnetic properties of nuclei, and the manner in which these properties affect measurements of chemical interest.

NUCLEAR PARTICLES AND UNITS

The static properties of nuclei, with which we shall be largely concerned, may be discussed in terms of a model in which nuclei contain neutrons and protons only. Even these particles have been shown to have an inner structure, which may be revealed by electron-scattering experiments. The distributions of charge as a function of distance from the centre of the particle are shown in Fig. 35.1, from which it will be seen that, while both protons and neutrons may have positive cores, the outer shell of the proton is positive and that of the neutron is negative. These outer shells may be

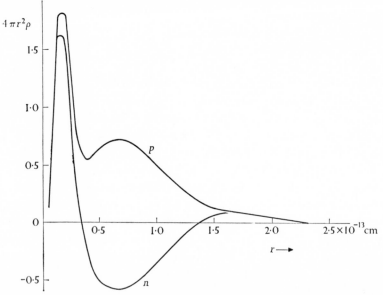

FIG. 35.1. Charge distribution for the proton and the neutron from electron scattering (after Olson, Schipper, and Wilson, *Phys. Rev. Letters*, 1961, **6**, 286). The positive cores are to some extent a matter of interpretation.

interpreted in terms of each nucleon existing partly as the other with a π-meson (pion), in such a way as to conserve electric charge and angular momentum. Thus

$$\text{proton } (\uparrow \text{spin}) \rightleftharpoons \text{neutron } (\downarrow \text{spin}) + \pi^+ \quad (l = 1, \; m_z = +1)$$
$$\text{neutron } (\downarrow \text{spin}) \rightleftharpoons \text{proton } (\uparrow \text{spin}) + \pi^- \quad (l = 1, \; m_z = -1).$$

The mutual interaction of neutrons and protons has been described in terms of a π-meson field. Other 'fundamental' particles are only required in order to discuss the dynamic properties of nucleons at very high energies (> 1000 MeV).

Nuclear masses are customarily quoted for neutral atoms, i.e. for nuclei *plus* electrons, as these are the masses most readily determined by mass spectroscopy. In 1960 the International Union of Pure and Applied Physics defined the standard scale for nuclear masses by setting the mass of the ^{12}C atom as $12 \cdot 0000...$, and the figures quoted in this book are based on this scale (Everling, König, Mattauch, and Wapstra). The previous physical scale was based on ^{16}O as the standard, and care should be exercised since many tables have been published using this scale. The ratio between the ^{16}O and ^{12}C scales is 0.99968218 (e.g. $^{131}Xe = 130.94670$ on the ^{16}O scale, 130.90509 on the ^{12}C scale). The main reason for the change is the greater convenience of ^{12}C for mass-spectroscopic measurements. One atomic unit is equivalent to 1.66032×10^{-24} g or to 931.437 MeV, since mass and energy are interrelated by the Einstein equation

$$E = mc^2.$$

We shall use the symbol Z for the number of protons in a nucleus (i.e. the atomic number) and N for the number of neutrons, so that $A = Z+N$, where A is the mass number or 'rounded' atomic weight. All nuclei of the same Z are called isotopes, of the same N isotones, and of the same A isobars. Nuclei with the same Z and N which differ from one another only in their energy content are called isomers. Nuclear species are referred to in general as nuclides.

35.2. Structures and binding energies

STRUCTURE

Nuclear forces are only exerted over very small distances of the order of 10^{-13} to 10^{-12} cm. The potential energy of a neutron or a proton in the vicinity of a nucleus may be represented as in Fig. 35.2, the difference between the two nucleons arising from the simple electrostatic repulsion between a proton and a nucleus, which is absent in the case of a neutron. The nuclear radius, R, is related to the mass number by the approximate relation

$$R = 1.2A^{\frac{1}{3}} \text{ (units of } 10^{-13} \text{ cm).}$$

Thus in contrast to atoms, the volume of a nucleus is proportional to the number of particles: nuclear matter is incompressible. The reason is that at short distances, of the order of 0.4×10^{-13} cm, nucleons strongly repel one another. This may be demonstrated by scattering experiments with protons and/or neutrons. Nucleons have thus a 'hard core', the size of which is of a similar order of magnitude as the distance over which they attract one another. As a result, the structure of nuclei is in some ways analogous to that of a liquid drop, in which molecules attract one another over relatively short distances of the same order of magnitude as molecular sizes. Since nuclear constituents only attract a limited number of their neighbours, nuclear forces are said to show the phenomenon of 'saturation'.

Moreover, just as in a liquid drop, nucleons at the surface of the nucleus will be unsaturated, so that—to a first approximation—the binding energy of a nucleus may be represented by an attractive term proportional to the nuclear volume and a disruptive term proportional to its surface area.

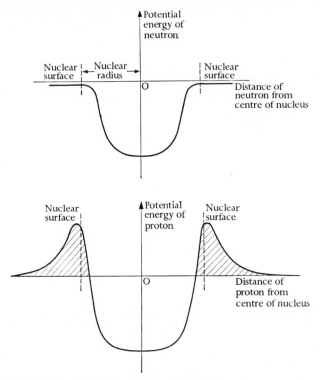

FIG. 35.2. Potential energy of neutron or proton as a function of its distance from the centre of a nucleus.

A further disruptive term arises from the electrostatic repulsion between the protons. This increases with Z and is the reason why heavy nuclei become unstable and tend to have high neutron/proton ratios.

Both neutrons and protons obey the Pauli principle ($\frac{1}{2}$ unit spins, antisymmetric wave functions), and into any possible nuclear state it is only possible to place two of each nucleon. This pairing process is associated with a relatively great stability of nuclei with even numbers of protons and/or neutrons. Further details of nuclear structure may be explained in terms of the energy levels which the nucleons may occupy within the nucleus. These levels are in some ways analogous to the electron energy levels outside the nucleus (e.g. $3s$, $3p$, $3d$, etc.), and are also interpreted in terms of a wave-mechanical model, the so-called shell model. The essentially different potentials in the atomic and nuclear problems give rise, however,

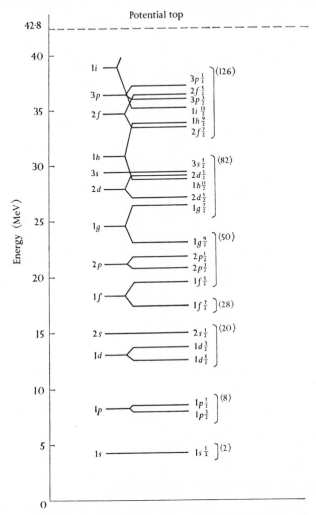

FIG. 35.3. Energy levels for particles in an approximately square-well potential. The letters correspond to the l values, $s = 0$, $p = 1$, $d = 2$, etc. The numbers to the left of each letter give the n values and to the right the j values. The numbers on the extreme right are the magic numbers at the filling of the shells (after Moore).

to distinctly different orders in the levels, and spin-orbit coupling is given a more dominant role in the nuclear problem.

The left-hand side of Fig. 35.3 gives the order of levels for an assumed approximately square-well nuclear potential (for the order with an harmonic oscillator potential see problem 35.35). The letter in each label corresponds to the orbital angular momentum of the nucleon, just as for the extra-nuclear electrons, i.e. s, p, d, f, g levels correspond to l values of 0, 1, 2, 3, 4 respectively. The number in each label corresponds to the number of zeros (excluding the origin) in the radial part of the wave function (see especially Burcham). The sum of this number and the l value would correspond to the principal quantum number, n, for electrons, but n no longer has the importance which it carries in the extra-nuclear problem.

In combination with the l values, the spin of $\pm\frac{1}{2}$ for each nucleon gives rise to the j values shown in the labelling of the spin-orbit coupling levels given on the right-hand side of Fig. 35.3. This spin-orbit coupling is assumed to be so strong that the original order of levels is altered, different j states of an original level at times being part of different nuclear shells. Each level may hold $2j+1$ protons and $2j+1$ neutrons, so that the successive shells are filled with one kind of nucleon when 2, 8, 20, 28, 50, 82, and 126 particles of that kind have been placed in the lowest energy levels available. These numbers are called *magic numbers*. A nucleus with a magic number of either protons or neutrons is in general likely to be stable. Nuclei with magic numbers both of protons and neutrons are *especially* stable, for instance ^{4}He, ^{16}O, ^{40}Ca, and ^{208}Pb. The magic numbers correspond in some measure to the numbers of electrons for the various noble-gas atoms in the extra-nuclear problem. Just as these electron numbers were known before they could be explained theoretically, so empirical nuclear-stability rules gave rise to the magic numbers before they were interpreted theoretically. Moreover, the nuclear wave-mechanical arguments are much more empirical and incomplete than are their extra-nuclear counterparts. They do, however, enable a correlation of a surprising number of nuclear properties.

BINDING ENERGIES

In Fig. 35.4 the binding energy per nucleon is plotted against the number of nucleons. The binding energy is calculated by multiplying the number of protons in the nucleus by the proton mass, and adding to the product the number of neutrons times the neutron mass. This number less the observed weight of the nucleus gives the loss in mass on formation of the nucleus, which is equivalent to the total binding energy. The general form of the plot in Fig. 35.4 can be related to energy contributions of two kinds.

(1) As the number of nucleons is increased, the exchange interaction becomes nearly proportional to the number of nucleons, for the

nucleons get further apart and, so far as these very short-range forces are concerned, out of range of all but a few other nucleons. This contribution to the binding energy *per nucleon* therefore approaches an asymptotic limit.

(2) The electrostatic energy of repulsion between the protons varies as Z^2, so that this contribution of the binding energy *per nucleon* is nearly proportional to Z.

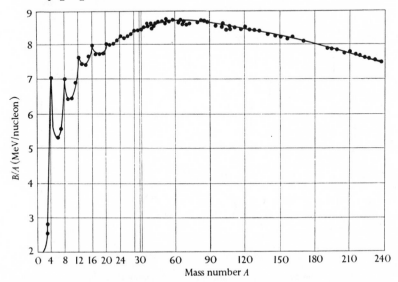

FIG. 35.4. Average binding energy for the naturally-occurring nuclides. Note scale change at $A = 30$.

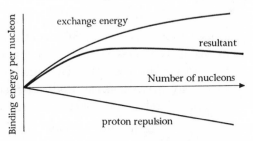

FIG. 35.5. Illustrative diagram showing the main cause of the maximum in the variation of nuclear stability with atomic number.

The sum of these two effects is shown in Fig. 35.5. In addition Fig. 35.4 has several other maxima. These occur at the magic numbers, especially at the values of ^{4}He, ^{12}C, ^{16}O. All these nuclei are considerably more stable than expected from the smooth curve. Their stability suggests that the sub-unit $^4_2$He has a special stability, as might have been suspected from the appearance of the α particle as a product of nuclear decay. That elements of odd atomic number are less common than elements of even atomic number may be most readily demonstrated in the lanthanide series (Fig. 35.6) where the elements are relatively little separated in nature.

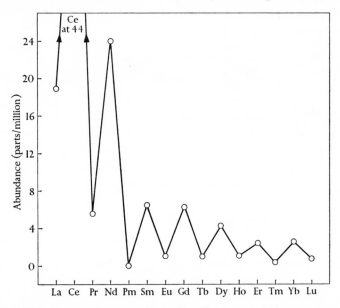

FIG. 35.6. The abundances of the lanthanide elements in igneous rocks.

FUSION AND FISSION

It is clear from Fig. 35.4 that the fusion of small nuclei or the fission of large nuclei would lead to a considerable release of energy. In section 35.4 we shall discuss fusion processes which are thought to have taken place in the cosmic synthesis of the elements. The possibility of using such reactions as a source of energy on earth has naturally attracted considerable attention. The only reactions likely to proceed fast enough to be of practical value are

$$^2_1D + {}^2_1D \Bigg\langle {}^{\displaystyle ^3_2He + {}^1_0n + 3\cdot2\ MeV}_{\displaystyle ^3_1T + {}^1_1H + 4\cdot0\ MeV}$$

in which the activation energy is about $0\cdot1$ MeV, and the critical temperature for self-sustaining fusion about 400×10^6 °K, and

$$^3_1T + {}^2_1D \rightarrow {}^4_2He + {}^1_0n + 17\cdot6\ MeV$$

which has a critical temperature about 45×10^6 °K. Various ingenious attempts have been made to confine a gas plasma at temperatures of this order, but as yet (1965) none has proved to be practicable. Such temperatures are, however, achieved in a nuclear-fission bomb, and the hydrogen or thermonuclear bomb makes use of both fission and fusion processes.

Heavy nuclei would be reduced in mass and would release energy if they were divided into two smaller nuclei. Thus heavy nuclei will all be thermodynamically unstable with respect to division into two nuclei of comparable size. As an example, the reaction

$$^{206}_{82}\text{Pb} \rightarrow 2\ ^{103}_{41}\text{Nb} \rightarrow 2\ ^{103}_{45}\text{Rh} + 8\beta^-$$

would in theory yield about 150 MeV. However, nearly all such fission processes take place at an unobservably slow rate as a result of the potential barrier which has to be overcome in the separation into the two nuclei. Some of the heaviest nuclei undergo spontaneous fission, e.g. the spontaneous-fission half-lives of ^{235}U and ^{254}Cf are 2×10^7 years and 55 days respectively. However, the excited ^{236}U nucleus, produced by the capture of slow neutrons by ^{235}U, has a fission half-life less than 10^{-14} seconds. Processes of this type are used in atomic bombs and nuclear reactors.

35.3. Radioactivity and related properties

NATURAL AND ARTIFICIAL NUCLIDES

The atoms which constitute the earth and the solar system are believed to have been formed about 3×10^9 years ago. The naturally-occurring nuclei are therefore either stable, unstable with half-lives of the order of 10^9 years or longer, or are derived from relatively long-lived parent nuclei. Other nuclei may be produced artificially in nuclear reactions such as fission or particle bombardment. Some 800 new nuclides have thus been produced: all are radioactive. The factors determining the lifetimes of alpha- and beta-unstable nuclei appear to be general, and there is no important distinction in this respect between naturally-occurring and artificial nuclei.

The naturally-occurring nuclides with $Z \leqslant 83$ are shown in Fig. 35.7, and the heavier natural and artificial nuclides in Fig. 35.8. Fig. 35.7 demonstrates the increasing ratio of N/Z with increasing Z. In the region covered by Fig. 35.8 the line of stability with respect to beta-decay has a slope of about 1·8, so that the addition of two protons requires the addition of about four neutrons to obtain comparable beta-stability. Two hundred and one beta-stable nuclides contain an even number of protons and an even number of neutrons, sixty-nine are even-odd, i.e. contain an even

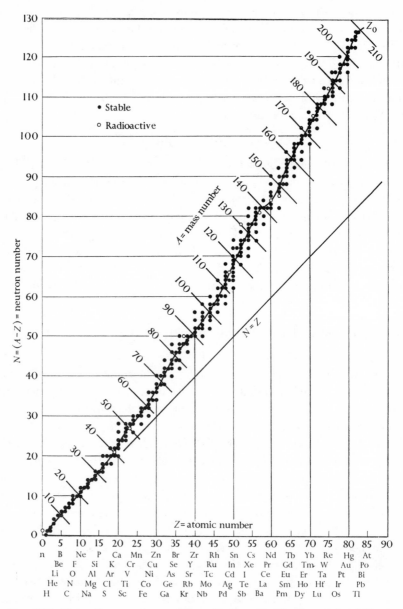

FIG. 35.7. Naturally-occurring nuclides with $Z \leqslant 83$. The line of β-stability is marked Z_0 (after Evans).

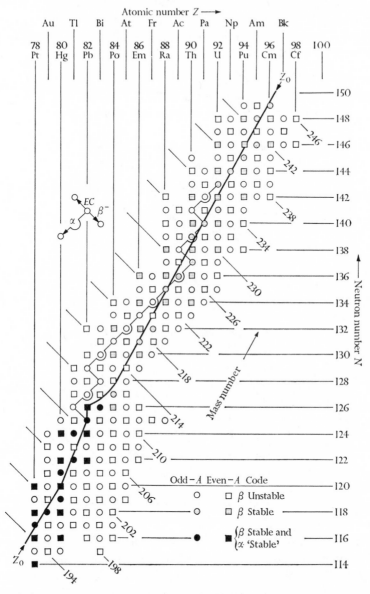

FIG. 35.8. Nuclides of $Z \geqslant 78$. The line of β-stability is marked Z_0. The main line of descent of the actinium $(4n+3)$ series from ^{235}U is also shown (after Evans). EC = electron capture.

number of protons and an odd number of neutrons, while sixty-one are odd-even and only four ($^2_1$H, $^6_3$Li, $^{10}_5$B, and $^{14}_7$N) are odd-odd.

The variation in stability for nuclei with a given A (isobars) or given Z (isotopes) is illustrated by Fig. 35.8, and the data quoted in Table 35.I.

TABLE 35.I. *Stability and mass excesses (atomic mass—A) of nuclides with $A = 12$, and of nuclides with $Z = 6$. A low value for the mass excess corresponds to a high nuclear binding energy*

Symbol	Z	A	Stability	Mass excess (10^{-6} a.m.u.)
B	5	12	radioactive	14,353
C	6	12	stable	0
N	7	12	radioactive	18,900
C	6	10	radioactive	16,830
C	6	11	radioactive	11,433
C	6	12	stable	0
C	6	13	stable	3,354
C	6	14	radioactive	3,242

TABLE 35.II. *Parent radioactive nuclides found in nature (after Evans)*

Nuclide Z	A	Atom per cent abundance	Half-life (years)	Radiation observed
19(K)	40	0·0119	$1·2 \times 10^9$	β^-, EC, γ
23(V)	50	0·24	?	?
37(Rb)	87	27·85	6×10^{10}	β^-
49(In)	115	95·77	6×10^{14}	β^-
52(Te)	130	34·49	$\sim 10^{21}$	Growth of $^{130}_{54}$Xe
57(La)	138	0·089	$\sim 2 \times 10^{11}$	β^-, EC
60(Nd)	144	23·9	$\sim 1·5 \times 10^{15}$	α
62(Sm)	147	15·07	$1·4 \times 10^{11}$	α
71(Lu)	176	2·6	$7·5 \times 10^{10}$	β^-, γ
75(Re)	187	62·93	4×10^{12}	β^-
90(Th)	232	100	$1·39 \times 10^{10}$	α
92(U)	235	0·715	$7·13 \times 10^8$	α
92(U)	238	99·28	$4·49 \times 10^9$	α

Table 35.II gives the parent radioactive nuclides found in nature. The three heaviest nuclides give rise to the three natural radioactive series, which include some forty shorter-lived nuclides such as radium. The $4n+3$ (i.e. $A = 4n+3$) series is related to the parent ^{235}U, and is outlined in Fig. 35.8. The $4n+2$ series is related to ^{238}U, and the $4n$ series to ^{232}Th. ^{237}Np is the longest-lived nuclide (half-life $2·25 \times 10^6$ years) of the artificial $4n+1$ series.

ALPHA-DECAY

All nuclei with $A > 150$ are unstable with respect to alpha-particle emission (see Problem 35.18), but in practice relatively few nuclides exhibit alpha-decay. This distinction is associated with the potential barrier (see Fig. 35.2) through which the alpha-particle has to pass. The probability of passing through this barrier depends exponentially on the decay energy (Geiger–Nuttall rule). The alpha-particle energies from a given nuclide show a discrete spectrum as is illustrated in Fig. 35.9. The relationship between decay energy and nuclear structure is brought out in Fig. 35.10, where the effect of neutron-shell closure at $N = 82$ is shown.

BETA-DECAY

The term beta-decay includes three processes, each of which involves the interaction of an electron with a nucleus. These are the emission of a positive electron (positron) denoted by β^+ or e^+, or of a negative electron denoted by β^- or e^-, and the capture of an orbital electron, usually from the K-shell but occasionally from the L-shell. Whereas in alpha-decay the mass number of the nucleus decreases by four and the atomic number by two, in beta-decay the mass number of the nucleus is unchanged, while the atomic number decreases (positron emission or orbital-electron capture, EC) or increases (negative-electron emission) by one. The emission of alpha-particles, positrons, and electrons has been found to be independent of the physical or chemical state of the radioelement, but electron capture is slightly affected by the type of chemical combination. Thus the electron-capture half-life of ^{7}Be is about 0·013 per cent greater in the metal than in BeO, and about 0·074 per cent greater in the metal than in BeF$_2$.

As was outlined in Chapter 1, electrons cannot, because of their low mass, exist in nuclei as stable species: their effective volumes for reasonable kinetic energies must be considerably larger than that of an atomic nucleus. Once formed they are emitted, and there is no comparable problem to the potential-energy barrier for alpha-particle emission. This is one reason why beta-decay is in general faster and more common than alpha-decay. Relatively heavy nuclides, i.e. containing a relative excess of neutrons, tend to be β^- active (see, e.g., Fig. 35.8). The beta-emitters in all the natural radioactive series are negative-electron emitters. Natural examples of electron capture are provided by ^{40}K, ^{138}La, and possibly ^{50}V. Positron emission is only observed in artificial nuclides containing a relative excess of protons. The relative stability and beta-decay processes in an isobaric

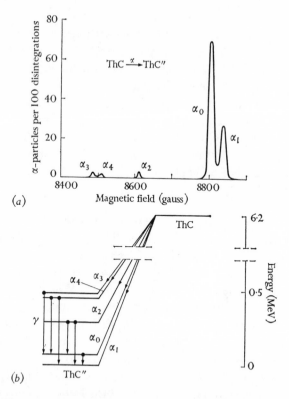

FIG. 35.9. Fine structure of α-particle spectra; (a) ThC $\xrightarrow{\alpha}$ ThC″ (disintegration) with (b) γ-ray emissions of ThC″ nucleus (after Evans).

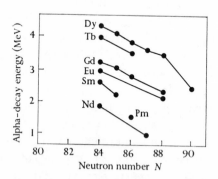

FIG. 35.10. Energy release in α-decay of the lanthanides showing the effect of the shell closure at $N = 82$ (after Hanna, 'Alpha-Radioactivity', *Experimental Nuclear Physics*, vol. iii, ed. E. Segrè, Wiley, New York, 1959).

series are illustrated in Fig. 35.11, while Table 35.III gives the decay properties of the carbon isotopes. Of these ^{14}C is the most generally useful for radioactive-tracer work: it has a relatively long half-life, but the

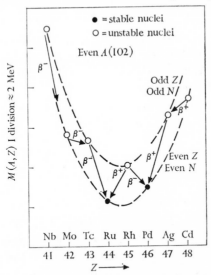

Fig. 35.11. Stability of isobars for $A = 102$. There are two stable isobars $^{102}_{44}Ru$ and $^{102}_{46}Pd$, both even-even, in the series (after Evans).

radiation is rather weak or 'soft' so that special counting procedures are necessary. It may be produced by the reaction

$$^{14}N + n \rightarrow ^{14}C + p,$$

which also takes place by the interaction of cosmic rays with atmospheric nitrogen. As a result, atmospheric CO_2 and living matter in equilibrium

TABLE 35.III. *The isotopes of carbon*

Isotope	Activity	Half-life or relative abundance
^{14}C	β^-	5600 years
^{13}C	stable	1·11 per cent
^{12}C	stable	98·89 per cent
^{11}C	β^+ (γ)	20·4 minutes
^{10}C	β^+	8·8 seconds

with the atmosphere contain small quantities of radioactive carbon. The decay of this in dead organic matter is the basis of the radio-carbon-dating procedure. The stable ^{13}C isotope may be enriched by chemical-exchange processes and used for tracer work with a mass spectrometer. The ^{11}C isotope emits 'hard' positron radiation which makes it easy to assay, but its half-life is too short for many experiments. In general a radioisotope is effectively useful in an experiment lasting up to about ten times its half-life. ^{11}C may be produced by the reaction

$$^{10}B + {}^{2}D \rightarrow {}^{11}C + {}^{1}n.$$

Beta-decay is often accompanied by gamma-emission, but, even when allowance has been made for the gamma-energy, it is found that the spectrum of beta-energies is a continuum. This was for a long time a fundamental problem in nuclear physics.

Alternative decay schemes such as

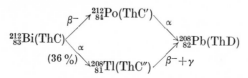

can, however, be made equivalent in energy if the upper limit of the electron energy is used. In any beta-decay it is this upper limit which corresponds to conservation of energy. For all other electron energies there appeared to be a disappearance of energy in the reaction. In many beta-decays there was also an apparent non-conservation of angular momentum. The difficulty was resolved by postulating the simultaneous emission of another particle, called the neutrino, of zero charge and zero or near zero rest mass. By assuming also that the neutrino has an angular momentum, conservation of angular momentum as well as of energy can be maintained. There is now considerable independent evidence for the neutrino and its antiparticle, the antineutrino. In one of the most convincing experiments both the positron and the neutron were detected from the reaction

$$\text{antineutrino} + p \rightarrow \beta^{+} + n,$$

induced by the intense antineutrino flux near a nuclear reactor.

GAMMA-EMISSION

A product nucleus is often formed in an excited state as a result of a primary radioactive process involving alpha- or beta-decay. This isomer can then decay either to the ground state or to another excited state with the emission of a high-energy photon or gamma-ray. An example is shown in Fig. 35.9. Gamma-emission is commonly a very rapid phenomenon and half-lives of the order of 10^{-10} second or less are quite common. On the other hand, quite long-lived isomers can occur when the selection rules for gamma-ray emission are violated, just as metastable atoms occur in the atomic case. The very high precision of gamma-energy determination in the Mössbauer method has already been discussed in connexion with the light which it throws on electron densities near nuclei (Chapter 5 and section 24.9).

NEUTRON CAPTURE

At extreme values of the neutron-proton ratio, emission of a proton or a neutron by a nucleus becomes energetically possible. However, in such

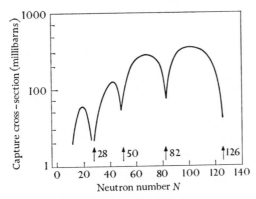

FIG. 35.12. Periodicity of capture cross-section for neutrons in a reactor (after Codd, Shepherd, and Tait, *Prog. Nucl. Energy*, 1956, **1**, 296).

circumstances beta-decay is extremely rapid, and neither proton nor neutron radioactivity has been observed as a competitive decay process for nuclear ground states, although nucleon emission from highly excited nuclear states is a common phenomenon in nuclear reactions. Bombardment of nuclei with protons and other particles is used in the production of new nuclides, including new elements. We shall restrict our discussion to the capture of slow neutrons by nuclei. This nuclear reaction is simplified by the absence of charge-repulsion effects, and is of some significance in theories of atomic abundance, as will be shown in the next section.

Neutron-capture efficiencies are usually measured in terms of nuclear cross-sections, for which the whimsical unit the 'barn' has been devised. Cross-sections are a function of atomic number and reflect the nuclear-shell structures, as is shown by the experimental results plotted in Fig. 35.12. They are also a function of neutron energy, and thus reflect the nuclear energy levels of different isomers (see Fig. 35.13). Radionuclides, identifiable by their half-lives and the energies of their radiation, may be produced by irradiation with neutrons or other particles. This is the basis of the delicate analytical method known as radioactivation analysis. The sensitivities of this method for various elements are shown in Table 35.IV.

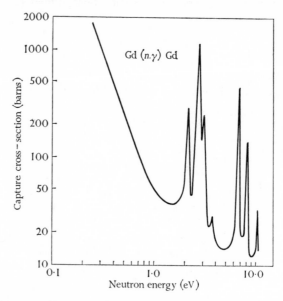

FIG. 35.13. Capture cross-section for the interaction of slow neutrons with gadolinium (after Hughes and Schwartz, *Neutron Cross Sections*, Brookhaven National Laboratory 325).

35.4. Cosmic abundance

The relative cosmic abundances of the elements are given in Fig. 35.14. The striking features of the figure are:

(1) 90–95 per cent of the atoms in the universe are hydrogen.

(2) 5–10 per cent of the atoms are helium.

(3) All the other elements taken together amount to some 1 per cent of the universe even by weight.

(4) Lithium, beryllium, and boron are anomalously rare.

(5) There is a general fall in abundances from oxygen to lead.

(6) A very pronounced maximum occurs in the iron group of elements around $A = 50$–60, i.e. $N = 28$ or $Z = 28$.

(7) There are no stable elements above $A = 250$.

We shall now outline a theory which accounts for the major features of the distribution. One starting-point is the postulate that everything has been made from neutrons, for *free* neutrons are known to beta-decay with

TABLE 35.IV. *Estimated sensitivities for some elements in neutron activation (from Atkins and Smales)*

Element	Radionuclide formed	Half-life	Estimated sensitivity[†] (grams)
Dy	^{165}Dy	2·3 hr	1×10^{-12}
Eu	^{152m}Eu	9·2 hr	1×10^{-12}
Au	^{198}Au	2·7 day	5×10^{-12}
In	^{116}In	54 min	1×10^{-11}
Mn	^{56}Mn	2·6 hr	1×10^{-11}
As	^{76}As	26·5 hr	5×10^{-11}
La	^{140}La	40 hr	5×10^{-11}
W	^{187}W	24·1 hr	5×10^{-11}
Cu	^{64}Cu	12·8 hr	1×10^{-10}
Ga	^{72}Ga	14·1 hr	1×10^{-10}
Ta	^{182}Ta	111 day	1×10^{-10}
Na	^{24}Na	15 hr	1×10^{-10}
Cs	^{134}Cs	2·3 yr	5×10^{-10}
Co	^{60}Co	5·3 yr	5×10^{-10}
P	^{32}P	14·3 day	5×10^{-10}
Rb	^{86}Rb	18·6 day	5×10^{-10}
Ba	^{139}Ba	85 min	1×10^{-9}
Hg	^{203}Hg	47 day	1×10^{-9}
Cl	^{38}Cl	37·3 min	5×10^{-9}
U	^{140}Ba	12·8 day	5×10^{-9}
Mo	^{99}Mo	68 hr	1×10^{-8}
Ni	^{65}Ni	2·6 hr	1×10^{-8}
Cr	^{51}Cr	27·8 day	1×10^{-7}
Sr	^{89}Sr	50 day	1×10^{-7}
Ca	^{45}Ca	164 day	1×10^{-7}
S	^{35}S	87·1 day	5×10^{-7}

† Estimated using slow neutron flux of 10^{12} neutrons $cm^{-2} sec^{-1}$, irradiation period of one month or saturation, whichever is less, a 2-hr period for radiochemical processing, and 100 per cent chemical yield.

a half-life of about ten minutes to give protons and electrons, the constituents of hydrogen atoms. Thus

$$n \rightarrow p + e^- + \text{antineutrino} + 780 \text{ keV}.$$

Alternatively we could assume that hydrogen atoms were present initially. The next step in the reaction sequence is the formation of the stable helium nucleus from protons or from protons and neutrons, i.e. reactions with the overall effect

$$4\ ^1H \rightarrow\ ^4He + 2\beta^+ + 2 \text{ neutrinos.}$$

Such reactions are highly exothermic, so the system does not remain at a fixed temperature. As the temperature rises toward 10^7 and 10^8 °K, a series of reactions of the ^4He nucleus occur, e.g.

$$2\ ^4He \rightarrow\ ^8Be$$

$$^8Be + ^4He \rightarrow\ ^{12}C.$$

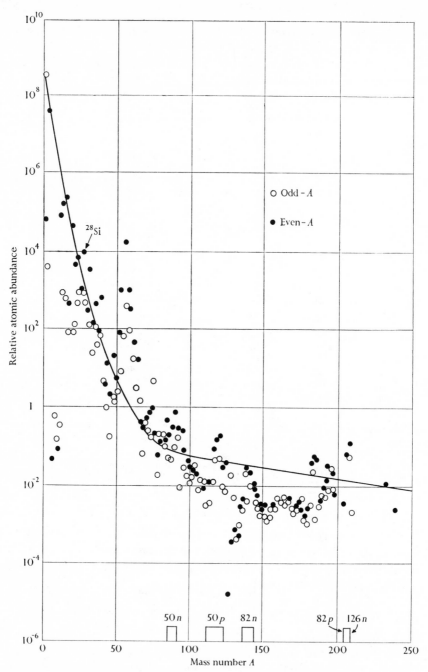

Fig. 35.14. Relative cosmic abundances of nuclides normalized to 10,000 atoms of silicon. The solid curve gives calculated abundances for successive (n, γ) capture processes, see text (after Evans).

^{8}Be is an unstable intermediate. This type of ^{4}He polymerization cannot give rise to atoms such as ^{6}Li or ^{10}B. These elements are of very low abundance. The ^{4}He polymerization, the so-called helium burning, produces a very great further release of energy and the reacting mass may now reach a temperature of 10^9 ° K. Further reactions, known in the laboratory, now occur giving rise to the elements N, O, F, and Ne.

The ^{12}C nuclei produced from ^{4}He nuclei may react with more protons as follows

$$^{12}C + p \rightarrow \, ^{13}N + \gamma$$
$$^{13}N \rightarrow \, ^{13}C + \beta^+ + \text{neutrino}$$
$$^{13}C + p \rightarrow \, ^{14}N + \gamma$$
$$^{14}N + p \rightarrow \, ^{15}O + \gamma$$
$$^{15}O \rightarrow \, ^{15}N + \beta^+ + \text{neutrino}$$
$$^{15}N + p \rightarrow \, ^{12}C + \, ^4He.$$

Several completed cycles of this, followed by an interrupted cycle, would produce helium and also explain the production of ^{13}C and ^{15}N and (by combination of ^{13}C with ^{4}He nuclei) of ^{17}O and ^{21}Ne. Because of the weak binding of the odd neutron in these nuclei, the following exothermic reactions then occur:

$$^{13}C + \, ^4He \rightarrow \, ^{16}O + n$$
$$^{17}O + \, ^4He \rightarrow \, ^{20}Ne + n$$
$$^{21}Ne + \, ^4He \rightarrow \, ^{24}Mg + n.$$

Now the elements from above mass number 20 begin to have quite high neutron-capture cross-sections (section 35.3), and the great importance of the reactions just given is that the liberated neutrons will be preferentially absorbed by the heavier elements, and thus serve to generate many of the nuclides heavier than iron. If such a process were operative, the abundance of a nuclide should be in inverse relation to its cross-section for capturing neutrons. This is, indeed, found to be true: measured neutron-capture cross-sections show a general rise with increasing mass number up to $A \simeq 100$, and become approximately constant for $A > 100$. Also, those nuclides which have a magic number of neutrons (iron group with $N = 28$, molybdenum group with $N = 50$, lanthanides near $N = 82$), and which therefore have an abnormally small cross-section for capturing an additional neutron, are found to be abnormally abundant in nature. Thus once the fusion of hydrogen into helium and ^{12}C starts, it appears that the heavier elements are formed in abundances suggestive of some sort of equilibrium distribution. Other features of abundances which suggest a near equilibrium at the higher atomic numbers are the relative abundances of isotopes (see earlier), the odd–even atomic number variations in abundances of the lanthanides (Fig. 35.6), and the absence of an accumulation of very heavy

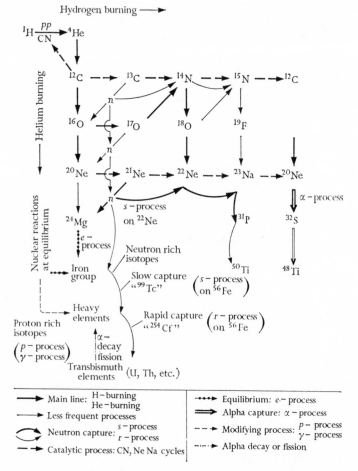

FIG. 35.15. The formation of the elements (after Burbidge, Burbidge, Fowler, and Hoyle, *Rev. Mod. Phys.*, 1957, **29**, 547).

elements. Very heavy elements, like very high polymers, are the results of chain reactions.

The chart, Fig. 35.15, summarizes the outlined theory of the origin of the elements. Whatever one is inclined to think of this theory, the startling fact remains that the universe is a very long way from an equilibrium position: for example, there is still so much hydrogen and helium. It appears that we can make but one observation, an analysis of products, on a reaction which has barely begun. The earth itself represents a particular frozen state of the products, for most of the hydrogen and helium has been lost. Abundances on the earth follow cosmic abundances from about oxygen onwards. Life which is carried on in a high abundance of *oxygen* and water is a very peculiar offspring of the frozen kinetic pattern of the abundances.

35.5. Magnetic and electric properties

NUCLEAR SPIN

The magnetic properties of nuclei result from components due to

(1) the spins of the protons,
(2) the spins of the neutrons, and
(3) the orbital motion of the charged protons.

The vector sum of these may be expressed as a nuclear angular momentum vector, or nuclear spin I. In this way the nucleus is treated as a particle with an intrinsic magnetic moment arising from its 'spin'. The spins of even–even nuclei are always zero because of the 'pairing off' of the neutrons and of the protons. The spins of odd–odd nuclei are always integral, in units of $h/2\pi$, but are difficult to calculate theoretically in an unambiguous manner. The half-integral spins of odd A nuclei can nearly always be correctly predicted from the shell model by ascribing the nuclear spin entirely to the orbital motion and spin of the single unpaired nucleon. For instance, the shell-model sequence of levels (Fig. 35.3) shows that the odd neutron in ^{17}O must be in the $1d_{\frac{5}{2}}$ level, so the nuclear spin is $\frac{5}{2}$. Similarly ^{15}N lacks one proton in the $1p_{\frac{1}{2}}$ level as compared with the spin-zero ^{16}O nucleus. The spin of ^{15}N is therefore $\frac{1}{2}$. This prediction of spins, together with the explanation of the magic numbers, is a major reason for adopting the nuclear-shell model with a square-well type of potential.

The spin properties of nuclei greatly affect the possibilities of radioactive transitions between them, and are thus of considerable importance in the theoretical consideration of half-lives. They give rise to a hyperfine structure in optical spectra and limit the transition possibilities of rotational spectra. An example of the latter is the H_2 molecule which exists in two forms not readily convertible into one another. In *para*-hydrogen the nuclear spins ($\frac{1}{2}$) are opposed and even, 0, 2, 4, 6,..., rotational levels are occupied, while in *ortho*-hydrogen the nuclear spins are parallel and odd, 1, 3, 5, 7,..., rotational levels are occupied.

In an applied magnetic field the nucleus can orient itself in $2I+1$ ways. I can therefore be measured by passing an atomic (or molecular) beam through an inhomogeneous magnetic field, when the beam is split and the separate components may be collected, e.g. on buttons of sulphur to which

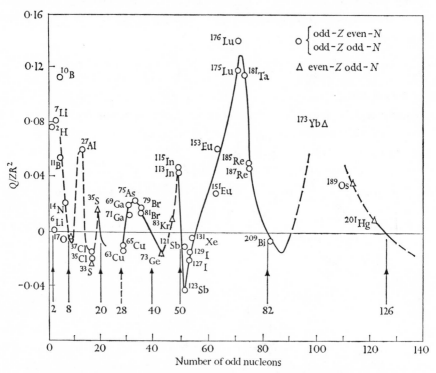

Fig. 35.16. Observed quadrupole moments, Q, divided by the nuclear charge Z and the square of the nuclear radius, R. The ordinate is then a measurement of nuclear ellipticity. Arrows represent closing of nucleon shells (after Evans).

the atoms stick readily. Of greater interest to chemists is the behaviour of magnetic nuclei in an applied magnetic field of great homogeneity. In this case the frequency required to induce transitions from one nuclear orientation to another may be measured, the technique of nuclear magnetic resonance. We have already referred to some of the results which this technique provides, but one of the most useful is the measurement of the chemical shift, which arises because different nuclei are in slightly different effective magnetic fields as a result of their different chemical combination. Thus in the low-resolution proton-resonance spectrum of ethyl alcohol there are three peaks of relative intensity $3:2:1$, corresponding to the protons in the CH_3, CH_2, and OH groups. The proton-spin resonance is observed with frequencies around 40 Mc/s for magnetic fields of the order of 10,000 gauss. At much higher frequencies the spin resonance of electrons in paramagnetic substances may be observed. The ESR spectrum is itself split by interaction with the magnetic field of the nucleus (see also sections 24.9 and 28.10).

ELECTRIC QUADRUPOLES

The distribution of electric charge throughout a nucleus is not always spherical, so that in addition to possessing a charge the nucleus can have electric polarity. The lowest-order electric moment observable as a static nuclear property is a nuclear quadrupole, and is positive for a prolate (cf. a rugby-ball) nucleus, and negative for an oblate (cf. the earth) nucleus. It is non-zero only for nuclei with $I \geqslant 1$. The nuclei of the lanthanides are found experimentally to be strongly prolate (see Fig. 35.16).

The electric-field gradient near the nucleus interacts with the nuclear quadrupole, so that the energy of the system depends on the orientation of the spin with respect to this gradient. Transitions from one orientation to another may be induced by frequencies in the neighbourhood of a few hundred megacycles per second. The application of nuclear quadrupole coupling to the detection of covalent bonding has been referred to earlier (Chapter 4 and section 25.7).

Problems

1. Show that, as a result of the Heisenberg Uncertainty Principle, the uncertainty in the kinetic energy of a neutron or proton confined within a distance of 10^{-12} cm will be of the order of 2 MeV. What will be the corresponding uncertainties in the kinetic energy of an electron confined within (a) the same distance, and (b) a distance of 10^{-8} cm? Comment on your results (see Chapter 1).

2. The density of nuclear material is about 10^{14} g cm^{-3}. Calculate the mass that a nucleus would have if it were the size (a) of an atom, and (b) of a tennis ball.

3. Show that the forces of gravitation are too weak by a factor of about 10^{37} to account for nucleon interactions.

4. Calculate the percentage loss in mass when 100 g of a hydrocarbon–oxygen mixture is burnt with the evolution of 100 kcal.

5. Estimate the difference in mass between two hydrogen atoms and a hydrogen molecule, if the dissociation energy of a hydrogen molecule is 103 kcal mole^{-1}.

6. Calculate an equilibrium constant for the reaction

$$4H \rightleftharpoons He$$

at room temperature, if the entropy of a H atom is 27·40 e.u., and that of a He atom is 30·13 e.u., and the masses of a H atom and a He atom are 1·00783 and 4·00260 respectively. One mass unit is equivalent to $9·3 \times 10^8$ eV.

7. Binding energies in nuclei are about 10^6 greater than the binding energies of the outer electrons in atoms. On this basis make an order of magnitude estimate of the energy which might be released in a nuclear explosion (e.g. of ^{235}U) and a chemical explosion (e.g. of TNT).

8. Estimate the total binding energy of the protons, neutrons, and electrons in the $^{11}_5$B atom (11·009305 atomic mass units) and compare this with the nucleus-electron binding energy obtained from the sum of ionization potentials (values given at the end of Chapter 2).

9. The density of a nucleus is fairly uniform throughout most of its mass, in contrast to the density of the electron cloud around a nucleus which is much greater near the nucleus. The volume of a nucleus is approximately proportional to its mass but atomic volumes increase on average very little with atomic number. Comment on these distinctions and their significance.

10. The binding energy of a nucleus per nucleon is very roughly independent of the number of nucleons (Fig. 35.4), so that its properties are more like those of a liquid than of electrons in atoms. Comment on this in relation to short-range and long-range forces.

11. ^{4}He is very stable but ^{4}H and ^{4}Li do not appear to exist. Comment.

12. What do the following nuclei have in common: He, O, Ca, Sn, Pb? Do you think that when eka-plutonium is discovered it will be found to have any particularly interesting nuclear properties?

13. Suggest why it is that the bottom of the packing fraction

$$\left(\frac{\text{Isotopic weight} - A}{A} \times 10^4 \right)$$

curve should occur near Fe.

14. There is a general *but not a precise* relation between the curves for (a) packing fraction, and (b) binding energy per nucleon, each as a function of atomic number. Explain why this should be so.

15. Estimate a minimum size for an atomic bomb from the following data.

The energy release of an atomic bomb is approximately equivalent to that of the explosion of 20,000 tons of TNT.

The explosion of 1 ton of TNT releases about 2×10^6 kcal.

The fission of a ^{235}U atom takes place in a number of ways but the following reaction may be taken as typical:

$$^{235}\text{U} + n \rightarrow \,^{95}\text{Mo} + \,^{139}\text{La} + 2n.$$

The masses of ^{235}U, ^{95}Mo, ^{139}La and of a neutron are 235·044, 94·906, 138·906, and 1·009 respectively.

One mass unit is equivalent to $9·3 \times 10^8$ eV.

16. When a U atom undergoes fission the products include neutrons and a large number of β-active radioelements. Comment.

17. From measurements of the range of α particles in a cloud chamber, Cockcroft and Walton calculated that the nuclear reaction

$$^1_1\text{H} + \,^7_3\text{Li} \rightarrow 2\,^4_2\text{He}$$

was exothermic to the extent of about 17 MeV. Mass spectroscopic measurements give the rest mass of $^1_1$H as 1·00783, of $^7_3$Li as 7·01600, and of $^4_2$He as 4·00260 (^{12}C scale). Show that these observations are in conformity with the Einstein relation, $\mathsf{E} = mc^2$ (1 eV $\equiv 1·602 \times 10^{-12}$ ergs).

18. From Fig. 35.4 show that α-decay is likely to become an exothermic process for masses greater than (very approximately) 150 a.m.u.

19. Show that, if it occurred, the α-emission of ^{22}Na represented by the equation

$$^{22}\text{Na} \rightarrow \,^4\text{He} + \,^{18}\text{F}$$

would be endothermic to the extent of 8·49 MeV. (Masses are 21·99443, 4·00260, and 18·00095.)

20. The energies required to remove a neutron from various Pb isotopes are 6·37 MeV for ^{207}Pb, 7·38 MeV for ^{208}Pb, and 3·87 MeV for ^{209}Pb. Comment.

21. Show that ^{235}U is β-stable, is able to emit α particles, and could in theory disintegrate spontaneously into two smaller nuclei of roughly equal size. (^{235}U = 235·0439, ^{235}Np = 235·0441, ^{235}Pa = 235·0454, ^{231}Th = 231·0364, ^{4}He = 4·0026, ^{96}Mo = 95·9045, ^{139}La = 138·9061.)

22. The radioactive decay of ^{7}Be is accompanied by the emission of X-rays characteristic of the K-series of Li. The half-life of ^{7}Be is greater in Be metal than in the oxide BeO or in the fluoride BeF_2. Comment.

23. What would you think would be the mode of decay (if any) of the following isotopes of oxygen: 14, 15, 16, 17, 18, 19?

24. The lightest stable isotope in which the difference between the number of neutrons and the number of protons is 3 is ^{37}Cl, and in which this difference is 4 is ^{36}S. Comment.

25. On absorption of a slow neutron a ^{238}U atom is transformed into atom A, which emits a β particle to give atom B, which then emits a second β particle to give atom C. C is slowly changed into D by α-emission. What are A, B, C, and D?

26. A boy carves a stick from a tree which grows alongside the Frankfurt autobahn. In the year 2100 the stick is dug up by an archaeologist who dates it as A.D. 500 ± 100 using the radiocarbon procedure. Comment.

27. A man weighing 85 kg is injected with 5 ml of water containing tritium (9×10^8 counts per minute). After some hours a sample of 1 ml of plasma water taken from the same man had an activity of $1 \cdot 5 \times 10^4$ counts per minute. Estimate the weight per cent of water in the man.

28. Comment on the difference in the ordinate scales of Figs. 35.12 and 35.13.

29. The following (10^{-4} g/g) are the abundances in igneous rocks and in metallic meteorites respectively:

Ca (363, 5), Ti (44, 1), V ($1 \cdot 5$, $0 \cdot 06$), Cr (2, $2 \cdot 4$), Mn (10, 3), Fe (500, 9080), Co ($0 \cdot 4$, 63), Ni (1, 860), Cu ($0 \cdot 7$, $3 \cdot 1$).

Comment.

30. Sn has ten stable isotopes with relative abundances:

$1 \cdot 1$ (112), $0 \cdot 8$ (114), $0 \cdot 4$ (115), $15 \cdot 5$ (116), $9 \cdot 1$ (117), $22 \cdot 5$ (118), $9 \cdot 8$ (119), $28 \cdot 5$ (120), $5 \cdot 5$ (122), $6 \cdot 8$ (124).

Comment.

31. Comment on the following series of relative abundances of stable isotopes:

Ba ($Z = 56$)		Ce ($Z = 58$)		Nd ($Z = 60$)	
130	0·1	136	0·2	142	26·0
132	0·1	138	0·3	143	13·0
134	2·4	140	88·5	144	22·6
135	6·6	142	11·1	145	9·2
136	7·8			146	16·5
137	11·3			148	6·8
138	71·7			150	6·0

32. Comment on the following percentage abundances by weight in the earth's crust as estimated for the most abundant nuclides: $^{16}_{8}O = 48$, $^{28}_{14}Si = 26$, $^{27}_{13}Al = 8·5$, $^{56}_{26}Fe = 5$, $^{40}_{20}Ca = 3·5$, $^{23}_{11}Na = 2·8$, $^{39}_{19}K = 2·5$, $^{24}_{12}Mg = 2·0$.

33. Comment on the following abundance figures (composition of the earth's atmosphere by volume in parts per 10^6: general abundance in the universe estimated in terms of atoms relative to Kr) for the noble gases:

He (5·2: $4·0 \times 10^7$), Ne (18: $4·4 \times 10^4$), Ar (9300: 1150), Kr (1: 1), Xe (0·08: 0·017).

34. The nuclei ^{11}B, ^{13}C, ^{15}N, and ^{17}O have spins $\frac{3}{2}$, $\frac{1}{2}$, $\frac{1}{2}$, and $\frac{5}{2}$ respectively. Correlate these observations with the j values in the shell model as shown in Fig. 35.3.

35. Parity of nuclear particles may be defined by $(-1)^l$ where l is the angular momentum quantum number. For an oscillator potential (as opposed to a square-wave potential), the solution of the wave equation gives the following order of evenly-spaced levels (cf. $1/n^2$ in the atomic problem) starting with the lowest energy state:

$$1s; \quad 1p; \quad 1d = 2s; \quad 1f = 2p; \quad 1g = 2d = 3s; \quad 1h = 2f = 3p;$$
$$1i = 2g = 3d = 4s.$$

Show that this conforms to a steady alternation of odd and even parities.

Bibliography

D. H. F. ATKINS and A. A. SMALES, Activation Analysis, *Advances in Inorganic Chemistry and Radiochemistry*, vol. 1, ed. H. J. Eméleus and A. G. Sharpe, Academic Press, New York, 1959.

H. J. M. BOWEN and D. GIBBONS, *Radioactivation Analysis*, Oxford University Press, 1963.

W. E. BURCHAM, *Nuclear Physics. An Introduction*, Longmans, London, 1963.

G. B. COOK and J. F. DUNCAN, *Modern Radiochemical Practice*, Oxford University Press, 1952.

H. CRAIG, S. L. MILLER, and G. J. WASSERBURG, ed., *Isotopic and Cosmic Chemistry*, North Holland, Amsterdam, 1964.

J. G. CUNINGHAME, *Introduction to the Atomic Nucleus*, Elsevier, Amsterdam, 1964.

R. D. Evans, *The Atomic Nucleus*, McGraw-Hill, New York, 1955.

F. Everling, L. A. König, J. H. E. Mattauch, and A. H. Wapstra, 'Relative Nuclidic Masses', *Nucl. Phys.*, 1960, **18**, 529.

W. A. Fowler, 'The Origin of the Elements', *The Universe, A Scientific American Book*, Bell, London, 1958.

S. Glasstone, *Sourcebook on Atomic Energy*, 2nd ed., Van Nostrand, Princeton, N.J., 1958.

J. Hamilton, 'Nuclear Structure', *Endeavour*, 1960, **19**, 163.

B. G. Harvey, *Introduction to Nuclear Physics and Chemistry*, Prentice-Hall, Englewood Cliffs, New Jersey, 1962.

A. G. Maddock and E. H. Willis, Atmospheric Activities and Dating Procedures, *Advances in Inorganic Chemistry and Radiochemistry*, vol. 3, ed. H. J. Emeléus and A. G. Sharpe, Academic Press, New York, 1961.

G. N. Walton, 'Nuclear Fission', *Quart. Rev. Chem. Soc.*, 1961, **15**, 71.

APPENDIX I

Redox couples in aqueous acid ($a_H = 1 \cdot 0$) solutions at 25 °C (after W. M. Latimer, *Oxidation Potentials*, 2nd ed., Prentice-Hall, Englewood Cliffs, N.J., 1952).

$E°$	Couple
$-3 \cdot 09$	$\frac{3}{2}N_2, H^+/HN_3$
$-3 \cdot 045$	Li^+/Li
$-2 \cdot 925$	K^+/K
$-2 \cdot 925$	Rb^+/Rb
$-2 \cdot 923$	Cs^+/Cs
$-2 \cdot 92$	Ra^{2+}/Ra
$-2 \cdot 90$	Ba^{2+}/Ba
$-2 \cdot 89$	Sr^{2+}/Sr
$-2 \cdot 87$	Ca^{2+}/Ca
$\cdot-2 \cdot 714$	Na^+/Na
$-2 \cdot 52$	La^{3+}/La
$-2 \cdot 48$	Ce^{3+}/Ce
$-2 \cdot 44$	Nd^{3+}/Nd
$-2 \cdot 41$	Sm^{3+}/Sm
$-2 \cdot 40$	Gd^{3+}/Gd
$-2 \cdot 37$	Mg^{2+}/Mg
$-2 \cdot 37$	Y^{3+}/Y
$-2 \cdot 32$	Am^{3+}/Am
$-2 \cdot 25$	Lu^{3+}/Lu
$-2 \cdot 25$	$\frac{1}{2}H_2/H^-$
$-2 \cdot 10$	$H^+/H(g)$
$-2 \cdot 08$	Sc^{3+}/Sc
$-2 \cdot 07$	Pu^{3+}/Pu
$-2 \cdot 07$	$AlF_6^{3-}/Al, 6F^-$
$-1 \cdot 90$	Th^{4+}/Th
$-1 \cdot 86$	Np^{3+}/Np
$-1 \cdot 85$	Be^{2+}/Be
$-1 \cdot 80$	U^{3+}/U
$-1 \cdot 70$	Hf^{4+}/Hf
$-1 \cdot 66$	Al^{3+}/Al
$-1 \cdot 63$	Ti^{2+}/Ti
$-1 \cdot 53$	Zr^{4+}/Zr
$-1 \cdot 2$	$SiF_6^{2-}/Si, 6F^-$
$-1 \cdot 19$	$TiF_6^{2-}/Ti, 6F^-$
$-1 \cdot 18$	Mn^{2+}/Mn
$c. -1 \cdot 18$	V^{2+}/V

$E°$	Couple
$c. -1\cdot1$	Nb^{3+}/Nb
$-0\cdot89$	$TiO^{2+},2H^+/Ti,H_2O$
$-0\cdot87$	$H_3BO_3,3H^+/B,3H_2O$
$-0\cdot86$	$SiO_2,4H^+/Si,2H_2O$
$-0\cdot81$	$Ta_2O_5,10H^+/2Ta,5H_2O$
$-0\cdot763$	Zn^{2+}/Zn
$-0\cdot753$	$TlI/Tl,I^-$
$-0\cdot74$	Cr^{3+}/Cr
$-0\cdot72$	$Te,2H^+/H_2Te$
$-0\cdot658$	$TlBr/Tl,Br^-$
$-0\cdot65$	$Nb_2O_5,10H^+/2Nb,5H_2O$
$-0\cdot61$	U^{4+}/U^{3+}
$-0\cdot60$	$As,3H^+/AsH_3(g)$
$-0\cdot557$	$TlCl/Tl,Cl^-$
$-0\cdot53$	Ga^{3+}/Ga
$-0\cdot51$	$Sb,3H^+/SbH_3(g)$
$-0\cdot51$	$H_3PO_2,H^+/P,2H_2O$
$-0\cdot50$	$H_3PO_3,2H^+/H_3PO_2,H_2O$
$-0\cdot440$	Fe^{2+}/Fe
$-0\cdot43$	Eu^{3+}/Eu^{2+}
$-0\cdot41$	Cr^{3+}/Cr^{2+}
$-0\cdot403$	Cd^{2+}/Cd
$-0\cdot40$	$Se,2H^+/H_2Se$
$c. -0\cdot37$	Ti^{3+}/Ti^{2+}
$-0\cdot365$	$PbI_2/Pb,2I^-$
$-0\cdot356$	$PbSO_4/Pb,SO_4^{2-}$
$-0\cdot342$	In^{3+}/In
$-0\cdot3363$	Tl^+/Tl
$-0\cdot30$	$PtS,2H^+/Pt,H_2S$
$-0\cdot280$	$PbBr_2/Pb,2Br^-$
$-0\cdot277$	Co^{2+}/Co
$-0\cdot276$	$H_3PO_4,2H^+/H_2O,H_3PO_3$
$-0\cdot268$	$PbCl_2/Pb,2Cl^-$
$-0\cdot255$	V^{3+}/V^{2+}
$-0\cdot253$	$V(OH)_4^+,4H^+/V,4H_2O$
$-0\cdot25$	$SnF_6^{2-}/Sn,6F^-$
$-0\cdot250$	Ni^{2+}/Ni
$-0\cdot23$	$N_2,5H^+/N_2H_5^+$
$-0\cdot22$	$2SO_4^{2-},4H^+/S_2O_6^{2-}$
$c. -0\cdot2$	Mo^{3+}/Mo
$-0\cdot196$	$CO_2,2H^+/HCOOH(aq)$
$-0\cdot185$	$CuI/Cu,I^-$
$-0\cdot151$	$AgI/Ag,I^-$
$-0\cdot136$	Sn^{2+}/Sn
$-0\cdot13$	$O_2,H^+/HO_2$
$-0\cdot126$	Pb^{2+}/Pb
$-0\cdot15$	$GeO_2,4H^+/Ge,2H_2O$

$E°$	Couple
-0.09	$WO_3(c),6H^+/W,3H_2O$
-0.08	$2H_2SO_3,H^+/HS_2O_4^-,2H_2O$
-0.04	$HgI_4^{2-}/Hg,4I^-$
0.00	$2H^+/H_2$
$+0.01$	$Ag(S_2O_3)_2^{3-}/Ag,2S_2O_3^{2-}$
$+0.033$	$CuBr/Cu,Br^-$
$+0.05$	UO_2^{2+}/UO_2^+
$+0.056$	$HCOOH(aq),2H^+/HCHO(aq),H_2O$
$+0.06$	$P,3H^+/PH_3(g)$
$+0.095$	$AgBr/Ag,Br^-$
$+0.1$	$TiO^{2+},2H^+/Ti^{3+},H_2O$
$+0.102$	$Si,4H^+/SiH_4$
$+0.13$	$C,4H^+/CH_4$
$+0.137$	$CuCl/Cu,Cl^-$
$+0.141$	$S,2H^+/H_2S$
$+0.147$	Np^{4+}/Np^{3+}
$+0.15$	Sn^{4+}/Sn^{2+}
$+0.152$	$Sb_2O_3,6H^+/2Sb,3H_2O$
$+0.153$	Cu^{2+}/Cu^+
$+0.16$	$BiOCl,2H^+/Bi,H_2O,Cl^-$
$+0.17$	$SO_4^{2-},4H^+/H_2SO_3,H_2O$
$+0.19$	$HCHO(aq),2H^+/CH_3OH(aq)$
$+0.21$	$HgBr_4^{2-}/Hg,4Br^-$
$+0.222$	$AgCl/Ag,Cl^-$
$+0.23$	$(CH_3)_2SO_2,2H^+/(CH_3)_2SO,H_2O$
$+0.247$	$HAsO_2(aq),3H^+/As,2H_2O$
$+0.252$	$ReO_2,4H^+/Re,2H_2O$
$+0.32$	$BiO^+,2H^+/Bi,H_2O$
$+0.33$	$HCNO,H^+/\frac{1}{2}C_2N_2,H_2O$
$+0.334$	$UO_2^{2+},4H^+/U^{4+},2H_2O$
$+0.337$	Cu^{2+}/Cu
$+0.35$	$AgIO_3/Ag,IO_3^-$
$+0.36$	$Fe(CN)_6^{3-}/Fe(CN)_6^{4-}$
$+0.361$	$VO^{2+},2H^+/V^{3+},H_2O$
$+0.363$	$ReO_4^-,8H^+/Re,4H_2O$
$+0.37$	$\frac{1}{2}C_2N_2,H^+/HCN(aq)$
$+0.40$	$2H_2SO_3,2H^+/S_2O_3^{2-},3H_2O$
$+0.44$	$RhCl_6^{3-}/Rh,6Cl^-$
$+0.446$	$Ag_2CrO_4/2Ag,CrO_4^{2-}$
$+0.45$	$H_2SO_3,4H^+/S,3H_2O$
$+0.48$	$Sb_2O_5,2H^+/Sb_2O_4,H_2O$
$+0.49$	$Ag_2MoO_4/2Ag,MoO_4^{2-}$
$+0.496$	$H_2N_2O_2,6H^+/2NH_3OH^+$
$+0.51$	$ReO_4^-,4H^+/ReO_2,2H_2O$
$+0.51$	$4H_2SO_3,4H^+/S_4O_6^{2-},6H_2O$
$+0.52$	$C_2H_4,2H^+/C_2H_6$
$+0.521$	Cu^+/Cu

$E°$	Couple
$+0.529$	$TeO_2(c), 4H^+/Te, 2H_2O$
$+0.5355$	$I_2/2I^-$
$+0.536$	$I_3^-/3I^-$
$+0.538$	$Cu^{2+}, Cl^-/CuCl$
$+0.55$	$AgBrO_3/Ag, BrO_3^-$
$+0.559$	$TeOOH^+, 3H^+/Te, 2H_2O$
$+0.559$	$H_3AsO_4, 2H^+/HAsO_2, 2H_2O$
$+0.564$	$AgNO_2/Ag, NO_2^-$
$+0.564$	MnO_4^-/MnO_4^{2-}
$+0.57$	$S_2O_6^{2-}, 4H^+/2H_2SO_3$
$+0.58$	$PtBr_4^{2-}/Pt, 4Br^-$
$+0.581$	$Sb_2O_5, 6H^+/2SbO^+, 3H_2O$
$+0.586$	$CH_3OH(aq), 2H^+/CH_4, H_2O$
$+0.6$	$PdBr_4^{2-}/Pd, 4Br^-$
$+0.60$	$RuCl_5^{2-}/Ru, 5Cl^-$
$+0.62$	$UO_2^+, 4H^+/U^{4+}, 2H_2O$
$+0.62$	$PdCl_4^{2-}/Pd, 4Cl^-$
$+0.640$	$Cu^{2+}, Br^-/CuBr$
$+0.643$	$AgC_2H_3O_2/Ag, C_2H_3O_2^-$
$+0.653$	$Ag_2SO_4/2Ag, SO_4^{2-}$
$+0.66$	$Au(CNS)_4^-/Au, 4CNS^-$
$+0.68$	$PtCl_6^{2-}/PtCl_4^{2-}, 2Cl^-$
$+0.682$	$O_2, 2H^+/H_2O_2$
$+0.69$	$HN_3, 11H^+/3NH_4^+$
$+0.70$	$Te, 2H^+/H_2Te$
$+0.71$	$2NO, 2H^+/H_2N_2O_2$
$+0.72$	$H_2O_2, H^+/OH, H_2O$
$+0.73$	$PtCl_4^{2-}/Pt, 4Cl^-$
$+0.73$	$C_2H_2, 2H^+/C_2H_4$
$+0.74$	$H_2SeO_3, 4H^+/Se, 3H_2O$
$+0.75$	$NpO_2^+, 4H^+/Np^{4+}, 2H_2O$
$+0.77$	$(CNS)_2/2CNS^-$
$+0.77$	$IrCl_6^{3-}/Ir, 6Cl^-$
$+0.771$	Fe^{3+}/Fe^{2+}
$+0.789$	$Hg_2^{2+}/2Hg$
$+0.7991$	Ag^+/Ag
$+0.80$	$2NO_3^-, 4H^+/N_2O_4, 2H_2O$
$c. +0.8$	Rh^{3+}/Rh
$+0.85$	$OsO_4(c), 8H^+/Os, 4H_2O$
$+0.86$	$2HNO_2, 4H^+/H_2N_2O_2, 2H_2O$
$+0.86$	$Cu^{2+}, I^-/CuI$
$+0.87$	$AuBr_4^-/Au, 4Br^-$
$+0.920$	$2Hg^{2+}/Hg_2^{2+}$
$+0.94$	$NO_3^-, 3H^+/HNO_2, H_2O$
$+0.93$	PuO_2^{2+}/PuO_2^+
$+0.96$	$NO_3^-, 4H^+/NO, 2H_2O$
$+0.96$	$AuBr_2^-/Au, 2Br^-$

E°	Couple
$+0.97$	Pu^{4+}/Pu^{3+}
$+0.98$	$Pt(OH)_2,2H^+/Pt,2H_2O$
$+0.987$	Pd^{2+}/Pd
$+0.99$	$IrBr_6^{3-}/IrBr_6^{4-}$
$+1.00$	$HNO_2,H^+/NO,H_2O$
$+1.00$	$AuCl_4^-/Au,4Cl^-$
$+1.00$	$V(OH)_4^+,2H^+/VO^{2+},3H_2O$
$+1.017$	$IrCl_6^{2-}/IrCl_6^{3-}$
$+1.02$	$H_6TeO_6(c),2H^+/TeO_2,4H_2O$
$+1.03$	$N_2O_4,4H^+/NO,2H_2O$
$+1.04$	$PuO_2^{2+},4H^+/Pu^{4+},2H_2O$
$+1.06$	$ICl_2^-/2Cl^-,\frac{1}{2}I_2$
$+1.0652$	$Br_2(l)/2Br^-$
$+1.07$	$N_2O_4,2H^+/2HNO_2$
$+1.12$	$Cu^{2+},2CN^-/Cu(CN)_2^-$
$+1.15$	$PuO_2^+,4H^+/Pu^{4+},2H_2O$
$+1.15$	$SeO_4^{2-},4H^+/H_2SeO_3,H_2O$
$+1.15$	NpO_2^{2+}/NpO_2^+
$+1.18$	$CCl_4/4Cl^-,C$
$+1.19$	$ClO_4^-,2H^+/ClO_3^-,H_2O$
$+1.195$	$IO_3^-,6H^+/\frac{1}{2}I_2,3H_2O$
$+1.21$	$ClO_3^-,3H^+/HClO_2,H_2O$
$+1.229$	$O_2,4H^+/2H_2O$
$+1.23$	$S_2Cl_2/2S,2Cl^-$
$+1.23$	$MnO_2,4H^+/Mn^{2+},2H_2O$
$+1.25$	Tl^{3+}/Tl^+
$+1.26$	$AmO_2^+,4H^+/Am^{4+},2H_2O$
$+1.275$	$N_2H_5^+,3H^+/2NH_4^+$
$+1.275$	$ClO_2,H^+/HClO_2$
$+1.288$	$PdCl_6^{2-}/PdCl_4^{2-},2Cl^-$
$+1.29$	$2HNO_2,4H^+/N_2O,3H_2O$
$+1.33$	$Cr_2O_7^{2-},14H^+/2Cr^{3+},7H_2O$
$+1.35$	$NH_3OH^+,2H^+/NH_4^+,H_2O$
$+1.3595$	$Cl_2/2Cl^-$
$+1.42$	$2NH_3OH^+,H^+/N_2H_5^+,2H_2O$
$+1.45$	$Au(OH)_3,3H^+/Au,3H_2O$
$+1.45$	$HIO,H^+/\frac{1}{2}I_2,H_2O$
$+1.455$	$PbO_2,4H^+/Pb^{2+},2H_2O$
$+1.50$	Au^{3+}/Au
$+1.5$	$HO_2,H^+/H_2O_2$
$+1.51$	Mn^{3+}/Mn^{2+}
$+1.51$	$MnO_4^-,8H^+/Mn^{2+},4H_2O$
$+1.52$	$BrO_3^-,6H^+/\frac{1}{2}Br_2,3H_2O$
$+1.59$	$HBrO,H^+/Br_2,H_2O$
$+1.59$	$Bi_2O_4,2H_2O,4H^+/2BiO^+$
$+1.6$	$H_5IO_6,H^+/IO_3^-,3H_2O$
$+1.6$	Bk^{4+}/Bk^{3+}

	E°	*Couple*
	$+1\cdot61$	Ce^{4+}/Ce^{3+}
	$+1\cdot63$	$HClO,H^+/\frac{1}{2}Cl_2,H_2O$
	$+1\cdot64$	AmO_2^{2+}/AmO_2^+
	$+1\cdot64$	$HClO_2,2H^+/HClO,H_2O$
$c.$	$+1\cdot68$	Au^+/Au
	$+1\cdot68$	$NiO_2,4H^+/Ni^{2+},2H_2O$
	$+1\cdot685$	$PbO_2,SO_4^{2-},4H^+/PbSO_4,2H_2O$
	$+1\cdot69$	$AmO_2^{2+},4H^+/Am^{3+},2H_2O$
	$+1\cdot695$	$MnO_4^-,4H^+/MnO_2,2H_2O$
	$+1\cdot725$	$AmO_2^+,4H^+/Am^{3+},2H_2O$
	$+1\cdot77$	$H_2O_2,2H^+/2H_2O$
	$+1\cdot82$	Co^{3+}/Co^{2+}
	$+1\cdot9$	$FeO_4^{2-},8H^+/Fe^{3+},4H_2O$
	$+1\cdot96$	$HN_3,3H^+/NH_4^+,N_2$
	$+1\cdot98$	Ag^{2+}/Ag^+
	$+2\cdot01$	$S_2O_8^{2-}/2SO_4^{2-}$
	$+2\cdot07$	$O_3,2H^+/O_2,H_2O$
	$+2\cdot1$	$F_2O,2H^+/H_2O,2F^-$
	$+2\cdot18$	Am^{4+}/Am^{3+}
	$+2\cdot42$	$O(g),2H^+/H_2O$
	$+2\cdot87$	$F_2/2F^-$
	$+2\cdot8$	$OH,H^+/H_2O$
	$+2\cdot85$	$H_2N_2O_2,2H^+/N_2,2H_2O$
	$+3\cdot06$	$F_2,2H^+/2HF(aq)$

APPENDIX II

General Bibliography

In addition to the special bibliographies at the end of each chapter a general reference list is given below. This is divided into six sections. In the first source-books of detailed chemical information about inorganic compounds are listed. The second gives the corresponding information about structures. Tabulated data are to be found in the third list while the fourth is one of review journals in which inorganic articles are well represented. The fifth section is devoted to text-books which deal with inorganic chemistry in a more conventional manner than the present text and the last list is one of practical inorganic chemistry books.

SOURCE-BOOKS

GMELIN's *Handbuch der anorganischen Chemie*, Verlag Chemie, Weinheim.

MELLOR's *Comprehensive Treatise on Inorganic and Theoretical Chemistry*, Longmans, London.

P. PASCAL, *Nouveau Traité de Chimie Minérale*, Masson, Paris.

N. V. SIDGWICK, *The Chemical Elements and their Compounds*, Oxford University Press, 1950.

M. C. SNEED, J. L. MAYNARD, and R. C. BRASTED, eds., *Comprehensive Inorganic Chemistry*, Van Nostrand, Princeton, N.J.

INORGANIC STRUCTURES

W. HÜCKEL, *Structural Chemistry of Inorganic Compounds*, trans. L. H. LONG, Elsevier, Amsterdam, 1950.

A. F. WELLS, *Structural Inorganic Chemistry*, 3rd ed., Oxford University Press, 1962.

R. W. G. WYCKOFF, *Crystal Structures*, Interscience, New York.

Structural Reports, Oosthoek, Utrecht.

TABULATED DATA

J. F. ELLIOTT and M. GLEISER, *Thermochemistry for Steel-making*, vol. 1, Addison-Wesley, Reading, Mass., 1960.

O. KUBASCHEWSKI and E. LL. EVANS, *Metallurgical Thermochemistry*, 2nd ed., Pergamon Press, London, 1956. (Data on heats of formation, boiling-points, melting-points, etc.)

LANDOLT-BÖRNSTEIN, *Zahlenwerte und Funktionen aus Physik, Chemie, Astronomie, Geophysik und Technik*, Springer-Verlag, Berlin.

W. M. LATIMER, *The Oxidation States of the Elements and their Potentials in Aqueous Solution*, 2nd ed., Prentice-Hall, Englewood Cliffs, N.J., 1952.

A. E. MARTELL, and L. G. SILLÉN, eds., *Stability Constants of Metal-Ion Complexes*, Chemical Society, London, 1964.

C. E. MOORE, *Atomic Energy Levels*, Circular of the National Bureau of Standards No. 467, Vols. I, II, and III, Washington, D.C., 1949, 1952, and 1958.

A. SEIDELL, *Solubilities of Inorganic and Metal Organic Compounds*, 3rd ed., Van Nostrand, Princeton, N.J. 1940.

L. E. SUTTON, ed., *Tables of Interatomic Distances and Configurations in Molecules and Ions*, Special Publications Nos. 11 and 18, Chemical Society, London, 1958 and 1965.

Selected Values of Chemical Thermodynamic Properties, National Bureau of Standards Circular No. 500, Washington, D.C., 1952.

International Critical Tables, McGraw-Hill, New York.

REVIEW JOURNALS AND BOOKS

Advances in Inorganic Chemistry and Radiochemistry, ed. H. J. Emeléus and A. G. Sharpe, Academic Press, New York.

Progress in Inorganic Chemistry, ed. F. A. Cotton, Interscience, New York.

Advances in Organometallic Chemistry, ed. F. G. A. Stone and R. West, Academic Press, New York.

Annual Surveys of Organometallic Chemistry, ed. D. Seyfurth and R. B. King, Elsevier, Amsterdam.

Bi-annual reports on International Conferences in Coordination Chemistry.

Annual Reports on the Progress of Chemistry, Chemical Society, London.

Quarterly Reviews, Chemical Society, London.

Chemical Reviews, American Chemical Society.

Reviews of Pure and Applied Chemistry, Royal Australian Chemical Institute.

GENERAL TEXTBOOKS

E. DE B. BARNETT and C. L. WILSON, *Inorganic Chemistry*, 2nd ed., Longmans, London, 1957.

F. A. COTTON and G. WILKINSON, *Advanced Inorganic Chemistry*, Interscience, New York, 1962.

H. J. EMELÉUS and J. S. ANDERSON, *Modern Aspects of Inorganic Chemistry*, 3rd ed., Routledge and Kegan Paul, London, 1960.

K. B. HARVEY and G. B. PORTER, *Introduction to Physical Inorganic Chemistry*, Addison-Wesley, Reading, Mass., 1963.

R. B. HESLOP and P. L. ROBINSON, *Inorganic Chemistry*, 2nd ed., Elsevier, Amsterdam, 1963.

J. KLEINBERG, W. J. ARGERSINGER, and E. GRISWOLD, *Inorganic Chemistry*, Heath, Boston, 1960.

T. MOELLER, *Inorganic Chemistry*, Wiley, New York, 1952.

H. REMY, *Treatise on Inorganic Chemistry*, trans. J. S. ANDERSON, Elsevier, Amsterdam, 1956.

PRACTICAL INORGANIC CHEMISTRY (excluding books on analytical chemistry)

G. BRAUER, *Handbuch der präparativen anorganischen Chemie*, Enke, Stuttgart.

R. E. DODD and P. L. ROBINSON, *Experimental Inorganic Chemistry*, Elsevier, Amsterdam, 1954.

H. LUX, *Anorganisch-chemische Experimentierkunst*, 2nd ed., Barth, Leipzig, 1959.

W. G. PALMER, *Experimental Inorganic Chemistry*, Cambridge University Press, 1954.

Inorganic Syntheses, McGraw-Hill, New York.

Preparative Inorganic Reactions, ed. W. L. Jolly, Interscience, New York.

Technique of Inorganic Chemistry, ed. H. B. Jonassen and A. Weissberger, Interscience, New York.

ELEMENT INDEX

HEAVY type gives the number of the chapter which deals with the element in greatest detail. Less significant references are in ordinary type and in parentheses.

GENERAL INDEX TO PARTS I, II, AND III

THE chapters which are most directly concerned with the chemistry of a particular element are listed in the Element Index, above. Thus, for example, it should be noted that while in Chapter 11 the general and comparative chemistry of hydrides is described, hydrides of particular groups of elements, non-metals in Part II and metals in Part III, are discussed in the individual chapters appropriate to the elements concerned. The General Index which follows is a complete index to Volume I and Volume II. Page references to Volume I are in italics.

'a' class acceptors, *453, 629*, 533.
'a' class cations, 533.
A metals, organometallic compounds of, 550, 554.
A-subgroup ions:
  general chemistry of, *48–90*.
  reaction rates, *364*.
abundance:
  cosmic, 636–41.
  in the earth's crust, 607.
  of the lanthanide elements, *626*.
acceptor and donor ligands, 214, 327.
acceptor properties of Group III elements, *630*.
acceptors:
  'a' class, *453, 629*, 533.
  'b' class, *453, 629*, 533.
  donor-acceptor intermediates, *350*.
accumulator, lead, 541.
acetates, dimerized, 265.
acetic acids, substituted, ionization of, *253*.
acetylene complexes, 334.
acetylide complexes, *622*, 334.
acid-base catalysis, *354, 379*, 435.
'acid-base' combination, of halides, *444*.
acid-base properties:
  oxide classification in terms of, 585.
  of sulphides, *578*, 592.
acid-base ranges in solvents, *564*.
acid/base strengths of hydrides, *418*.
acid dissociation constants, *530, 536, 636*.
acid strengths of oxyacids, *529*.
acids:
  catenated, *531*.
  definition of, *516*.
  of Group V, *635*.
  of Group VII, *457*.
  and hydroxides, ionization of, *536*.
  hydride, *418*.
acidity and selectivity of organic reagents, *567*, 601.

actinide atoms, structure of, 129.
actinide compounds and complexes:
  heats of formation of, 136–8.
  hydrides, nitrides, and carbides, 142.
  oxo-complexes, 140.
  spectra and magnetism, 143–6.
  stability of, 139, 140.
  structures, 135, 138, 140.
  valence states in, 132.
actinide elements, separation of, 146.
actinide metals:
  atomic volumes of, 17.
  binding energies of, *88*, 17.
  and lanthanide metals, 16.
  melting-points of, 17.
actinium, see *under* actinide.
activation energy, *333*.
  for diffusion, *373*.
  of electron-transfer reactions, 444.
  of nuclear reactions, 626.
  radical reactions, *348*.
  for self-diffusion, *373*.
  of substitution reactions, *363*, 444, 437.
activity, *249*.
addition reactions, *354*.
adenosine triphosphate, *385, 87*.
adsorption on surfaces, kinetics, *375*.
aerobic and anaerobic systems, *386*.
age of the Earth, 627.
alkali metals:
  alloys, 14.
  aromatic compounds, 554.
  compounds and complexes, *48–90*.
alkali-metal atoms, ionization potentials of, 53.
alkyl organometallic compounds, σ-bonded, 352, Chap. 33.
alkylated cations, 530.
allotropic changes, *246*.
allotropy:
  of carbon, *246*.
  of metals, 7.
  of phosphorus, *608*.